STATICS OF
DEFORMABLE SOLIDS

This book is in the
ADDISON-WESLEY Series in
MECHANICS AND THERMODYNAMICS

Consulting Editors
BERNARD BUDIANSKY and HOWARD W. EMMONS

STATICS OF
DEFORMABLE SOLIDS

RAYMOND L. BISPLINGHOFF
National Aeronautics and Space Administration

JAMES W. MAR
Massachusetts Institute of Technology

THEODORE H. H. PIAN
Massachusetts Institute of Technology

 ADDISON-WESLEY · READING, MASSACHUSETTS

ADDISON-WESLEY PUBLISHING COMPANY, INC.

READING, MASSACHUSETTS · Palo Alto · London

NEW YORK · DALLAS · ATLANTA · BARRINGTON, ILLINOIS

Preface

This book, like so many others, had its genesis in notes. These particular notes were prepared to aid in the teaching of a first course in solid mechanics to second-term sophomores in the Department of Aeronautics and Astronautics at the Massachusetts Institute of Technology. The material is intended to build on the mechanics background normally obtained from a first course in physics in an engineering curriculum.

The content of the book and the philosophy of approach which has been adopted are based upon convictions which the authors have developed over a period of several years of experiment with solid mechanics curricula. Although the book represents a solution to their particular curriculum problems, the authors are the first to admit that there is no unique solution to all the needs of mechanics curricula.

The attempt has been made throughout the book to reveal the subject in its fundamentals and at the same time to attend to details in such a way as to retain the student's interest. The teaching of elementary solid mechanics in the classical engineering college curriculum of the past tended to subdivide the subject in the student's mind to give him a facility in methods applicable to special cases, and to give him only a vague picture of the broader principles. Graduate students often found that their elementary mechanics courses had not provided a sound foundation and that no special thought or planning had gone into the integration between elementary and advanced mechanics. Introducing solid mechanics in a fundamental way at the sophomore level, just as fluid mechanics is commonly introduced, is necessary in a modern engineering curriculum in order to overcome some of these difficulties.

The instructor in mechanics is faced with the dilemma of finding a technique for teaching and illustrating the fundamental principles without getting bogged down in so much detail that the student loses sight of the main stream of thought. The art of teaching mechanics consists largely in effectively introducing fundamental principles with a minimum of detail. The fundamental principles of solid mechanics involve, for example, the concepts of force, the principles of equilibrium and compatibility, and the idea of constitutive relationships. The details embrace, for example, geometry and kinematics, mathematical notation, and moments and products of inertia.

The present book proceeds directly to a full exposition of the underlying principles. As a result, the book divides naturally into two parts. The first, consisting of Chapters 1 through 4, introduces these fundamental principles, but illustrates them only by means of simple discrete elastic systems, without becoming involved with the geometry of the continua. The second part, comprising Chapters 5 through 9, deals with the application of these principles to three-dimensional continua, both elastic and plastic. Although it may appear at first glance that the two parts of the book represent different orders of rigor and difficulty, it has been the authors' aim to drive home the fundamental principles of solid mechanics in the first and attend to details of the continua in the second.

Chapter 2 presents the laws of Newtonian mechanics fundamental to the entire field, including particle, rigid, solid, and fluid mechanics. This introductory portion of the subject is covered in its broadest form so that the student can relate it to companion courses in mechanics. In Chapter 3, the laws introduced in Chapter 2 are applied to problems concerning the static equilibrium of particles and bodies under the action of forces and moments. Chapters 2 and 3 thus present in an abbreviated manner the material generally covered in an introductory course in statics.

It has been the authors' experience that undergraduates grasp more easily the concepts of force and equilibrium than other principles of mechanics. It is believed, then, that some of the problem drill ordinarily conducted at this stage may be profitably carried out after the principles of statically indeterminate structures have been introduced. In Chapter 4, simple statically indeterminate systems are presented by supplementing the principles of static equilibrium with constitutive relations and conditions of consistent deformation. The problem drill is designed to exercise the student's ability not only to apply equilibrium principles, but also to supplement them when necessary with compatibility conditions.

In Chapters 5 and 6, strain and stress in three-dimensional solids are dealt with, and the notions of strain and stress tensors and their properties are discussed. Chapter 7 ties together Chapters 5 and 6 through Hooke's law, and introduces the theory of elasticity in its elementary form. Chapter 8 deals with the stress-strain relations for plastic solids. Finally, Chapter 9 introduces energy principles in solid continuum. This chapter embraces not only the concepts of work and energy, but also the principle of virtual work and the theorems of minimum potential energy, minimum complementary energy, least work, and Castigliano's two theorems.

Each chapter is followed by a concise summary of the important principles which have been introduced, a bibliography, and a list of problems. The bibliography is not intended to be exhaustive, but rather to include at least one reference to an original source as well as a few selected references to contemporary books for supplementary reading. Many of the problems are taken from home assignments and examinations used at the Massachusetts Institute of Technology.

Deep appreciation is due to the many people who have aided in bringing the book to completion. Several colleagues on the Aeronautics and Astronautics staff at M.I.T., as well as former students, read portions of the manuscript and offered valuable criticism. These include Professors Paul Sandorff, Emmett Witmer, and John Dugundji. Work on the figures and associated calculations was contributed by Messrs. Oscar Orringer and Charles Bruggeman. The typing, preparation, and reproduction of the manuscript were skillfully handled by Miss Ann Gorrasi. The preparation of the class notes was supported in part by a grant made to the Massachusetts Institute of Technology by the Ford Foundation. This support is gratefully acknowledged.

Washington, D.C.	R. L. B.
Cambridge, Mass.	J. W. M.
June, 1965	T. H. H. P.

Contents

Chapter 8   **Plastic Behavior of Solids**

Chapter 9   **Energy Principles in Solid Continuum**

Appendix   **Mathematical Themes**

I

Foundation of Solid Mechanics

1.1 INTRODUCTION

A deformable body is distinguished from a rigid body by its susceptibility to changes in shape under the influence of forces. Strictly speaking, all of nature's bodies are deformable, but in problems of mechanics one may sometimes assume with sufficient precision that certain bodies retain their shape under load, that is, they are perfectly rigid. A deformable body may, however, be a solid or a fluid. The term "solid" is used to identify a solid deformable body in contrast to a fluid with the restriction that a solid possesses shear strength while a fluid does not. Our concern will be limited, furthermore, to the static behavior of solids, that is, to shape changes resulting from static loads only. Our interest in the behavior of solid bodies will extend to a full definition of the deformations, strains, and stresses throughout the volume and over the surface.

Why should the present-day engineer study solid mechanics? In the profession of engineering, for example in the field of aeronautics and astronautics, there is always an end product in mind—a supersonic transport, a launch vehicle, a spacecraft. All these systems, in order to fulfill their missions, must possess physical strength and rigidity. The provision of strength and rigidity can be accomplished relatively simply, but in the process the flight vehicle may become so heavy, so impractical, or so uneconomical that it will not be useful. For example, the structure of a supersonic transport airplane is subjected to widely fluctuating loads as well as temperature excursions of as much as 500° F during each flight. In addition, its users demand a lifetime of some 50,000 hours of flying. In the design of such an airplane, a structural weight of say 23 percent of the gross weight would ensure economic success, whereas a comparable figure only a few percent higher would result in economic failure. The difference between a spacecraft which achieves orbit and one which remains earthbound is sometimes measured in ounces. Thus the structural design of flight vehicles requires exotic materials, sophisticated methods of analysis, and ingenious structural design. Such demands for high structural efficiency are not peculiar to aeronautical and space systems. Because of the high temperatures usually required in energy conversion devices, solid mechanics plays a dominant role in their analysis and design. Higher structural efficiencies are increasingly demanded for civil engineering structures as well as for ground vehicles and marine vessels.

1.2 WAYS OF THINKING

A student of solid mechanics is at first confronted with a dichotomy in his way of thinking about the subject. There is first the physical way of thinking which relates directly to the real world in which we live and to the problems which we seek to solve. These problems are posed to us in a physical way: to predict the deformation of a bridge under load or to compute the stresses in a rocket booster case during launch. Then there is the mathematical way of thinking in which the theorems of mathematics are employed as tools for swift and accurate reasoning.

It is the purpose of a course in solid mechanics to interrelate in the student's mind these two ways of thinking, and to help him develop as second nature a facility for transition from the physical to the mathematical and back again. The student has already experienced this in its simplest manifestation during his study of geometry. Plane Euclidean geometry is a legitimate branch of mathematics regardless of whether there exist in the real world the physical entities of points, lines, and planes. The student, however, easily recognizes these as physical entities at the outset, and the axioms and theorems of geometry thereby provide him with tools for studying their behavior. Other branches of mathematics pose a more subtle transition between physical and mathematical ways of thinking, and a methodology is required to aid in our thinking.

1.3 METHODOLOGY IN SOLID MECHANICS

In general, five successive stages are involved in the study of solid mechanics and in the solution of problems.

(1) A physical system is presented as an object of analysis or design. This may range from a complete system such as a vehicle or a bridge to a single subsystem such as a beam, column, or fastener.

(2) An ideal model is conceived and sketched.

(3) Mathematical reasoning is applied to the ideal model which now becomes a mathematical model. The equations which result from this application are derived and solved.

(4) The mathematical results are interpreted physically in terms pertinent to the original object of the analysis or design.

(5) The results are compared with the results of physical observations. These observations may be made on a laboratory model or on the finished object.

Although it is the purpose of a large portion of the present book to discuss these five stages, certain remarks can be made about them at this point.

Stage 1 implies that man has a curiosity concerning the physical world about him and desires to infer information about it beyond that which he can immediately observe. This curiosity is generally motivated by a desire to construct an engineering system.

It is probably evident that the second stage, conception of the ideal model, is the key element in making the transition from physical to mathematical ways of thinking. Nature is, in general, so complex that it does not permit itself to be expressed exhaustively in a single model, equation, or thought. The scientist or engineer is invariably faced with a task of constructing simplified models of nature to represent levels of abstraction consistent with the results which are sought. If he seeks, for example, to describe the position of the atomic particles of a solid under load, the model he adopts must be vastly different from that required to describe the gross change of external shape. The most difficult task that confronts him is then one of introducing only those simplifying assumptions important to the physical process he is studying, and of neglecting all influences of lower order.

Applications of science at all levels involve conceptual models of nature which are used for mathematical or physical reasoning. The different divisions of basic science may be classified by their conceptual models. For example, to the student of solid mechanics a metal beam is a mass of homogeneous, isotropic, sometimes elastic and sometimes plastic material subjected to force and displacement boundary conditions; to the metallurgist, a collection of randomly oriented grains and crystals; to the chemist, a collection of atoms and molecules; and to the solid-state physicist, a swarm of nuclei and electrons. We can construct an approximate model of a portion of the physical world and trace the relations between its parts, but we cannot by such methods reveal the total intrinsic reality of nature. By applying the mathematical tools of reasoning to models, we can infer new information. If the model is consistent with experimental observation, it is regarded as a valid model. Pure scientists are engrossed in improving nature's models; engineers or applied scientists apply them to machines. In the student's professional life, his success in the use of mechanics will depend as much on his skill in the game of "mathematical make-believe" as on any other single factor. The art of stripping away physical complexities which are unimportant for the problem at hand, and of designing ideal models which yield to analysis is at the heart of successful engineering practice. The student will recognize that the development of these skills and viewpoints is, in fact, a requirement in all branches of the engineering sciences.

The third stage, application of mathematical reasoning, requires an application of physical laws to the ideal model. These laws, which in the present book rest upon the foundation of Newtonian mechanics, provide an experimentally verified basis for constructing mathematical equations to describe the behavior of the physical system. Mathematical reasoning is then brought into play by employing the axioms and theorems governing the mathematical equations which have been constructed.

The fourth stage, physical interpretation of mathematical results, presents no difficulty providing the physical laws introduced in the third stage are fully understood. Under these circumstances there should be a clear realization of the relationship between the parameters of the mathematical model and their counterparts in nature.

The fifth step, comparison with physical observations, is an important step in the process, although it will not be one of the objects of the present book to deal explicitly with the experimental sciences. The engineer or applied scientist must learn from experience. The tools he employs should be those which experience has shown will yield accurate, experimentally verified results. Mechanical, aeronautical, civil, and other engineers have learned from experience that certain ideal models provide accurate representations of physical systems with which they have traditionally dealt. The ideal models used to represent pulley systems, cantilever airplane wings, and bridge trusses are examples of accumulated experience based on experimental observation. The engineer working at the forefront of his technology may need to construct ideal models for systems which are entirely new and for which there is no accumulated experience. He may desire, in such cases, to construct experimental laboratory models or to make careful confirmatory measurements on the first version of the operational system in order to verify his design calculations. Thus he accumulates additional experience which gives him a unique advantage.

FIGURE 1.1

A simple example may serve to illustrate at this point the nature of the five stages. There are many structural problems associated with the design of an airplane. In principle, one ideal model or one gigantic mathematical equation covering the entire airplane (Fig. 1.1) is possible, but solving it would be impractical and even impossible. The engineer is forced to break the airplane down into its separate structural components and examine them individually. For instance, in the analysis and design of a wing structure to carry the flight loads, the five stages may be described in the following terms:

(1) The wing provides the lift necessary to sustain flight, and as such must be strong enough to resist the aerodynamic pressures created by the air flow over the wing and must be rigid enough to prevent excessive deflections and wing flutter.

(2) The wing is idealized as a one-dimensional structure rigidly attached to a wall. Such a structure, illustrated by Fig. 1.2, is called a cantilever beam. The bending-stiffness properties of the beam are condensed into a single parameter called the bending-stiffness factor, EI, and the airloads are condensed into a load per unit length, $p(x)$.

Air load $p(x)$

FIG. 1.2   Airplane wing as a cantilever beam.

Bending stiffness $EI(x)$

(3) The equation which describes the bending behavior of the idealized model is

$$\frac{d^2}{dx^2}\left(EI\,\frac{d^2w}{dx^2}\right) = p(x), \tag{1.1}$$

where $w(x)$ is the lateral deflection of the beam as a function of x. Since EI is also a function of x, the above equation is most easily integrated in numerical form.

(4) The lateral deflection of the wing is obtainable directly from $w(x)$, and the strains and stresses may also be computed from the result by employing additional mathematical formulas.

(5) The structural designer often verifies his computations and obtains additional information from static tests in the laboratory of models or of a full-scale wing. The ultimate verification of the analysis and design, however, is the successful flight operation of the prototype airplane.

Other examples are abundant, and as the subject is gradually developed these will become evident. It will become increasingly clear to the student that mathematics plays an important role in the study of solid mechanics. Even though the problems are generally motivated by an engineering objective, and although the ultimate verification lies in the performance of a hardware object, a reasonably high proficiency in mathematics is required for participation in the challenging engineering projects which are at the forefront of new technologies. Of course, many of the fundamental principles of solid mechanics were laid down by men blessed with tremendous intuitive gifts and mental abilities. Fortunately, it is not necessary to possess these same attributes in order to understand the principles of solid mechanics and to apply them effectively to engineering problems.

Principles of Mechanics

2.1 INTRODUCTION

We shall find in subsequent developments of the present book that four fundamental laws provide a foundation for the subject of mechanics. These laws
represent in concise form an acceptable mathematical model of a segment of
nature. They are listed below for the sake of convenient reference, and they
are discussed in detail in the following articles of the present chapter.

(a) Law of the Parallelogram of Forces (Section 2.3)
(b) Law of Transmissibility of Forces (Section 2.4)
(c) Law of Motion (Section 2.5)
(d) Law of Action and Reaction (Section 2.6)

These four laws provide an experimentally verified foundation for Newtonian
mechanics upon which, by mathematical analysis, such vast subjects as particle,
rigid-body, solid, and fluid mechanics may be erected. These laws can be fully
understood only by applying them to diverse problems. It is quite important
that the student adopt a philosophy of seeking an understanding of their full
meaning by numerous applications to problems. Several examples are given
in the present and later chapters to illustrate their application, and additional
problems are listed at the ends of the chapters.

2.2 THE CONCEPT OF FORCE

All normal human beings are familiar in their day-to-day activities with the
notion of a force. The opening and closing of doors, the lifting of weights, and
the steering of an automobile are experiences which require one to exert force.
It is evident from daily activities that the notion of a force involves both magnitude and direction; that is, a force is a vector quantity. Furthermore, a force
is associated with a point of application. Forces are therefore represented in
mechanics by vectors acting at specific points. In mechanics as in everyday

experience, forces are usually produced by the action of one body on another. Since forces are vector quantities, they will be represented by bold-face letters such as **F**, **P**, and **Q**. On the blackboard or in manuscript they are usually denoted by arrows over the letters, such as $\vec{F}$, $\vec{P}$, and $\vec{Q}$.

The vector qualities of a force permit it to be represented in space by a directed line segment. In Fig. 2.1 a force **F** acting at a point p is schematically represented in three-dimensional space by the line segment pa. As explained in the Appendix, for the summation notation and tensor notation to be used in this text, the three rectangular Cartesian coordinates are represented by y_1, y_2, and y_3, respectively.

The force **F** can be written as the vector sum of three independent components,

$$\mathbf{F} = F_1\mathbf{i}_1 + F_2\mathbf{i}_2 + F_3\mathbf{i}_3 = \sum_{m=1}^{3} F_m\mathbf{i}_m,$$

$$(2.2.1a)$$

where $\mathbf{i}_1$, $\mathbf{i}_2$, and $\mathbf{i}_3$ are the unit vectors associated with the rectangular Cartesian coordinates y_1, y_2, and y_3. According to the summation notation (see Appendix, Section A.2) this is represented simply as

$$\mathbf{F} = F_m\mathbf{i}_m. \qquad (2.2.1b)$$

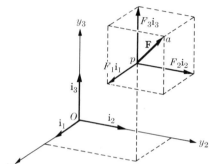

FIG. 2.1   Cartesian representation of a force vector.

The repeated index, such as the m in Eq. (2.2.1b), is to be summed from one to three. Geometrically, the vector components $F_1\mathbf{i}_1$, $F_2\mathbf{i}_2$, and $F_3\mathbf{i}_3$ are seen to form the edges of a rectangular parallelepiped which has **F** as its main diagonal. The magnitude of **F** is given by the scalar product (see Appendix, Section A.12):

$$|\mathbf{F}| = \sqrt{\mathbf{F} \cdot \mathbf{F}} = [(F_m\mathbf{i}_m) \cdot (F_n\mathbf{i}_n)]^{1/2},$$

$$|\mathbf{F}| = (F_m F_n \delta_{mn})^{1/2},$$

$$(2.2.2)$$

where δ_{mn} is called the Kronecker delta (Appendix, Section A.3), which is equal to unity if the two indices are equal, and is zero if the two indices are unequal. The vertical bars on either side of a vector, e.g., $|\mathbf{F}|$, signify the magnitude or length of a vector.

Equation (2.2.2) is written in expanded form as

$$|\mathbf{F}| = [(F_1)^2 + (F_2)^2 + (F_3)^2]^{1/2}. \qquad (2.2.3)$$

Hence the scalar quantities F_1, F_2, F_3 are seen to be the magnitudes of the vector components of **F**.

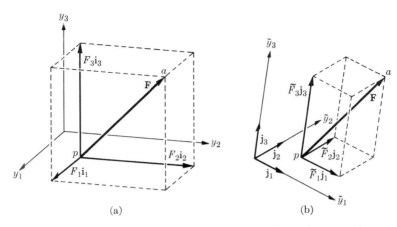

FIG. 2.2   Components of the same vector in different Cartesian coordinate systems.

The coordinate system consisting of the axes y_1, y_2, and y_3 has been arbitrarily chosen. It should be evident that the force $\mathbf{F}$ does not depend upon the choice of a coordinate system. In another coordinate system, for example, $\tilde{y}_1$, $\tilde{y}_2$, and $\tilde{y}_3$, the force is written as

$$\mathbf{F} = \tilde{F}_m \mathbf{j}_m, \tag{2.2.4}$$

where the $\mathbf{j}_m$ are the unit vectors associated with the new coordinate system, and where $\tilde{F}_1 \mathbf{j}_1$, $\tilde{F}_2 \mathbf{j}_2$, and $\tilde{F}_3 \mathbf{j}_3$ are the vector components which describe $\mathbf{F}$ relative to the $\tilde{y}_n$-axes (see Fig. 2.2).

Since Eqs. (2.2.1b) and (2.2.4) describe the same vector, we may combine them to obtain

$$\tilde{F}_m \mathbf{j}_m = F_n \mathbf{i}_n. \tag{2.2.5}$$

In order to express the $\tilde{F}_m$-components in terms of the F_n-components, we need only take the scalar product of both sides of Eq. (2.2.5) with $\mathbf{j}_r$:

$$\mathbf{j}_r \cdot \tilde{F}_m \mathbf{j}_m = \tilde{F}_m \delta_{mr} = \mathbf{j}_r \cdot \mathbf{i}_n F_n. \tag{2.2.6}$$

The scalar products on the right-hand side of Eq. (2.2.6) are the cosines of the angles between the axes of the two axis systems (see Appendix, Section A.12). These are called direction cosines, and will be denoted by $l_{\tilde{r}n}$, that is,

$$l_{\tilde{r}n} = \mathbf{j}_r \cdot \mathbf{i}_n. \tag{2.2.7}$$

Then Eq. (2.2.6) becomes

$$\tilde{F}_r = l_{\tilde{r}n} F_n. \tag{2.2.8}$$

Equation (2.2.8) is the transformation law (see Appendix, Section A.6) for a first-order tensor, and therefore the components of a force form a first-order tensor.

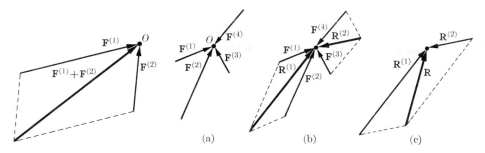

FIG. 2.3 Addition of vectors   FIG. 2.4 Addition of forces by repeated application of
by parallelogram method.   parallelogram law.

2.3 LAW OF THE PARALLELOGRAM OF FORCES—RESULTANT OF CONCURRENT FORCES

In dealing with the subject of mechanics, one is very often confronted with situations in which several forces act at once at a specified point. The first question to be raised in such a situation is, what is the resultant of all of these forces? This question is answered traditionally by the *Law of the Parallelogram of Forces: When two forces,* $\mathbf{F}^{(1)}$ *and* $\mathbf{F}^{(2)}$*, act simultaneously at a specified point, they are together equivalent to a single force,* $\mathbf{F}^{(1)} + \mathbf{F}^{(2)}$*, acting at that point,* as shown by the parallelogram construction of Fig. 2.3. It is seen that the so-called Law of the Parallelogram of Forces may be interpreted as a consequence of the vector addition of two concurrent forces (see preceding section). When more than two forces are acting, the Parallelogram Law may be applied repeatedly to obtain the resultant. For example, in Fig. 2.4, the forces $\mathbf{F}^{(1)}$, $\mathbf{F}^{(2)}$, $\mathbf{F}^{(3)}$, and $\mathbf{F}^{(4)}$ acting at O may be replaced by the force $\mathbf{R}$ at O. The latter is obtained by constructing $\mathbf{R}^{(1)}$ from a parallelogram formed with $\mathbf{F}^{(1)}$ and $\mathbf{F}^{(2)}$, $\mathbf{R}^{(2)}$ from a parallelogram with $\mathbf{F}^{(3)}$ and $\mathbf{F}^{(4)}$, and finally $\mathbf{R}$ from a parallelogram with $\mathbf{R}^{(1)}$ and $\mathbf{R}^{(2)}$. These repeated steps are represented by the vector equation

$$\mathbf{F}^{(1)} + \mathbf{F}^{(2)} + \mathbf{F}^{(3)} + \mathbf{F}^{(4)} = \mathbf{R}. \qquad (2.3.1)$$

The vector sum represented by Eq. (2.3.1) may be found graphically by the polygon construction shown in Fig. 2.5, provided that all the forces are in a plane. When the forces are not coplanar, a space construction of the vector sum is required.

If a coordinate system y_1, y_2, y_3 is chosen, then each of the four forces in Eq. (2.3.1) can be written in the form

$$\mathbf{F}^{(n)} = F_m^{(n)}\mathbf{i}_m, \qquad n = 1, 2, 3, 4, \qquad (2.3.2)$$

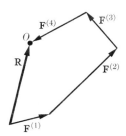

FIG. 2.5 Addition of vectors by polygon construction.

where the enclosed superscript is an identifying tag. The resultant can also be written in vector form with respect to the same axes,

$$\mathbf{R} = R_m \mathbf{i}_m,$$ (2.3.3)

and therefore Eq. (2.3.1) yields the result

$$R_m = \sum_{n=1}^{4} F_m^{(n)}.$$ (2.3.4)

2.4 LAW OF TRANSMISSIBILITY OF FORCES

Another fundamental feature of the action of a force on a rigid body is the *Law of Transmissibility of a Force: When a force is acting upon a rigid body, it may be translated along its line of action so that it acts on any point of the rigid body which coincides with the line of action.* It may be seen from the above that two forces of equal magnitude and opposite direction acting upon opposite sides of a rigid body and along a common line of action, as illustrated by Fig. 2.6, cancel each other entirely. This is evident since the two forces may be slid along their common line of action to the same point of application. When the parallelogram law is applied to this pair, their resultant is seen to vanish.

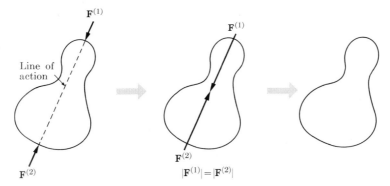

Fig. 2.6   One consequence of the principle of force transmissibility.

This law applies only to rigid bodies, i.e., to bodies in which the deformations may be considered negligible. We will see that such an assumption is justified for some analyses and not for others.

2.5 LAW OF MOTION

Let us assume that experiments are being conducted to determine the influence of forces on bodies. Perhaps the simplest of all experiments is that of observing the falling of a body in the gravitational field of the earth. Suppose that the weight of a body at a given location on the surface of the earth is measured by a very sensitive spring scale, and that the acceleration of gravity in a vacuum is also measured by sensitive timing devices at the same location. If this process is repeated with the same object at other locations on the surface of the earth, it will be found that

$$\frac{w^{(1)}}{g^{(1)}} = \frac{w^{(2)}}{g^{(2)}} = \cdots = \frac{w^{(n)}}{g^{(n)}} = m, \qquad (2.5.1)$$

where $w^{(i)}$ and $g^{(i)}$ are the weights and accelerations of gravity, respectively. The ratio of weight to acceleration of gravity, called the mass of the body, m, is invariant with respect to location on the earth's surface.

The action of the earth's gravitational field upon a body can be summarized by the formula

$$\mathbf{W} = m\mathbf{g}, \qquad (2.5.2)$$

where $\mathbf{W}$ is a force vector with magnitude equal to the body weight and direction along a plumb line, $\mathbf{g}$ is an acceleration vector with magnitude equal to the local acceleration of gravity and direction also along the local plumb line.

Experience has shown that formula (2.5.2) can be generalized to other forces and accelerations, providing one selects a suitable frame of reference relative to which the accelerations are measured. This generalization, known as *Newton's Second Law of Motion*, may be stated as follows: *A particle which is unrestrained and acted upon by a force vector* $\mathbf{F}$, *accelerates at a rate* $\mathbf{a}$ *which is proportional in magnitude to the magnitude of* $\mathbf{F}$ *and along the line of action and in the sense of direction of* $\mathbf{F}$. This proportionality may be represented by the equation

$$\mathbf{F} = m\mathbf{a}, \qquad (2.5.3)$$

where m is a scalar mass, the value of which depends upon the body and on the choice of units of force, length, and time.

The first requirement which must be placed upon the frame of reference is that it be either fixed or moving with constant velocity. Such a frame of reference is called Newtonian. Experimental evidence shows that a suitable system is the astronomical frame of reference in which the mass center of the solar system is fixed and which is without rotation relative to the fixed stars as a whole.* Another frame of reference which is nearly Newtonian is that of the earth's surface. Strictly speaking, there are differences between experimental evidence and predictions of Eq. (2.5.3) due to the earth's rotation, when the earth's surface is used as a reference frame. However, these differences are negligible in most engineering calculations.

---

* Equation (2.5.3) provides excellent although not perfect agreement with astronomical observations in the solar system. The agreement is, however, sufficiently good so that it is usually used as a basis for the study of the mechanics of the solar system.

In scientific and engineering work involving the use of forces, it is of fundamental importance to be able to describe the magnitude of a given force. This requires that some definite force be selected as a standard unit. For example, one might employ a spring scale for this purpose. The scale could be calibrated by measuring the deflection produced by the weight of a standard body at a particular location on the earth's surface. Calibration units frequently employed in scientific and engineering work are the British gravitational unit of the pound and the metric gravitational unit of the kilogram. The former is defined as the weight, measured at sea level and at a latitude of 45°, of a standard pound platinum body kept at the Standards Office of the London Board of Trade. The latter is the weight, also measured at sea level and at a latitude of 45°, of a standard kilogram platinum body kept at the International Bureau of Weights and Measures, Sèvres, France.

In mechanics, three fundamental dimensions are necessary to form a complete mechanical dimension system. With length and time as a common basis, a single additional independent dimension is required. One may choose from among mass, force, power, energy and others. We shall consider two of these possibilities.

(a) Dynamical or physical systems. In these systems, we select the fundamental dimensions of length, mass, and time. Perhaps the best known system in this category is the *CGS (centimeter-gram-second) system*. In this system the unit of mass is taken as the gram-mass, which is 1/1000 of the mass of the standard kilogram body. The force which is required to produce an acceleration of 1 cm/sec² of 1-gm mass is termed a *dyne*. Thus the fundamental units of the CGS system are the centimeter, the gram-mass, and the second. A derived quantity is the dyne force having the units of g-cm/sec². Another system similar to the cgs-system is the mks-system in which the fundamental units are the meter, the kilogram-mass, and the second. The force is again a derived quantity; the force necessary to give a 1-kg mass an acceleration of 1 m/sec² is defined as the *newton*. In terms of the fundamental units of the mks-system, the newton has the units of kg-m/sec². The *English dynamical system* employs the fundamental units of the foot, the pound-mass, and the second. The force is derived from these quantities; the force necessary to give a 1-lb mass an acceleration of 1 ft/sec² is defined as the *poundal*. The poundal has the fundamental units of lb-ft/sec².

(b) Gravitational or technical systems. In contrast to the dynamical or physical systems of units, we now select as the fundamental units in the gravitational or technical systems the units of length, force, and time. Mass is left as a derived quantity. Such systems are primarily used by engineers, with some advantages accruing from the fact that force is a fundamental rather than a derived quantity. The *English gravitational system* is probably the most widely used of all such systems, and it employs as its fundamental units feet, pounds-force, and seconds. Thus, if a force of 1 lb produces an acceleration of 1 ft/sec², the body

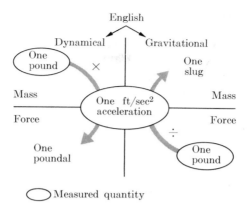

FIG. 2.7   Comparison of the English dynamical and gravitational systems of unity.

in question has a unit mass. This unit of mass is termed a *slug*, and in terms of the fundamental units of the system it has the units lb-sec^2/ft. The two English systems are compared in Fig. 2.7.

2.6   LAW OF ACTION AND REACTION

Finally, we state the important *Law of Action and Reaction: When two particles exert forces on each other, whether in direct contact or at a distance from each other, these forces are equal in magnitude and opposite in sense, and act along a line joining the two particles.* According to the Law of Action and Reaction, the mutual effect of one particle on another, whether it be by direct contact or at a distance through the agency of magnetism, gravitation, or electrostatic action, involves pairs of forces of equal magnitude and opposite direction. Thus, if the gravitational pull of the earth on an orbiting satellite is a force **F** along a line joining the satellite with the center of the earth, the gravitational pull of the satellite on the earth is a force **F** acting along the same line. If a landing airplane exerts a maximum downward force of 100,000 lb by its tire on the runway, the runway exerts an equal and opposite upward force of 100,000 lb on the tire. These statements may all be summed up succinctly by saying that action and reaction are equal and opposite.

2.7   EQUILIBRIUM OF A PARTICLE

A particle is regarded in mechanics as a body which has dimensions sufficiently small that it may be regarded as situated at a point. Thus, when a particle is situated at a point O, and acted on by several forces, it may be said that the forces are concurrent at O. We have seen (Section 2.5) that the motion of a particle under the action of a resultant external force **F** is governed by the Law of

Motion, Eq. (2.5.3). Application of this law to the prediction of particle motion constitutes the field of particle dynamics. It is not our intention to enter into a discussion of this field here, but rather to enunciate the fundamental principle of equilibrium of an unrestrained particle acted on by external forces. This principle, known as *d'Alembert's Principle*, reads: *The system of forces composed of the external forces,* **F**, *and the reversed inertial forces,* $-m\mathbf{a}$, *taken together in vector addition, add up to zero for equilibrium.* Thus, we find that if there are a number of external force vectors $\mathbf{F}^{(1)}$, $\mathbf{F}^{(2)}$, $\mathbf{F}^{(3)}$, ... , $\mathbf{F}^{(n)}$ acting on a particle at O, the particle is in equilibrium providing

$$\sum_{i=1}^{n} \mathbf{F}^{(i)} + (-m\mathbf{a}) = 0. \quad (2.7.1)$$

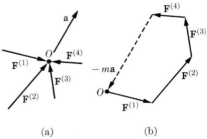

This is equivalent to stating that the particle is in equilibrium when and only when the vectors $\mathbf{F}^{(i)}$ and $-m\mathbf{a}$ drawn successively, beginning to end, form a closed polygon. Such a polygon is illustrated by Fig. 2.8(b). Note that the vector representing the inertia force [$m\mathbf{a}$]

(a)   (b)

FIG. 2.8   Equilibrium of a particle.

in the polygon construction has a sense opposite to the acceleration vector of Fig. 2.8(a). The force polygon will, of course, be a plane figure only when the forces $\mathbf{F}^{(i)}$ are coplanar. Otherwise, it will be a space figure, and methods of descriptive geometry will be required to represent it on a plane.

It is evident that in a statical system where constraints are applied to the particle so that it cannot move, thus requiring that $\mathbf{a} = 0$, the condition of equilibrium simplifies to

$$\sum_{i=1}^{n} \mathbf{F}^{(i)} = 0. \quad (2.7.2)$$

The preceding formula is a vector equation which expresses the equilibrium of the particle; by expressing each force $\mathbf{F}^{(i)}$ in component form, Eq. (2.7.2) becomes

$$\sum_{i=1}^{n} F_r^{(i)} \mathbf{i}_r = 0. \quad (2.7.3)$$

The scalar product of $\mathbf{i}_p$ with Eq. (2.7.3) leads to three scalar equations of equilibrium,

$$\sum_{i=1}^{n} F_p^{(i)} = 0, \quad p = 1, 2, 3. \quad (2.7.4)$$

When p is set equal to one, Eq. (2.7.4) states that the sum of the y_1-components of all the forces acting on the particle is zero. Similarly, the other two values of p state that the sum of y_2- and y_3-components must be zero independently. Thus we may speak of the "three" independent equations for the equilibrium of a particle.

2.8   SUMMARY OF THE PRINCIPLES OF MECHANICS

(a) A *force* has direction, magnitude and a point of application.

(b) *Law of the Parallelogram of Forces.* When two forces, $\mathbf{F}^{(1)}$ and $\mathbf{F}^{(2)}$, act simultaneously at a specified point, they are together equivalent to a single force, $\mathbf{F}^{(1)} + \mathbf{F}^{(2)}$, acting at that point.

(c) *Law of Transmissibility of Forces.* When a force is acting upon a rigid body, it may be translated along its line of action so that it acts on any point of the rigid body which coincides with the line of action.

(d) *Law of Motion.* A particle which is unrestrained and acted upon by a force vector $\mathbf{F}$ acquires an acceleration $\mathbf{a}$ which is proportional in magnitude to the magnitude of $\mathbf{F}$ and along the line of action and in the sense of direction of $\mathbf{F}$.

(e) *Law of Action and Reaction.* When two particles exert forces, one upon the other, whether in direct contact or at a distance from each other, these forces are equal in magnitude and opposite in sense and act along a line joining the two particles.

PROBLEMS

2.1   Expand each of the following sets of equations written with the indicial notation:

(a) $\sigma_m i_m = k_{mn}\sigma_{mn}$,

(b) $\alpha_m \sigma_{am} + \beta_q \sigma_{aq} = \gamma_r \sigma_{ar}$,

(c) $A_{mn}\sigma_m = C_{mr}\sigma_{nr}i_m$,

(d) $\delta_{mn}a_{ms}b_{nt} = C_{st}$.

FIGURE P.2.2

2.2   What is the consequence of the Law of Transmissibility of Forces in the situation illustrated by Fig. P.2.2?

2.3   Write a vector expression for the acceleration of the particle shown in Fig. P.2.3 (forces are expressed in pounds):

$$\mathbf{F}^{(1)} = \mathbf{i}_1 + \mathbf{i}_2 + \mathbf{i}_3,$$
$$\mathbf{F}^{(2)} = 3\mathbf{i}_1 + \mathbf{i}_2 - 2\mathbf{i}_3,$$
$$\mathbf{F}^{(3)} = 4\mathbf{i}_1 - 3\mathbf{i}_2 + 7\mathbf{i}_3,$$
$$\mathbf{F}^{(4)} = 2\mathbf{i}_1 + 5\mathbf{i}_2 + 2\mathbf{i}_3.$$

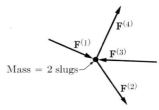

Mass = 2 slugs

FIGURE P.2.3

2.4   A 5000-lb airplane is in a steady glide with the flight path at an angle θ below the horizontal (Fig. P.2.4). The drag force in the direction of the flight path is 750 lb. Find the lift force L normal to the flight path, and angle θ.

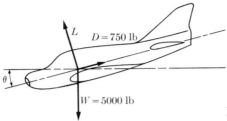

L $D = 750$ lb

θ

$W = 5000$ lb

FIGURE P.2.4

2.5   Three coplanar forces $\mathbf{F}^{(1)}$, $\mathbf{F}^{(2)}$, and $\mathbf{F}^{(3)}$ are acting on a particle in equilibrium (Fig. P.2.5). If $\mathbf{F}^{(1)}$ and α are fixed quantities, determine $\mathbf{F}^{(2)}$, $\mathbf{F}^{(3)}$, and β such that $|\mathbf{F}^{(3)}|$ is a minimum.

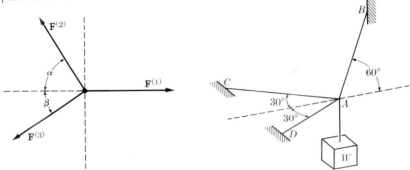

$\mathbf{F}^{(2)}$

α

β

$\mathbf{F}^{(1)}$

$\mathbf{F}^{(3)}$

FIGURE P.2.5

B

$60°$

C $30°$

$30°$

A

D

W

FIGURE P.2.6

2.6   A weight W is supported by three strings AB, AC, and AD (Fig. P.2.6). A, D, and C are on one horizontal plane; AB is at an angle of $60°$ with respect to this plane. Calculate the forces in the strings. [Neglect the change in geometry, i.e., the deflection of point A due to the elongation of the strings.]

2.7   Given the two coordinate systems shown in Fig. P.2.7, and that $\tilde{y}_1$ and $\tilde{y}_2$ lie in the y_1y_2-plane.
(a) Fill in the table of nine direction cosines $l_{\tilde{m}n}$.

	y_1	y_2	y_3
$\tilde{y}_1$			
$\tilde{y}_2$			
$\tilde{y}_3$			

(b) Given the force vector $\mathbf{F} = \mathbf{i}_1 - 2\mathbf{i}_2 + \mathbf{i}_3$ expressed in the $y_1y_2y_3$-system. Express this vector in the new $\tilde{y}_1\tilde{y}_2\tilde{y}_3$-system.

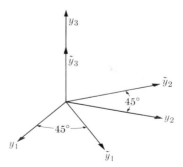

y_3

$\tilde{y}_3$

$\tilde{y}_2$

$45°$

y_2

$45°$

y_1

$\tilde{y}_1$

FIGURE P.2.7

2.8   Three mutually perpendicular strings, OP, OQ, and OR, are attached to the corner, O, of a cube. The edges of the cube are represented by OA, OB, and OC. Each string carries a tensile force. The magnitudes of the string forces are shown in Fig. P.2.8. The direction cosines between the strings and the cube edges are:

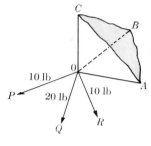

	OP	OQ	OR
OA	$-\dfrac{1}{\sqrt{2}}$	$\dfrac{1}{\sqrt{2}}$	0
OB	$-\dfrac{1}{2}$	$-\dfrac{1}{2}$	$\dfrac{1}{\sqrt{2}}$
OC	$-\dfrac{1}{2}$	$-\dfrac{1}{2}$	$-\dfrac{1}{\sqrt{2}}$

FIGURE P.2.8

(a) Find the magnitude of the resultant force which acts on the corner of the cube.
(b) Find the components of the resultant force with respect to the edges of the cube. [All results may be left in radical form.]

2.9   A weight W is suspended by two identical springs, each with a spring constant k (lb/in). The length of each spring in its unstretched position is L. The upper ends of the springs are located a distance L apart (Fig. P.2.9). Write the equations which can be used to determine H, the final length of the spring, in terms of L, k, and W. [*Note:* In this problem the change in geometry has been included in the equilibrium equations. What is the parameter which must be large before the change in geometry can be neglected?]

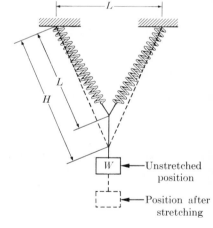

FIGURE P.2.9

3

Statics

3.1 INTRODUCTION

In the preceding chapter we discussed four laws basic to the whole subject of mechanics. We shall take up now the application of these laws to problems of the static equilibrium of particles and bodies under the action of forces and moments. We introduce this subject by discussing some of the special properties of forces and moments and their interrelations. Finally, we examine in detail some important scientific and engineering applications of statics.

3.2 PROPERTIES OF FORCE AND MOMENTS

(a) The moment of a force about a point. We will consider a force vector **F** which is arbitrarily oriented with respect to a point p, and calculate the moment produced by **F** about p. Let us construct the plane $ABCD$ defined by the vector **F** and the point p, as shown by Fig. 3.1, and draw in the plane the perpendicular line a from p to **F**. Then the magnitude of the moment of **F** about p is given by the product of **F** and the distance a.

$$|\mathbf{M}| = a|\mathbf{F}|. \tag{3.2.1}$$

It is convenient to assign a positive direction to the moment, and we do this by regarding it as a vector defined by

$$\mathbf{M} = \mathbf{r} \times \mathbf{F}, \tag{3.2.2}$$

where **r** is any vector drawn in the plane $ABCD$ from p to a point on the line of action of **F**. The positive direction of the moment vector **M**, according to the rule for vector products (see Appendix, Section A.13), is as shown by Fig. 3.1 and is along a line perpendicular to the plane $ABCD$. It is in the direction in which a right-hand screw will advance if the vectors **r** and **F** are translated along their lines of action so that they act at a common point, and the vector **r** is turned into the vector **F** through the smallest possible angle.

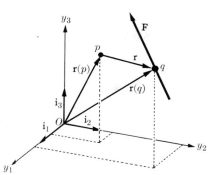

Fɪɢ. 3.1   Moment of a force about a point.

Fɪɢ. 3.2   The component form of the moment of **F** about p is required.

Since **M** is a vector, it can also be written in component form:

$$\mathbf{M} = M_m \mathbf{i}_m. \tag{3.2.3}$$

The meaning of the components $M_1 \mathbf{i}_1$, $M_2 \mathbf{i}_2$, and $M_3 \mathbf{i}_3$ can be determined with the aid of the right-hand rule.

It is evident that the moment of **F** about p is unchanged by moving **F** along its line of action, and that the moment will vanish only when **F** passes through p which means $a = |\mathbf{r}| = 0$.

Exᴀᴍᴘʟᴇ: To compute in component form the moment of an arbitrary force about a point.

Solution: Referring to Fig. 3.2 we designate the force vector by **F**, and the point about which the moment is to be taken by p. Both quantities are assumed to be embedded in an orthogonal Cartesian coordinate system y_1, y_2, and y_3 with the unit vectors $\mathbf{i}_1$, $\mathbf{i}_2$, and $\mathbf{i}_3$. The point p is located by the position vector $\mathbf{r}(p)$. Suppose that the vector **r** is drawn from the point p to any point q along the line of action of **F**. Then the moment of **F** about p is given by

$$\mathbf{M} = \mathbf{r} \times \mathbf{F} = [\mathbf{r}(q) - \mathbf{r}(p)] \times \mathbf{F}, \tag{3.2.4}$$

where $\mathbf{r}(q)$ is the vector connecting the origin of coordinates with q. The component forms of these vectors are

$$
\begin{aligned}
\mathbf{r} &= y_1 \mathbf{i}_1 + y_2 \mathbf{i}_2 + y_3 \mathbf{i}_3 = y_m \mathbf{i}_m, \\
\mathbf{r}(p) &= y_1(p) \mathbf{i}_1 + y_2(p) \mathbf{i}_2 + y_3(p) \mathbf{i}_3 = y_m(p) \mathbf{i}_m, \\
\mathbf{r}(q) &= y_1(q) \mathbf{i}_1 + y_2(q) \mathbf{i}_2 + y_3(q) \mathbf{i}_3 = y_m(q) \mathbf{i}_m, \\
\mathbf{F} &= F_1 \mathbf{i}_1 + F_2 \mathbf{i}_2 + F_3 \mathbf{i}_3 = F_m \mathbf{i}_m.
\end{aligned}
\tag{3.2.5}
$$

Inserting Eq. (3.2.5) into (3.2.4) yields the following component form of the moment vector:

$$\mathbf{M} = \{[y_2(q) - y_2(p)]F_3 - [y_3(q) - y_3(p)]F_2\}\mathbf{i}_1$$
$$+ \{[y_3(q) - y_3(p)]F_1 - [y_1(q) - y_1(p)]F_3\}\mathbf{i}_2$$
$$+ \{[y_1(q) - y_1(p)]F_2 - [y_2(q) - y_2(p)]F_1\}\mathbf{i}_3. \qquad (3.2.6)$$

Although it may appear at first glance that the magnitude of $\mathbf{M}$ is dependent upon the location of the terminus of $\mathbf{r}(q)$ on the line of action of $\mathbf{F}$, closer inspection will show that the result is independent of this location.

The use of the permutation tensor, e_{mnp} (see Appendix, Section A.3) very neatly yields the results shown in Eqs. (3.2.4), (3.2.5), and (3.2.6). Thus Eq. (3.2.4) can be written as

$$\mathbf{M} = [y_m(q)\mathbf{i}_m - y_m(p)\mathbf{i}_m] \times F_r\mathbf{i}_r, \qquad (3.2.7a)$$

or

$$\mathbf{M} = [y_m(q) - y_m(p)]F_r(\mathbf{i}_m \times \mathbf{i}_r). \qquad (3.2.7b)$$

The vector products of the unit vectors (see Appendix, Section A.13) can be expressed as

$$\mathbf{i}_m \times \mathbf{i}_r = e_{mrk}\mathbf{i}_k, \qquad (3.2.8)$$

and hence

$$\mathbf{M} = [y_m(q) - y_m(p)]F_r\, e_{mrk}\, \mathbf{i}_k. \qquad (3.2.9)$$

The components of $\mathbf{M}$ are seen to be

$$M_k = [y_m(q) - y_m(p)]F_r\, e_{mrk}. \qquad (3.2.10)$$

(b) The moment of a force about an axis. In the previous subsection we saw that the moment of a force $\mathbf{F}$ about a point is given by Eq. (3.2.2), in which any position vector $\mathbf{r}$ drawn from the point to the line of action of the force is crossed into the force vector. Suppose that a line l is drawn through the point p, and we now compute the moment of $\mathbf{F}$ about this line. Of the two possible senses of l, we take one as positive and designate it by a unit vector $\mathbf{e}$ collinear with l, as illustrated by Fig. 3.3. Since the line l is assigned a positive sense of direction, we refer to it as an axis. The scalar component of the moment of $\mathbf{F}$ about l is defined as the component M_l of $\mathbf{M}$ in the positive sense of l. Then

$$M_l = \mathbf{e} \cdot \mathbf{M} = \mathbf{e} \cdot (\mathbf{r} \times \mathbf{F}). \qquad (3.2.11)$$

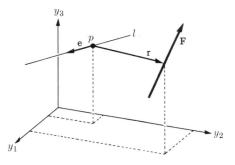

FIG. 3.3   Moment of a force about an axis.

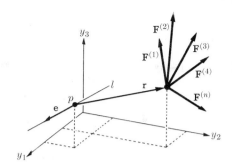

Fig. 3.4   Moment of a force about the   Fig. 3.5   Moment of several force vec-
y_3-axis.   tors about a line.

Equation (3.2.11) announces that the moment of a force $\mathbf{F}$ about an axis is equal to the component of $\mathbf{r} \times \mathbf{F}$ along that axis. Clearly the vector $\mathbf{r}$ may be any vector drawn from the axis to the line of action of $\mathbf{F}$.

EXAMPLE: To compute in component form the moment of an arbitrary force about the y_3-axis.

Solution: We take the vector $\mathbf{r}$ which connects the y_3-axis with the line of action of $\mathbf{F}$, as illustrated by Fig. 3.4. Then the solution is obtained by substituting into

$$M_3 = \mathbf{i}_3 \cdot (\mathbf{r} \times \mathbf{F}) \tag{3.2.12}$$

the component forms

$$\mathbf{r} = y_m \mathbf{i}_m, \qquad \mathbf{F} = F_r \mathbf{i}_r. \tag{3.2.13}$$

This yields the final result,

$$M_3 = y_m F_r e_{rm3} = y_1 F_2 - y_2 F_1. \tag{3.2.14}$$

(c) Theorem of Varignon.   We consider next the question of computing the moment about the line l of several force vectors having a common origin A as illustrated by Fig. 3.5 for the forces $\mathbf{F}^{(1)}$, $\mathbf{F}^{(2)}$, $\mathbf{F}^{(3)}$, . . . , $\mathbf{F}^{(n)}$. This moment is the sum of the moments of the individual vectors, and

$$M_l = \mathbf{e} \cdot (\mathbf{r} \times \mathbf{F}^{(1)}) + \mathbf{e} \cdot (\mathbf{r} \times \mathbf{F}^{(2)}) + \cdots + \mathbf{e} \cdot (\mathbf{r} \times \mathbf{F}^{(n)}), \tag{3.2.15}$$

which reduces, since the vector-product law is distributive, to

$$M_l = \mathbf{e} \cdot [\mathbf{r} \times (\mathbf{F}^{(1)} + \mathbf{F}^{(2)} + \cdots + \mathbf{F}^{(n)})]. \tag{3.2.16}$$

It is evident that if $\mathbf{R}$ is the resultant of the forces $\mathbf{F}^{(k)}$,

$$\mathbf{R} = \mathbf{F}^{(1)} + \mathbf{F}^{(2)} + \cdots + \mathbf{F}^{(n)}, \tag{3.2.17}$$

then we may conclude that the moment of the resultant is equal to the sum of the moments of the individual forces. This result, known as the Theorem of

Varignon, is stated in detail as follows: *The sum of the moments about an axis of several force vectors with a common origin is equal to the moment about the axis of the resultant of these vectors.*

(d) Couples. A pair of forces of equal magnitude, opposite direction, and different but parallel lines of action is known as a *couple*. Figure 3.6 illustrates a couple consisting of forces $\mathbf{F}$ and $-\mathbf{F}$ lying in a plane designated by $ABCD$. It is evident that the vector sum of a couple is zero. Let us consider the moment of the couple about an arbitrary line s perpendicular to this plane. Referring to the notation of Fig. 3.6, we see that this moment is

$$\mathbf{C} = \mathbf{r}(q) \times \mathbf{F} - \mathbf{r}(p) \times \mathbf{F} = [\mathbf{r}(q) - \mathbf{r}(p)] \times \mathbf{F} = \mathbf{r} \times \mathbf{F}. \qquad (3.2.18)$$

Then

$$\mathbf{C} = a|\mathbf{F}|\mathbf{n}, \qquad (3.2.19)$$

where a is the perpendicular distance between the parallel force vectors and $\mathbf{n}$ is a unit vector which is perpendicular to the plane $ABCD$. The positive sense of $\mathbf{n}$ is given by the right-hand rule. Equation (3.2.19) indicates that the total moment of the forces forming a couple is independent of the location of s. The symbol $\mathbf{C}$ is used to distinguish a couple from the moment vector $\mathbf{M}$, which is a function of location. Note also that the couple vector does not have a definite point of application. We refer therefore to the magnitude of the moment of a couple in an absolute sense as the product of the magnitude of the forces of the couple times the perpendicular distance between these forces. The direction of the moment of the couple is determined by the same rule of direction that governs the moments of forces. For example, in Fig. 3.6 the moment vector associated with the couple points in the plus $\mathbf{n}$-direction, since a right-hand screw turned in the direction of rotation of the couple would advance in this direction.

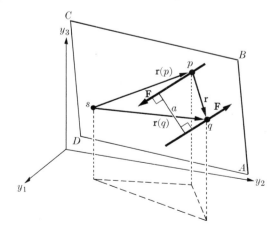

FIG. 3.6   Moment produced by a couple.

(e) Equipollent force systems. Two systems of forces are said to be *equipollent* when either system may be replaced by the other. (Pollent is Greek, meaning "powerful," and thus, equipollent means equally powerful.) In more detail we say that the two systems are equipollent if

  (1) the resultant of the forces of one system is equal to the resultant of forces of the other system, and
  (2) the sum of the moments of the forces of one system about an arbitrary base point is equal to the sum of the moments of the forces of the other system about the same point.

It is evident, for example, that system A which consists of a force vector $\mathbf{F}$ and a position vector $\mathbf{r}$ is equipollent to system B in which the force vector $\mathbf{F}$ is moved to the origin and a moment $\mathbf{r} \times \mathbf{F}$ is added.

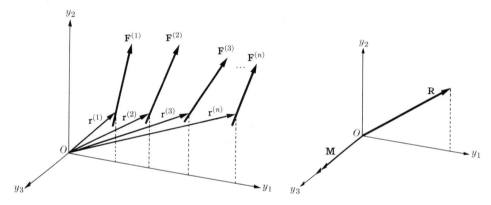

FIG. 3.7   Arbitrary system of coplanar forces.   FIG. 3.8   Reduced system of coplanar forces.

(f) Reduction of coplanar force systems. Let us consider next for simplicity a number of forces lying in the y_1y_2-plane, as illustrated by Fig. 3.7. Let $\mathbf{R}$ be their sum and $\mathbf{M}$ their total moment about the y_3-axis. The system consisting of $\mathbf{R}$ and $\mathbf{M}$ shown in Fig. 3.8 is evidently plane equipollent to the given system of forces.

   We may also state in a slightly different way that any system of forces in a plane may be reduced to a single force located at some arbitrary point s and a moment about s. This reduction process may be carried out analytically. Let us suppose, for example, that we wish to reduce the system of Fig. 3.7 to a single force at the origin and a moment about the origin. This result is illustrated by Fig. 3.8, where

$$\mathbf{R} = \sum_{i=1}^{n} \mathbf{F}^{(i)}, \tag{3.2.20}$$

$$\mathbf{M} = \sum_{i=1}^{n} \mathbf{r}^{(i)} \times \mathbf{F}^{(i)}, \tag{3.2.21}$$

and $\mathbf{r}^{(i)}$ are position vectors from the origin to points on the lines of action of the force vectors $\mathbf{F}^{(i)}$. In component form, Eq. (3.2.20) becomes

$$R_1 = \sum_{i=1}^{n} F_1^{(i)}, \qquad R_2 = \sum_{i=1}^{n} F_2^{(i)}, \tag{3.2.22}$$

where the subscripts 1 and 2 indicate components along the y_1- and y_2-axes, respectively. Similarly, Eq. (3.2.21) has the scalar form of

$$|\mathbf{M}| = \sum_{i=1}^{n} (y_1^{(i)} F_2^{(i)} - y_2^{(i)} F_1^{(i)}). \tag{3.2.23}$$

We have so far demonstrated how a system of forces may be reduced to a single force at a point and a moment about this same point. There can be further reductions. For example, let us consider a case where $\mathbf{R} \neq 0$ and $\mathbf{M} \neq 0$, and replace $\mathbf{M}$ in Fig. 3.8 by a couple with forces $\pm\mathbf{R}$. Thus we may replace the system of Fig. 3.8 by another equipollent system shown in Fig. 3.9. The perpendicular distance OA in Fig. 3.9, that is, the arm of the couple, is equal to $|\mathbf{M}|/|\mathbf{R}|$. Since the vectors $\pm\mathbf{R}$ at the origin cancel each other, it is evident that the system represented by a single force vector $\mathbf{R}$ located at the perpendicular distance OA from the origin is plane equipollent to the system of Fig. 3.8 and the original system of Fig. 3.7.

Let us consider next a case when $\mathbf{R} = 0$ and $\mathbf{M} \neq 0$. It is obvious that in this case the equipollent system consists of a couple. Finally, we summarize the results stated above by saying that an arbitrary coplanar force system may be reduced to (1) a single force at an arbitrary point plus a moment about this point, (2) to a single force at a unique point if there are no couples, or (3) to a couple if there is no resultant force.

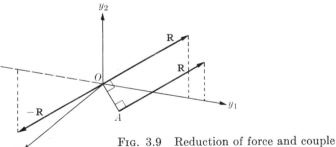

FIG. 3.9 Reduction of force and couple to single force.

(g) Reduction of force systems in space. In the preceding section we discussed the reduction of arbitrary coplanar force systems to a single force and a couple about an arbitrary point. The same conclusion may be drawn also for force systems in space. We may, for example, reduce any system of forces in space to its equipollent system consisting of a single force and moment as represented

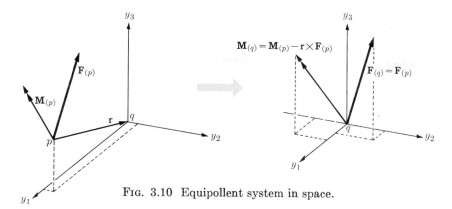

FIG. 3.10 Equipollent system in space.

by the vectors $\mathbf{F}(p)$ and $\mathbf{M}(p)$, respectively, on the left-hand side of Fig. 3.10. If we change the base point p to another base point q, and if we wish to construct another equipollent system at q, we move the force $\mathbf{F}$ without alteration to q, but affix the new moment vector

$$\mathbf{M}(q) = \mathbf{M}(p) - \mathbf{r} \times \mathbf{F}(p), \tag{3.2.24}$$

where $\mathbf{r}$ is the displacement vector connecting base points p and q. Thus, under a change in base point, the original force $\mathbf{F}$ and moment $\mathbf{M}$ at p are transformed at q to $\mathbf{F}(q)$ and $\mathbf{M}(q)$ given by

$$\mathbf{F}(q) = \mathbf{F}(p), \qquad \mathbf{M}(q) = \mathbf{M}(p) - \mathbf{r} \times \mathbf{F}(p). \tag{3.2.25}$$

3.3 EQUILIBRIUM OF A PARTICLE

(a) Condition of equilibrium. In mechanics a particle is regarded as a body which is concentrated in a single point. It may be of such small dimensions that it can be considered to occupy a vanishingly small area represented by a point P. The forces on the particle may, therefore, be regarded as concurrent at the point P. However, of greater practical importance, we may regard any body as a particle so long as the forces are applied such that when they are shifted along their lines of action they may be made concurrent at some point P in the body.

A particle is said to be in static equilibrium when the vector sum of the concurrent forces acting at the point P is zero (cf. Eq. 2.7.2). That is, if the forces acting on the particle are represented by $\mathbf{F}^{(1)}, \mathbf{F}^{(2)}, \ldots, \mathbf{F}^{(n)}$, the condition for equilibrium is represented by the vector equation,

$$\sum_{i=1}^{n} \mathbf{F}^{(i)} = 0. \tag{3.3.1}$$

The vector equation (3.3.1) may also be expressed in component form. If we take components along the orthogonal y_1-y_2-y_3 triad, we have as the scalar form of Eq. (3.3.1):

$$\sum_{i=1}^{n} F_1^{(i)} = 0, \qquad \sum_{i=1}^{n} F_2^{(i)} = 0, \qquad \sum_{i=1}^{n} F_3^{(i)} = 0. \tag{3.3.2}$$

Equations (3.3.2) require that the sums of the forces in each of the three orthogonal directions be individually equal to zero.

Equation (3.3.1) may be satisfied in a geometric sense by constructing a polygon of forces where the vectors $\mathbf{F}^{(i)}$ are drawn successively tail-to-head to form a space polygon.

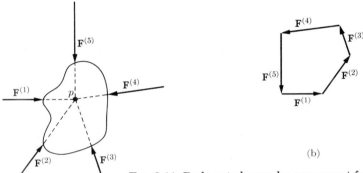

(a)

(b)

Fig. 3.11 Body acted upon by concurrent forces in static equilibrium: (a) free-body diagram; (b) polygon of forces.

(b) Free-body diagram. A free-body diagram in mechanics represents a diagram in which the body is drawn free and clear of all its supports or reacting bodies, with their influence represented by appropriate reactive forces. Figure 3.11(a) illustrates a coplanar free-body diagram with forces concurrent at a single point. Figure 3.11(b) shows the corresponding coplanar force polygon which represents the particle equilibrium.

As a simple illustration of how one arrives at a free-body diagram, we refer to Fig. 3.12, which shows a circular cylinder resting on a flat surface. The physical diagram of Fig. 3.12(a) is replaced by the free-body diagram of Fig. 3.12(b) by removing the horizontal surface and replacing it by the normal reaction R. This step puts one in position to write the equations of equilibrium of the particle, which in this case are

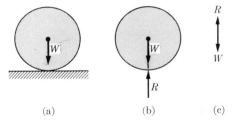

(a)   (b)   (c)

Fig. 3.12 Circular cylinder resting on table: (a) physical diagram; (b) free-body diagram; (c) force polygon.

obtained merely by summing the vertical forces (see Fig. 3.12c):

$$R - W = 0, \tag{3.3.3}$$

where W is the weight of the cylinder. Equation (3.3.3) allows one to compute the reaction of the circular cylinder on the plane as $R = W$.

EXAMPLE: To compute the reactions on a circular cylinder resting in a smooth trough, as illustrated by Fig. 3.13(a).

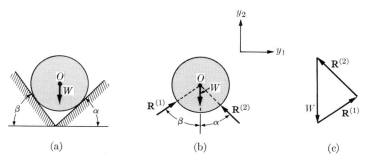

(a)   (b)   (c)

FIG. 3.13 Circular cylinder resting in a smooth trough: (a) physical diagram; (b) free-body diagram; (c) force polygon.

Solution: We may construct the free-body diagram of Fig. 3.13(b) by removing the trough and replacing it by two reactions $\mathbf{R}^{(1)}$ and $\mathbf{R}^{(2)}$ perpendicular to the surfaces of the trough. Since the surfaces of the trough are assumed smooth these reactions pass through the center O of the circular cylinder. We have a system of forces which are concurrent at O, and the cylinder may be treated as a particle. The two unknowns of the problem, $\mathbf{R}^{(1)}$ and $\mathbf{R}^{(2)}$, may be computed by applying Eqs. (3.3.2), that is, by requiring that the sum of the horizontal and the sum of the vertical forces each be zero. We find that

$$\sum_{i=1}^{3} F_1^{(i)} = R^{(1)} \sin \beta - R^{(2)} \sin \alpha = 0,$$

$$\sum_{i=1}^{3} F_2^{(i)} = R^{(1)} \cos \beta + R^{(2)} \cos \alpha - W = 0, \tag{3.3.4}$$

from which we obtain the reactions

$$|\mathbf{R}^{(1)}| = \frac{W \sin \alpha}{\sin (\alpha + \beta)}, \qquad |\mathbf{R}^{(2)}| = \frac{W \sin \beta}{\sin (\alpha + \beta)}. \tag{3.3.5}$$

(c) Supports. There are some symbols employed in solid mechanics to represent special kinds of supports which are used to restrain structures. The symbol

⊥⊥⊥ or ⟂ represents a support which can only supply a force of either sense along a line perpendicular to the surface. The symbol ⟂ represents a support

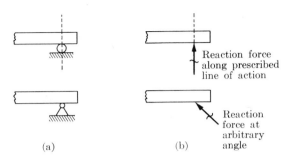

FIG. 3.14 Schematic representation of supports: (a) physical diagrams; (b) free-body diagrams.

which fixes the point of application but not the line of action of the force. Generally these supports are used only in planar structures and such supports are actually used. (The next time you sail under a simple bridge, look at the supports for each span.) Their properties are shown schematically in Fig. 3.14. In this figure the symbol ⤴ is used to indicate a reaction force.

3.4 EQUILIBRIUM OF A SYSTEM OF PARTICLES

(a) Conditions of equilibrium. Let us consider in detail the conditions for static equilibrium of a system of particles which may be interconnected in any manner whatsoever. In such a problem we must be very careful and clear at the outset as to which particles constitute the total system. For example, we might regard the solar system as a system of several particles consisting of the sun and the planets; or we might regard the earth and moon as a two-particle system. A pile of n books lying on a table, where we regard each book and the table as a separate particle, may comprise a system of $n + 1$ particles. It is quite clear that the choice of individual particles and definition of their aggregate system from a given arrangement in nature is an important preliminary step in the discussion of a system of particles.

In examining a given particle in a system of particles, we find two kinds of forces, internal and external. A force on a particle is internal when it is exerted by another particle of that system. The Law of Action and Reaction comes into play in dealing with internal forces. The law asserts that internal forces occur in equal and opposite pairs, each pair representing the mutual interaction of a pair of particles, one upon the other. These internal forces may be due, for example, to surface contact of the particles, mechanical connections between the particles, or electromagnetic, electrostatic, and gravitational forces. Figure 3.15 shows an example of a three-particle system under the influence of external forces. $\mathbf{P}^{(i)}$ is the vector sum of all external forces on the ith particle, $\mathbf{R}^{(ij)}$ is the internal force on the ith particle due to jth particle. For example, mass (1) is acted on by a resultant external force $\mathbf{P}^{(1)}$ and two internal forces $\mathbf{R}^{(12)}$ and

$\mathbf{R}^{(13)}$. In general, for a system of n particles, the equation of equilibrium for the ith particle is

$$\mathbf{P}^{(i)} + \sum_{i \neq j}^{n} \mathbf{R}^{(ij)} = 0, \qquad i, j = 1, 2, \ldots, n, \tag{3.4.1}$$

or the force polygon formed by these force vectors must be closed. Note that

$$\mathbf{R}^{(ij)} = -\mathbf{R}^{(ji)}, \qquad i, j = 1, 2, \ldots, n, \tag{3.4.2}$$

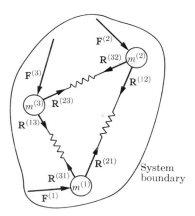

FIG. 3.15   A system of particles.

because action equals reaction, and quantities such as $\mathbf{R}^{(11)}$, $\mathbf{R}^{(22)}$, etc., do not exist. Equation (3.4.2), which states that the internal forces between any two particles are equal in magnitude and opposite in direction, applies irrespective of how the particles are interconnected.

By summing the forces on all the particles of the system, that is, by summing Eq. (3.4.1) on i, we obtain

$$\sum_{i=1}^{n} \mathbf{P}^{(i)} + \sum_{i=1}^{n} \sum_{j=1}^{n} \mathbf{R}^{(ij)} = 0. \tag{3.4.3}$$

This merely represents the addition of all n of the equations represented by Eq. (3.4.1). If the double summation term is written out explicitly, it will be observed that the terms can be grouped in pairs such as $\mathbf{R}^{(12)} + \mathbf{R}^{(21)}$, $\mathbf{R}^{(23)} + \mathbf{R}^{(32)}$, etc., and by virtue of Eq. (3.4.2) these terms will vanish; hence the equilibrium equation (3.4.3) reduces to

$$\sum_{i=1}^{n} \mathbf{P}^{(i)} = 0. \tag{3.4.4}$$

Equation (3.4.4) states one of the requirements of equilibrium; that the sum of the external forces on the system be equal to zero. Another requirement for equilibrium is derived from Eq. (3.4.1). Let $\mathbf{r}^{(i)}$ be the position vector of the ith particle with respect to some axis system located at point O. Then we can form the vector product of $\mathbf{r}^{(i)}$ with Eq. (3.4.1),

$$\mathbf{r}^{(i)} \times \mathbf{P}^{(i)} + \sum_{j=1}^{n} \mathbf{r}^{(i)} \times \mathbf{R}^{(ij)} = 0, \tag{3.4.5}$$

which becomes, after summing on i (that is, adding up all n equations),

$$\sum_{i=1}^{n} \mathbf{r}^{(i)} \times \mathbf{P}^{(i)} + \sum_{i=1}^{n} \sum_{j=1}^{n} \mathbf{r}^{(i)} \times \mathbf{R}^{(ij)} = 0. \tag{3.4.6}$$

We may regroup the second term in the above equation as

$$\frac{1}{2} \sum_{i=1}^{n} \sum_{j=1}^{n} (\mathbf{r}^{(i)} - \mathbf{r}^{(j)}) \times \mathbf{R}^{(ij)},$$

by applying Eq. (3.4.2). Since the two vectors, $(\mathbf{r}^{(i)} - \mathbf{r}^{(j)})$ and $\mathbf{R}^{(ij)}$, are parallel, this term is identically zero. We obtain

$$\sum_{i=1}^{n} \mathbf{r}^{(i)} \times \mathbf{P}^{(i)} = 0. \qquad (3.4.7)$$

Equation (3.4.7) states that the total moment about O of the external force system is zero.

Thus the two requirements for a system of particles to be in equilibrium are that (1) the sum of the external forces on the system be equal to zero [vector equation (3.4.4)] and (2) the sum of the moments of the external forces about some arbitrary point be equal to zero [vector equation (3.4.7)]. If we resolve the vectors in their component form with respect to an orthogonal triad y_1-y_2-y_3 with origin at O, we have the following six scalar equations of equilibrium:

$$\sum_{i=1}^{n} P_1^{(i)} = 0, \qquad (3.4.8)$$

$$\sum_{i=1}^{n} P_2^{(i)} = 0, \qquad (3.4.9)$$

$$\sum_{i=1}^{n} P_3^{(i)} = 0, \qquad (3.4.10)$$

$$\sum_{i=1}^{n} (y_2^{(i)} P_3^{(i)} - y_3^{(i)} P_2^{(i)}) = 0, \qquad (3.4.11)$$

$$\sum_{i=1}^{n} (y_3^{(i)} P_1^{(i)} - y_1^{(i)} P_3^{(i)}) = 0, \qquad (3.4.12)$$

$$\sum_{i=1}^{n} (y_1^{(i)} P_2^{(i)} - y_2^{(i)} P_1^{(i)}) = 0. \qquad (3.4.13)$$

The first three equations state that the resultants of the y_1-, y_2-, and y_3-components, respectively, of all the external forces must be equal to zero. The last three equations state that the moments of all the forces about the y_1-, y_2-, and y_3-axes, respectively, must be zero.

The entire theory of statics rests on the vector equations (3.4.4) and (3.4.7), or alternatively on their scalar representation, Eqs. (3.4.8) through (3.4.13). We have stated previously that the particles of the body may be connected in any manner whatsoever. Thus these equations may be applied to a rigid body, an elastic or plastic deformable body, or a volume of fluid. We shall illustrate several examples of the equilibrium of bodies of various kinds.

EXAMPLE 1: As a current example of a system of particles let us consider the reentering Mercury capsule shown in Fig. 3.16. All forces and accelerations are parallel to the y_1-axis, and it is assumed that the parachute and capsule centers of gravity lie on a common line parallel to the y_1-axis. For such a system the three equilibrium equations for moment [Eqs. (3.4.11) through (3.4.13)] do not appear in the problem, and only one equilibrium equation for the external forces is required. The external forces acting on the system are

$$\mathbf{D}^{(i)} \quad \text{(drag forces on parachute and capsule),}$$
$$\mathbf{W}^{(i)} \quad \text{(weights of parachute and capsule),}$$

where $i = p, c$. In addition, d'Alembert forces $-m^{(i)}\mathbf{a}$ may also be considered as external forces acting on the capsule and parachute because of the deceleration of the system.

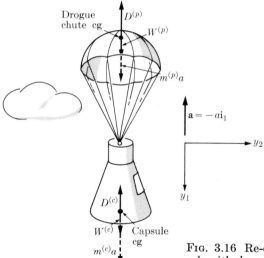

FIG. 3.16 Re-entering Mercury capsule with drogue parachute deployed.

All the forces acting may be transferred to the center of gravity of the entire system, and the following equilibrium equation may be written in the y_1-direction:

$$\mathbf{W}^{(p)} + \mathbf{W}^{(c)} - (m^{(p)} + m^{(c)})\mathbf{a} - \mathbf{D}^{(p)} - \mathbf{D}^{(c)} = 0. \qquad (3.4.14)$$

Equation (3.4.14) completes the analysis of the parachute and capsule as a one-particle system. Figure 3.17 illustrates the manner in which we may represent the capsule and parachute as a two-particle system. In addition to

FIG. 3.17 Mercury capsule and drogue parachute as a two-particle system.

the external and d'Alembert forces, we must now delineate the internal forces,

$\mathbf{F}^{(pc)}$ on the parachute from the capsule,

$\mathbf{F}^{(cp)}$ on the capsule from the parachute.

The equations of equilibrium for each of the particles now read

$$\mathbf{F}^{(pc)} + \mathbf{W}^{(p)} - m^{(p)}\mathbf{a} - \mathbf{D}^{(p)} = 0 \quad \text{(parachute)},$$
$$\mathbf{F}^{(cp)} + \mathbf{W}^{(c)} - m^{(c)}\mathbf{a} - \mathbf{D}^{(c)} = 0 \quad \text{(capsule)}. \tag{3.4.15}$$

If we make an imaginary cut to obtain the two-particle representation, as shown at the left of Figure 3.17, we see that the internal force, $\mathbf{F}^{(pc)}$, has been added to the parachute to account for the effects of the external forces on the parachute through the capsule, that is,

$$\mathbf{F}^{(pc)} = \mathbf{W}^{(c)} - m^{(c)}\mathbf{a} - \mathbf{D}^{(c)}. \tag{3.4.16}$$

Similarly, the internal force, $\mathbf{F}^{(cp)}$, has been added to the capsule to account for the effects of the external forces on the capsule through the parachute,

$$\mathbf{F}^{(cp)} = \mathbf{W}^{(p)} - m^{(p)}\mathbf{a} - \mathbf{D}^{(p)}. \tag{3.4.17}$$

The equilibrium equation (3.4.14) for the original one-particle representation may be rewritten

$$\mathbf{W}^{(p)} - m^{(p)}\mathbf{a} - \mathbf{D}^{(p)} = -[\mathbf{W}^{(c)} - m^{(c)}\mathbf{a} - \mathbf{D}^{(c)}], \tag{3.4.18}$$

which, when combined with Eqs. (3.4.16) and (3.4.17), yields the expected

$$\mathbf{F}^{(cp)} = -\mathbf{F}^{(pc)}. \tag{3.4.19}$$

Thus we have developed an alternative view of internal forces. We begin with an entire system in equilibrium with a set of applied external forces. When a particular particle of the system is isolated for detailed study, internal forces arise at the particle-system interfaces from the transmission of the action of external forces on the rest of the system.

FIG. 3.18. Hammerhead crane structure.

EXAMPLE 2: As another example which may be considered as a collection of particles, let us consider the so-called hammerhead crane which is used in the erection of buildings (see Fig. 3.18). The crane consists of a vertical tower (the handle of a hammer) and a long horizontal boom (the head). The concrete bucket (or other useful load) is suspended on a cable at one end of the boom, and a large mass of concrete which serves as a counterweight is fixed at the other end. There are many possible subdivisions which can be made of the structural system depicted in Fig. 3.18. One such system is shown in Fig. 3.19. An explanation follows.

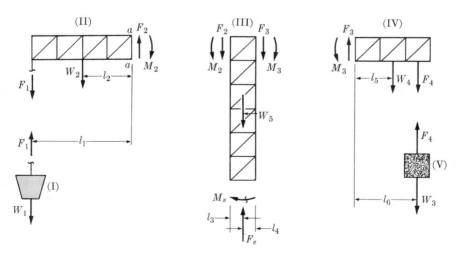

FIG. 3.19   Free-body diagram of subdivided hammerhead crane structure.

In subcollection I, W_1 represents the weight of the bucket plus contents and a portion of the cable, F_1 is the force in the cable at this point, and for equilibrium

$$F_1 = W_1. \tag{3.4.20}$$

For subcollection II, F_2 and M_2 are a force and moment equipollent to the internal forces at section a–a of the boom, and F_1 is the cable force which by the Law of Action and Reaction (see Section 2.6) is the equal and opposite of the F_1-force shown in subcollection I.

For the vertical equilibrium of subsystem II

$$F_2 = F_1 + W_2, \tag{3.4.21}$$

and for rotational or moment equilibrium,

$$M_2 = F_1 l_1 + W_2 l_2, \tag{3.4.22}$$

where W_2 is the weight of the boom and cable included in II, l_2 locates its center of gravity, and l_1 is the length of the boom. The horizontal equilibrium of part II is assured because there are no externally applied forces with horizontal components.

For subcollections IV and V the corresponding equations are

$$F_3 = W_4 + F_4, \tag{3.4.23}$$

$$M_3 = F_4 l_6 + W_4 l_5, \tag{3.4.24}$$

$$F_4 = W_3. \tag{3.4.25}$$

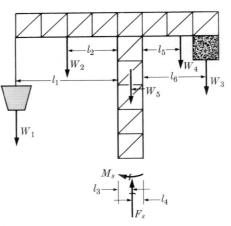

The central vertical tower has acting on it the internal forces transmitted from the two portions of the horizontal boom, the dead weight W_5 of the tower, and the support force and moment F_s and M_s. Equilibrium of subcollection III requires that

$$F_s = F_2 + F_3 + W_5, \tag{3.4.26}$$

$$M_s = M_2 + F_2 l_2 - M_1 - F_3 l_4. \tag{3.4.27}$$

Fig. 3.20   Free-body diagram of complete hammerhead crane structure.

We can obtain the support reactions more directly by reassembling the five subcollections into the total structure (see Fig. 3.20). Then the internal forces are no longer visible. The equations of equilibrium obtained by examining Fig. 3.20 are

$$F_s = W_1 + W_2 + W_3 + W_4 + W_5, \tag{3.4.28}$$

$$M_s = W_1(l_1 + l_3) + W_2(l_2 + l_3) - W_3(l_4 + l_6) - W_4(l_4 + l_5). \tag{3.4.29}$$

It can be easily verified that the simultaneous solution of Eqs. (3.4.20) through (3.4.27) will yield Eqs. (3.4.28) and (3.4.29).

Example 3: Let us next compute the forces required to maintain an airplane in equilibrium in steady level flight. Figure 3.21 shows a simplified free-body diagram of an airplane of weight W in steady level flight. Let it be assumed that at the flight speed of the airplane the drag D is known. It is required to compute the lift on the wing $L^{(w)}$, the lift on the tail $L^{(t)}$, and the engine thrust T for steady level flight.

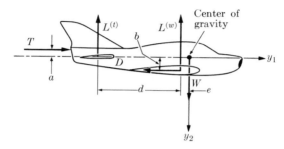

Fig. 3.21   Free-body diagram of an airplane in steady level flight.

Solution: This is a problem of plane statics, and we assume airplane body axes y_1 and y_2, as illustrated by Fig. 3.21. Summing forces along y_1 and y_2 we obtain respectively

$$T - D = 0, \tag{3.4.30}$$

$$-L^{(w)} - L^{(t)} + W = 0. \tag{3.4.31}$$

Summing moments about the center of gravity of the airplane yields

$$Ta + Db + L^{(t)}d + L^{(w)}e = 0. \tag{3.4.32}$$

From Eq. (3.4.30) we obtain the thrust,

$$T = D. \tag{3.4.33}$$

Solving Eqs. (3.4.31) and (3.4.32) simultaneously, we compute the following for the tail lift $L^{(t)}$, and the wing lift $L^{(w)}$:

$$L^{(t)} = -\frac{D(a + b) + We}{d - e}, \tag{3.4.34}$$

$$L^{(w)} = W + \frac{D(a + b) + We}{d - e}. \tag{3.4.35}$$

It is evident in this example that a downward tail load is required for equilibrium.

(b) Special force systems. Equations (3.4.8) through (3.4.13) show that in general the external forces on a system of particles or a rigid body are governed by six scalar equations of equilibrium. In many special force systems, some of these conditions are satisfied identically so that fewer equations of equilibrium remain to be satisfied. Some of these special cases are listed below:

(1) *Coplanar force systems, where all force vectors are in one plane.* If this is the $y_1 y_2$-plane, then

$$y_3^{(i)} = 0, \tag{3.4.36}$$

and

$$P_3^{(i)} = 0. \tag{3.4.37}$$

Thus Eqs. (3.4.10), (3.4.11), and (3.4.12) are satisfied identically, and the equations which remain to be satisfied are

$$\sum_{i=1}^{n} P_1^{(i)} = 0, \tag{3.4.38}$$

$$\sum_{i=1}^{n} P_2^{(i)} = 0, \tag{3.4.39}$$

$$\sum_{i=1}^{n} (y_1^{(i)} P_2^{(i)} - y_2^{(i)} P_1^{(i)}) = 0. \tag{3.4.40}$$

(2) *Parallel force systems, where all the forces are parallel to the y_2-axis.* Then

$$P_1^{(i)} = 0, \tag{3.4.41}$$

$$P_3^{(i)} = 0. \tag{3.4.42}$$

Thus Eqs. (3.4.8), (3.4.10), and (3.4.12) are satisfied identically, and the equations which remain to be satisfied are

$$\sum_{i=1}^{n} P_2^{(i)} = 0, \tag{3.4.43}$$

$$\sum_{i=1}^{n} y_3^{(i)} P_2^{(i)} = 0, \tag{3.4.44}$$

$$\sum_{i=1}^{n} y_1^{(i)} P_2^{(i)} = 0. \tag{3.4.45}$$

Note the reduction of the moment equations (3.4.11) and (3.4.13) to only one group of terms.

(3) *Concurrent force systems, where all forces pass through one single point.* If this point is chosen as the origin, then the sums of moments of all forces about

the three coordinate axes are identically zero. The remaining condition to be satisfied is that the sums of forces along each of the three perpendicular directions be zero. When the concurrent force system is also coplanar, the number of equations of equilibrium is reduced to two.

(4) *Systems where the lines of action of all forces pass through the same axis.* It is obvious that the sum of moments of all forces about this axis is identically zero, and only five equations of equilibrium remain to be satisfied.

3.5 EXAMPLES OF THE USE OF THE FREE-BODY DIAGRAM

Before we proceed to the examples, it is desirable to reiterate the importance of the free-body diagram and lay down some general principles for its construction. The first step in any problem in statics is to isolate that physical object or portion of a physical object which is to be studied. A diagram is then drawn showing this object free and clear of its supports or connecting members, these latter having been replaced by appropriate reactive forces. Such a diagram is a *free-body diagram* (read Section 3.3b). All the forces supplied by the supports or connecting members to the isolated free body are then considered as external forces.

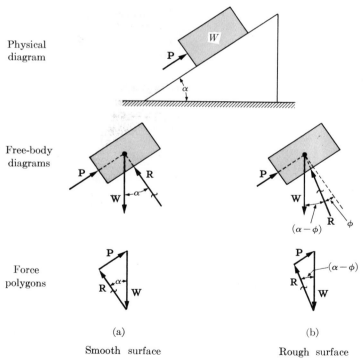

Physical diagram

Free-body diagrams

Force polygons

(a)   (b)

Smooth surface   Rough surface

FIG. 3.22 Free-body diagrams and force polygons of block on inclined surface: (a) smooth surface; (b) rough surface.

When a body is resting on a surface, removal of the surface requires that it be replaced by a reaction **R**. When the surface is smooth, **R** is normal to the surface. If the surface is rough, **R** makes an angle with the surface normal. For example, if the body is on the verge of slipping on a surface having a coefficient of sliding friction, μ, **R** will make an angle, $\phi = \tan \mu$, with the normal and in a direction opposite to the motion. Figure 3.22 illustrates, for example, free-body diagrams of a block on a smooth and on a rough surface. The force **P** in the diagram is externally applied, and is of just sufficient magnitude to keep the block from sliding down. The reaction **R** is normal to the surface in free-body diagram (a), whereas it makes an angle with the surface normal in (b). The force polygons corresponding to each free-body diagram are shown also in Fig. 3.22. In these polygons the directions of all the force vectors are known; however, only the magnitude of **W** is known, and the magnitudes of **P** and **R** remain to be found.

In the force polygon of free-body diagram (a) the vectors **R** and **W** have an included angle α, whereas in (b) the angle is $\alpha - \phi$, where ϕ is the friction angle. It is evident that the magnitude of **P** is reduced as ϕ approaches α, and goes to zero for $\phi = \alpha$. In the latter case, the surface is sufficiently rough to prevent the block from sliding without application of an external force **P**.

Fɪɢ. 3.23 Frictionless pin joint: (a) physical diagram; (b) free-body diagram.

Fɪɢ. 3.24 Cutaway view of ball-and-socket joint.

In some cases a body is supported by frictionless pin joints. For example, in Fig. 3.23 the attachment of the end of a beam to its support through a pin is shown. Such a joint obviously is not capable of resisting any moment about the axis of the pin. Thus the resultant of the reactive forces must pass through the center of the pin. The corresponding free-body diagram is shown at the right of the figure. Such a support has also been described in a previous section (see Fig. 3.13).

A pin-joint support, of course, can transmit a moment about any axis which is normal to the axis of the pin. A joint which will not transmit any moment at all is a ball-and-socket joint, as shown in Fig. 3.24.

A body is often supported by or attached to cables. By definition, a cable can transmit only tension (although one must admit that the cables of the Golden Gate Bridge or the George Washington Bridge can resist bending and compression, the efficiency of a suspension bridge derives from designing the cables to carry only tension). In a free-body diagram these cables are shown

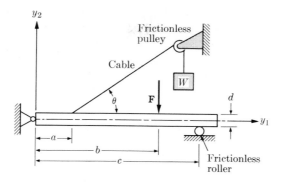

FIG. 3.25 Physical diagram of beam-cable system.

cut and replaced by reactive forces along their lines of action. Figure 3.25 illustrates a planar uniform member supported by a pin joint at one end and a frictionless roller at the other. The member is acted upon by a vertical force **F** and is attached to a weight **W** through a cable-pulley system as shown. If the pulley is frictionless, the tension in the cable becomes a known force equal to the weight **W**. The unknown forces are the reactions $\mathbf{R}^{(1)}$ and $\mathbf{R}^{(2)}$ at both ends of the member.

FIG. 3.26 Free-body diagram of beam-cable system.

Since only coplanar forces are involved, the vector expressions for $\mathbf{R}^{(1)}$ and $\mathbf{R}^{(2)}$ are

$$\mathbf{R}^{(1)} = R_1^{(1)}\mathbf{i}_1 + R_2^{(1)}\mathbf{i}_2, \tag{3.5.1}$$

$$\mathbf{R}^{(2)} = R_2^{(2)}\mathbf{i}_2. \tag{3.5.2}$$

These two reactions involve the three unknown quantities $R_1^{(1)}$, $R_2^{(1)}$, and $R_2^{(2)}$. The three equations which will yield the solution are the three equations of coplanar force systems given by (3.4.38), (3.4.39), and (3.4.40). The free-body diagram is shown in Fig. 3.26.

We first resolve the tension in the cable into its two components, $|\mathbf{W}| \cos \theta$ and $|\mathbf{W}| \sin \theta$. From the first two equilibrium conditions we have

$$\sum_{i=1}^{n} P_1^{(i)} = R_1^{(1)} + |\mathbf{W}| \cos \theta = 0 \tag{3.5.3}$$

and

$$\sum_{i=1}^{n} P_2^{(i)} = R_2^{(1)} + |\mathbf{W}| \sin \theta - |\mathbf{F}| + R_2^{(2)} = 0. \tag{3.5.4}$$

From (3.5.3) we obtain

$$R_1^{(1)} = - |\mathbf{W}| \cos \theta. \tag{3.5.5}$$

If we choose the reference axis to coincide with the axis of the pin joint at the left-hand end of the member, we obtain

$$\sum_{i=1}^{n} (y_1^{(i)} F_2^{(i)} - y_2^{(i)} F_1^{(i)}) = - |\mathbf{W}| \frac{d}{2} \cos \theta + |\mathbf{W}| a \sin \theta - |\mathbf{F}| b + R_2^{(2)} c = 0. \tag{3.5.6}$$

Solving for $R_2^{(2)}$, we have

$$R_2^{(2)} = \frac{1}{c} \left[|\mathbf{W}| \frac{d}{2} \cos \theta - |\mathbf{W}| a \sin \theta + |\mathbf{F}| b \right]. \tag{3.5.7}$$

From (3.5.4),

$$R_2^{(1)} = |\mathbf{F}| - |\mathbf{W}| \sin \theta - R_2^{(2)}, \tag{3.5.8}$$

or

$$R_2^{(1)} = |\mathbf{F}| \left(1 - \frac{b}{c} \right) - |\mathbf{W}| \sin \theta \left(1 - \frac{a}{c} \right) - \frac{|\mathbf{W}| d}{2c} \cos \theta. \tag{3.5.9}$$

It should be noted that the third equilibrium equation applies to the moment about any arbitrary axis perpendicular to the $y_1 y_2$-plane. For example, the sum of moments about an axis at the right-hand end of the member should also be zero,

$$\sum_{i=1}^{n} M_3^{(i)} = - |\mathbf{W}| \frac{d}{2} \cos \theta - |\mathbf{W}|(c - a) \sin \theta + |\mathbf{F}|(c - b) - R_2^{(1)} c = 0, \tag{3.5.10}$$

which is an easy method of checking the accuracy of the previous calculations.

It can easily be verified that the solutions for the forces $R_2^{(2)}$ and $R_2^{(1)}$ can be obtained by using Eqs. (3.5.4) and (3.5.10), or by using the two moment equations (3.5.6) and (3.5.10). Thus although one may have infinitely many ways to write the moment equilibrium conditions, one can find only three independent equations of equilibrium for this coplanar force system. The most efficient procedure depends upon the specific problem, the "art" of solving such problems will come with experience.

We shall consider another typical support which consists of a weightless bar with hinges at both ends, as shown in Fig. 3.27(a). The rigid bar AB is isolated, and a free-body diagram for this bar is drawn as shown in Fig. 3.27(b). The reactions at the end points are $\mathbf{F}^{(1)}$ and $\mathbf{F}^{(2)}$. We shall show first that when a rigid body is in equilibrium under only two external forces, these must be collinear, equal in magnitude, and opposite in direction.

From the equilibrium condition $\sum \mathbf{F}^{(i)} = 0$ we obtain

$$\mathbf{F}^{(1)} + \mathbf{F}^{(2)} = 0 \qquad \text{or} \qquad \mathbf{F}^{(1)} = -\mathbf{F}^{(2)}. \tag{3.5.11}$$

Since the sum of the moments of all forces about A must be zero,

$$\mathbf{r}^{(12)} \times \mathbf{F}^{(2)} = 0. \tag{3.5.12}$$

This means that $\mathbf{r}^{(12)}$ and $\mathbf{F}^{(2)}$ are collinear. Similarly, since the sum of the moments of all forces about B is zero, $\mathbf{r}^{(12)} \times \mathbf{F}^{(1)} = 0$, or $\mathbf{r}^{(12)}$ and $\mathbf{F}^{(1)}$ are also collinear. We have thus proved that the force at A must be in line with the axis of the bar AB. This demonstrates a very important rule concerning pin-ended bars: *for a weightless bar which has two pin ends, and is loaded only at its ends, the reactive force must be in line with the bar.*

Figure 3.28 shows a vertical bar at the right-hand end of the uniform member. When this bar is removed, it must be replaced by a reaction along AB, which is in this case perpendicular to the member. Thus the effect of a vertical bar with hinged ends is identical to that of the frictionless roller shown in Fig. 3.25.

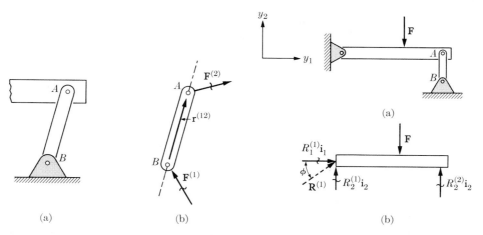

(a)   (b)   (a)

(b)

FIG. 3.27 Equilibrium of a pin-ended bar: (a) physical diagram; (b) free-body diagram.

FIG. 3.28 Equilibrium of a pin-ended beam: (a) physical diagram; (b) free-body diagram.

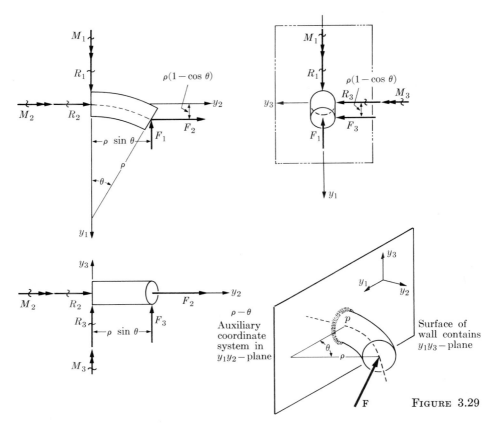

FIGURE 3.29

As a final example of a free-body diagram, let us consider a curved rod clamped to the wall and loaded by a force **F** at the other end, as shown in Fig. 3.29. We want to find the force system that must be applied at the support when the wall is removed.

The junction of the wall and the bar is a plane surface, but it is more convenient to represent the action of the wall on the bar by an equipollent system acting at the center of the bar. We saw in Section 3.2(e) that a force system in space can be reduced to an equipollent system consisting of a single force vector and a single moment vector. Thus the equipollent system representing the action of the wall on the bar at point p is a force vector and a moment vector. These have been resolved into their components R_1, R_2, R_3, and M_1, M_2, M_3. Note that the unit vectors have been omitted from the labels attached to the various force and moment components. This generally leads to better clarity, since the location of the arrowheads on the lines will pictorially give the sense of the vector.

A straightforward application of the six scalar equations of equilibrium, Eqs. (3.4.8) through (3.4.13), will yield the solutions for the reactions.

First we resolve the applied load $\mathbf{F}$ into three components, F_1, F_2, F_3,

$$\sum P_1^{(i)} = 0 \qquad \text{or} \qquad F_1 + R_1 = 0,$$
$$\therefore R_1 = -F_1; \tag{3.5.13}$$

$$\sum P_2^{(i)} = 0 \qquad \text{or} \qquad F_2 + R_2 = 0,$$
$$\therefore R_2 = -F_2; \tag{3.5.14}$$

$$\sum P_3^{(i)} = 0 \qquad \text{or} \qquad F_3 + R_3 = 0,$$
$$\therefore R_3 = -F_3; \tag{3.5.15}$$

$$\sum M_1^{(i)} = 0 \qquad \text{or} \qquad F_3\rho \sin \theta + M_1 = 0,$$
$$\therefore M_1 = -F_3\rho \sin \theta; \tag{3.5.16}$$

$$\sum M_2^{(i)} = 0 \qquad \text{or} \qquad M_2 - F_3\rho(1 - \cos \theta) = 0,$$
$$\therefore M_2 = +F_3\rho(1 - \cos \theta); \tag{3.5.17}$$

$$\sum M_3^{(i)} = 0 \qquad \text{or} \qquad F_1\rho \sin \theta + F_2\rho(1 - \cos \theta) + M_3 = 0,$$
$$\therefore M_3 = -F_1\rho \sin \theta - F_2\rho(1 - \cos \theta). \tag{3.5.18}$$

Thus the reaction at the clamped end can be replaced by three moments and three forces, these being the components of a moment vector and a force vector, respectively.

3.6 SYSTEMS OF PARALLEL FORCES—CENTER OF GRAVITY

When all the forces $\mathbf{F}^{(i)}$ in a system are parallel (Fig. 3.30a), they are also parallel to their resultant,

$$\mathbf{F} = \sum_{i=1}^{n} \mathbf{F}^{(i)},$$

and the sum of the moments about any point O due to these forces is always a moment vector perpendicular to $\mathbf{F}$. The equipollent force system (Fig. 3.30b)

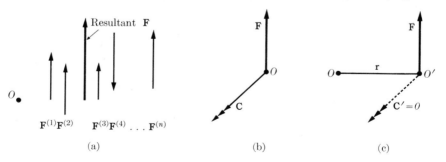

FIG. 3.30   System of parallel forces: (a) original system with resultant; (b) equipollent system with force at O; (c) equipollent system with force at O'.

is thus a force **F** at O and a couple **C**. If we choose another point O', the equipollent force system becomes a force **F** along the same direction and a couple **C'**,
given by

$$\mathbf{C'} = \mathbf{C} - \mathbf{r} \times \mathbf{F} \qquad (3.6.1)$$

(see Fig. 3.30c). Here $\mathbf{r} \times \mathbf{F}$ is also perpendicular to **F**, and we can always ar-
range the magnitude and direction of **r** such that $\mathbf{C} = \mathbf{r} \times \mathbf{F}$ and hence **C'**
becomes zero. Thus the system of parallel forces can be replaced by a single
equipollent resultant force with its line of action passing through O'.

Consider a system of parallel forces
$\mathbf{F}^{(i)}$ $(i = 1, 2, \ldots, n)$ with their direction oriented along the y_3-axis (Fig.
3.31). We intend to determine the location **r** of the resultant force **F**. We can
write each force as

$$\mathbf{F}^{(i)} = F_3^{(i)} \mathbf{i}_3. \qquad (3.6.2)$$

Thus the resultant is

$$\mathbf{F} = \sum_{i=1}^{n} \mathbf{F}^{(i)} = \left(\sum_{i=1}^{n} F_3^{(i)} \right) \mathbf{i}_3.$$

$$(3.6.3)$$

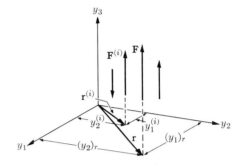

FIG. 3.31   System of parallel forces in
space.

Let us choose the origin O as the ref-
erence point and let all position vectors be on the $y_1 y_2$-plane. Thus we can
locate each force by

$$\mathbf{r}^{(i)} = y_1^{(i)} \mathbf{i}_1 + y_2^{(i)} \mathbf{i}_2. \qquad (3.6.4)$$

The location of the resultant force is given by

$$\mathbf{r} = (y_1)_r \mathbf{i}_1 + (y_2)_r \mathbf{i}_2. \qquad (3.6.5)$$

We have

$$\mathbf{M} = \sum_{i=1}^{n} (\mathbf{r}^{(i)} \times \mathbf{F}^{(i)}) = \mathbf{r} \times \mathbf{F};$$

therefore

$$\sum_{i=1}^{n} (-y_1^{(i)} F_3^{(i)} \mathbf{i}_2 + y_2^{(i)} F_3^{(i)} \mathbf{i}_1) = -(y_1)_r \left(\sum_{i=1}^{n} F_3^{(i)} \right) \mathbf{i}_2 + (y_2)_r \left(\sum_{i=1}^{n} F_3^{(i)} \right) \mathbf{i}_1.$$

This is equivalent to

$$(y_1)_r = \frac{\sum_{i=1}^{n} y_1^{(i)} F_3^{(i)}}{\sum_{i=1}^{n} F_3^{(i)}}, \qquad (3.6.6)$$

$$(y_2)_r = \frac{\sum_{i=1}^{n} y_2^{(i)} F_3^{(i)}}{\sum_{i=1}^{n} F_3^{(i)}}. \qquad (3.6.7)$$

An application of the above discussion is found when the parallel forces are taken as the gravitational forces acting on the various particles of a body. The center of gravity (cg) of a body is defined as the point of action of a single resultant force equipollent to the system of gravitational forces. Here

$$F_3^{(i)} = -m^{(i)}g,$$

and the cg position is given by

$$(y_1)_c = \frac{\sum y_1^{(i)} m^{(i)}}{\sum m^{(i)}}, \tag{3.6.8}$$

$$(y_2)_c = \frac{\sum y_2^{(i)} m^{(i)}}{\sum m^{(i)}}. \tag{3.6.9}$$

We may rotate the body as well as the axes such that the other axis (say y_1) becomes vertical; by following the same treatment, we obtain

$$(y_3)_c = \frac{\sum y_3^{(i)} m^{(i)}}{\sum m^{(i)}}. \tag{3.6.10}$$

Equations (3.6.8), (3.6.9), and (3.6.10) can be written as

$$(\mathbf{r})_c = \frac{\sum \mathbf{r}^{(i)} m^{(i)}}{\sum m^{(i)}}, \tag{3.6.11}$$

and the point which locates $(\mathbf{r})_c$ may also be called the *center of mass*. For a continuous system,

$$(\mathbf{r})_c = \frac{\int_{\text{volume}} \mathbf{r}\, dm}{\int_{\text{volume}} dm}. \tag{3.6.12}$$

If the density distribution is $\rho = \rho(y_k)$, $k = 1, 2, 3$, we have $dm = \rho\, dV$ and

$$(\mathbf{r})_c = \frac{\iiint \rho(y_1, y_2, y_3)\mathbf{r}\, dy_1\, dy_2\, dy_3}{\iiint \rho(y_1, y_2, y_3)\, dy_1\, dy_2\, dy_3}. \tag{3.6.13}$$

EXAMPLE: To compute the center of mass of a homogeneous right circular cone of height h and base radius r.

Solution: Let the axis of symmetry of the cone be placed along the y_2-axis with the origin at the apex as illustrated by Fig. 3.32. Since the center of mass is on the y_2-axis, that is, $(y_1)_c = (y_3)_c = 0$, we need to find

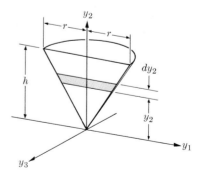

FIG. 3.32   Right circular cone.

only the distance $(y_2)_c$ from the vertex to the center of mass. Applying Eq. (3.6.13), we have

$$(y_2)_c = \frac{\iiint_v \rho y_2 \, dV}{\iiint_v \rho \, dV} . \tag{3.6.14}$$

Taking a slice parallel to the base of thickness dy_2, we have for the volume element

$$dV = \pi y_1^2 \, dy_2. \tag{3.6.15}$$

Putting

$$y_1 = \frac{r}{h} y_2$$

and introducing Eq. (3.6.15) in (3.6.14) we find that

$$(y_2)_c = \frac{\rho(r^2/h^2)\pi \int_0^h (y_2)^3 \, dy_2}{\rho(r^2/h^2)\pi \int_0^h (y_2)^2 \, dy_2} = \frac{3}{4} h. \tag{3.6.16}$$

3.7 PLANE AND SPACE TRUSSES

A truss is a structure which consists of a group of straight members connected to each other only at their ends by frictionless joints (Fig. 3.27). In a plane truss where all the members and the loads are coplanar, these joints (Fig. 3.33) are of pin connections; in a space truss, they are ball-and-socket joints (Fig. 3.34). For an ideal truss, all external loads are applied only at the joints. Under such conditions each member of the truss is subjected only to two forces at its two end points. These two forces must necessarily be equal and opposite, and must act along the direction of the member (see discussion relative to Fig. 3.27). Thus each member is subjected to either an axial tension or compression, constant along its length, but to no other force. The so-called truss analysis is to determine the force in each member of the truss under externally applied loads.

In the general practical truss the members are usually bolted, riveted, or welded at the ends. However, it has been found that an analysis of such a

FIG. 3.33   Plane truss.

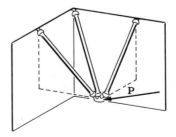

FIG. 3.34   Space truss.

structure based on the assumption of an idealized truss yields approximately the correct values for the forces in the members. This is true mainly because the lengths of the truss members are much greater (say 10 or more times) than the dimensions of the cross sections.

Before proceeding with the details of truss analysis, let us summarize the characteristics of an ideal truss as follows:

(1) The truss members are connected at their ends (called the joints) by frictionless pins.
(2) The loads and reactions are applied only at the joints.
(3) The axis of each bar is straight, and coincides with the line connecting the joints.
(4) The force system equipollent to the internal forces in a truss member consists only of a component coinciding with the centroidal axis.

In this chapter we shall consider only statically determinate trusses, for which all the forces can be determined by the equations of equilibrium. This means that when we isolate the complete structure or a portion of the structure, and draw the corresponding free-body diagram, we expect the number of unknown quantities to be equal to the available number of equations of equilibrium. Thus, in general, for a space truss we have six equations, and for a plane truss or a concurrent force system we have only three equations. For a coplanar and concurrent force system we have only two equations of equilibrium to be satisfied.

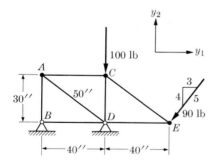

FIG. 3.35 Statically determinate plane truss.

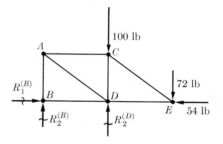

FIG. 3.36 Free-body diagram of entire truss.

We shall demonstrate the method of truss analysis by a typical plane truss problem illustrated in Fig. 3.35. Note that the members of the ideal truss are represented by lines which coincide with the axes of the members. The truss is supported at B and D, and two loads are applied at C and E. It is desired to evaluate the axial forces carried by each member of the truss. The first step in the analysis is to draw the free-body diagram (Fig. 3.36) of the complete system, replacing the supports by the three unknown reactions, $R_1^{(B)}$, $R_2^{(B)}$, and

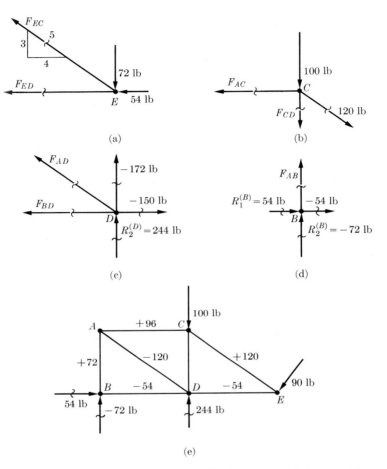

FIG. 3.37   The method of joints: (a) free-body diagram of joint E; (b) free-body diagram of joint C; (c) free-body diagram of joint D; (d) free-body diagram of joint B; (e) truss diagram with bar forces.

$R_2^{(D)}$. It is seen that these unknown reactions can be determined by the three equations of equilibrium for a coplanar force system as follows:

$$\sum_{i=1}^{n} F_1^{(i)} = R_1^{(B)} - 54 = 0, \tag{3.7.1}$$

$$\sum_{i=1}^{n} F_2^{(i)} = R_2^{(B)} + R_2^{(D)} - 100 - 72 = 0, \tag{3.7.2}$$

$$\sum_{i=1}^{n} M_3^{(i)} = -(100)(40) + 40 R_2^{(D)} - (72)(80) = 0. \tag{3.7.3}$$

From these equations we obtain

$$R_1^{(B)} = 54 \text{ lb}, \qquad R_2^{(D)} = 244 \text{ lb}, \qquad \text{and} \qquad R_2^{(B)} = -72 \text{ lb}.$$

We can proceed to determine the axial load in each member by isolating individual joints. For example, when we consider joint E (Fig. 3.37a), we replace the members EC and ED by unknown axial forces, F_{EC} and F_{ED}, which are assumed to be positive in tension, as shown in the diagram. If the numerical answer is positive, then the *bar force* (as the force in the truss member is called) is tension. Conversely, if the numerical answer is negative, then the bar force is compression. For this coplanar and concurrent force system the two equations of equilibrium are

$$\sum_{i=1}^{n} F_1^{(i)} = 0 \qquad \text{or} \qquad -F_{ED} - \frac{4}{5} F_{EC} - 54 = 0, \qquad (3.7.4)$$

$$\sum_{i=1}^{n} F_2^{(i)} = 0 \qquad \text{or} \qquad \frac{3}{5} F_{EC} - 72 = 0. \qquad (3.7.5)$$

From these equations we obtain $F_{EC} = 120$ lb, and $F_{ED} = -150$ lb. This means that member EC is under a tension force of 120 lb, while member ED is under a compressive force of 150 lb.

The determination of axial forces in various members by considering equilibrium at a joint is called the *method of joints*. We can now proceed to isolate joint C (Fig. 3.37b) and replace member CE by a known tension of 120 lb, and members CD and AC by unknown external forces F_{CD} and F_{AC}. Again we apply the two equations of equilibrium,

$$\sum_{i=1}^{n} F_1^{(i)} = -F_{AC} + (\tfrac{4}{5})(120) = 0, \qquad (3.7.6)$$

$$\sum_{i=1}^{n} F_2^{(i)} = -F_{CD} - 100 - (120)(\tfrac{3}{5}) = 0. \qquad (3.7.7)$$

From these we obtain $F_{AC} = 96$ lb, and $F_{CD} = -172$ lb. When we proceed to joint D (Fig. 3.37c), we see that we have already evaluated the reaction $R_2^{(D)}$, and we again have only two unknown axial forces to be determined. The two equilibrium equations are

$$\sum_{i=1}^{n} F_1^{(i)} = -F_{BD} - \frac{4}{5} F_{AD} - 150 = 0, \qquad (3.7.8)$$

$$\sum_{i=1}^{n} F_2^{(i)} = \frac{3}{5} F_{AD} - 172 + 244 = 0, \qquad (3.7.9)$$

from which we obtain

$$F_{AD} = -120 \text{ lb},$$

$$F_{BD} = -150 + 96 = -54 \text{ lb}.$$

The only remaining unknown quantity F_{AB} can be determined by considering either joint B or joint A. If we consider B (Fig. 3.37d), we find from

$$\sum_{i=1}^{n} F_2^{(i)} = F_{AB} - 72 = 0 \qquad (3.7.10)$$

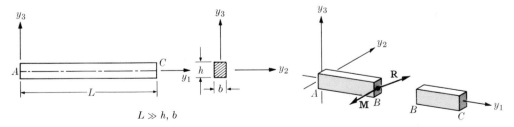

FIG. 3.38 The method of sections.

that $F_{AB} = 72$ lb. Figure 3.37(e) shows the completely solved truss.

It is possible to determine the forces in some members of the truss without analyzing the complete truss. For example, if we are interested only in the axial force F_{AC}, we can cut AC, AD, and BD and isolate the structure at the right-hand side of the cut. The free body is shown in Fig. 3.38. Such a procedure, of course, is tantamount to adding up only a selected few of the equations given by Eq. (3.4.1). Here three of the four unknown quantities F_{AC}, F_{AD}, F_{BD}, and $R_2^{(D)}$ act at joint D. Hence, by setting the sum of moments about D equal to zero, we can calculate the unknown force F_{AC} immediately. We have, then, $(F_{AC})(30) - (72)(40) = 0$, $F_{AC} = 96$ lb. This last method is called the *method of sections*. For a more complete exposition of truss analysis the reader is referred to Norris and Wilbur (Ref. 3.1).

3.8 INTERNAL FORCES AND MOMENTS IN SLENDER BEAMS

A very common structural component is called a beam. Just as in the case of an ideal truss, a structural member is called an ideal beam because certain restrictions are first placed on its geometry. Then, because of the restrictions on the geometry, further restrictions are placed on the types of forces and moments which can be developed. In Fig. 3.39, the geometrical restrictions on a beam are shown. A beam is a three-dimensional structure with one dimension (called the *span* or *length*) much larger (say 10 times) than the other two dimensions

FIG. 3.39 Beam geometry.

FIG. 3.40 Beam as a two-particle system—equipollent forces on portion AB.

(i.e. dimensions of the *cross section*). It is assumed that the externally applied loads are coplanar with the $y_1 y_3$-plane, where y_1 is in the span direction of the beam.

In order to apply the results of Section 3.4 to a beam, we need only to visualize the beam as a collection of particles. The particles in this case are the atoms, but the atoms are so numerous that the usual engineering structure can be treated as a continuum. The internal forces in a beam are the forces between atoms, but the notion of equipollent force systems makes it possible to ignore the details of the actual distribution of the internal forces. We can form a subcollection of particles by figuratively cutting the beam into two parts by a plane perpendicular to the y_1-axis of the beam (see Fig. 3.40). The action of the portion BC on the portion AB can be represented by an equipollent system consisting of a force vector $\mathbf{R}$ and a moment vector $\mathbf{M}$. Since the beam is assumed to be loaded only by coplanar forces, the vector forms of $\mathbf{R}$ and $\mathbf{M}$ are

$$\mathbf{R} = F\mathbf{i}_1 - S\mathbf{i}_3, \tag{3.8.1}$$

$$\mathbf{M} = -M\mathbf{i}_2. \tag{3.8.2}$$

The somewhat irrational combination of signs attached to the preceding two equations is an outgrowth of the manner in which beam analysis has developed. There is such a tremendous quantity of numerical data which conform to the above sign conventions that it is not feasible to adopt a more rational approach. The component F is called the *axial force*, S is called the *shear force*, and M is called the *bending moment*. These are shown in Fig. 3.41, where in conformity with the usual practice, the moment component M is shown as a curved vector.

$$\text{F{\small IG}. 3.41} \quad \text{Sign conventions for axial force, shear force, and bending moment.}$$

Note carefully that the positive directions for F, S, and M are defined on the positive face of the cut at B, the positive face being the face which has an outward normal vector in the positive $\mathbf{i}_1$-direction. On the other face of the cut, which has an outward normal in the negative $\mathbf{i}_1$-direction, the forces F and S and the moment M must all point in the opposite direction by virtue of Eq. (3.4.2).

The sign conventions associated with beam theory are apt to be confusing. Another scheme for remembering what constitutes positive and negative is shown in Fig. 3.42.

The assumption that the forces acting on a beam are coplanar means that the cross-sectional shape is unimportant to the analysis of internal forces, F, S, and M. Thus a beam can be schematically represented by a thick line (see Fig.

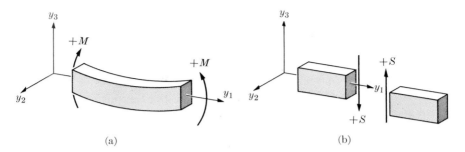

(a)   (b)

FIG. 3.42   Sign conventions, shear force and bending moment: (a) positive bending moment tends to apply compression to the upper fibers of the beam, tension, to the lower; (b) positive shear tends to lower the right half of the beam relative to the left half.

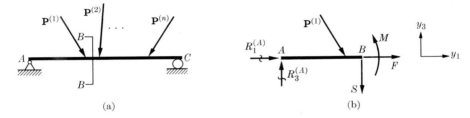

(a)   (b)

FIG. 3.43   Schematic representation of a beam: (a) physical diagram; (b) free-body diagram.

FIG. 3.44   Physical diagram of a beam under a system of coplanar forces.

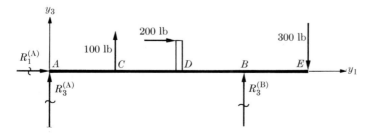

FIG. 3.45   Free-body diagram of the complete beam.

3.43). However, the cross-sectional shape of a beam is important to the determination of the distribution of the forces, i.e., of internal stresses (see Chapter 6, "Analysis of Stress").

EXAMPLE: Consider a beam (Fig. 3.44) supported at A by a pin joint and at B by a roller. Two of the applied forces are in the vertical direction, while the third one, $P^{(2)}$, is in the horizontal direction. The force $P^{(2)}$ acts at the end of a vertical post which is 5 in. in height. We make the assumption that the deformations of the beam under the action of the loads will not significantly change the specified dimensional relations between the loads and the structure. This will later be shown to be true for most problems of structural analysis. It is desired to determine the distribution of internal forces and moment along the beam.

Referring to Fig. 3.45 we observe that the three reactions $R_1^{(A)}$, $R_3^{(A)}$, and $R_3^{(B)}$ can be determined by using three equations of statics:

$$\sum_{i=1}^{n} F_1^{(i)} = R_1^{(A)} + 200 = 0, \tag{3.8.3}$$

$$\sum_{i=1}^{n} F_3^{(i)} = R_3^{(A)} + 100 + R_3^{(B)} - 300 = 0, \tag{3.8.4}$$

$$\sum_{i=1}^{n} M_2^{(i)} = (100)(10) - (200)(5) + (R_3^{(B)})(30) - (300)(40)$$
$$= 0 \quad \text{(about } A\text{)}. \tag{3.8.5}$$

From these equations we obtain

$$R_1^{(A)} = -200 \text{ lb}, \qquad R_3^{(A)} = -200 \text{ lb}, \qquad R_3^{(B)} = 400 \text{ lb}. \tag{3.8.6}$$

In order to determine the internal forces and moments at a given station we need to make a cut perpendicular to the axis of the beam at this station, and isolate either part of the beam. Let us consider first, a station located between A and C (i.e., for $0 < y_1 < 10$), and isolate the part of the beam to the left of this station, as shown in Fig. 3.46(a). The three unknowns, internal forces $F(y_1)$ and $S(y_1)$ and moment $M(y_1)$, can be determined by the three equations for static equilibrium:

$$\sum_{i=1}^{n} F_1^{(i)} = -200 + F(y_1) = 0, \tag{3.8.7}$$

$$\sum_{i=1}^{n} F_3^{(i)} = -200 - S(y_1) = 0, \tag{3.8.8}$$

$$\sum_{i=1}^{n} M_2^{(i)} = 200y_1 + M(y_1) = 0 \quad \text{(about } P\text{)}. \tag{3.8.9}$$

The last equation refers to the sum of the moments about the point P which is located on the axis of beam at the station where the cut has been made. In this case a counterclockwise moment is considered as positive. It should be realized that the reference point for the equation of moment equilibrium may be any point along the beam. However, a judicious choice of the reference point can simplify the algebra and arithmetic. The internal forces and moment obtained by these three equations are

$$F(y_1) = 200 \text{ lb}, \qquad S(y_1) = -200 \text{ lb}, \qquad M(y_1) = -200 \, y_1 \text{ in.-lb.} \quad (3.8.10)$$

These results can also be obtained by isolating the part of the beam to the right of the station, as shown in Fig. 3.46(b). The internal forces and moment

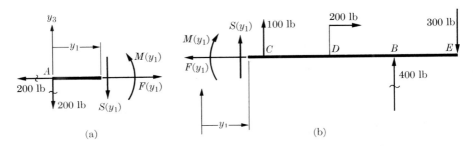

Fig. 3.46 Free-body diagrams for determination of internal forces and moment between B and C: (a) left-hand part of a cut at a station between A and C; (b) right-hand part of a cut at a station between A and C.

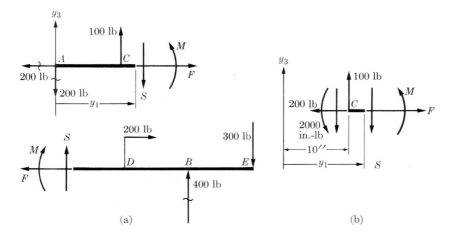

Fig. 3.47 Free-body diagrams for determination of internal forces and moment between C and D: (a) left- and right-hand parts of a cut at a station between C and D; (b) a small segment to the left of a cut between C and D.

which are in the opposite direction to those in the previous figure can also be calculated by the three equations for static equilibrium:

$$\sum_{i=1}^{n} F_1^{(i)} = 200 - F(y_1) = 0, \tag{3.8.11}$$

$$\sum_{i=1}^{n} F_3^{(i)} = S(y_1) + 500 - 300 = 0, \tag{3.8.12}$$

$$\sum_{i=1}^{n} M_2^{(i)} = -M(y_1) + 100(10 - y_1) - (200)(5) + 400(30 - y_1)$$
$$-300(40 - y_1) = 0 \quad \text{(about } P\text{)}. \tag{3.8.13}$$

These equations yield

$$F(y_1) = 200 \text{ lb}, \qquad S(y_1) = -200 \text{ lb},$$
$$M(y_1) = -200 \, y_1 \text{ in-lb}. \tag{3.8.14}$$

At a station located at an infinitesimally small distance to the left of C the internal forces and moments are

$$F(10-) = 200 \text{ lb}, \qquad S(10-) = -200 \text{ lb},$$
$$M(10-) = -2000 \text{ in-lb}. \tag{3.8.15}$$

The symbol "10−" is used to indicate that y_1 is slightly smaller than 10, and similarly "10+" that y_1 is slightly larger than 10.

To determine the internal forces and moment at a station between C and D we again make a cut at this station and isolate either part of the beam shown in Fig. 3.47(a). It can also be seen that since we have already determined the internal forces and moment at the left of station C, we may make a cut there and replace the left-hand part of that cut by the known forces and moment. The free-body diagram of this shorter segment of the beam is shown in Fig. 3.47(b). Let us consider only the last diagram and write the following conditions of static equilibrium:

$$\sum_{i=1}^{n} F_1^{(i)} = -200 + F = 0, \tag{3.8.16}$$

$$\sum_{i=1}^{n} F_3^{(i)} = -200 + 100 - S = 0, \tag{3.8.17}$$

$$\sum_{i=1}^{n} M_2^{(i)} = 2000 + M - S(y_1 - 10) = 0 \quad \text{(about } C\text{)}. \tag{3.8.18}$$

We obtain from these equations, for $10 < y_1 < 20$,

$$F(y_1) = 200 \text{ lb},$$
$$S(y_1) = -100 \text{ lb}, \qquad (3.8.19)$$
$$M(y_1) = -100 \, y_1 - 1000,$$

and

$$F(20-) = 200 \text{ lb},$$
$$S(20-) = -100 \text{ lb}, \qquad (3.8.20)$$
$$M(20-) = -3000 \text{ in-lb}.$$

FIG. 3.48 A small segment to the left of a cut between D and B.

To determine the internal forces and moment at a station between D and B we consider a short segment to the left of this station, as shown in Fig. 3.48. The equilibrium conditions are

$$\sum_{i=1}^{n} F_1^{(i)} = -200 + 200 + F = 0, \qquad (3.8.21)$$

$$\sum_{i=1}^{n} F_3^{(i)} = -100 - S = 0, \qquad (3.8.22)$$

$$\sum_{i=1}^{n} M_2^{(i)} = 3000 - (200)(5) + M - S(y_1 - 20)$$
$$= 0 \quad (\text{about } D). \qquad (3.8.23)$$

These yield, for $20 < y_1 < 30$,

$$F(y_1) = 0, \qquad S(y_1) = -100 \text{ lb}, \qquad M(y_1) = -100 \, y_1 \text{ in-lb}, \qquad (3.8.24)$$

$$F(30-) = 0, \qquad S(30-) = 100 \text{ lb}, \qquad M(30-) = -3000 \text{ in-lb}. \qquad (3.8.25)$$

Finally, when we calculate the sectional forces and moment at a station to the left of B, we isolate the right-hand part of the cut as shown in Fig. 3.49. The equations of static equilibrium are

$$\sum_{i=1}^{n} F_1^{(i)} = -F + 0 = 0, \qquad (3.8.26)$$

$$\sum_{i=1}^{n} F_3^{(i)} = S - 300 = 0, \qquad (3.8.27)$$

$$\sum_{i=1}^{n} M_2^{(i)} = -M - S(40 - y_1) = 0 \quad (\text{about } E). \qquad (3.8.28)$$

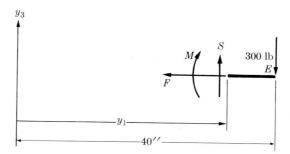

FIG. 3.49   A segment to the right of a cut between B and E.

We obtain, for $30 < y_1 < 40$,

$$F(y_1) = 0, \qquad S(y_1) = 300, \qquad M(y_1) = 300\,y_1 - 12{,}000, \quad (3.8.29)$$

and

$$F(40-) = 0, \qquad S(40-) = 300, \qquad M(40-) = 0. \qquad (3.8.30)$$

The distributions of axial force, shear force, and bending moment along the beam are shown in Fig. 3.50. These diagrams are called the axial-force, shear, and bending-moment diagrams.

Axial force diagram

Shear diagram

Bending-moment diagram

FIGURE 3.50

3.9 RELATIONS BETWEEN LOAD, SHEAR, AND BENDING MOMENT

The beam, as has been pointed out, is treated as a continuum and hence the applied loads, the internal forces F and S, and the bending moment M, must obey certain differential relationships. In general, we consider a slender beam (Fig. 3.51) under a continuously distributed load $p(y_1)$ per unit length of the beam. Note that loads with lines of action parallel to the axis of the beam are omitted. Beams are seldom called upon to transmit loads of this kind. If there are loads of this nature, then the application of the force equilibrium equation in the y_1-direction will yield the internal axial force.

Let us isolate a very small segment of length dy_1 and draw a free-body diagram as shown in Fig. 3.52. When the distributed load $p(y_1)$ is continuous and because the element dy_1 is an infinitesimal, the resultant of the distributed load within this segment may be represented approximately by $p(y_1)\,dy_1$ and may be considered to act at the center of this segment. The force system acting on this segment is shown in Fig. 3.53. The two equations of static equilibrium are

$$\sum_{i=1}^{n} F_3^{(i)} = S + p(y_1)\,dy_1 - \left(S + \frac{dS}{dy_1}\,dy_1\right) = 0, \qquad (3.9.1)$$

and

$$\sum_{i=1}^{n} M_2^{(i)} = -M - S\frac{dy_1}{2} - (S + dS)\frac{dy_1}{2} + \left(M + \frac{dM}{dy_1}\,dy_1\right) = 0$$

$$\text{(about center of element).} \qquad (3.9.2)$$

Equation (3.9.1) may be simplified to

$$\frac{dS}{dy_1} = p(y_1), \qquad (3.9.3)$$

and Eq. (3.9.2) may be reduced to

$$\frac{dM}{dy_1} = S + \frac{dS}{2}. \qquad (3.9.4)$$

FIG. 3.51 Beam under distributed load.

Consider the case where the distribution of shear is continuous. Then, in the limit as dy_1 approaches zero, dS becomes negligibly small in comparison to S, and we obtain

$$\frac{dM}{dy_1} = S(y_1). \qquad (3.9.5)$$

Equations (3.9.3) and (3.9.5) are the two basic differential equations relating the load distribution $p(y_1)$, shear distribution $S(y_1)$, and bending-moment distribution $M(y_1)$. They state respectively that *the slope of the shear diagram is equal to the magnitude of the distributed load p, and the slope of the bending-*

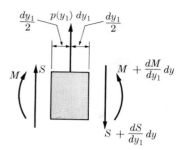

FIG. 3.52   Free-body diagram of a small segment of the beam.

FIG. 3.53   Free-body diagram of the segment with the distributed load replaced by its resultant.

moment diagram is equal to the magnitude of the shear force S. Thus, if the load distribution is given, the shear and bending-moment distribution can be obtained by integration.

Integrating Eq. (3.9.3), we obtain

$$S(y_1^{(B)}) = \int_{y_1^{(A)}}^{y_1^{(B)}} p(y_1)\,dy_1 + S(y_1^{(A)}), \qquad (3.9.6)$$

where $S(y_1^{(A)})$ and $S(y_1^{(B)})$ are the values of the shear at stations A and B, respectively. Similarly, from Eq. (3.9.5) we have

$$M(y_1^{(B)}) = \int_{y_1^{(A)}}^{y_1^{(B)}} S(y_1)\,dy_1 + M(y_1^{(A)}), \qquad (3.9.7)$$

where $M(y_1^{(A)})$ and $M(y_1^{(B)})$ are the values of the bending moment at stations A and B, respectively.

EXAMPLE: Consider a cantilever beam with the tapered load distribution shown in Fig. 3.54. It is desired to determine the shear and bending-moment diagrams.

The free-body diagram of the beam is shown in Fig. 3.55. The shear force S_0 and the bending moment M_0 at the clamped end of the beam can be obtained

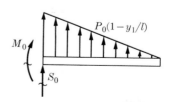

FIG. 3.54   Physical diagram of cantilever beam with tapered load.

FIG. 3.55   Free-body diagram of the complete beam.

first by the two equations of static equilibrium,

$$\sum_{i=1}^{n} F_3^{(i)} = S_0 + \int_0^l p(y_1)\, dy_1 = 0, \tag{3.9.8}$$

$$\sum_{i=1}^{n} M_2^{(i)} = -M_0 + \int_0^l p(y_1)y_1\, dy_1 \quad \text{(about clamped end)}. \tag{3.9.9}$$

From these we obtain

$$S_0 = -\int_0^l \frac{p_0}{l}(l - y_1)\, dy_1 = -\frac{p_0 l}{2},$$

$$M_0 = \int_0^l \frac{p_0}{l}(l - y_1)y_1\, dy_1 = +\frac{p_0 l^2}{6}. \tag{3.9.10}$$

The shear and bending-moment distributions can thus be calculated by Eqs. (3.9.6) and (3.9.7):

$$S(y_1) = \int_0^{y_1} \frac{p_0}{l}(l - y_1)\, dy_1 - \frac{p_0 l}{2}, \qquad S(y_1) = -\frac{p_0}{2l}(l - y_1)^2,$$

$$\tag{3.9.11}$$

$$M(y_1) = -\int_0^{y_1} \frac{p_0}{2l}(l - y_1)^2\, dy_1 + \frac{p_0 l^2}{6}, \qquad M(y_1) = \frac{p_0}{6l}(l - y_1)^3.$$

The shear and bending-moment diagrams are shown in Fig. 3.56.

A remark should now be made concerning concentrated loads. A *concentrated load* may be considered as a load distributed within a segment of infinitesimally small length. We can write the magnitude of a concentrated load as

$$P = p(y_1)\Delta y_1 \tag{3.9.12}$$

when Δy_1 approaches zero or

$$p(y_1) = \lim_{\Delta y_1 \to 0} \left(\frac{P}{\Delta y_1}\right). \tag{3.9.13}$$

It is seen that when P is finite, $p(y_1)$ must be infinitely large. From Eq. (3.9.3) we can conclude that at a station where a concentrated load is acting, the slope of the shear diagram is infinite, i.e., the shear diagram is discontinuous. It is obvious that if a concentrated load P

FIG. 3.56   Cantilever beam with tapered load.

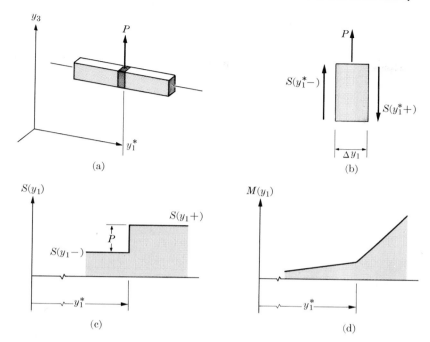

FIG. 3.57   The effects of a concentrated load: (a) physical diagram of beam subjected to concentrated load; (b) free-body diagram of a small segment at a concentrated load; (c) infinite slope and finite jump of shear diagram at concentrated load; (d) discontinuity in slope of bending-moment diagram at concentrated load.

acts at y_1^*, the shear force at the right-hand side of this station is equal to the shear force at the left-hand side plus P. This is shown in Fig. 3.57. The bending moment at a station is given by the differential relation $dM/dy_1 = S$. Since the shear forces are different on either side of a concentrated load, the slope of the bending-moment diagram will be discontinuous at the loading station, as shown in Fig. 3.57(d).

3.10 GENERAL BEAM THEORY

The results of planar beam theory can be extended to the more general case in which loads are also applied parallel to the $y_1 y_2$-plane. Then the equipollent force and moment vectors will each have three components (see Fig. 3.58):

$$\mathbf{F} = F\mathbf{i}_1 - S_2\mathbf{i}_2 - S_3\mathbf{i}_3, \tag{3.10.1}$$

$$\mathbf{M} = T\mathbf{i}_1 - M_2\mathbf{i}_2 + M_3\mathbf{i}_3, \tag{3.10.2}$$

where, by the application of the right-hand rule, it is seen that T represents a torsional moment.

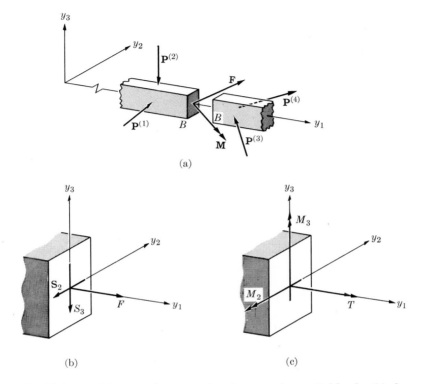

Fig. 3.58   (a) Internal force and moment in a beam under spatial loads; (b) shear and axial force conventions; (c) bending and torsion moment conventions.

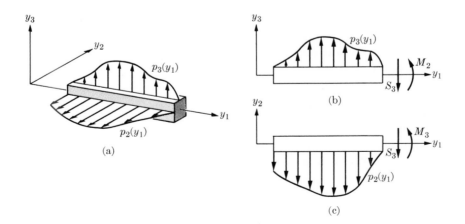

Fig. 3.59   Beam under lateral forces in y_1y_2- and y_1y_3-planes: (a) perspective view of beam under lateral loads; (b) side elevation; (c) plan view.

The differential relations between load and shear, and between shear and bending moment may be extended to include lateral forces in both the $y_1 y_2$- and $y_1 y_3$-planes, as shown in Fig. 3.59.

These relations are

$$\frac{dS_3}{dy_1} = p_3(y_1), \tag{3.10.3}$$

$$\frac{dM_2}{dy_1} = S_3(y_1), \tag{3.10.4}$$

$$\frac{dS_2}{dy_1} = p_2(y_1), \tag{3.10.5}$$

$$\frac{dM_3}{dy_1} = S_2(y_1). \tag{3.10.6}$$

3.11 TORSION OF A ROD

Differential relations can also be obtained between distributed torque and internal torsional moment. Consider a slender rod under a distributed torque of $t(y_1)$ per unit length, shown in Fig. 3.60(a). Let us isolate a small segment of length dy_1, and draw the free-body diagram shown in Fig. 3.60(b). The equilibrium of all moments about the y_1-axis yields

$$\sum_{i=1}^{n} M_1^{(i)} = -T + t\, dy_1 + T + \frac{dT}{dy_1}\, dy_1 = 0. \tag{3.11.1}$$

We obtain from this

$$\frac{dT}{dy_1} = -t(y_1). \tag{3.11.2}$$

Equation (3.11.2) states that *the slope of the torsional-moment diagram is equal to the negative value of the torque distribution at that station.*

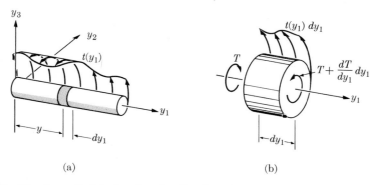

FIG. 3.60   Slender cylindrical rod under distributed torque load: (a) physical diagram; (b) free-body diagram of a small segment.

3.12 SUMMARY

Moment of a force about a point p

$$\mathbf{M} = \mathbf{r} \times \mathbf{F}, \qquad\qquad (3.12.1)$$

where $\mathbf{r}$ is position vector from p to any point along line of action of $\mathbf{F}$.

$$\mathbf{M} = [y_m(q) - y_m(p)]F_r\, e_{mrk}\, \mathbf{i}_k, \qquad\qquad (3.12.2)$$

where $y_m(q)$ represents coordinates of a point on line of action of $\mathbf{F}$, $y_m(p)$ co-ordinates of point p, and F_r components of $\mathbf{F}$.

Moment of a force about an axis collinear with the unit vector $\mathbf{e}$

$$M_l = \mathbf{e} \cdot (\mathbf{r} \times \mathbf{F}), \qquad\qquad (3.12.3)$$

where $\mathbf{r}$ is the vector from line of axis of $\mathbf{e}$ to line of action of $\mathbf{F}$.

Equipollent force systems
  (1) The resultant of the forces of one system is equal to the resultant of forces of the other system.
  (2) The sum of the moments of the forces of one system about an arbitrary base point is equal to the sum of the moments of the forces of the other system about the same point.

Equilibrium of a system of particles
  Vector sum of external forces acting on system is zero:

$$\sum_{i=1}^{n} \mathbf{P}^{(i)} = 0. \qquad\qquad (3.12.4)$$

Total moment about arbitrary origin O of the external forces acting on system is zero:

$$\sum_{i=1}^{n} \mathbf{r}^{(i)} \times \mathbf{P}^{(i)} = 0. \qquad\qquad (3.12.5)$$

The scalar form of Eq. (3.12.4) is

$$\sum_{i=1}^{n} P_1^{(i)} = 0, \qquad\qquad (3.12.6)$$

$$\sum_{i=1}^{n} P_2^{(i)} = 0, \qquad\qquad (3.12.7)$$

$$\sum_{i=1}^{n} P_3^{(i)} = 0. \qquad\qquad (3.12.8)$$

and similarly, the scalar form of Eq. (3.12.5) is

$$\sum_{i=1}^{n} (y_2^{(i)}P_3^{(i)} - y_3^{(i)}P_2^{(i)}) = 0, \tag{3.12.9}$$

$$\sum_{i=1}^{n} (y_3^{(i)}P_1^{(i)} - y_1^{(i)}P_3^{(i)}) = 0, \tag{3.12.10}$$

$$\sum_{i=1}^{n} (y_1^{(i)}P_2^{(i)} - y_2^{(i)}P_1^{(i)}) = 0, \tag{3.12.11}$$

where

$$\mathbf{P}^{(i)} = P_m^{(i)}\mathbf{i}_m, \tag{3.12.12}$$

$$\mathbf{r}^{(i)} = y_m^{(i)}\mathbf{i}_m. \tag{3.12.13}$$

Equilibrium of a force system coplanar with the y_1y_2-plane

$$\sum_{i=1}^{n} P_1^{(i)} = 0, \tag{3.12.14}$$

$$\sum_{i=1}^{n} P_2^{(i)} = 0, \tag{3.12.15}$$

$$\sum_{i=1}^{n} (y_1^{(i)}P_2^{(i)} - y_2^{(i)}P_1^{(i)}) = 0, \tag{3.12.16}$$

where

$$\mathbf{P}^{(i)} = P_1^{(i)}\mathbf{i}_1 + P_2^{(i)}\mathbf{i}_2, \tag{3.12.17}$$

$$\mathbf{r}^{(i)} = y_1^{(i)}\mathbf{i}_1 + y_2^{(i)}\mathbf{i}_2. \tag{3.12.18}$$

Equilibrium of a force system parallel to y_2-axis

$$\sum_{i=1}^{n} P_2^{(i)} = 0, \tag{3.12.19}$$

$$\sum_{i=1}^{n} y_3^{(i)}P_2^{(i)} = 0, \tag{3.12.20}$$

$$\sum_{i=1}^{n} y_1^{(i)}P_2^{(i)} = 0. \tag{3.12.21}$$

Characteristics of ideal truss

(1) Members are connected at their ends by frictionless joints.
(2) Loads and reactions are applied only at the joints.

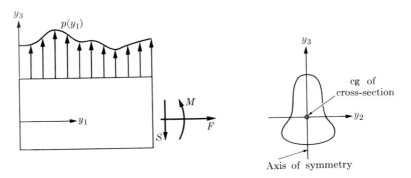

FIG. 3.61 Beam under lateral forces in y_1y_3-plane.

(3) Centroidal axis of each bar is straight and passes through the joints at the two ends.
(4) Internal forces in each truss member may be represented by a force along the centroidal axis.

Force analysis of ideal truss

(1) Method of joints
(2) Method of sections

Characteristics of ideal beam

(1) Span y_1 is much larger than dimensions of cross section y_2, y_3.
(2) Externally applied loads are coplanar in the y_1y_3-plane (see Figs. 3.61 and 3.39).
(3) Internal forces are replaced by equipollent system consisting of axial force F parallel to y_1, transverse shear force S parallel to y_3, and bending moment M about y_2-axis.

Relations between load, shear, and bending moment

$$\frac{dS}{dy_1} = p, \tag{3.12.22}$$

$$\frac{dM}{dy_1} = S. \tag{3.12.23}$$

PROBLEMS

3.1 (a) Referring to Fig. 3.2 (in the text), use vector analysis to prove that the moment of **F** about point p is independent of the location of point q on the line of action of **F**. (b) Referring to Fig. 3.3, prove that the moment of **F** about the axis l is independent of the choice of **r** from l to **F**.

3.2 Reduce each of the following force and moment systems (a) through (e) to the simplest equipollent system.

	Force	Acts at
(a)	$\mathbf{F}^{(1)} = -3(\mathbf{i}_1 + \mathbf{i}_2)$	$(0, 3)$
	$\mathbf{F}^{(2)} = +3\mathbf{i}_2$	$(2, 0)$
	$\mathbf{F}^{(3)} = 4(\mathbf{i}_1 + \mathbf{i}_2)$	$(3, 0)$

	Force	Acts at
(b)	$\mathbf{F}^{(1)} = 3\mathbf{i}_2$	$(3, 3)$
	$\mathbf{F}^{(2)} = 2\mathbf{i}_1 + 3\mathbf{i}_2$	$(3, 3)$
	$\mathbf{F}^{(3)} = 3\mathbf{i}_1 + 2\mathbf{i}_2$	$(3, 3)$
	$\mathbf{F}^{(4)} = 4\mathbf{i}_1$	$(3, 3)$
	$\mathbf{F}^{(5)} = -3\mathbf{i}_1 + 4\mathbf{i}_2$	$(0, 4)$
	$\mathbf{F}^{(6)} = 2\mathbf{i}_1$	$(0, 2)$

	Force	Acts at
(c)	$\mathbf{F}^{(1)} = \mathbf{i}_1 + 2\mathbf{i}_2$	$(0, 1, 2)$
	$\mathbf{F}^{(2)} = 3\mathbf{i}_1 - \mathbf{i}_2$	$(1, 2, 0)$
	$\mathbf{F}^{(3)} = 4\mathbf{i}_1 + 3\mathbf{i}_2$	$(3, 2, 2)$

	Force	Acts at
(d)	$\mathbf{F}^{(1)} = 2\mathbf{i}_1 + 3\mathbf{i}_2$	$(-2, 3)$
	$\mathbf{F}^{(2)} = -5\mathbf{i}_1 + 2\mathbf{i}_2$	$(3, 1)$
	$\mathbf{F}^{(3)} = -3\mathbf{i}_1 - \mathbf{i}_2$	$(6, -1)$

	Force or moment	Acts at
(e)	$\mathbf{F}^{(1)} = \mathbf{i}_1 + \mathbf{i}_2 + \mathbf{i}_3$	$(0, 0, 0)$
	$\mathbf{F}^{(2)} = \mathbf{i}_1 - 2\mathbf{i}_2 + 3\mathbf{i}_3$	$(1, 1, 1)$
	$\mathbf{C}^{(1)} = \mathbf{i}_1 - \mathbf{i}_2$	$(4, 4, 4)$

3.3   Given the force vector $\mathbf{F}$ of magnitude 5 lb, lying in the y_2y_3-plane, and passing through the point q at $(0, 1, 1)$ as shown in Fig. P.3.3.   (a) Determine the moment $\mathbf{M}$ of this force about point p at $(1, 1, 0)$.   (b) Determine the magnitude of the moment about the axis Op.   (c) Find the couple $\mathbf{C}$ that would be produced by this force $\mathbf{F}$, together with an equal and opposite force passing through the point a at $(0, 1, 2)$.

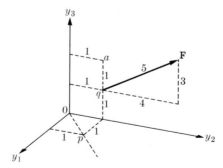

FIGURE P.3.3

3.4   An airplane, as shown in Fig. P.3.4, weighs 2500 lb, develops a maximum thrust of 143 lb, and sustains a tail load of 10.2 lb while cruising in level unaccelerated flight at 150 mph.   Determine the lift, drag, and moment about the aerodynamic center a.c. (so called because it is the reference point for a set of forces equipollent to the aerodynamic pressures acting on the wing).

FIGURE P.3.4

FIGURE P.3.5   FIGURE P.3.6

3.5   A wind-tunnel model of an airplane wing is suspended as shown by Fig. P.3.5. Find the loads in members B, C, and E if the forces at A are $L = 50$ lb, $D = 5$ lb, and the moment about A is $M = 25$ in-lb.

3.6   The astronaut is sitting calmly in the capsule, waiting for the parachute to collapse when the capsule hits the water, as shown in Fig. P.3.6. Assuming that the capsule is descending at constant velocity, draw and define the parachute, capsule, and astronaut as a three-particle system. Isolate and show all the internal and external forces acting on each particle. In another drawing, show the additional forces acting on each particle at the instant the capsule hits the water.

3.7   The rocket shown in Fig. P.3.7(a) is rising vertically with acceleration

$$\mathbf{a} = \frac{T - (D + W)}{m}\, \mathbf{i}_2,$$

where T is the thrust of the motor, D the total aerodynamic drag, m the total mass of the rocket, and $W = mg$ its weight. An idealized model of the rocket is shown in Fig. P.3.7(b), in which the mass m is "lumped" into three particles, m_1, m_2, and m_3, such that

$$m_1 + m_2 + m_3 = m.$$

The lumped masses are connected by rigid, massless rods. Treat the idealized model

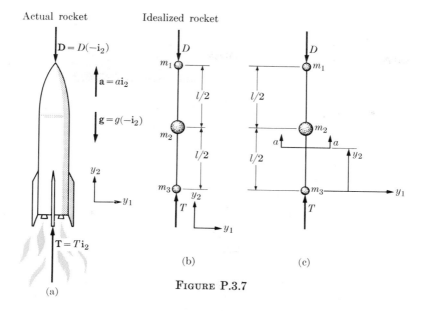

Actual rocket   Idealized rocket

(a)

(b)   (c)

FIGURE P.3.7

as a two-particle system by making the imaginary cut represented by section a–a in Fig. P.3.7(c). Plot the internal forces $\mathbf{F}^{(LU)}$ on the lower particle from the upper, and $\mathbf{F}^{(UL)}$ on the upper particle from the lower, as the position of section a–a sweeps up the rocket ($0 \leq y_2 \leq l$).

3.8   Determine the center-of-gravity locations y_1, y_2, and y_3 (see Fig. P.3.8) of (a) three masses:

Mass	Weight, lb	Location
$m^{(1)}$	1	(1, 1, 0)
$m^{(2)}$	1	(2, 2, 0)
$m^{(3)}$	2	(−1, 3, 0)

(b) a triangular plate, where h = uniform thickness; and (c) a half-cylinder, where R = radius.

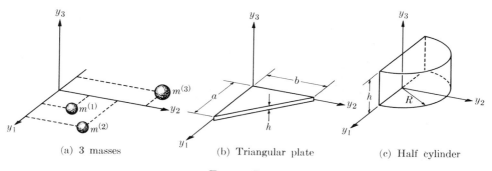

(a) 3 masses   (b) Triangular plate   (c) Half cylinder

FIGURE P.3.8

3.9 Using the *method of joints*, determine the internal forces in all the bars of the truss shown in Fig. P.3.9.

3.10 Find the reactions at the points of support, and the bar forces in all the members of the truss (Fig. P.3.10).

FIGURE P.3.9   FIGURE P.3.10

3.11 Using the *method of sections*, determine the internal forces in bars *AB*, *BD*, *DC* (these bars probably have the greatest loads). See Fig. P.3.11.

3.12 Find the reactions on the truss, and determine the axial forces in bars *CK*, *JD*, *CD* by the *method of sections*. Only the lettered intersections are joints (Fig. P.3.12).

3.13 In the space truss shown in Fig. P.3.13 the members *AB*, *BC*, *CD*, and *AD* form a square base in the y_1y_2-plane while the member *AE* coincides with the y_3-axis. $AB = BC = CD = AD = AE = 5$ ft. The truss is supported by a ball-and-socket joint at *A*, and by members *BB'*, *DD'*, and *EE'* at *B*, *D*, and *E*, respectively. *BB'* is parallel with the y_3-axis, *DD'* is parallel with the y_2-axis, and *EE'* is parallel with the

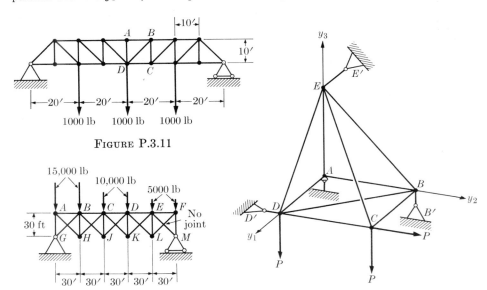

FIGURE P.3.11

FIGURE P.3.12   FIGURE P.3.13

y_1-axis. Under the external load shown in the figure, calculate forces in EE' and AB. [*Hint:* For each solution try to cut and isolate the truss in such a manner that the equation of moment equilibrium about a certain line will contain only one unknown force, i.e., the one which you are seeking.]

3.14 A beam CE (see Fig. P.3.14) which is supported by pin-ended members BD, BE, and AB is acted upon by a concentrated load W and a couple M (about an axis parallel to the y_2-axis). C is a pin joint. Determine the axial forces in AB, BD, and BE, and the reaction at C.

FIGURE P.3.14

3.15 Calculate the reactions, and plot the shear and bending-moment diagrams for each of the beams shown in Fig. P.3.15. Verify your solution for (d) by superposing solutions (a) and (b).

3.16 Determine the load, shear, and bending-moment diagrams for a beam of the configuration shown in Fig. P.3.16.

3.17 Determine the shear, bending-moment, and axial load distributions along the beam shown in Fig. P.3.17.

FIGURE P.3.15

FIGURE P.3.16

FIGURE P.3.17

FIGURE P.3.18

FIGURE P.3.19

FIGURE P.3.20

3.18   A beam (see Fig. P.3.18) with a heavy mass at the tip is attached to the end of a vertical shaft by a pin joint. The shaft with the attached beam is rotating at a constant angular velocity ω. The mass distribution of the beam is m/unit length. The tip mass M is equal to one-third of the beam mass ($M = ml/3$). Determine the angle of inclination θ, and the spanwise location at which the bending moment is a maximum.

3.19   (a) Draw a free-body diagram of the beam and kingpost, ABC and BD, respectively (Fig. P.3.19).   (b) Calculate the tension forces in wires DE and CE. (c) Calculate and plot the shear and bending-moment diagrams for the beam ABC.

3.20   A beam is supported by a pin at one end and by a wire at the other end as shown in Fig. P.3.20. The weight of the beam per unit length is w(lb/in). A weight W is hanging at point D. Determine the tension in the wire BC, and the reaction at A. What is the bending moment at section D?

FIGURE P.3.21   FIGURE P.3.22

3.21 A three-dimensional, cantilevered beam with an L-shaped planform (Fig. P.3.21) is acted on by forces $\mathbf{P}^{(A)} = 10\mathbf{i}_2 + 5\mathbf{i}_3$, $\mathbf{P}^{(B)} = 10\mathbf{i}_1 - 10\mathbf{i}_3$, and a torque $T = -20\mathbf{i}_2$ parallel to the y_2-axis. The forces are in units of pounds, and the torque is in inch-pounds. Find the reactions at the wall, and draw shear and bending-moment diagrams for both sections of the beam.

3.22 A horizontal frame shown in Fig. P.3.22 consists of three rods AD, CD, and BC, which are connected at D and C by ball-and-socket joints. The frame is supported at A and B by ball-and-socket joints, and at G and H by cables which are attached to the wall at point I. A beam 60 in. long is placed on top of this frame. The weight of the beam is 2 lb/in., and the weight of the rigid rods AD and BC is 1 lb/in. Rod DC may be considered weightless. Determine the tension in the wire HI (or GI), and the maximum bending moment in the bar BC (or AD).

3.23 A curved beam whose axis is a circular arc of radius r is acted on by an upward (y_3-direction) distributed load $p_3(\theta)$ (lb/unit arc length) and a radial (y_2-direction) distributed load $p_2(\theta)$ (lb/unit arc length). See Fig. P.3.23. For a given section the three axes are defined by x_1 = circumferential direction, x_2 = radial direction, x_3 = vertical direction. The corresponding internal forces F, S_2, S_3 and moments T, M_2, M_3 are defined as shown in Fig. P.3.23(a). Consider the equilibrium of an element of arc length $r \times d\theta$ (Fig. P.3.23b), and show that the following differential relations are valid:

$$(1) \quad \frac{dS_3}{d\theta} = p_3 r, \qquad\qquad (4) \quad -\frac{dM_2}{d\theta} + S_3 r - T = 0,$$

$$(2) \quad \frac{dS_2}{d\theta} = p_2 r - F, \qquad\qquad (5) \quad \frac{dM_3}{d\theta} = S_2 r,$$

$$(3) \quad \frac{dF}{d\theta} = S_2, \qquad\qquad (6) \quad \frac{dT}{d\theta} - M_2 = 0.$$

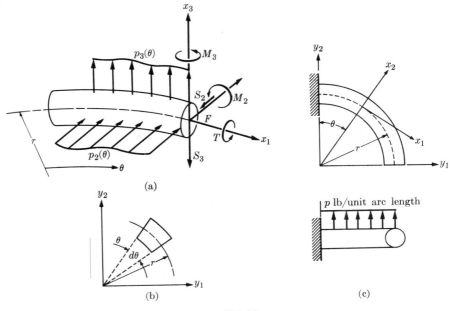

$$\text{F{\small IGURE} P.3.23}$$

A beam in the form of a quadrant of a circle (Fig. P.3.23.c) is clamped at one end and is acted on by uniform loads of p lb/unit arc length as shown in the sketch. Determine the bending moment $M_2(\theta)$ and torsional moment $T(\theta)$. Check to see whether your results satisfy Eq. (6) above.

REFERENCE

(1) C. H. N{\small ORRIS} and J. B. W{\small ILBUR}, *Elementary Structural Analysis*, 2nd Ed., Chaps. 3 and 4, McGraw-Hill, New York, 1960.

4

Simple Statically
Indeterminate Systems

4.1 INTRODUCTION

Chapter 3 was devoted to the principles of statics and to the analysis of statically determinate systems. We saw that many systems can be analyzed completely by merely carrying out the two steps:

(1) constructing a free-body diagram, and

(2) applying the principles of static equilibrium.

There are, however, many problems which involve a number of unknown reactions and/or internal forces greater than the number of independent equations that can be found from the principles of static equilibrium. For example, Fig. 4.1 shows a cantilever beam with three unknown reactions, $R_1^{(A)}$, $R_3^{(A)}$, and $M_2^{(A)}$, at the clamped end; since there are three equations of static equilibrium for this coplanar force system, the problem is statically

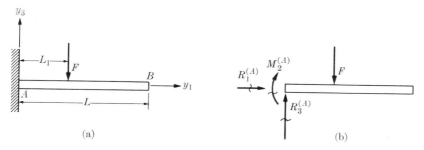

(a)   (b)

FIG. 4.1   Statically determinate beam: (a) physical diagram; (b) free-body diagram.

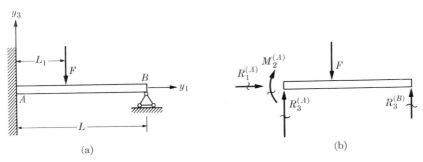

(a)   (b)

FIG. 4.2   Statically indeterminate beam: (a) physical diagram (b) free-body diagram.

determinate. Now if the beam is additionally supported by a hinge on a roller at the other end B (see Fig. 4.2), there is one additional reaction $R_3^{(B)}$. But there are still only three equations of static equilibrium that can be used.

For another example, let us consider a plane truss (Fig. 4.3) for which the members AD and BC are not connected. It is apparent that there are only three unknown reactions, $R_1^{(B)}$, $R_3^{(B)}$, and $R_3^{(D)}$, and there are three equations of static equilibrium for the complete structure. But when we begin to analyze the internal force in each member, we discover that there are three unknown forces at each joint, but only two equations of static equilibrium for each joint.

Problems which cannot be solved by using the equations of static equilibrium alone are termed *statically indeterminate*, and their analysis requires a knowledge of the deformation characteristics of the system.

Navier (Ref. 4.1) was the first to outline the method for solving statically indeterminate problems. He observed that such problems are indeterminate only if the bodies and the supports are considered as being completely rigid, but that if elasticity is considered, enough additional equations may be derived to evaluate all the unknown quantities. The present chapter is devoted to an

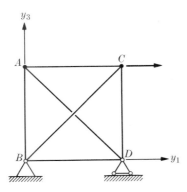

FIG. 4.3   Statically indeterminate truss.

FIG. 4.4   Physical diagram of rigid hinged beam supported on two springs.

elementary exposition of the principles of analysis of statically indeterminate systems. We shall see that two additional kinds of equations are required: (1) *constitutive relations* which express the deformation response of the structure and its supports to forces and to changes in environment such as temperature variations, and (2) *consistent deformation relations* which ensure the contiguity of the system. The principles are introduced and illustrated by examples involving simple systems. More complicated problems will be deferred to a later stage in this text, after more of the fundamentals of solid mechanics have been presented.

4.2   PRINCIPLES OF ANALYSIS OF STATICALLY INDETERMINATE SYSTEMS

We shall develop these principles by means of the simple planar system illustrated by Fig. 4.4. This illustration shows a completely rigid beam of length L, hinged at one end, supported by two springs of equal spring constants k, and loaded by a single force F. The object of the problem is to compute the internal forces in the springs and the reaction supplied by the hinge.

(a) Free-body diagrams. In this problem, as in any other problem in solid mechanics, the first steps are those of drawing free-body diagrams and selecting notation for the unknown quantities. These steps are illustrated by Fig. 4.5, where $R_3^{(1)}$ is designated as the reaction provided by the hinge, and $R_3^{(2)}$ and $R_3^{(3)}$ are the internal forces in the springs.

FIG. 4.5   Free-body diagram corresponding to Fig. 4.4.

(b) Equations of static equilibrium. The principles of static equilibrium require that Eqs. (3.4.8), (3.4.10), and (3.4.12) be satisfied for a planar system. We have then the following two independent equations of equilibrium:

$$\sum_{i=1}^{3} P_3^{(i)} = R_3^{(1)} + R_3^{(2)} + R_3^{(3)} - F = 0 \tag{4.2.1}$$

and

$$\sum_{i=1}^{3} M_2^{(i)} = R_3^{(3)}L + R_3^{(2)}b - Fa = 0 \quad \text{(about the hinge).} \tag{4.2.2}$$

Since there are three unknown quantities, namely $R_3^{(1)}$, $R_3^{(2)}$, and $R_3^{(3)}$, the two equations of statics are insufficient to provide a complete solution. The problem is said to be statically indeterminate with one *redundant* quantity or statically indeterminate to the first degree.

(c) Constitutive equations.   In order to supplement the equations of static equilibrium we must turn to the deformations and seek equations which relate forces and displacements of the system. Referring to Fig. 4.5 we see that since the beam is considered rigid and the springs elastic, the only pertinent force-displacement relations are

$$R_3^{(2)} = k\delta^{(2)}, \tag{4.2.3}$$

$$R_3^{(3)} = k\delta^{(3)}, \tag{4.2.4}$$

where $\delta^{(2)}$ and $\delta^{(3)}$ are the displacements of the springs (2) and (3), respectively. Equations (4.2.3) and (4.2.4) are of a mathematical form which is applicable not only to springs* but to all structural components of any degree of complexity. For our present purposes it is assumed that k is available; actually, the difficult task lies in the determination of k, a task which is a portion of the subject of solid mechanics. Figure 4.6 illustrates graphically the linear relations between force and the displacement of the system. The balance sheet of equations and unknowns now reads: four equations, (4.2.1) through (4.2.4) and five unknowns, $R_3^{(1)}$, $R_3^{(2)}$, $R_3^{(3)}$, $\delta^{(2)}$, and $\delta^{(3)}$.

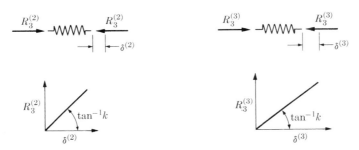

FIG. 4.6   Force-displacement properties of the system.

(d) Equations of consistent deformation.   The final step in the process is to require that the deformations at points (2) and (3) be consistent with each other and with the geometric constraints which have been placed upon the system. We shall require the displacements to be small, so that the angle of rotation, θ, of the rigid bar is of a magnitude such that $\sin \theta \cong \theta$ (in radians). In Fig. 4.7

---

* Springs are usually constructed of bars with circular cross section wound into helicoidal shapes. Such a structural form presents an unusual and interesting problem for analysis.

FIG. 4.7   Diagram showing consistency of deformations with geometric constraints.

it is evident that if the spring deflections are small, then

$$\frac{\delta^{(2)}}{b} = \frac{\delta^{(3)}}{L}. \tag{4.2.5}$$

Equation (4.2.5) is called the *equation of consistent deformation*.

We have seen that by (a) constructing a free-body diagram, and deriving (b) equilibrium equations, (c) force-displacement equations, and (d) equations of consistent deformation, we are led to a system of independent equations equal in number to the unknowns of the system. In summary, the unknowns are $R_3^{(1)}$, $R_3^{(2)}$, $R_3^{(3)}$, $\delta^{(2)}$, and $\delta^{(3)}$, and the five available equations are:

$$\left. \begin{array}{l} R_3^{(1)} + R_3^{(2)} + R_3^{(3)} - F = 0 \\ R_3^{(3)}L + R_3^{(2)}b - Fa = 0 \end{array} \right\} \quad \text{equilibrium equations,}$$

$$\left. \begin{array}{l} R_3^{(2)} = k\delta^{(2)} \\ R_3^{(3)} = k\delta^{(3)} \end{array} \right\} \quad \text{constitutive equations,}$$

$$\frac{\delta^{(2)}}{b} = \frac{\delta^{(3)}}{L}, \quad \text{equation of consistent deformation.}$$

The equations are solved by following a pattern in which the constitutive equations and the equation of consistent deformation are combined to yield a single equation relating $R_3^{(2)}$ and $R_3^{(3)}$ as follows:

$$\frac{R_3^{(2)}}{R_3^{(3)}} = \frac{b}{L}. \tag{4.2.6}$$

Combining Eq. (4.2.6) with the equilibrium equations (4.2.1) and (4.2.2) we find for the three unknown reactions:

$$R_3^{(1)} = F\left[1 - \frac{a(b + L)}{L^2(1 + b^2/L^2)}\right],$$

$$R_3^{(2)} = \frac{Fab}{L^2(1 + b^2/L^2)}, \qquad R_3^{(3)} = \frac{Fa}{L(1 + b^2/L^2)}. \tag{4.2.7}$$

4.3 EXAMPLE: AIRPLANE LANDING GEAR

We shall further illustrate the principles of Section 4.2 by applying them
to the landing gear shown by Fig. 4.8.
The rigid member ABC is assumed to
be fixed against translation at C, attached to a shock strut spring at B, and
restrained against rotation by a torsion
spring at C. The spring constant of the
linear spring at B is designated as
k_1 lb/in., and the spring constant of
the torsion spring at C is designated as
k_2 in.-lb/radian.

Fig. 4.8   Physical   diagram   of   landing
gear.

(a) Free-body diagrams.   Free-body diagrams of the isolated component parts
of the tripod landing gear, together with the notation for unknown reactions
and internal forces and moments, are illustrated by Fig. 4.9.   The force in
the linear spring is designated by $R_3^{(1)}$, the moment supplied by the torsion
spring by $M_2^{(1)}$, and the reaction at the hinged support at C by $R_3^{(2)}$.   The
reaction at C is vectored in the y_3-direction, since no y_1- or y_2-components of
force are acting on the rigid beam ABC.

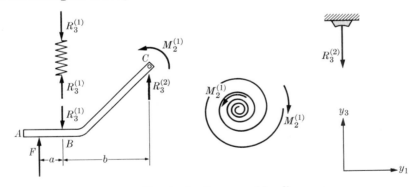

Fig. 4.9   Free-body diagram of landing gear.

(b) Equations of static equilibrium.   Treating the free-body diagram of the
beam in Fig. 4.9 as a planar system, we find the following equations of static
equilibrium:

$$\sum_{i=1}^{3} P_3^{(i)} = F + R_3^{(2)} - R_3^{(1)} = 0 \qquad (4.3.1)$$

and

$$\sum_{i=1}^{3} M_2^{(i)} = F(a + b) - R_3^{(1)}b - M_2^{(1)} = 0 \quad \text{(about hinge).} \quad (4.3.2)$$

The balance sheet of equations and unknowns reads: two equations, (4.3.1) and (4.3.2), and three unknowns, $R_3^{(1)}$, $R_3^{(2)}$, and $M_2^{(1)}$.

(c) Constitutive relations. The force-displacement equations of the system, when we assume complete rigidity of the beam member ABC, read:

$$R_3^{(1)} = k_1 \delta, \tag{4.3.3}$$

$$M_2^{(1)} = k_2 \theta. \tag{4.3.4}$$

In the preceding two examples the structural members have been assumed to be rigid. The same three types of equation, i.e., equilibrium, constitutive, and consistency, would be used if the flexibility of the members were taken into account; additional constitutive equations to account for the flexibility of the members would be combined with those of the springs. In real life there are no rigid members, and thus the neglect of flexibility implies that some structural component is much more rigid (or much more flexible) than some other. Thus in the examples used, the assumption of rigid members can be justified only if the flexibility of the springs (this means $1/k$) is much larger than that of the members, or conversely, the stiffness of the members is much greater than that of the springs. In solid mechanics, the terms "much larger" or "much greater" usually mean at least by one order of magnitude.

4.4 EXAMPLES OF PLANE TRUSSES

Statically Indeterminate Truss. Figure 4.10 shows a pin-jointed truss consisting of three bars meeting at the vertex D, and loaded by a force F. The bar BD has an area A_1 and modulus of elasticity E_1, and the bars AD and CD each have area A_2 and modulus of elasticity E_2. The length of the bar BD is L and the angle ABD and BDC is α.

 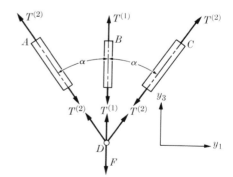

Fɪɢ. 4.10 Physical diagram of statically indeterminate planar truss.

Fɪɢ. 4.11 Free-body diagrams of planar truss.

(a) Free-body diagrams. The appropriate free-body diagrams of the planar truss are shown in Fig. 4.11. Here we have isolated the pin at D, and each of the individual bars. Each bar is assumed to be in tension. The tension force in bar BD is designated as $T^{(1)}$, and in bars AD and CD it is designated as $T^{(2)}$. It is evident from the symmetry of the truss and its loading system that the internal forces will also be symmetrically disposed, and that bars AD and CD will therefore have equal internal forces.

(b) Equations of static equilibrium. One equation of static equilibrium may be found from the equilibrium of the pin at D in Fig. 4.11.

$$\sum_{i=1}^{3} P_3^{(i)} = T^{(1)} + 2T^{(2)} \cos \alpha - F = 0. \tag{4.4.1}$$

Symmetry has in effect used the equilibrium equation in the y_1-direction to show that $T_{AD} = T_{CD}$:

$$\sum_{i=1}^{3} P_1^{(i)} = -T_{AD} \sin \alpha + T_{CD} \sin \alpha = 0;$$

$$\therefore T_{AD} = T_{CD} = T^{(2)},$$

as stated above. The balance sheet of equations and unknowns reads: one equation, (4.4.1), and two unknowns, $T^{(1)}$ and $T^{(2)}$.

(c) Constitutive relations. In order to construct the force-displacement relations for a truss system such as that of Fig. 4.11, it is necessary to derive the relation between force and displacement for a uniform elastic bar with constant axial force. As has been stated in Section 4.2, the force-displacement relationship is of the form

$$T = k\delta. \tag{4.4.2}$$

It will be shown in subsequent chapters that k for a bar under uniform tension has the form

$$k = \frac{AE}{L}, \tag{4.4.3}$$

where A is the cross-sectional area and E is the modulus of elasticity of the material. We can then construct the following force-displacement relations for our planar truss example:

$$T^{(1)} = \frac{A_1 E_1}{L} \delta^{(1)}, \tag{4.4.4}$$

$$T^{(2)} = \frac{A_2 E_2 \cos \alpha}{L} \delta^{(2)}, \tag{4.4.5}$$

where $\delta^{(1)}$ and $\delta^{(2)}$ are the deflections of bars BD and AD (or CD), respectively. At this point in the problem there are three equations, (4.4.1), (4.4.4), and (4.4.5), and four unknowns, $T^{(1)}$, $T^{(2)}$, $\delta^{(1)}$, and $\delta^{(2)}$.

(d) Equations of consistent deformation. A single equation of consistent deformation may be derived by requiring that the stretching of the bars be compatible with their common point of attachment at D. From Fig. 4.12 it is easily seen that the equation of consistent deformation is simply

$$\delta^{(1)} \cos \alpha = \delta^{(2)}. \qquad (4.4.6)$$

Equations (4.4.1), (4.4.4), (4.4.5), and (4.4.6) are sufficient for the computations of the four unknowns $T^{(1)}$, $T^{(2)}$, $\delta^{(1)}$, and $\delta^{(2)}$. Combining Eqs. (4.4.4), (4.4.5), and (4.4.6), we find the following relation between $T^{(1)}$ and $T^{(2)}$:

$$\frac{T^{(1)}}{T^{(2)}} = \frac{A_1 E_1}{A_2 E_2 \cos^2 \alpha}. \qquad (4.4.7)$$

Equation (4.4.7) when combined with Eq. (4.4.1) yields

$$T^{(1)} = \frac{F}{1 + 2A_2 E_2 \cos^3 \alpha / A_1 E_1}, \qquad (4.4.8)$$

$$T^{(2)} = \frac{F \sec \alpha}{2 + A_1 E_1 / A_2 E_2 \cos^3 \alpha}. \qquad (4.4.9)$$

Statically Determinate Truss. Let us examine the behavior of a two-bar truss (Fig. 4.13). This is a statically determinate structure in which $T_{AD} = T_{CD}$, as shown previously for the similar three-bar truss. We apply the equilibrium relation for the y_3-direction:

$$\sum_{i=1}^{2} P_3^{(i)} = 2T^{(2)} \cos \alpha - F = 0$$

or

$$T^{(2)} = F/2 \cos \alpha.$$

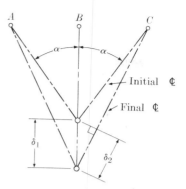

Fig. 4.12 Diagram showing consistency of stretching of bars of planar truss.

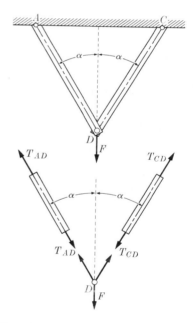

Fig. 4.13 Statically determinate plane truss.

It is clear that in the limit where $A_1 = 0$, Eqs. (4.4.8) and (4.4.9) reduce to

$$T^{(1)} = 0 \quad \text{and} \quad T^{(2)} = F/2 \cos \alpha,$$

which is the same answer that results if A_1 is set equal to zero in Eq. (4.4.9), i.e., if bar BD is removed from the indeterminate truss of Fig. 4.11.

4.5 EXAMPLE OF THERMAL STRESSES IN BOLT-AND-BUSHING ASSEMBLY

In Fig. 4.14 an assembly is shown which consists of a steel bolt inserted in a bronze bushing. The nut is pulled up snugly against the bushing while the whole assembly is at an ambient temperature of 50°F. It is desired to compute the stresses in the bolt and bushing when the temperature of the assembly is raised to 170°F.

Bronze sleeve   Steel bolt

2″   3″

20″

Fig. 4.14   Physical diagram of bolt-and-sleeve assembly.

(a) Free-body diagrams. Figure 4.15 illustrates the free-body diagrams which follow from Fig. 4.14. The bolt is assumed to be in tension with load $P^{(s)}$, and the bushing in compression with load $P^{(b)}$. The bolt head is in equilibrium under the forces $P^{(b)}$ and $P^{(s)}$. In this discussion superscripts b refer to the bronze bushing, and s to the steel bolt.

(b) Equations of static equilibrium. One equation of static equilibrium may be formed from the equilibrium of the bolt head (cf. Fig. 4.15) as follows:

$$\sum_{i=1}^{2} P_1^{(i)} = P^{(s)} - P^{(b)} = 0. \tag{4.5.1}$$

The balance sheet of unknowns and equations reads: one equation (4.5.1), and two unknowns, $P^{(b)}$ and $P^{(s)}$. The problem is therefore statically indeterminate, and we must seek additional equations from sources other than equilibrium.

(c) Constitutive relations. In determining the deformations of components of the assembly we must take into account the fact that the materials of which the bolt and bushing are made expand with an increase in temperature. The elongation of the bolt due to a change in temperature ΔT by an amount $\delta^{(s)}$ is given by

$$\delta_T^{(s)} = \alpha_s L\, \Delta T, \tag{4.5.2}$$

where

α_s = coefficient of thermal expansion of the steel bolt material per degree change in temperature,

L = length of the bolt,

ΔT = change in temperature.

The coefficient of thermal expansion of a material represents an experimentally

Bolt head

FIG. 4.15 Free-body diagrams of bolt and sleeve assembly.

determined constant which measures the expansion of the material per unit length of material per unit change of temperature.

The expansion of the bushing due to temperature change is expressed by

$$\delta_T^{(b)} = \alpha_b L \, \Delta T, \tag{4.5.3}$$

where

α_b = coefficient of thermal expansion of the bronze bushing material per degree change in temperature.

It is evident that there will also be changes in length of the bolt and bushing due to the loads $P^{(s)}$ and $P^{(b)}$, respectively. For the bolt, the stretching due to P_s is given by

$$\delta_P^{(s)} = \frac{P^{(s)}}{k_s}, \tag{4.5.4}$$

where the form of k_s will be the same as for the truss members of Section 4.4,

$$k_s = \frac{A_s E_s}{L}, \tag{4.5.5}$$

and

A_s = cross-sectional area of bolt,

E_s = modulus of elasticity of the steel bolt.

The reduction in length of the bushing due to the compressive load $P^{(b)}$ is given by

$$\delta_P^{(b)} = -\frac{P^{(b)}L}{A_b E_b} = -\frac{P^{(b)}}{k_b}, \tag{4.5.6}$$

where

$$k_b = \frac{A_b E_b}{L}, \tag{4.5.7}$$

and

A_b = cross-sectional area of the bushing,

E_b = modulus of elasticity of the bronze bushing.

(d) Equation of consistent deformation. In order for the head and nut of the bolt to remain in contact with the ends of the bushing, the following condition on the deformation must be met:

$$\delta_T^{(b)} + \delta_P^{(b)} = \delta_P^{(s)} + \delta_T^{(s)}. \tag{4.5.8}$$

(e) Numerical solution. The six equations, (4.5.1) through (4.5.6), are sufficient to compute the six unknowns $P^{(b)}$, $P^{(s)}$, $\delta_T^{(b)}$, $\delta_P^{(b)}$, $\delta_T^{(s)}$, and $\delta_P^{(s)}$. Let us suppose that the properties of the bolt and bushing material are given by

$$\begin{aligned}
E_b &= (10)(10^6) \text{ lb/in}^2, \\
\alpha_b &= (10.1)(10^{-6})/°\text{F}, \\
E_s &= (30)(10^6) \text{ lb/in}^2, \\
\alpha_s &= (6.1)(10^{-6})/°\text{F}.
\end{aligned} \tag{4.5.9}$$

Substituting Eqs. (4.5.2) through (4.5.5) in Eq. (4.5.8), and combining with Eq. (4.5.1), we get

$$P = P^{(b)} = P^{(s)} = 13{,}300 \text{ lb}. \tag{4.5.10}$$

Since these answers were obtained with plus signs, we conclude that the assumed directions of $P^{(b)}$ and $P^{(s)}$ in Fig. 4.15 are correct.

4.6 EXAMPLE OF ASSEMBLY STRESSES IN BOLT-AND-NUT ASSEMBLY

Let us suppose that the bolt of the example in Section 4.5 has 20 threads to the inch, and that we wish to compute the loads in the bolt and bushing when the nut is given one-half turn after it has been brought snugly against the bushing. In such a problem the equilibrium equation is the same as (4.5.1), and the force-displacement equations are the same as (4.5.4) and (4.5.5). Since one-half turn advances the nut 0.025 in., the compatibility equation is

$$\delta_P^{(b)} = \delta_P^{(s)} - 0.025. \tag{4.6.1}$$

Combining Eqs. (4.5.1), (4.5.4), (4.5.5), and (4.6.1), and introducing the numerical data of (4.5.7), we obtain

$$P^{(b)} = P^{(s)} = 34{,}700 \text{ lb}. \tag{4.6.2}$$

4.7 EXAMPLE OF STATICALLY INDETERMINATE BEAM

Let us now consider the statically indeterminate beam which was discussed previously in Section 4.1, and is illustrated again in Fig. 4.16.

(a) Free-body diagram. Figure 4.16(b) illustrates the free-body diagram corresponding to Fig. 4.16(a). There are four unknown reactions, $R_1^{(A)}$, $R_3^{(A)}$, $M_2^{(A)}$, and $R_3^{(B)}$.

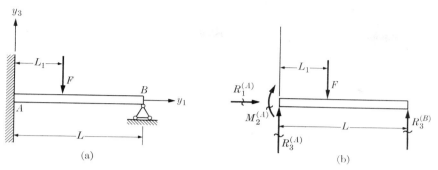

FIG. 4.16   Statically indeterminate beam: (a) physical diagram; (b) free-body diagram.

(b) Equations of static equilibrium. The three equations of equilibrium for this coplanar force system are

$$\sum P_1^{(i)} = R_1^{(A)} = 0, \tag{4.7.1}$$

$$\sum P_3^{(i)} = R_3^{(A)} - F + R_3^{(B)} = 0, \tag{4.7.2}$$

$$\sum M_2^{(i)} = M_2^{(A)} + L_1 F - L R_3^{(B)} = 0 \quad \text{(about } A). \tag{4.7.3}$$

It is seen that $R_1^{(A)}$ is zero. The balance sheet of unknowns and equations reads: two equations, (4.7.2) and (4.7.3), and three unknowns, $R_3^{(A)}$, $M_2^{(A)}$, and $R_3^{(B)}$. The problem is therefore statically indeterminate and we must seek an additional equation.

(c) Constitutive relations. Let us assume that we can determine the tip deflection δ_B of a cantilever uniform beam, due to a vertical load P acting at any distance x from the fixed end of the beam (Fig. 4.17). The expression for the tip deflection is

$$\delta_B = \frac{Px^2}{2EI} (L - \tfrac{1}{3}x), \tag{4.7.4}$$

FIG. 4.17   Cantilever beam under a concentrated load.

where E is the modulus of elasticity, and I is the section moment of inertia about the y_2-axis. We can, of course, always determine the tip deflections through a series of experiments. In Chapters 7 and 9 we shall discuss analytical methods for evaluating this expression.

(d) Equations of consistent deformation. From Fig. 4.16(b) we can see that the statically indeterminate beam may be considered as a cantilever beam acted upon by a load $P = -F$ at a distance $x = L_1$ from A, and an unknown load $P = R_3^{(B)}$ acting at a distance $x = L$ from A. The deflection at B due to these two loads must necessarily be zero because B is a fixed support. The equation of consistent deformation is thus

$$\delta_B^{(F)} + \delta_B^{(R_3^B)} = 0. \tag{4.7.5}$$

Substituting

$$\delta_B^{(F)} = -\frac{FL_1^2}{2EI}(L - \tfrac{1}{3}L_1) \qquad \text{and} \qquad \delta_B^{(R_3^B)} = \frac{R_3^{(B)}L^2}{2EI}(L - \tfrac{1}{3}L),$$

$$\tag{4.7.6}$$

we can solve for the unknown reaction $R_3^{(B)}$. The result is

$$R_3^{(B)} = \frac{FL_1^2}{L^2}\left(\frac{3}{2} - \frac{1}{2}\frac{L_1}{L}\right). \tag{4.7.7}$$

Knowing $R_3^{(B)}$, we can evaluate the other three reactions by means of Eqs. (4.7.2) and (4.7.3).

4.8   SUMMARY

We have now completed the development of the tools necessary for the analysis of structures "in the large." We have seen that if the number of unknowns is equal to the number of equilibrium equations available, a problem may be solved with the equations of statics alone. When the number of unknowns exceeds the number of available equilibrium equations, the structure is called statically indeterminate. Such structures can be solved by simultaneous considerations of the following three groups of equations:

(1) equations of static equilibrium,
(2) constitutive equations or force displacement relations,
(3) conditions of consistent deformation.

Whether the problem is determinate or indeterminate, we observe that the unknowns are always forces and displacements, i.e., integrated-effect quantities. In the remainder of this volume we shall retrace our steps through these fundamental equations, examining the structure in greater detail. Instead of forces and displacements, we shall be interested in forces per unit area and displacements per unit length, and our general problem will be to solve for these quantities as functions of position in the structure.

PROBLEMS

4.1   Compute the reactions on the beam shown in Fig. P.4.1. Also compute the deflections at the supports. The beam may be considered rigid and weightless. The deformation of each spring is small in comparison to the length of the beam.

FIGURE P.4.1

FIGURE P.4.2

4.2   A rigid beam weighing w lb/unit length is supported by three springs as shown in Fig. P.4.2. Given that the beam is loaded by an additional concentrated load W acting at point B, compute the bending moment at section B.

FIGURE P.4.3

FIGURE P.4.4

4.3   Compare the effects of thermal expansion on the one-material and two-material bars shown in Fig. P.4.3. Compute the loads which arise in each material, and the deflections of the midspan stations of each bar for a rise in temperature of 100F°.

Bar	Area	Material	$\alpha/°F$ $(\times 10^{-6})$	E, psi $(\times 10^{6})$
1	A	Titanium	6	17
2	A	Concrete	6	3.4

4.4   Three bars of different materials are built into a rigid wall at one end and connected at the other by a common end plate. The end plate is rigid and is constrained by rigid tracks against rotation (Fig. P.4.4). Calculate the load in each bar, and the deflection of the end plate for a decrease in termperature of 200° F.

Bar	Area	Material	$\alpha/°F$ $(\times 10^{-6})$	E, psi $(\times 10^{7})$
1	1 in^2	Gun metal	10.2	1
2	2 in^2	Tungsten	2.4	5.2
3	3 in^2	Copper	7.8	1.8

4.5 The bar-and-plate system shown in the Fig. P.4.5 is built into rigid walls at either end, and the tie plate is constrained to horizontal motion. The system is in equilibrium under zero stress at 0°F. Compute the bar loads and the deflection, δ, at a temperature of $-100°F$. Each bar is 10 in. long.

Bar	Area	Material	$\alpha/°F$ $(\times 10^{-6})$	E, psi $(\times 10^7)$
1	2 in^2	Molybdenum	2.7	4.3
2	1 in^2	Aluminum, 2024–T3	13	1.05
3	1 in^2	Steel, SAE 4130	6.5	2.9

4.6 A rigid beam is suspended by three elastic bars as shown by the figure. All bars are 1 in^2 in cross section and 20 in. long. Bar BE is made of steel, and bars AF and CD are made of bronze. Assuming that the bars are stress-free prior to loading, compute the forces in each bar for the loading shown by Fig. P.4.6. Suppose that the temperature of the entire assembly is raised by 100°F. Compute the forces in the bars

FIGURE P.4.5

FIGURE P.4.6

FIGURE P.4.7

FIGURE P.4.8

under the combined external loading and temperature environment. Sketch the bending-moment and shear diagrams of the beam.

Moduli of elasticity:

$$E_{steel} = 30 \times 10^6 \text{ lb/in}^2,$$

$$E_{bronze} = 17 \times 10^6 \text{ lb/in}^2.$$

Coefficients of thermal expansion:

$$\alpha_{steel} = 6.5 \times 10^{-6}/°F,$$

$$\alpha_{bronze} = 10.1 \times 10^{-6}/°F.$$

4.7   The wires shown in the Fig. P.4.7 are cooled by an amount $\Delta T = -100°F$. Calculate the axial tension in each wire in terms of the properties and dimensions of the wires, and the angle of rotation of the rigid bar. The dimensions and properties of the wires are

Wire No. 1: $A_1, L_1, E_1, \alpha_1,$ Wire No. 2: $A_2, L_2, E_2, \alpha_2,$

where A = cross section area, L = length of member, E = modulus of elasticity, and α = coefficient of thermal expansion.

4.8   Prestressed concrete is widely used as a building material today. A prestressed concrete member is formed by applying tension to a set of steel rods while concrete is poured around them. When the concrete sets, the external loads are removed from the steel rods, and the concrete is subjected to compression. The prestressed concrete member derives its great strength from the facts that (1) concrete can withstand large compressive loads but only small tensile loads, and (2) the precompression prevents an externally applied large tensile load from actually putting the concrete in tension. Figure P.4.8 illustrates an idealized prestressed concrete member, in which the steel rod is "fixed" to the concrete only by the rigid end plates.

   (a) If the length of the steel rod was equal to L during the time the tensile load P was applied, calculate the length l of the prestressed member after P is removed. (b) Speculate on what might happen to a prestressed concrete floor beam in a building which has been burning long enough for the beam to become heated throughout. Given:

$$E_{steel} = 30 \times 10^6 \text{ psi},$$

$$E_{concrete} = 3.4 \times 10^6 \text{ psi},$$

$$\alpha_{steel} = 6.5 \times 10^{-6}/°F,$$

$$\alpha_{concrete} = 6 \times 10^{-6}/°F.$$

4.9   A cantilever beam is supported at its end by a wire of area A in tension. The beam with a moment of inertia I is loaded by a uniformly distributed load of w lb/in. Both the beam and the wire are made of the same material, with modulus of elasticity E (Fig. P.4.9). Compute the load in the wire and the reactions of the wall on the beam.

FIGURE P.4.9

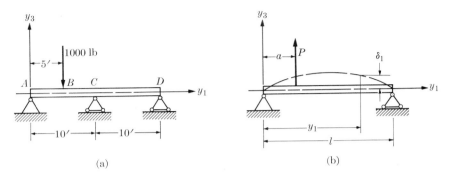

(a)

(b)

FIGURE P.4.10

4.10   Determine the reactions for the beam on three supports in Fig. P.4.10(a). *Note:* For the statically determinate uniform beam loaded as shown in Fig. P.4.10(b) the deflection δ_1 at any point y_1 is:

$$
\delta_1 = \begin{cases} \dfrac{Py_1(l-a)(2la-a^2-y_1^2)}{6EIl} & \text{for } y_1 \leq a, \\[4mm] \dfrac{Pa(l-y_1)(2ly_1-a^2-y_1^2)}{6EIl} & \text{for } y_1 \geq a. \end{cases}
$$

4.11   The rigid beam AB weighing w lb/unit length is pinned at its upper end A and attached at its lower end B to two cables BC and BD (Fig. P.4.11). Compute the loads in the cables and the reaction at A. The two wires have the same elastic modulus and cross-section area.

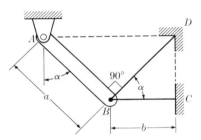

FIGURE P.4.11

REFERENCE

(1) C. L. M. H. NAVIER, *Résumé des leçons sur l'application de la méchanique*, Paris, France, 1833.

5

Analysis of Strain

5.1 INTRODUCTION

The analytical treatment of forces has been presented in Chapters 2 and 3. In Chapters 3 and 4, the effect of the gross deformations of a body on the distribution of forces in a statically indeterminate structure has been discussed. We must now delve more deeply into the detailed nature of the deformations in deformable bodies. The information we desire is contained in the strain tensor. This chapter will be concerned with the analysis of the state of strain in a deformed body.

It is an experimental fact that bodies subjected to forces will be deformed. For a structure constructed of rubber or wood, the deformations under load are easily discernible and can be measured by relatively crude instruments. For one constructed of an aluminum or a steel alloy, the strains can be detected only with precision instruments.

The state of strain at a point P in the deformed body supplies the following information:

(a) the differences in length of all linear elements, dS, originating at a point P in the deformed structure and the corresponding elements, ds, originating at the point p in the undeformed structure (in undergoing deformation, a material particle point at point p in the undeformed body moves in a continuous fashion to its final position at point P in the deformed body), and

(b) the differences between the angles, $d\widehat{S_1 dS_2}$, formed by all pairs of linear elements originating at point P and the angles, $d\widehat{s_1 ds_2}$ formed by the corresponding linear elements ds_1 and ds_2 originating at point p in the undeformed structure.

The quantities described in (a) are called the *extensional strains*, while those of (b) are called the *shear strains*. We will shortly discover that knowledge of any combination of six strains (e.g., three extensional and three shear, or four extensional and two shear) is sufficient to completely specify the strain at a point P.

The geometrical meanings of (a) and
(b) are depicted in Fig. 5.1, wherein
point p is any point in the undeformed
body. It is assumed that point p moves
to point P in a continuous fashion (from
causes which need not be of concern
here), and this is schematically shown
by placing P within a boundary which
is labeled "deformed body." Similarly,
points q and r which are infinitesimally
close to p displace to the points labeled
Q and R. The vector joining p to P will

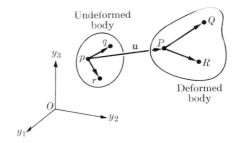

Fig. 5.1   Relation between points in
the undeformed and deformed body.

be denoted by $\mathbf{u}$, and it can be specified as a function of the coordinates of p.
The state of strain at point P (or p, since p is uniquely related to P by $\mathbf{u}$) is
specified if the following two items of geometry are known:

(a) $|PQ| - |pq|$ for all points q in the neighborhood of p ($dS = |PQ|$ and
$ds = |pq|$),

(b) $\angle QPR - \angle qpr$ for all pairs of line segments formed by points q and r
in the vicinity of p ($dS_1 = |PQ|$, $dS_2 = |PR|$, $ds_1 = |pq|$, $ds_2 = |pr|$,
$d\widehat{S_1 dS_2} = \angle QPR$, and $d\widehat{s_1 ds_2} = \angle qpr$).

It will be shown that this information is contained in the fundamental metric
tensors of the deformed and undeformed structure.

In what follows, lower-case letters will identify points or quantities in the
undeformed body, and the same upper-case letters will identify similar quantities
in the deformed body (see Fig. 5.1).

5.2   THE FUNDAMENTAL METRIC TENSORS

Basically, the task in the analysis of strain is to chart the course of every
material particle from its original to its final position. The material particle
can be identified on the basis either of its initial coordinates or final coordinates,
the former being called the *Lagrangian representation*, the latter, the *Eulerian
representation*. In general, it is more convenient to use the Lagrangian coordinates because the undeformed structure will possess some regularities or
symmetries which make it susceptible to description by a common coordinate
frame such as rectangular Cartesian, cylindrical, or spherical. The deformed
structure usually does not possess any regularities or symmetries.

The developments are to be undertaken with respect to a rectangular Cartesian
coordinate frame y_1, y_2, and y_3. In Fig. 5.2, point p with coordinates y_1, y_2, y_3
is a material point in the undeformed structure, and point P with coordinates
Y_1, Y_2, Y_3 is the location of the same particle of material after deformation.
Both y_n and Y_n are measured with respect to the same origin O and same system
of axes. A neighboring point with coordinates $y_1 + dy_1$, $y_2 + dy_2$, $y_3 + dy_3$

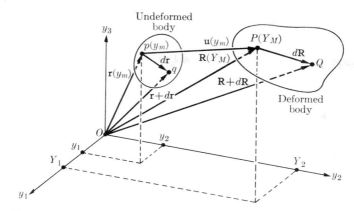

FIG. 5.2   Position vectors to undeformed and deformed body.

is identified as q, and its final position is Q with coordinates $Y_1 + dY_1$, $Y_2 + dY_2$, $Y_3 + dY_3$.

The position vector to p is denoted by $\mathbf{r}$ and its component form is

$$\mathbf{r} = y_m \mathbf{i}_m, \tag{5.2.1}$$

where the $\mathbf{i}_m$'s are the unit vectors of the y_n-frame. Similarly, $\mathbf{R}$ is the position vector to point P in the deformed body with components given by

$$\mathbf{R} = Y_m \mathbf{i}_m. \tag{5.2.2}$$

It is assumed that the particle of material moves continuously from point p to P, and that the final coordinates Y_m must be continuous and differentiable functions of the initial coordinates y_m. This is specified mathematically by writing

$$Y_m = Y_m(y_1, y_2, y_3). \tag{5.2.3}$$

If the loads or other causes of distortion do not rupture the structure, and this will be assumed, then Eq. (5.2.3) can be solved to yield the inverse relation,*

$$y_m = y_m(Y_1, Y_2, Y_3). \tag{5.2.4}$$

The differential element of length in the undeformed body is the distance between points p and q, its square being given by

$$(ds)^2 = d\mathbf{r} \cdot d\mathbf{r}. \tag{5.2.5}$$

---

* A necessary and sufficient condition that Eq. (5.2.3) be solvable for y_m, i.e., for Eq. (5.2.4) to exist, is that the Jacobian shall not vanish. Further information on tensors is to be found in the mathematical appendix.

The differential of the position vector is

$$d\mathbf{r} = \frac{\partial \mathbf{r}}{\partial y_m} \, dy_m. \tag{5.2.6}$$

The vectors $\partial \mathbf{r}/\partial y_m$ are called the *base vectors* of the coordinate frame y_n. Since the y_n's form a rectangular Cartesian frame, we have

$$\frac{\partial \mathbf{r}}{\partial y_m} = \mathbf{i}_m \tag{5.2.7}$$

and

$$(ds)^2 = dy_m \, dy_m. \tag{5.2.8}$$

Equation (5.2.8) owes its simplicity to the use of rectangular Cartesian coordinates. It is a special case of the more general quadratic form

$$(ds)^2 = g_{mn} \, dx_m \, dx_n, \tag{5.2.9}$$

where the collection of the g_{mn}'s is called the *fundamental metric tensor*, and the x_m's are *general curvilinear coordinates* (which need not be orthogonal). The fundamental metric tensor has the important property that

$$g_{mn} = g_{nm}, \tag{5.2.10}$$

which means that g_{mn} is a symmetric tensor.

The general form, Eq. (5.2.9), is suitable regardless of the coordinate frame employed. Simplifications will result for special cases. Thus, if the coordinate frame is orthogonal,

$$g_{mn} = 0, \quad \text{for} \quad m \neq n, \tag{5.2.11}$$

and if, in addition to being orthogonal, the frame is also Cartesian, then

$$g_{mn} = \delta_{mn}, \tag{5.2.12}$$

where δ_{mn} is the Kronecker delta symbol. Thus for rectangular Cartesian coordinates, Eq. (5.2.9) is written as

$$(ds)^2 = \delta_{mn} \, dy_m \, dy_n, \tag{5.2.13}$$

in which additional emphasis is placed on the specialized nature of the frame by using y_m instead of x_m. The form of Eq. (5.2.13) will seem to be a somewhat abstruse way to express a rather simple result (Eq. 5.2.8), but the use of Eq. (5.2.13) will put the student in the proper frame of mind for the eventual transition to general curvilinear coordinates.

Since the final coordinates are continuous functions of the initial coordinates (cf. Eq. 5.2.3), the differential of $\mathbf{R}$ can be written as

$$d\mathbf{R} = \frac{\partial \mathbf{R}}{\partial y_m} \, dy_m, \tag{5.2.14}$$

where the vectors $\partial \mathbf{R}/\partial y_m$ are called the *base vectors* of the deformed body. In tensor analysis these base vectors are given the symbol $\mathbf{G}_m$.

Now, the square of the line element in the deformed body is

$$(dS)^2 = \left(\frac{\partial \mathbf{R}}{\partial y_m} dy_m\right) \cdot \left(\frac{\partial \mathbf{R}}{\partial y_n} dy_n\right), \tag{5.2.15}$$

which can be put into the form

$$(dS)^2 = G_{mn} \, dy_m \, dy_n, \tag{5.2.16}$$

where the functions denoted by G_{mn} are given by the scalar products,

$$G_{mn} = \frac{\partial \mathbf{R}}{\partial y_m} \cdot \frac{\partial \mathbf{R}}{\partial y_n}. \tag{5.2.17}$$

The collection of the G_{mn}'s is the fundamental metric tensor of the deformed body with respect to the Lagrangian coordinates. It should be carefully observed that this fundamental metric tensor of the deformed body is also symmetric, that is,

$$G_{mn} = G_{nm}. \tag{5.2.18}$$

5.3 THE STRAIN TENSOR

The squares of the line elements in the undeformed and deformed body have been defined in Eqs. (5.2.13) and (5.2.16) in terms of the initial (Lagrangian) coordinates. It will be found convenient and expedient to introduce the concept of a *strain tensor*, which will be denoted by γ_{mn}. The strain tensor is introduced by writing the difference of the squares of the undeformed and deformed line elements in the convenient mathematical form

$$2\gamma_{mn} \, dy_m \, dy_n = (dS)^2 - (ds)^2. \tag{5.3.1}$$

The above definition, which at first glance may appear to be clumsy, will later prove convenient for mathematical purposes. Equation (5.3.1) means that the strain tensor is defined as one-half the difference between the deformed and undeformed metric tensors (cf. Eqs. 5.2.13 and 5.2.16),*

$$\gamma_{mn} = \tfrac{1}{2}(G_{mn} - \delta_{mn}). \tag{5.3.2}$$

---

* We will discover in our study of the strain tensor that the definition given by Eqs. (5.3.1) and (5.3.2) is well suited for most of the engineering problems concerned with small strains. For the analysis of large strains, it has been found that the Eulerian approach is more convenient. For example, the Eulerian approach has been used more extensively in the treatment of fluid mechanics.

The strain tensor, like the fundamental metric tensors, is symmetric, so that

$$\gamma_{mn} = \gamma_{nm}, \tag{5.3.3}$$

because both G_{mn} and δ_{mn} are symmetric. Thus, although there are nine elements in the strain tensor, there are only six independent ones.

5.4   THE GEOMETRICAL MEANING OF THE STRAIN TENSOR

The vector, $d\mathbf{r}$, which joins two neighboring points in the undeformed body can be enclosed by a rectangular parallelepiped with edges represented by

$$d\mathbf{r} = dy_m \frac{\partial \mathbf{r}}{\partial y_m} = dy_m \mathbf{i}_m. \tag{5.4.1}$$

This is shown in Fig. 5.3 with a perspective which is different from that used in Fig. 5.2. The lengths of the vectors $dy_1\mathbf{i}_1$, $dy_2\mathbf{i}_2$, and $dy_3\mathbf{i}_3$ are shown in Fig. 5.3 as the edges pa, pb, and pc, respectively. Similarly, the vector $d\mathbf{R}$, which joins the points P and Q in the deformed body, is enclosed in a parallelepiped which is no longer rectangular.*

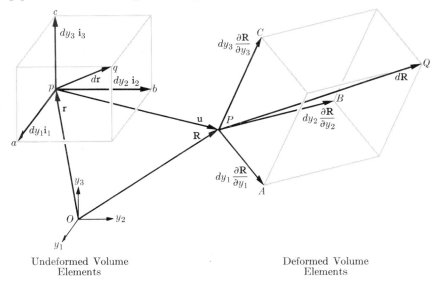

Undeformed Volume
Elements

Deformed Volume
Elements

FIG. 5.3 Vector representations of edges of undeformed and deformed volume elements.

* The element of volume surrounding $d\mathbf{R}$ is a parallelepiped only in the limit as $|d\mathbf{R}|$ approaches zero.

Since the Lagrangian approach has been adopted, it is informative to consider the rectangular parallelepiped *pabc* as the reference element of volume. The process of deformation distorts this element of volume such that the corners *pabc* become *PABC*, respectively. It follows that this figure must be considered the element of volume in the deformed body.

The geometrical meaning of the components of the strain tensor can best be appreciated by finding the changes in length of the edges of the element of volume, and the changes in angles formed by the edges. Thus the change in length of edge *pa* as it is deformed into *PA* is given by $dS_1 - ds_1$, where dS_1 denotes the length of *PA* and ds_1 is dy_1, the length of *pa*. It is more convenient to deal with the relative elongation defined as

$$E_1 = \frac{dS_1 - ds_1}{ds_1} = \frac{dS_1}{ds_1} - 1 \qquad (5.4.2)$$

than with the actual change in length. Note carefully that the reference length is the original length which is natural for the Lagrangian formulation.* In words, Eq. (5.4.2) states

$$E_1 = \frac{\text{change in length of } pa}{\text{original length of } pa} = \frac{|PA| - |pa|}{|pa|}, \qquad (5.4.3)$$

where $|PA|$ and $|pa|$ represent the lengths of the edges *PA* and *pa*, respectively, of Fig. 5.3. By making use of the scalar product and Eq. (5.2.17) we have

$$|PA|^2 = \frac{\partial \mathbf{R}}{\partial y_1} dy_1 \cdot \frac{\partial \mathbf{R}}{\partial y_1} dy_1 = G_{11}(dy_1)^2. \qquad (5.4.4)$$

Similarly, the original length is given by

$$|pa|^2 = \mathbf{i}_1 \, dy_1 \cdot \mathbf{i}_1 \, dy_1 = (dy_1)^2. \qquad (5.4.5)$$

With the substitution of Eqs. (5.4.4) and (5.4.5), Eq. (5.4.3) becomes

$$E_1 = \sqrt{G_{11}} - 1. \qquad (5.4.6)$$

By definition (see Eq. 5.3.2) the component of the strain tensor γ_{11} is the one related to G_{11},

$$\gamma_{11} = \tfrac{1}{2}(G_{11} - 1). \qquad (5.4.7)$$

The replacement of G_{11} in Eq. (5.4.6) by its equivalent from Eq. (5.4.7) yields the desired result,

$$E_1 = \frac{dS_1}{ds_1} - 1 = \sqrt{1 + 2\gamma_{11}} - 1. \qquad (5.4.8)$$

---

* In the Eulerian formulation, the reference length would be the final length dS_1, which would then appear in the denominator.

Similarly, the relative elongations of the other two edges can be obtained:

$$E_2 = \frac{dS_2}{ds_2} - 1 = \sqrt{1 + 2\gamma_{22}} - 1, \tag{5.4.9}$$

$$E_3 = \frac{dS_3}{ds_3} - 1 = \sqrt{1 + 2\gamma_{33}} - 1. \tag{5.4.10}$$

The changes in length of the line elements along the coordinate directions $\mathbf{i}_1$, $\mathbf{i}_2$, $\mathbf{i}_3$ are thus seen to be related to the components of the strain tensor γ_{11}, γ_{22}, and γ_{33}, respectively. These are generally referred to as the *extensional components* of strain.

Next, the changes in angles will be calculated in terms of the strain tensor. Since the angle between edges pa and pb is a right angle, it is convenient and customary to denote the angle between PA and PB as $(\pi/2 - \phi_{12})$. Thus ϕ_{12} is the change which the originally right angle undergoes during deformation. The definition of the scalar product yields for this angle:

$$\cos\left(\frac{\pi}{2} - \phi_{12}\right) = \frac{[(\partial\mathbf{R}/\partial y_1)\,dy_1] \cdot [(\partial\mathbf{R}/\partial y_2)\,dy_2]}{(dS_1)(dS_2)}, \tag{5.4.11}$$

wherein use has again been made of the fact that $(\partial\mathbf{R}/\partial y_1)\,dy_1$ and $(\partial\mathbf{R}/\partial y_2)\,dy_2$ are the vector representations of the edges PA and PB. The numerator of Eq. (5.4.11) is included in Eq. (5.2.17) as

$$G_{12} = \frac{\partial\mathbf{R}}{\partial y_1} \cdot \frac{\partial\mathbf{R}}{\partial y_2}, \tag{5.4.12}$$

and the denominator contains (see Eqs. 5.4.8 and 5.4.9)

$$dS_1 = \sqrt{1 + 2\gamma_{11}}\,dy_1 = (1 + E_1)\,dy_1, \tag{5.4.13}$$

$$dS_2 = \sqrt{1 + 2\gamma_{22}}\,dy_2 = (1 + E_2)\,dy_2. \tag{5.4.14}$$

If these are substituted in Eq. (5.4.11), it becomes

$$\cos\left(\frac{\pi}{2} - \phi_{12}\right) = \sin\phi_{12} = \frac{2\gamma_{12}}{(1 + E_1)(1 + E_2)}, \tag{5.4.15}$$

where (see Eq. 5.3.2)

$$\gamma_{12} = \tfrac{1}{2}G_{12}. \tag{5.4.16}$$

Similarly, the changes which angles bpc and cpa undergo during deformation are given by

$$\sin\phi_{23} = \frac{2\gamma_{23}}{(1 + E_2)(1 + E_3)}, \tag{5.4.17}$$

$$\sin\phi_{31} = \frac{2\gamma_{31}}{(1 + E_3)(1 + E_1)}. \tag{5.4.18}$$

Thus the angular changes between adjacent edges of the rectangular parallelepiped are related to the components γ_{12}, γ_{23}, and γ_{31}, as well as to the relative elongations. These components of the strain tensor are referred to as the *shearing components*.

In the preceding few paragraphs, the components of the strain tensor have been given geometrical substance which is certainly not evident in the definition, Eq. (5.3.1). It has been shown that those components which have both subscripts identical, such as γ_{11}, γ_{22}, γ_{33}, are related to the changes in length along the coordinate axes. Those components which have two different subscripts, such as γ_{12}, γ_{23}, γ_{31}, are related to the changes in angle between line segments which were originally oriented along the coordinate axes. The geometrical interpretations which have been presented may not be entirely satisfying, since the relative elongations E_n are not linearly related to the strain tensor. Also, the angular interpretations involve a trigonometric function as well as the relative elongations. A more explicit and hence more satisfying geometrical picture will result when the magnitudes of the changes in length and angle are suitably restricted, as will be done in the following section. At this stage of the development, however, no restrictions have been placed on the strain tensor. It is equally applicable to materials such as steel or rubber, which differ widely in response to forces.

5.5 SMALL STRAIN

The magnitudes of the relative elongations E_1, E_2, and E_3, as well as the changes in angles ϕ_{12}, ϕ_{23}, and ϕ_{31}, encountered in engineering practice are generally very small. For example, the largest relative elongation in the wing of a transport airplane even in very turbulent weather will be less than 0.006. Its largest value in a steel railroad bridge under a locomotive will be less than 0.001. Even if rupture of the wing or of a steel girder in the bridge were to take place, the largest relative elongations would still be small compared to unity. The changes in angle are of a correspondingly small order of magnitude. Thus the strains encountered are usually small in structures of high-strength materials such as metals. Obviously, the relative elongations in a rubber balloon will be much larger and, indeed, are of three or four orders of magnitude greater. However, for the usual engineering materials under nonfailure conditions the strains encountered in the usual structure are on the order of 10^{-3}, and such strains certainly merit the appellation of "small" strains. With this restriction placed on the magnitude, tremendous simplifications may be made in strain analysis.

The simplification and the resulting analytical benefits arise from the direct geometrical meanings which can be assigned to the components of the strain tensor. Previously [see Eqs. (5.4.8), (5.4.9), (5.4.10), (5.4.15), (5.4.17), and (5.4.18)], the components γ_{mm} (no sum) were related in not too simple a fashion to the relative elongations, E_m; and the components, γ_{mn} ($m \neq n$) were related in a comparatively complex fashion to the changes in angles, ϕ_{mn}. If Eq. (5.4.8) is rearranged into the form

$$E_1(E_1 + 2) = 2\gamma_{11}, \tag{5.5.1}$$

then under the assumption of small strains,

$$E_1 \ll 1 < 2, \tag{5.5.2}$$

and therefore

$$\gamma_{11} \cong E_1. \tag{5.5.3}$$

Similar results are obtained for γ_{22} and γ_{33}:

$$\gamma_{22} \cong E_2, \tag{5.5.4}$$

$$\gamma_{33} \cong E_3. \tag{5.5.5}$$

Thus the assumption of small strains means that the components of the Cartesian strain tensor, γ_{11}, γ_{22}, and γ_{33}, are the relative elongations E_1, E_2, E_3, respectively:

$$\gamma_{mm} \cong \frac{dS_m}{ds_m} - 1 \quad \text{(no sum)}. \tag{5.5.6}$$

In Eq. (5.4.15), the sine of the angle can be replaced by the angle itself for small strain. Also, the denominator on the right-hand side of the equation can be replaced by unity, because both E_1 and E_2 are small compared to unity. There results for Eq. (5.4.15) the simpler expression

$$\gamma_{12} \cong \tfrac{1}{2}\phi_{12}. \tag{5.5.7}$$

Similarly,

$$\gamma_{23} \cong \tfrac{1}{2}\phi_{23}, \tag{5.5.8}$$

$$\gamma_{31} \cong \tfrac{1}{2}\phi_{31}. \tag{5.5.9}$$

Thus under the assumption of small strains, the components of the strain tensor, γ_{12}, γ_{23}, and γ_{31}, are one-half of the changes in angles ϕ_{12}, ϕ_{23}, and ϕ_{31}, respectively.

The results of the "small strain" assumption are summarized in pictorial form in Fig. 5.4. This figure is similar to Fig. 5.3, except that the vectors have been omitted. In their place the scalar quantities which are the lengths and angles of the deformed element of volume under the restriction of small strain have been written.

A few remarks should be made at this point concerning semantics. As originally introduced and without the "smallness" restriction, γ_{mn} was called the *strain tensor*. In the ordinary usage of engineering, the term "strain" is used to

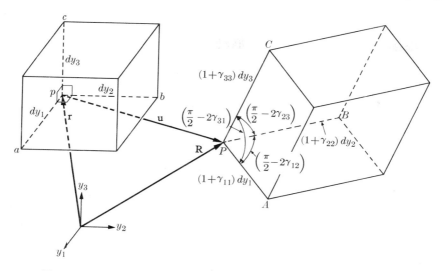

FIG. 5.4   Pictorial representation of components of small strain.

describe the nondimensional quantities and has been denoted herein by E_m and ϕ_{mn}. That is, the term "strain" refers to the relative changes in length and/or the changes which orthogonal directions in the unstrained body undergo. Thus it is customary to discuss the extensional or normal strains (which herein are E_1, E_2, E_3) and the shear strains (which herein are ϕ_{12}, ϕ_{23}, ϕ_{31}). The major part of engineering can restrict itself to a study of small strains and within this restriction, γ_{11}, γ_{22}, and γ_{33} are called the *extensional* or *normal strains*, and γ_{12}, γ_{23}, and γ_{31} are called the *shear strains*.

It appears worth while to mention the difference between the so-called engineering definition of strain components and the definition of strain tensor adopted in the present text. In most classical treatments relating to the theory of elasticity and plasticity published in the United States (for example, Refs. 1, 2, and 3), x, y, and z are often used as the rectangular Cartesian coordinates. For small strains, the normal strains are defined in the same way as the relative elongations of the elements along the x-, y-, and z-directions. They are usually denoted by ϵ_x, ϵ_y, and ϵ_z, respectively. The shear strains, in the engineering notation, are defined as the changes in angles between lines which are along the x-, y-, and z-axes prior to the deformation. They are denoted by γ_{xy}, γ_{yz}, and γ_{xz}, respectively. It is seen that if the x-, y-, and z-axes coincide with the y_1-, y_2-, and y_3-axes, respectively, the following relations exist:

$$\begin{aligned}
\epsilon_x &\equiv \gamma_{11}, & \gamma_{xy} &\equiv 2\gamma_{12}, \\
\epsilon_y &\equiv \gamma_{22}, & \gamma_{yz} &\equiv 2\gamma_{23}, \\
\epsilon_z &\equiv \gamma_{33}, & \gamma_{xz} &\equiv 2\gamma_{31}.
\end{aligned} \qquad (5.5.10)$$

5.6   THE STRAIN TRANSFORMATION LAWS

The components of the strain tensor have been defined by means of Eq. (5.3.1) in a rectangular Cartesian coordinate frame of reference y_1, y_2, y_3. It is of great practical importance, as well as of theoretical interest, to ascertain the manner in which the strain tensor changes under a coordinate transformation. The line elements PQ and pq (see Fig. 5.2) in the deformed and undeformed body remain the same irrespective of the coordinate system used. In other words, these are invariant quantities with respect to a transformation of coordinates. Consequently in a new coordinate system, $\tilde{y}_1$, $\tilde{y}_2$, $\tilde{y}_3$, Eq. (5.3.1) becomes

$$2\tilde{\gamma}_{mn}(\tilde{y}_1,\ \tilde{y}_2,\ \tilde{y}_3)\ d\tilde{y}_m\ d\tilde{y}_n\ =\ (dS)^2\ -\ (ds)^2, \tag{5.6.1}$$

and therefore the left-hand side of Eq. (5.6.1) is equal to the left-hand side of Eq. (5.3.1):

$$\tilde{\gamma}_{mn}(\tilde{y}_1,\ \tilde{y}_2,\ \tilde{y}_3)\ d\tilde{y}_m\ d\tilde{y}_n\ =\ \gamma_{mn}(y_1,\ y_2,\ y_3)\ dy_m\ dy_n. \tag{5.6.2}$$

The differentials, dy_m, are tensors of order one, and transform according to Eq. (A.6.2):

$$dy_m\ =\ \frac{\partial y_m}{\partial \tilde{y}_r}\ d\tilde{y}_r. \tag{5.6.3}$$

Equation (5.6.3) may also be obtained directly from the functional relations between the original and new coordinates,

$$y_m\ =\ y_m(\tilde{y}_1,\ \tilde{y}_2,\ \tilde{y}_3). \tag{5.6.4}$$

By virtue of the formula for the total derivative of a function of many variables, we have for the total differential of Eq. (5.6.4) the result given by Eq. (5.6.3). (See Ref. 5.4, Chapter 14.) Since both y_m and $\tilde{y}_r$ are rectangular Cartesian coordinates, it should be recognized that the partial derivatives $\partial y_m/\partial \tilde{y}_r$ are the direction cosines (see Appendix, Section A.4):

$$\frac{\partial y_m}{\partial \tilde{y}_r}\ =\ l_{m\tilde{r}}. \tag{5.6.5}$$

The substitution of Eqs. (5.6.4) and (5.6.2), and a minor bit of rearrangement give

$$(\gamma_{mn}l_{m\tilde{r}}l_{n\tilde{p}}\ -\ \tilde{\gamma}_{rp})\ d\tilde{y}_r\ d\tilde{y}_p\ =\ 0. \tag{5.6.6}$$

In obtaining Eq. (5.6.6) it was necessary to relabel the dummy indices in the term $\tilde{\gamma}_{mn}\ d\tilde{y}_m\ d\tilde{y}_n$ with r and p. Since $d\tilde{y}_1$, $d\tilde{y}_2$, and $d\tilde{y}_3$ are independent quantities, Eq. (5.6.6) then yields the desired strain transformation law:

$$\tilde{\gamma}_{rp}(\tilde{y}_1,\ \tilde{y}_2,\ \tilde{y}_3)\ =\ \gamma_{mn}(y_1,\ y_2,\ y_3)l_{m\tilde{r}}l_{n\tilde{p}}. \tag{5.6.7}$$

The preceding equation, which relates the components of the strain tensor in one coordinate system to the components in another coordinate system should be written out in full by the reader in order for him to fully appreciate the meaning of a second-order tensor. Observe that, in general, each component $\tilde{\gamma}_{rp}$ is related to all six components γ_{mn}, but that there are nine terms on the right-hand side of Eq. (5.6.7). Geometrical representations of special cases of Eq. (5.6.7) have been developed. One of these is known as *Mohr's circle* for strain, and is discussed in a problem at the end of the chapter.

5.7 PRINCIPAL STRAINS AND PRINCIPAL DIRECTIONS

It was stated at the beginning of this chapter that the goal of strain analysis is to specify the changes in length of all the line segments which originate at a point in the body, and the changes in angles subtended by all pairs of line segments. All this information is contained in the strain tensor, γ_{mn}. There are values of the strain tensor which merit special consideration. The points p and q (see Fig. 5.3) in the unstrained body have been arbitrarily chosen. If point p is held fixed and point q is varied such that the line segment pq assumes different directions in the body, then the quantity $(dS)^2 - (ds)^2$ will generally change in value.

Thus it is germane to seek those directions for which the relative elongation becomes an extremum, i.e., becomes a maximum and/or minimum (see Appendix, Section A.16). It will be shown that there are three such directions which are mutually orthogonal, and along which the shear components of strain are zero. These directions are called the *principal directions*, and the corresponding values of γ_{mn} are called the *principal strains*.

Let us assume that the six components of strain are known relative to the coordinates y_n. Then the component $\tilde{\gamma}_{11}$ relative to another coordinate set $\tilde{y}_n$ is given by (see Eq. 5.6.7)

$$\tilde{\gamma}_{11} = l_{\bar{1}m}l_{\bar{1}n}\gamma_{nm}. \tag{5.7.1}$$

Each admissible set of direction cosines $l_{\bar{1}m}$ corresponds to a different direction at point p of the body (see Fig. 5.3), and for each set, $\tilde{\gamma}_{11}$ will take on different values. Thus Eq. (5.7.1) can be viewed as an equation for $\tilde{\gamma}_{11}$ in which the independent variables are the three direction cosines. For emphasis of this aspect and also for ease of writing, we set

$$Q(\lambda) = \tilde{\gamma}_{11} = \lambda_m \lambda_n \gamma_{nm}, \tag{5.7.2}$$

where the direction cosines have been replaced by

$$\lambda_m = l_{\bar{1}m}. \tag{5.7.3}$$

It is observed that the trio $\lambda_1, \lambda_2, \lambda_3$ locates the orientation of the line segment pq relative to the axes y_1, y_2, and y_3, and this trio must satisfy the condition

$$(\lambda_1)^2 + (\lambda_2)^2 + (\lambda_3)^2 = \delta_{mn}\lambda_m\lambda_n = 1. \tag{5.7.4}$$

The relative elongation (see Eq. 5.4.8) in the $\tilde{y}_1$-direction is

$$\widetilde{E}_1 = \sqrt{1 + 2\tilde{\gamma}_{11}} - 1. \qquad (5.7.5)$$

We see from this expression that $\widetilde{E}_1$ will be an extremum when the quantity $Q(\lambda)$ is an extremum.

The extreme-value problem to be solved can now be stated in terms of $Q(\lambda)$ because the minimal and maximal values of $\tilde{\gamma}_{11}$ are directly related to the extreme value of $\widetilde{E}_1$. It is desired to find the values of $\lambda_1, \lambda_2, \lambda_3$ for which $Q(\lambda)$ assumes its largest and/or smallest value. However, not all values of $\lambda_1, \lambda_2, \lambda_3$ are admissible because Eq. (5.7.4) must be satisfied. The usual procedure for handling problems of this kind can be followed if Eq. (5.7.4) is used to eliminate one of the direction cosines from Eq. (5.7.2). Then the resulting equation will contain only two direction cosines, and the application of the necessary conditions, $\partial Q/\partial \lambda_m = 0$, will lead to a pair of simultaneous equations. However, there is a more convenient and elegant manner by which we may deal with the condition given by Eq. (5.7.4), which is known as a *constraint*. The determination of the extreme values of a quantity subject to a constraint is easily accomplished by Lagrange's method of undetermined multipliers (see Appendix, Section A.16). This method preserves the symmetries in the mathematics, in that no preference is given to any one of the variables λ_1, λ_2, or λ_3. The constraint, Eq. (5.7.4), is put into the form

$$P(\lambda) = \delta_{mn}\lambda_m\lambda_n - 1 = 0. \qquad (5.7.6)$$

A parameter α called the *Lagrange multiplier*, which is independent of the direction cosines, is introduced as an unknown factor.

It is shown in the Appendix that the necessary conditions for $Q(\lambda)$ to have an extreme value are given by the equations

$$\frac{\partial Q}{\partial \lambda_m} - \alpha \frac{\partial P}{\partial \lambda_m} = 0. \qquad (5.7.7)$$

Substitution of Eqs. (5.7.2) and (5.7.6) yields the set of homogeneous algebraic equations

$$(\gamma_{mn} - \alpha\delta_{mn})\lambda_n = 0. \qquad (5.7.8)$$

Equations (5.7.8) constitute three simultaneous equations for λ_1, λ_2, and λ_3, and because these are homogeneous, a nontrivial solution can exist if and only if the determinant of the coefficients is zero:

$$\begin{vmatrix} \gamma_{11} - \alpha & \gamma_{12} & \gamma_{13} \\ \gamma_{21} & \gamma_{22} - \alpha & \gamma_{23} \\ \gamma_{31} & \gamma_{32} & \gamma_{33} - \alpha \end{vmatrix} = 0. \qquad (5.7.9)$$

The expansion of the determinant yields a cubic equation in α, and because the determinant is symmetric, there are three real principal values. The expanded determinant can be written as

$$-(\alpha)^3 + J_1(\alpha)^2 - J_2\alpha + J_3 = 0, \tag{5.7.10}$$

in which J_1, J_2, J_3 are called the first, second, and third strain invariants, respectively. That J_1, J_2, J_3 are invariants will be subsequently demonstrated. It can be verified by the expansion of Eq. (5.7.9) that

$$J_1 = \gamma_{11} + \gamma_{22} + \gamma_{33}, \tag{5.7.11}$$

$$J_2 = \begin{vmatrix} \gamma_{11} & \gamma_{12} \\ \gamma_{21} & \gamma_{22} \end{vmatrix} + \begin{vmatrix} \gamma_{11} & \gamma_{13} \\ \gamma_{31} & \gamma_{33} \end{vmatrix} + \begin{vmatrix} \gamma_{22} & \gamma_{23} \\ \gamma_{32} & \gamma_{33} \end{vmatrix}, \tag{5.7.12}$$

$$J_3 = \begin{vmatrix} \gamma_{11} & \gamma_{12} & \gamma_{13} \\ \gamma_{21} & \gamma_{22} & \gamma_{23} \\ \gamma_{31} & \gamma_{32} & \gamma_{33} \end{vmatrix}. \tag{5.7.13}$$

The three values of α which are the roots of the cubic equation (5.7.10) will be labeled with Roman numeral subscripts as α_I, α_{II}, and α_{III}. (We will presently demonstrate that α_I, α_{II}, and α_{III} are the sought-after principal strains.) In order to find the corresponding principal directions, each of the roots is substituted individually back into Eqs. (5.7.8). The principal directions will be identified by a Roman numeral superscript. Thus $\lambda_1^{(I)}$, $\lambda_2^{(I)}$, $\lambda_3^{(I)}$ are the direction cosines of the direction along which the root α_I (principal strain) occurs. To find this triplet of numbers, α_I is put into Eqs. (5.7.8) yielding

$$(\gamma_{11} - \alpha_I)\lambda_1^{(I)} + \gamma_{12}\lambda_2^{(I)} + \gamma_{13}\lambda_3^{(I)} = 0,$$

$$\gamma_{21}\lambda_1^{(I)} + (\gamma_{22} - \alpha_I)\lambda_2^{(I)} + \gamma_{23}\lambda_3^{(I)} = 0, \tag{5.7.14}$$

$$\gamma_{31}\lambda_1^{(I)} + \gamma_{32}\lambda_2^{(I)} + (\gamma_{33} - \alpha_I)\lambda_3^{(I)} = 0.$$

However, these represent only two independent equations for $\lambda_m^{(I)}$, because the determinant of the coefficients of $\lambda_m^{(I)}$ is zero. The third independent equation is the constraint, Eq. (5.7.4), which now becomes

$$[\lambda_1^{(I)}]^2 + [\lambda_2^{(I)}]^2 + [\lambda_3^{(I)}]^2 = 1. \tag{5.7.15}$$

The actual computational procedure would be to solve for $\lambda_1^{(I)}$ and $\lambda_2^{(I)}$ in terms of $\lambda_3^{(I)}$ with any pair of Eqs. (5.7.14), and then to use Eq. (5.7.15) to calculate an explicit value for $\lambda_3^{(I)}$. The value of $\lambda_3^{(I)}$ would then be substituted back into Eqs. (5.7.14) to calculate explicit values for $\lambda_1^{(I)}$ and $\lambda_2^{(I)}$.

Once the direction cosines $\lambda_m^{(I)}$ have been determined, then the principal strain γ_I, which is $Q(\lambda_m^{(I)})$, is calculated from

$$\gamma_I = \gamma_{mn}\lambda_m^{(I)}\lambda_n^{(I)}. \tag{5.7.16}$$

There remains the task of demonstrating that the Lagrange multiplier α_I is the principal strain γ_I. Equation (5.7.8) is true for α_I and $\lambda_n^{(I)}$,

$$(\gamma_{mn} - \alpha_I\,\delta_{mn})\lambda_n^{(I)} = 0. \tag{5.7.17}$$

We multiply Eq. (5.7.17) by $\lambda_m^{(I)}$ and sum on m to obtain

$$\gamma_{mn}\lambda_n^{(I)}\lambda_m^{(I)} = \alpha_I\,\delta_{mn}\lambda_n^{(I)}\lambda_m^{(I)}. \tag{5.7.18}$$

The left-hand side of Eq. (5.7.18) is γ_I as indicated by Eq. (5.7.16), and the right-hand side by virtue of the properties of the direction cosines (see Eq. 5.7.4) reduces to α_I. Therefore Eq. (5.7.18) is the desired proof that

$$\gamma_I \equiv \alpha_I. \tag{5.7.19}$$

In a similar manner the equivalence of γ_{II} and α_{II}, as well as of γ_{III} and α_{III}, can be demonstrated. The three values are usually arranged such that

$$\gamma_I > \gamma_{II} > \gamma_{III}. \tag{5.7.20}$$

In factored form, the cubic equation (5.7.10) becomes

$$-(\gamma - \gamma_I)(\gamma - \gamma_{II})(\gamma - \gamma_{III}) = 0. \tag{5.7.21}$$

The strain invariants can then be expressed in terms of the principal strains:

$$J_1 = \gamma_I + \gamma_{II} + \gamma_{III}, \tag{5.7.22}$$

$$J_2 = \gamma_I\gamma_{II} + \gamma_{II}\gamma_{III} + \gamma_{III}\gamma_I, \tag{5.7.23}$$

$$J_3 = \gamma_I\gamma_{II}\gamma_{III}. \tag{5.7.24}$$

The fact that J_1, J_2, and J_3 are invariants should now be apparent. It is evident that the magnitudes of the principal strains γ_I, γ_{II}, γ_{III} are independent of the coordinate frame which is chosen, and therefore J_1, J_2, and J_3, the coefficients of Eq. (5.7.10), must also be independent of the frame of reference.

An important property of the three principal directions is that they are mutually orthogonal. This can be demonstrated as follows: First, Eqs. (5.7.8) are written for $\lambda_n^{(I)}$ and $\lambda_n^{(II)}$,

$$(\gamma_{mn} - \gamma_I\,\delta_{mn})\lambda_n^{(I)} = 0, \tag{5.7.25}$$

$$(\gamma_{mn} - \gamma_{II}\,\delta_{mn})\lambda_n^{(II)} = 0. \tag{5.7.26}$$

Second, Eq. (5.7.25) is multiplied by $\lambda_m^{(II)}$, and Eq. (5.7.26) is multiplied by $\lambda_m^{(I)}$:

$$(\gamma_{mn} - \gamma_I \; \delta_{mn})\lambda_n^{(I)} \; \lambda_m^{(II)} = 0, \tag{5.7.27}$$

$$(\gamma_{mn} - \gamma_{II} \; \delta_{mn})\lambda_n^{(II)}\lambda_m^{(I)} = 0. \tag{5.7.28}$$

Third, Eq. (5.7.27) is subtracted from Eq. (5.7.28) to yield

$$(\gamma_I - \gamma_{II}) \; \delta_{mn}\lambda_m^{(I)}\lambda_n^{(II)} = 0. \tag{5.7.29}$$

The symmetry of the strain tensor and of the Kronecker delta has permitted a rearrangement of the dummy indices according to the scheme:

$$\gamma_{mn}\lambda_n^{(II)}\lambda_m^{(I)} = \gamma_{mn}\lambda_m^{(II)} \lambda_n^{(I)},$$

$$\delta_{mn}\lambda_m^{(II)}\lambda_n^{(I)} = \delta_{mn}\lambda_m^{(I)} \lambda_n^{(II)}.$$

Finally, if the principal strains γ_I and γ_{II} are unequal, then Eq. (5.7.29) can be satisfied only if

$$\delta_{mn}\lambda_m^{(I)}\lambda_n^{(II)} = 0, \tag{5.7.30}$$

which can be recognized as the condition that the principal directions $\lambda_m^{(I)}$ and $\lambda_n^{(II)}$ are orthogonal (see Eq. A.5.12). A similar series of algebraic manipulations will demonstrate the orthogonalities between $\lambda_m^{(III)}$ and $\lambda_n^{(I)}$, and between $\lambda_m^{(III)}$ and $\lambda_n^{(II)}$.

Another important attribute of the principal directions is that the components of shear strain belonging to the orthogonal axes given by $\lambda_m^{(I)}$, $\lambda_m^{(II)}$, and $\lambda_m^{(III)}$ are all identically zero. Equation (5.7.25) can be rearranged with the aid of Eq. (5.7.3) to read

$$\gamma_{mn}l_{\bar{1}n} = \gamma_I \; \delta_{mn}l_{\bar{1}n}. \tag{5.7.31}$$

The multiplication of Eq. (5.7.31) by $l_{\bar{s}m}$ leads to

$$\gamma_{mn}l_{\bar{1}n}l_{\bar{s}m} = \gamma_I\delta_{mn}l_{\bar{1}n}l_{\bar{s}m}. \tag{5.7.32}$$

We make the observation that the left-hand side is the transformation law for the components represented by $\tilde{\gamma}_{1s}$ (see Eq. 5.6.2) while the right-hand side reduces to $\gamma_I\delta_{1s}$, that is,

$$\tilde{\gamma}_{1s} = \gamma_I \; \delta_{1s}, \tag{5.7.33}$$

where the subscripts 1 and s refer to the principal axes. Clearly, $\tilde{\gamma}_{12}$ and $\tilde{\gamma}_{13}$ (which we may also cumbersomely write as $\gamma_{I,II}$ and $\gamma_{I,III}$, respectively) are zero. In a similar manner the shear component, $\gamma_{II,III}$, can be shown to be zero.

The vanishing of the shear strains can also be shown by choosing the principal directions as the reference rectangular Cartesian frame (see Fig. 5.5) in which the coordinate axes y_I, y_{II}, and y_{III} represent the principal direction at point p.

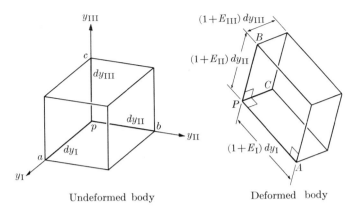

y_{III}

$(1+E_{III})\,dy_{III}$

B

$(1+E_{II})\,dy_{II}$

c

dy_{III}

C

dy_{II} b

P

p

y_{II}

$(1+E_I)\,dy_I$

a dy_I

A

y_I

Undeformed body   Deformed body

FIG. 5.5   Absence of shear strains for principal axes.

This is permissible since the principal directions are orthogonal. Roman numerals will be used to denote this special set of coordinates, and the corresponding components of the strain tensor will be denoted by $\gamma_{I,I}$, $\gamma_{I,II}$, $\gamma_{I,III}$, etc. However, a comparison of the two sets of expressions [Eqs. (5.7.22) through (5.7.24) and Eqs. (5.7.11) through (5.7.13)] for the strain invariants shows that the only nonzero components of the strain tensor, which is defined with respect to the principal directions, are $\gamma_{I,I}$, $\gamma_{II,II}$, and $\gamma_{III,III}$. More specifically, if Eqs. (5.7.13) and (5.7.24), which define the strain invariants, are compared, it is evident that

$$J_3 = \gamma_I\gamma_{II}\gamma_{III} = \begin{vmatrix} \gamma_I & 0 & 0 \\ 0 & \gamma_{II} & 0 \\ 0 & 0 & \gamma_{III} \end{vmatrix}. \tag{5.7.34}$$

This result means that the components which would be labeled $\gamma_{I,II}$, $\gamma_{II,III}$, $\gamma_{III,I}$ are zero, and that

$$\gamma_I \equiv \gamma_{I,I}, \qquad \gamma_{II} \equiv \gamma_{II,II}, \qquad \gamma_{III} \equiv \gamma_{III,III} \tag{5.7.35}$$

are the only nonzero components of strain with respect to the principal directions. Thus it has been shown that the strain tensor, if referred to the principal directions, consists only of the three extensional components.

Furthermore, we have found (see Eq. 5.4.15) that

$$\sin \phi_{I,II} = \frac{2\gamma_{I,II}}{(1 + E_I)(1 + E_{II})}, \tag{5.7.36}$$

where $\phi_{I,II}$ is defined as the change which the originally right angle apb undergoes during deformation. Since $\gamma_{I,II}$ is zero, then $\phi_{I,II}$ is also zero. Similar conclusions can be drawn for $\phi_{II,III}$ and $\phi_{III,I}$. This represents another way in which the principal directions may be interpreted; i.e., an element of volume defined in the undeformed body by means of the principal directions does not undergo any shearing deformations. It follows, then, that the element of volume in the deformed state is also a rectangular parallelepiped (see Fig. 5.5).

5.8 THE STRAIN-DISPLACEMENT RELATIONS

It is desirable to introduce at this stage the displacement vector $\mathbf{u}$, which connects the initial (undeformed) position p of the material particle and its final (deformed) position P, by the vector equation (cf. Fig. 5.2):

$$\mathbf{R}(y_1, y_2, y_3) = \mathbf{r}(y_1, y_2, y_3) + \mathbf{u}(y_1, y_2, y_3). \tag{5.8.1}$$

The component form of $\mathbf{u}$ is

$$\mathbf{u} = u_m(y_1, y_2, y_3)\mathbf{i}_m. \tag{5.8.2}$$

At this point the reader should clearly understand what is meant by the position vector $\mathbf{R}(y_1, y_2, y_3)$. In the undeformed body, the position vector $\mathbf{r}(y_1, c_2, c_3)$ will trace out a line which is parallel to the y_1-axis if y_1 is varied while y_2 and y_3 are set equal to constants c_2 and c_3 (see Fig. 5.6). However, the position vector $\mathbf{R}$ is dependent on the displacement vector $\mathbf{u}$,

$$\mathbf{R}(y_1, c_2, c_3) = \mathbf{r}(y_1, c_2, c_3) + \mathbf{u}(y_1, c_2, c_3). \tag{5.8.3}$$

An examination of Eq. (5.8.3) shows that $\mathbf{u}(y_1, c_2, c_3)$ can still have components in all three directions, and therefore $\mathbf{R}(y_1, c_2, c_3)$ will trace out a

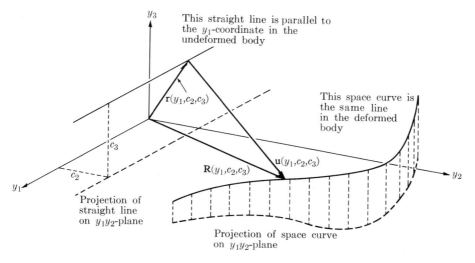

FIG. 5.6   Coordinate line in undeformed and deformed body.

curve in space. Thus, whereas points of the coordinate y_1 in the undeformed body lie on a straight line, the end-points of the position vector $\mathbf{R}(y_1, c_2, c_3)$ which identifies similar points in the deformed body, usually trace out a space curve.

Using Eq. (5.8.1) we find that the partial derivatives of the position vector $\mathbf{R}$ are

$$\frac{\partial \mathbf{R}}{\partial y_m} = \frac{\partial \mathbf{r}}{\partial y_m} + \frac{\partial \mathbf{u}}{\partial y_m} = \mathbf{1}_m + \frac{\partial u_n}{\partial y_m} \mathbf{i}_n, \tag{5.8.4}$$

where with the use of Eq. (5.8.2), we get

$$\frac{\partial \mathbf{u}}{\partial y_k} = \frac{\partial u_r}{\partial y_k} \mathbf{i}_r. \tag{5.8.5}$$

In detail, Eq. (5.8.4) becomes

$$\frac{\partial \mathbf{R}}{\partial y_1} = \left(1 + \frac{\partial u_1}{\partial y_1}\right) \mathbf{i}_1 + \frac{\partial u_2}{\partial y_1} \mathbf{i}_2 + \frac{\partial u_3}{\partial y_1} \mathbf{i}_3,$$

$$\frac{\partial \mathbf{R}}{\partial y_2} = \frac{\partial u_1}{\partial y_2} \mathbf{i}_1 + \left(1 + \frac{\partial u_2}{\partial y_2}\right) \mathbf{i}_2 + \frac{\partial u_3}{\partial y_2} \mathbf{i}_3, \tag{5.8.6}$$

$$\frac{\partial \mathbf{R}}{\partial y_3} = \frac{\partial u_1}{\partial y_3} \mathbf{i}_1 + \frac{\partial u_2}{\partial y_3} \mathbf{i}_2 + \left(1 + \frac{\partial u_3}{\partial y_3}\right) \mathbf{i}_3.$$

The fundamental metric tensor of the deformed body, G_{mn}, now can be expressed in terms of the displacement vector as

$$G_{mn} = \delta_{mn} + \frac{\partial \mathbf{u}}{\partial y_m} \cdot \mathbf{i}_n + \frac{\partial \mathbf{u}}{\partial y_n} \cdot \mathbf{i}_m + \frac{\partial \mathbf{u}}{\partial y_m} \cdot \frac{\partial \mathbf{u}}{\partial y_n}. \tag{5.8.7}$$

In order to further clarify the displacements, Fig. 5.7 is drawn with the deformed volume element moved by pure translation until points p and P coincide. The resulting figure shows the displacements of points a, b, c, relative to point p, and pictures more clearly the rotations of the line segments pa, pb, and pc as these are changed by the process of deformation into PA, PB, and PC, respectively. It can be seen that Fig. 5.7, in actuality, schematically represents the three vector equations (5.8.6). The dashed lines which are parallel to the y_n-axes are the orthogonal components of the vectors

$$\frac{\partial \mathbf{u}}{\partial y_1} dy_1, \qquad \frac{\partial \mathbf{u}}{\partial y_2} dy_2, \qquad \text{and} \qquad \frac{\partial \mathbf{u}}{\partial y_3} dy_3,$$

which connect points a to A, b to B, and c to C, respectively.

By introducing Eq. (5.8.7) we express the strain tensor in terms of the displacement vector as

$$\gamma_{mn} = \frac{1}{2}\left[\frac{\partial \mathbf{u}}{\partial y_m} \cdot \mathbf{i}_n + \frac{\partial \mathbf{u}}{\partial y_n} \cdot \mathbf{i}_m + \frac{\partial \mathbf{u}}{\partial y_m} \cdot \frac{\partial \mathbf{u}}{\partial y_n}\right], \tag{5.8.8}$$

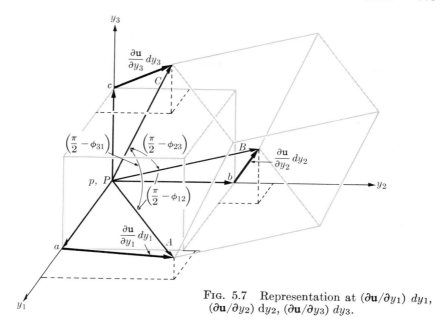

Fig. 5.7   Representation at $(\partial\mathbf{u}/\partial y_1)\,dy_1$, $(\partial\mathbf{u}/\partial y_2)\,dy_2$, $(\partial\mathbf{u}/\partial y_3)\,dy_3$.

which becomes, with the introduction of Eq. (5.8.5),

$$\gamma_{mn} = \frac{1}{2}\left(\frac{\partial u_m}{\partial y_n} + \frac{\partial u_n}{\partial y_m} + \frac{\partial u_r}{\partial y_m}\frac{\partial u_s}{\partial y_n}\,\delta_{rs}\right). \tag{5.8.9}$$

(See Eqs. (5.14.3b) for all six components of the strain-displacement relations given by Eq. 5.8.9)

It should be observed that the strain tensor is composed of a part which is linear in the derivatives of the displacements and a part which, since it involves the squares and products of the derivatives, is nonlinear. The linear portion is attributable to the first two terms of Eq. (5.8.8) or Eq. (5.8.9), and the nonlinear to the last term.

5.9   LINEAR STRAIN

There is one further restriction which is made in the analysis of strain, and this simplification is generally referred to as *infinitesimal strain* although the term *linear strain* is more connotative of the true implication of the simplification. The linear strain case encompasses the vast majority of the literature in all aspects of elasticity (and even plasticity), not only because the mathematical aspects are less complex, but also because the linear strain case does correctly describe the behavior of most structural forms with sufficient accuracy for engineering purposes. However, it should be pointed out that whenever stability of a structural form is in question, the case of linear strain is no longer applicable.

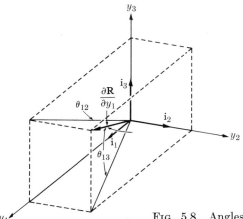

Fig. 5.8   Angles of rotation of $\partial \mathbf{R}/\partial y_1$.

The linear strain simplification neglects the nonlinear terms in the strain-displacement relations given by Eqs. (5.8.9). These are the terms involving the squares and products of the first derivatives of the components of the displacement vector $\mathbf{u}$. It can be seen that these nonlinear terms arise from the term formed by the scalar product $(\partial \mathbf{u}/\partial y_m) \cdot (\partial \mathbf{u}/\partial y_n)$ of Eq. (5.8.8); hence in the linear-strain case this term is omitted. Since linear strain requires basic modifications to the strain-displacement relations, a new symbol, ϵ_{mn}, will be used to denote the linear strain tensor. The definition for ϵ_{mn} is

$$\epsilon_{mn} = \frac{1}{2}\left(\frac{\partial \mathbf{u}}{\partial y_n} \cdot \mathbf{i}_m + \frac{\partial \mathbf{u}}{\partial y_m} \cdot \mathbf{i}_n\right), \tag{5.9.1}$$

or

$$\epsilon_{mn} = \frac{1}{2}\left(\frac{\partial u_m}{\partial y_n} + \frac{\partial u_n}{\partial y_m}\right). \tag{5.9.2}$$

There is a geometrical justification for neglecting the nonlinear terms. This can be shown by examining Fig. 5.8, which is a condensation of Fig. 5.3. In this figure, the vector which lies along the edge PA of the deformed element of volume has been translated so that the P-end coincides with the corner p of the undeformed element of volume. The two angles θ_{12} and θ_{13} represent the rotation of vector $\partial \mathbf{R}/\partial y_1$ out of the planes located by $\mathbf{i}_2$ and $\mathbf{i}_3$, respectively. Using the scalar product, we obtain

$$\left|\frac{\partial \mathbf{R}}{\partial y_1}\right| \cos\left(\frac{\pi}{2} - \theta_{12}\right) = \frac{\partial \mathbf{R}}{\partial y_1} \cdot \mathbf{i}_2, \tag{5.9.3}$$

$$\left|\frac{\partial \mathbf{R}}{\partial y_1}\right| \cos\left(\frac{\pi}{2} - \theta_{13}\right) = \frac{\partial \mathbf{R}}{\partial y_1} \cdot \mathbf{i}_3. \tag{5.9.4}$$

With the aid of Eqs. (5.2.17), (5.4.6) and (5.8.6), we can express the preceding two equations as

$$\sin \theta_{12} = \frac{1}{E_1 + 1} \frac{\partial u_1}{\partial y_2}, \tag{5.9.5}$$

$$\sin \theta_{13} = \frac{1}{E_1 + 1} \frac{\partial u_1}{\partial y_3}. \tag{5.9.6}$$

If we now stipulate that the magnitude of the elongation E_1 and the angles θ_{12} and θ_{13} be small, then we can write

$$\theta_{12} \approx \frac{\partial u_1}{\partial y_2}, \tag{5.9.7}$$

$$\theta_{13} \approx \frac{\partial u_1}{\partial y_3}. \tag{5.9.8}$$

In a similar manner we can derive the equation

$$\theta_{mn} \approx \frac{\partial u_m}{\partial y_n}. \tag{5.9.9}$$

The case of linear strain, as has already been stated, assumes that squares and products of θ_{mn} are negligible compared to θ_{mn} itself. However, it has been demonstrated that this premise is based upon angles of rotation which are suitably small.

It may prove informative to pursue this discussion from a slightly different viewpoint. The linearization of the strain-displacement relations is usually not discussed. Instead, the analysis of strain proceeds from the assumption that the derivatives of the components of displacement are infinitesimals. (We have shown in the preceding paragraph that these need be only suitably small.) Thus the base vectors of the deformed body (see Eqs. 5.8.6) can be simplified to

$$\frac{\partial \mathbf{R}}{\partial y_1} \cong \mathbf{i}_1 + \frac{\partial u_2}{\partial y_1} \mathbf{i}_2 + \frac{\partial u_3}{\partial y_1} \mathbf{i}_3,$$

$$\frac{\partial \mathbf{R}}{\partial y_2} \cong \frac{\partial u_1}{\partial y_2} \mathbf{i}_1 + \mathbf{i}_2 + \frac{\partial u_3}{\partial y_2} \mathbf{i}_3, \tag{5.9.10}$$

$$\frac{\partial \mathbf{R}}{\partial y_3} \cong \frac{\partial u_1}{\partial y_3} \mathbf{i}_1 + \frac{\partial u_2}{\partial y_3} \mathbf{i}_2 + \mathbf{i}_3,$$

because $\partial u_m / \partial y_n$, being an infinitesimal, can be neglected with respect to unity. Also the edges $(\partial \mathbf{R}/\partial y_m) \, dy_m$ (no sum) of the deformed element of volume have directions which are only infinitesimally different from the directions of the corresponding edges, $dy_m \mathbf{i}_m$ (no sum), of the undeformed element of volume (see Fig. 5.3). In other words, line segments (such as pa, pb, pc) undergo only infinitesimal rotations as the body becomes deformed. This can be visualized by projecting points A, B, a, and b of Fig. 5.4 onto the $y_1 y_2$-plane for this case

Fig. 5.9 Geometrical representation of displacements for calculation of linear strain components.

of infinitesimal deformation. In Fig. 5.9, the true lengths of lines PA and PB are shown to within an order of magnitude of an infinitesimal even though PA and PB do not lie in a plane parallel to the $y_1 y_2$-plane.

For the case at hand, the displacements and angles have been magnified for purposes of presentation. If the infinitesimal nature of the derivatives is considered, then as is done in the traditional manner, the strain in the y_1-direction is defined as

$$\epsilon_{11} = \frac{|PA| - |pa|}{|pa|} = \frac{(1 + (\partial u_1/\partial y_1)) \, dy_1 - dy_1}{dy_1} = \frac{\partial u_1}{\partial y_1}, \quad (5.9.11)$$

a result which was previously derived (see Eqs. 5.9.2) in a more rigorous manner as a simplification of an exact expression. Similarly, the change in angle ϕ_{12} (see Fig. 5.9) can be defined as

$$\phi_{12} = \alpha + \beta = \frac{(\partial u_2/\partial y_1) \, dy_1}{dy_1} + \frac{(\partial u_1/\partial y_2) \, dy_2}{dy_2}, \quad (5.9.12)$$

$$\phi_{12} = \frac{\partial u_2}{\partial y_1} + \frac{\partial u_1}{\partial y_2},$$

providing the infinitesimal nature of derivatives is kept in mind. This latter result is related to the linear strain tensor ϵ_{mn} by

$$\phi_{12} = 2\epsilon_{12}. \quad (5.9.13)$$

(See Eqs. 5.5.7 and 5.9.2.) Obviously, a figure such as 5.9 can also be drawn for the $y_2 y_3$- and $y_3 y_1$-planes.

We have presented two different classifications of strain tensors: small versus large strains, and linear versus nonlinear strain-displacement relations. In general, when the relative elongations (E_n) and/or angles of shearing (ϕ_{nm})

are large, the nonlinear strain-displacement relation must be used. Thus linear strain must also imply small strain. However, there are cases in which the elongations and shearing angles are extremely small but for which the rotations of the elements are considerable. In these cases it is still necessary to use the nonlinear strain-displacement relations. It should be clear that linear and small strains are not two mutually exclusive classes of strains. The generally used term of "infinitesimal strain" is then not an appropriate one for "linear strain" because it creates the erroneous impression that "linear strain" is even smaller than the so-called "small strain."

Whether or not the linear, small, or even the large components of a strain should be used depends on (1) the materials of construction, (2) the structural configuration, and (3) the mode of structural behavior. For example, if rubber is used in an inflated structure, then clearly the strains will be large. If the structure is a diving board constructed of oak, then the theory of small strains is sufficiently accurate. If the structure is a floor beam constructed of steel, it is generally adequate to use linear strain-displacement relations to describe the behavior. For flat sheets of metal which are subjected to in-plane compressive forces, it is necessary to use nonlinear strain-displacement relations in order to account for the possibility of buckling.

5.10 THE CHANGE IN VOLUME

The element of volume in the undeformed body is the volume of the rectangular parallelepiped whose edges are shown as $dy_1\mathbf{i}_1$, $dy_2\mathbf{i}_2$, and $dy_3\mathbf{i}_3$ in Fig. 5.3, and is given by

$$dV^{(0)} = dy_1\, dy_2\, dy_3. \tag{5.10.1}$$

The element of volume in the deformed body in the limit is the parallelepiped with edges shown as $(\partial \mathbf{R}/\partial y_1)\, dy_1$, $(\partial \mathbf{R}/\partial y_2)\, dy_2$, and $(\partial \mathbf{R}/\partial y_3)\, dy_3$ (see Fig. 5.3). Using the triple scalar product, we find the deformed element of volume to be

$$dV = \left(\frac{\partial \mathbf{R}}{\partial y_1}\, dy_1\right) \cdot \left(\frac{\partial \mathbf{R}}{\partial y_2}\, dy_2\right) \times \left(\frac{\partial \mathbf{R}}{\partial y_3}\, dy_3\right). \tag{5.10.2}$$

A much more useful form of Eq. (5.10.2) will be obtained if the components of strain are introduced by means of the following development: First, the vector formula, Eq. (A.14.3) is applied to Eq. (5.10.2) to yield

$$(dV)^2 = \begin{vmatrix} \dfrac{\partial \mathbf{R}}{\partial y_1} \cdot \dfrac{\partial \mathbf{R}}{\partial y_1} & \dfrac{\partial \mathbf{R}}{\partial y_1} \cdot \dfrac{\partial \mathbf{R}}{\partial y_2} & \dfrac{\partial \mathbf{R}}{\partial y_1} \cdot \dfrac{\partial \mathbf{R}}{\partial y_3} \\[2ex] \dfrac{\partial \mathbf{R}}{\partial y_2} \cdot \dfrac{\partial \mathbf{R}}{\partial y_1} & \dfrac{\partial \mathbf{R}}{\partial y_2} \cdot \dfrac{\partial \mathbf{R}}{\partial y_2} & \dfrac{\partial \mathbf{R}}{\partial y_2} \cdot \dfrac{\partial \mathbf{R}}{\partial y_3} \\[2ex] \dfrac{\partial \mathbf{R}}{\partial y_3} \cdot \dfrac{\partial \mathbf{R}}{\partial y_1} & \dfrac{\partial \mathbf{R}}{\partial y_3} \cdot \dfrac{\partial \mathbf{R}}{\partial y_2} & \dfrac{\partial \mathbf{R}}{\partial y_3} \cdot \dfrac{\partial \mathbf{R}}{\partial y_3} \end{vmatrix} (dy_1\, dy_2\, dy_3)^2. \tag{5.10.3}$$

Second, the fundamental metric tensor, G_{mn}, of the deformed body is used to replace the scalar products in Eq. (5.10.3). (See Eq. 5.2.17):

$$(dV)^2 = \begin{vmatrix} G_{11} & G_{12} & G_{13} \\ G_{21} & G_{22} & G_{23} \\ G_{31} & G_{32} & G_{33} \end{vmatrix} (dy_1 \, dy_2 \, dy_3)^2. \tag{5.10.4}$$

Third, the determinant is set equal to G,

$$G = \begin{vmatrix} G_{11} & G_{12} & G_{13} \\ G_{21} & G_{22} & G_{23} \\ G_{31} & G_{32} & G_{33} \end{vmatrix}, \tag{5.10.5}$$

with the result that

$$dV = \sqrt{G} \, dy_1 \, dy_2 \, dy_3. \tag{5.10.6}$$

Fourth, the strain tensor is made to appear in the determinant G by means of Eq. (5.3.2). This may be expressed in the determinant form

$$G = \begin{vmatrix} 1 + 2\gamma_{11} & 2\gamma_{12} & 2\gamma_{13} \\ 2\gamma_{21} & 1 + 2\gamma_{22} & 2\gamma_{23} \\ 2\gamma_{31} & 2\gamma_{32} & 1 + 2\gamma_{33} \end{vmatrix}. \tag{5.10.7}$$

Finally, Eq. (5.10.7) is expanded and the terms are grouped accordingly so that

$$G = 1 + 2J_1 + 4J_2 + 8J_3, \tag{5.10.8}$$

where J_1, J_2, J_3 are the previously defined strain invariants [see Eqs. (5.7.11), (5.7.12), and (5.7.13)]. The ratio of the original volume to the deformed volume is thus seen to be

$$\frac{dV}{dV^{(0)}} = \sqrt{1 + 2J_1 + 4J_2 + 8J_3}. \tag{5.10.9}$$

As for elongations, it is sometimes more informative to work with a ratio of the change in the volume to the original volume. This ratio is called the *cubical dilatation* or just simply the dilatation, and is expressed as

$$\frac{dV - dV^{(0)}}{dV^{(0)}} = \frac{dV}{dV^{(0)}} - 1 = \sqrt{1 + 2J_1 + 4J_2 + 8J_3} - 1. \tag{5.10.10}$$

For small strains, the volume-change ratio becomes simplified because the strain invariants J_2 and J_3 are of the order $(E_1)^2$ and $(E_1)^3$, respectively, and can be neglected with respect to J_1, which is of the order E_1 (see Section 5.4). Further, if the binominal expansion is used on $1 + 2J_1$, and if only the lowest-order terms are retained, then

$$\frac{dV}{dV^{(0)}} - 1 \cong J_1 = \gamma_{11} + \gamma_{22} + \gamma_{33}. \qquad (5.10.11)$$

Under the assumption of small strains, and hence linear strains, it is seen that the first strain invariant is the dilatation.

5.11 TWO SIMPLE EXAMPLES OF STRAIN

(a) Uniform strain. This example of strain is one of uniform extension in which the displacement vector **u** has the components given by

$$\mathbf{u} = c_1 y_1 \mathbf{i}_1 + c_2 y_2 \mathbf{i}_2 + c_3 y_3 \mathbf{i}_3, \qquad (5.11.1)$$

where c_1, c_2, and c_3 are constants. Since the position vector to points in the deformed body is

$$\mathbf{R} = \mathbf{r} + \mathbf{u} = (y_1 + c_1 y_1)\mathbf{i}_1 + (y_2 + c_2 y_2)\mathbf{i}_2 + (y_3 + c_3 y_3)\mathbf{i}_3, \qquad (5.11.2)$$

then

$$\frac{\partial \mathbf{R}}{\partial y_1} = (1 + c_1)\mathbf{i}_1, \qquad \frac{\partial \mathbf{R}}{\partial y_2} = (1 + c_2)\mathbf{i}_2, \qquad \frac{\partial \mathbf{R}}{\partial y_3} = (1 + c_3)\mathbf{i}_3. \qquad (5.11.3)$$

The fundamental metric tensor of the deformed body becomes

$$(G_{mn}) = \begin{pmatrix} (1 + c_1)^2 & 0 & 0 \\ 0 & (1 + c_2)^2 & 0 \\ 0 & 0 & (1 + c_3)^2 \end{pmatrix} \qquad (5.11.4)$$

and the determinant becomes

$$G = (1 + c_1)^2 (1 + c_2)^2 (1 + c_3)^2. \qquad (5.11.5)$$

The components of the strain tensor are then

$$(\gamma_{mn}) = \begin{pmatrix} \frac{1}{2}[(1 + c_1)^2 - 1] & 0 & 0 \\ 0 & \frac{1}{2}[(1 + c_2)^2 - 1] & 0 \\ 0 & 0 & \frac{1}{2}[(1 + c_3)^2 - 1] \end{pmatrix} \cdot \qquad (5.11.6)$$

It should be observed that the axes y_1, y_2, y_3 also coincide with the principal axes, since the strain tensor does not have any shearing components. The three strain invariants are

$$J_1 = \tfrac{1}{2}\{[(1 + c_1)^2 - 1] + [(1 + c_2)^2 - 1] + [(1 + c_3)^2 - 1]\},$$

$$J_2 = \tfrac{1}{4}\{[(1 + c_1)^2 - 1][(1 + c_2)^2 - 1] + [(1 + c_2)^2 - 1][(1 + c_3)^2 - 1]$$
$$+ [(1 + c_3)^2 - 1][(1 + c_1)^2 - 1]\}, \qquad (5.11.7)$$

$$J_3 = \tfrac{1}{8}[(1 + c_1)^2 - 1][(1 + c_2)^2 - 1][(1 + c_3)^2 - 1].$$

If the constants c_1, c_2, and c_3 are so small that their squares and products are negligible, then the strain tensor γ_{mn} can be replaced by the linear strain tensor ϵ_{mn}. Its components are

$$\epsilon_{mn} = \begin{pmatrix} c_1 & 0 & 0 \\ 0 & c_2 & 0 \\ 0 & 0 & c_3 \end{pmatrix}. \qquad (5.11.8)$$

Also the dilatation becomes simplified (see Eq. 5.10.10),

$$\frac{dV}{dV^{(0)}} - 1 \approx \epsilon_{11} + \epsilon_{22} + \epsilon_{33} = c_1 + c_2 + c_3. \qquad (5.11.9)$$

(b) Simple shear. This example is one of simple shear in which the displacement vector $\mathbf{u}$ has the components given by

$$\mathbf{u} = cy_2\mathbf{i}_1, \qquad (5.11.10)$$

where c is a constant. Each point in the undeformed body moves parallel to the y_1-axis by an amount which is proportional to its y_2-coordinate. Thus rectangles drawn on the body on the y_1y_2-plane before deformation become parallelograms after deformation (see Fig. 5.10).

The position vector, $\mathbf{R}$, to points in the deformed body is

$$\mathbf{R} = (y_1 + cy_2)\mathbf{i}_1 + y_2\mathbf{i}_2 + y_3\mathbf{i}_3, \qquad (5.11.11)$$

and the base vectors of the deformed body are

$$\frac{\partial \mathbf{R}}{\partial y_1} = \mathbf{i}_1, \qquad \frac{\partial \mathbf{R}}{\partial y_2} = c\mathbf{i}_1 + \mathbf{i}_2, \qquad \frac{\partial \mathbf{R}}{\partial y_3} = \mathbf{i}_3. \qquad (5.11.12)$$

Hence the fundamental metric tensor of the deformed body has the form

$$(G_{mn}) = \begin{pmatrix} 1 & c & 0 \\ c & 1 + c^2 & 0 \\ 0 & 0 & 1 \end{pmatrix} \qquad (5.11.13)$$

The determinant, G, has the value

$$G = 1, \qquad (5.11.14)$$

and the components of the strain tensor are given by

$$(\gamma_{mn}) = \begin{pmatrix} 0 & \frac{1}{2}c & 0 \\ \frac{1}{2}c & \frac{1}{2}c^2 & 0 \\ 0 & 0 & 0 \end{pmatrix}. \qquad (5.11.15)$$

Before deformation

Therefore, the three strain invariants have the value

$$J_1 = \tfrac{1}{2}c^2, \qquad J_2 = -\tfrac{1}{4}c^2, \qquad J_3 = 0. \qquad (5.11.16)$$

Again if c is sufficiently small, then γ_{mn} can be replaced by ϵ_{mn}:

$$\epsilon_{mn} = \begin{pmatrix} 0 & \frac{1}{2}c & 0 \\ \frac{1}{2}c & 0 & 0 \\ 0 & 0 & 0 \end{pmatrix}. \qquad (5.11.17)$$

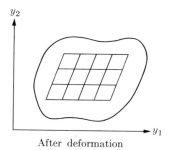

After deformation

FIG. 5.10 Simple shear strain.

Note that the dilatation for this case of linear simple shear is zero:

$$\frac{dV}{dV^{(0)}} - 1 = \epsilon_{11} + \epsilon_{22} + \epsilon_{33} = 0. \qquad (5.11.18)$$

5.12 THE DEVIATOR AND SPHERICAL STRAIN TENSORS

It will often be found convenient to consider the small strain tensor as the sum of two other strain tensors, called the *deviator* and *spherical strain tensors*. This is accomplished by defining

$$\gamma_{mn} = \hat{\gamma}_{mn} + \mathring{\gamma}_{mn}, \qquad (5.12.1)$$

where

$$\hat{\gamma}_{mn} = \gamma_{mn} - \tfrac{1}{3}\delta_{mn}\gamma_{rr}, \qquad (5.12.2)$$

$$\mathring{\gamma}_{mn} = \tfrac{1}{3}\delta_{mn}\gamma_{rr}. \qquad (5.12.3)$$

Here the symbols $\wedge$ and $\mathbin{\hat{\wedge}}$ are used to indicate a resolution of γ_{mn}, rather than a transformation to other coordinates. If Eqs. (5.12.2) and (5.12.3) are substituted in Eq. (5.12.1), an identity results. The tensor designated by $\hat{\gamma}_{mn}$ is called the deviator strain tensor and the one designated by $\mathring{\gamma}_{mn}$ is called the spherical strain tensor.

It should be observed that the extensional component of the deviator strain tensor is merely the strain tensor minus one-third of the first strain invariant. The extensional components of the spherical strain tensor are all identical, and are equal to one-third of the first strain invariant.

The concept of the strain invariants can be applied to both the deviator and the spherical strain tensors. These can be expressed in terms of the strain invariants of the strain tensor. There results

$$\hat{J}_1 = 0, \tag{5.12.4}$$

$$\hat{J}_2 = J_2 - \tfrac{1}{3}(J_1)^2, \tag{5.12.5}$$

$$\hat{J}_3 = J_3 - \tfrac{1}{3}J_1J_2 + \tfrac{2}{27}(J_1)^3, \tag{5.12.6}$$

$$\mathring{J}_1 = J_1, \tag{5.12.7}$$

$$\mathring{J}_2 = \tfrac{1}{3}(J_1)^2, \tag{5.12.8}$$

$$\mathring{J}_3 = \tfrac{1}{27}(J_1)^3. \tag{5.12.9}$$

The motivation for and the resulting convenience from splitting the strain tensor into two parts can be seen from an examination of the first strain invariants, $\hat{J}_1$ and $\mathring{J}_1$. We recall that the dilatation in the special case of small strain is equal to the first strain invariant. Since the first strain invariant $\hat{J}_1$ of the deviator strain tensor is zero, there is no volume change associated with the deviator strains. Consequently, all the volume change is attributable to the spherical strains. These results will be found to be of greater significance in plasticity than in elasticity.

5.13 COMPATIBILITY RELATIONS FOR LINEAR STRAINS

The linear strain tensor has been specified in terms of six components, ϵ_{mn}. However, the six components of strain are themselves functions of the three components of displacement u_m:

$$\epsilon_{mn} = \frac{1}{2}\left(\frac{\partial u_m}{\partial y_n} + \frac{\partial u_n}{\partial y_m}\right). \tag{5.13.1}$$

These strain-displacement relations can be considered as six partial differential equations for the determination of the three components of displacement. Obviously, there is a redundancy. Therefore the components of the strain tensor are not completely independent, and certain conditions, called the *compatibility relations*, must exist between the components of the strain.

The conditions of compatibility can be interpreted physically by examining the deformed body. In continuum elasticity, it is assumed that the process of deformation does not create cracks or holes in the body, i.e., the body remains continuous. The assumption that the deformed body is continuous can be formulated in terms of the difference in displacement between two points P and R in the deformed body.

Let Δ_1, Δ_2, and Δ_3 represent respectively the $\mathbf{i}_1$-, $\mathbf{i}_2$-, and $\mathbf{i}_3$-components of the difference in displacements between points P and R (see Fig. 5.11). This can be calculated by

$$\Delta_n = \oint_P^R du_n, \tag{5.13.2}$$

where $\oint_P^R$ represents a line integral. Since the deformed body is continuous, Δ_n should be independent of the path of integration, that is, Δ_n should have the same value regardless of whether the integration occurs along the path labeled (1), (2), or (3) (see Fig. 5.11) or any other path. Thus it will be shown that the mathematical requirement on the integral of Eq. (5.13.2) will lead to the compatibility relations.

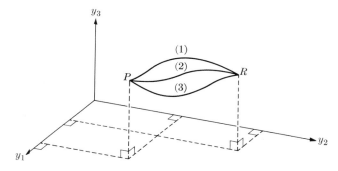

FIG. 5.11   Alternate paths of integration.

The derivative of Eq. (5.8.2) yields

$$du = \frac{\partial u_n}{\partial y_m} \mathbf{i}_n \, dy_m, \tag{5.13.3}$$

which can be rearranged to read

$$du = \left\{ \frac{1}{2}\left(\frac{\partial u_n}{\partial y_m} + \frac{\partial u_m}{\partial y_n} \right) + \frac{1}{2}\left(\frac{\partial u_n}{\partial y_m} - \frac{\partial u_m}{\partial y_n} \right) \right\} \mathbf{i}_n \, dy_m. \tag{5.13.4}$$

By introducing a new tensor, which is antisymmetric,*

$$\omega_{nm} = \frac{1}{2}\left(\frac{\partial u_n}{\partial y_m} - \frac{\partial u_m}{\partial y_n} \right), \tag{5.13.5}$$

we can write Eq. (5.13.4) in the form

$$du = (\epsilon_{nm} + \omega_{nm})\mathbf{i}_n \, dy_m. \tag{5.13.6}$$

_____

* An antisymmetric tensor has the property $\omega_{nm} = -\omega_{mn}$.

It is evident upon examining Eq. (5.13.6) that

$$du_n = (\epsilon_{nm} + \omega_{nm}) \, dy_m, \tag{5.13.7}$$

and hence Eq. (5.13.2) becomes

$$\Delta_n = \oint_P^R (\epsilon_{nm} + \omega_{nm}) \, dy_m. \tag{5.13.8}$$

An integration by parts of the second term in Eq. (5.13.8) leads to

$$\Delta_n = y_m \omega_{nm} \Big|_P^R + \oint_P^R \left[\epsilon_{nk} - y_m \frac{\partial \omega_{nm}}{\partial y_k} \right] dy_k, \tag{5.13.9}$$

where a dummy index on ϵ_{nm} has been relabeled.

It is easily verified by differentiating Eqs. (5.13.1) and (5.13.5) that

$$\frac{\partial \omega_{nm}}{\partial y_k} = \frac{\partial \epsilon_{nk}}{\partial y_m} - \frac{\partial \epsilon_{mk}}{\partial y_n}. \tag{5.13.10}$$

Combination of Eqs. (5.13.9) and (5.13.10) yields

$$\Delta_n = y_m \omega_{nm} \Big|_P^R + \oint_P^R \left[\epsilon_{nk} - y_m \left(\frac{\partial \epsilon_{nk}}{\partial y_m} - \frac{\partial \epsilon_{mk}}{\partial y_n} \right) \right] dy_k. \tag{5.13.11}$$

The first term in Eq. (5.13.11) depends only on the end points P and R, and hence is independent of the path of integration. Therefore, in order to fulfill the requirement only the integral term need be considered. It is shown in the theory of line integrals that the necessary and sufficient condition for the line integral to be independent of the path of integration (Ref. 5.4) is for the following equations to be satisfied:

$$\frac{\partial \xi_{nk}}{\partial y_l} = \frac{\partial \xi_{nl}}{\partial y_k}, \tag{5.13.12}$$

where for convenience, we introduce for the integrand,

$$\xi_{nk} = \epsilon_{nk} - y_m \left(\frac{\partial \epsilon_{nk}}{\partial y_m} - \frac{\partial \epsilon_{mk}}{\partial y_n} \right). \tag{5.13.13}$$

Introducing Eq. (5.13.13) into (5.13.12), we obtain

$$\frac{\partial \xi_{nk}}{\partial y_l} = \frac{\partial \epsilon_{nk}}{\partial y_l} - y_m \left[\frac{\partial^2 \epsilon_{nk}}{\partial y_m \, \partial y_l} - \frac{\partial^2 \epsilon_{mk}}{\partial y_n \, \partial y_l} \right] - \delta_{ml} \left[\frac{\partial \epsilon_{nk}}{\partial y_m} - \frac{\partial \epsilon_{mk}}{\partial y_n} \right],$$

$$\frac{\partial \xi_{nl}}{\partial y_k} = \frac{\partial \epsilon_{nl}}{\partial y_k} - y_m \left[\frac{\partial^2 \epsilon_{nl}}{\partial y_m \, \partial y_k} - \frac{\partial^2 \epsilon_{ml}}{\partial y_n \, \partial y_k} \right] - \delta_{mk} \left[\frac{\partial \epsilon_{nl}}{\partial y_m} - \frac{\partial \epsilon_{ml}}{\partial y_n} \right], \tag{5.13.14}$$

where

$$\frac{\partial y_m}{\partial y_l} = \delta_{ml}. \tag{5.13.15}$$

If we substitute Eqs. (5.13.14) in Eq. (5.13.12), we find that

$$\frac{\partial \xi_{nk}}{\partial y_l} - \frac{\partial \xi_{nl}}{\partial y_k} = y_m \left[\frac{\partial^2 \epsilon_{nk}}{\partial y_m \, \partial y_l} + \frac{\partial^2 \epsilon_{ml}}{\partial y_n \, \partial y_k} - \frac{\partial^2 \epsilon_{nl}}{\partial y_m \, \partial y_k} - \frac{\partial^2 \epsilon_{mk}}{\partial y_n \, \partial y_l} \right]. \tag{5.13.16}$$

Since the y_m are independent, the necessary and sufficient conditions that Δ_n be independent of the path of integration thus become

$$\frac{\partial^2 \epsilon_{nk}}{\partial y_m \, \partial y_l} + \frac{\partial^2 \epsilon_{ml}}{\partial y_n \, \partial y_k} - \frac{\partial^2 \epsilon_{nl}}{\partial y_m \, \partial y_k} - \frac{\partial^2 \epsilon_{mk}}{\partial y_n \, \partial y_l} = 0. \tag{5.13.17}$$

These are the sought-after *compatibility relations*.

The independent compatibility relations can be shown to result from an incompatibility tensor (which is symmetric) defined as

$$S_{mn} = e_{mpq} e_{nrs} R_{pqrs}, \tag{5.13.18}$$

where R_{pqrs} is called the *Riemann tensor:*

$$R_{pqrs} = \frac{\partial^2 \epsilon_{ps}}{\partial y_q \, \partial y_r} + \frac{\partial^2 \epsilon_{qr}}{\partial y_p \, \partial y_s} - \frac{\partial^2 \epsilon_{pr}}{\partial y_q \, \partial y_s} - \frac{\partial^2 \epsilon_{qs}}{\partial y_p \, \partial y_r}. \tag{5.13.19}$$

Then the independent relations, Eqs. (5.13.18), can be obtained by setting S_{11}, S_{12}, etc., equal to zero.

The development of the compatibility relations presented in this section has connected the requirements on the strain tensor to the assumption that the process of deformation has not created any cracks or holes. A more direct approach devoid of any physical meaning can be used. Thus, since

$$\epsilon_{11} = \frac{\partial u_1}{\partial y_1}, \qquad \epsilon_{22} = \frac{\partial u_2}{\partial y_2},$$

$$\epsilon_{12} = \frac{1}{2} \left(\frac{\partial u_1}{\partial y_2} + \frac{\partial u_2}{\partial y_1} \right), \tag{5.13.20}$$

and

$$\frac{\partial^2 \epsilon_{11}}{\partial y_2 \, \partial y_2} = \frac{\partial^3 u_1}{\partial y_1 \, \partial y_2 \, \partial y_2},$$

$$\frac{\partial^2 \epsilon_{22}}{\partial y_1 \, \partial y_1} = \frac{\partial^3 u_2}{\partial y_2 \, \partial y_1 \, \partial y_1}, \tag{5.13.21}$$

$$\frac{\partial^2 \epsilon_{12}}{\partial y_1 \, \partial y_2} = \frac{1}{2} \left(\frac{\partial^3 u_1}{\partial y_2 \, \partial y_1 \, \partial y_2} + \frac{\partial^3 u_2}{\partial y_1 \, \partial y_1 \, \partial y_2} \right),$$

the first of Eqs. (5.13.17), namely,

$$\frac{\partial^2 \epsilon_{11}}{\partial y_2 \, \partial y_2} + \frac{\partial^2 \epsilon_{22}}{\partial y_1 \, \partial y_1} - 2 \frac{\partial^2 \epsilon_{12}}{\partial y_1 \, \partial y_2} = 0,$$

is seen to be merely an expression of a mathematical identity, because the order of partial differentiation is not important. In a similar manner, the other five compatibility relations, which may be obtained by expanding Eqs. (5.13.17), can be shown to be mathematical identities. In general, the compatibility relations provide differential equations relating the displacement components, and are useful in obtaining solutions to problems in solid mechanics.

5.14 SUMMARY

The primary objective of this chapter has been to develop the equations of consistent deformations for a general strained-solid continuum. If the displacements u_m are continuous functions, the strain components γ_{mn} represented by the strain displacement relations will satisfy the conditions of consistent deformations. The conditions may also be represented by the six strain-compatibility equations which are derived from the strain-displacement relations.

The equations of consistent deformation are one of three sets of equations required for a complete solution for the internal forces and strains in a body under a general system of external loads and supports. The other two sets, the equilibrium equations and the constitutive equations, will be discussed in the following three chapters. The equations of consistent deformation and the equations of equilibrium are completely independent of the material properties of the body.

The expanded forms of some of the expressions and relations developed in this chapter are summarized below in terms of a rectangular Cartesian coordinate system.

Pythagorean relations for line elements

Undeformed body:

$$(ds)^2 = \delta_{mn} \, dy_m \, dy_n$$
$$= (dy_1)^2 + (dy_2)^2 + (dy_3)^2; \tag{5.14.1a}$$

Deformed body:

$$(dS)^2 = G_{mn} \, dy_m \, dy_n,$$
$$(dS)^2 = G_{11}(dy_1)^2 + G_{22}(dy_2)^2 + G_{33}(dy_3)^2 + 2G_{12} \, dy_1 \, dy_2$$
$$+ 2G_{23} \, dy_2 \, dy_3 + 2G_{31} \, dy_3 \, dy_1. \tag{5.14.1b}$$

Definition of strain tensor

$$2\gamma_{mn}\,dy_m\,dy_n = (dS)^2 - (ds)^2;\qquad(5.14.2a)$$

or

$$\gamma_{mn} = \tfrac{1}{2}(G_{mn} - \delta_{mn}),$$

$$\gamma_{11} = \tfrac{1}{2}(G_{11} - 1),\qquad \gamma_{12} = \tfrac{1}{2}G_{12},$$

$$\gamma_{22} = \tfrac{1}{2}(G_{22} - 1),\qquad \gamma_{23} = \tfrac{1}{2}G_{23},\qquad(5.14.2b)$$

$$\gamma_{33} = \tfrac{1}{2}(G_{33} - 1),\qquad \gamma_{31} = \tfrac{1}{2}G_{31}.$$

Strain-displacement relations for exact and small strains

$$\gamma_{mn} = \frac{1}{2}\left[\frac{\partial u_m}{\partial y_n} + \frac{\partial u_n}{\partial y_m} + \frac{\partial u_r}{\partial y_m}\frac{\partial u_s}{\partial y_n}\delta_{rs}\right];\qquad(5.14.3a)$$

$$\gamma_{11} = \frac{\partial u_1}{\partial y_1} + \frac{1}{2}\left[\left(\frac{\partial u_1}{\partial y_1}\right)^2 + \left(\frac{\partial u_2}{\partial y_1}\right)^2 + \left(\frac{\partial u_3}{\partial y_1}\right)^2\right],$$

$$\gamma_{22} = \frac{\partial u_2}{\partial y_2} + \frac{1}{2}\left[\left(\frac{\partial u_1}{\partial y_2}\right)^2 + \left(\frac{\partial u_2}{\partial y_2}\right)^2 + \left(\frac{\partial u_3}{\partial y_2}\right)^2\right],$$

$$\gamma_{33} = \frac{\partial u_3}{\partial y_3} + \frac{1}{2}\left[\left(\frac{\partial u_1}{\partial y_3}\right)^2 + \left(\frac{\partial u_2}{\partial y_3}\right)^2 + \left(\frac{\partial u_3}{\partial y_3}\right)^2\right],\qquad(5.14.3b)$$

$$\gamma_{12} = \frac{1}{2}\left[\frac{\partial u_1}{\partial y_2} + \frac{\partial u_2}{\partial y_1} + \frac{\partial u_1}{\partial y_1}\frac{\partial u_1}{\partial y_2} + \frac{\partial u_2}{\partial y_1}\frac{\partial u_2}{\partial y_2} + \frac{\partial u_3}{\partial y_1}\frac{\partial u_3}{\partial y_2}\right],$$

$$\gamma_{23} = \frac{1}{2}\left[\frac{\partial u_2}{\partial y_3} + \frac{\partial u_3}{\partial y_2} + \frac{\partial u_1}{\partial y_2}\frac{\partial u_1}{\partial y_3} + \frac{\partial u_2}{\partial y_2}\frac{\partial u_2}{\partial y_3} + \frac{\partial u_3}{\partial y_2}\frac{\partial u_3}{\partial y_3}\right],$$

$$\gamma_{31} = \frac{1}{2}\left[\frac{\partial u_3}{\partial y_1} + \frac{\partial u_1}{\partial y_3} + \frac{\partial u_1}{\partial y_3}\frac{\partial u_1}{\partial y_1} + \frac{\partial u_2}{\partial y_3}\frac{\partial u_2}{\partial y_1} + \frac{\partial u_3}{\partial y_3}\frac{\partial u_3}{\partial y_1}\right].$$

Relations between elongations, angle changes, dilation and strain components

$$E_1 = \sqrt{1 + 2\gamma_{11}} - 1,\qquad \sin\phi_{12} = \frac{2\gamma_{12}}{(1 + E_1)(1 + E_2)},$$

$$E_2 = \sqrt{1 + 2\gamma_{22}} - 1,\qquad \sin\phi_{23} = \frac{2\gamma_{23}}{(1 + E_2)(1 + E_3)},$$

$$E_3 = \sqrt{1 + 2\gamma_{23}} - 1,\qquad \sin\phi_{31} = \frac{2\gamma_{31}}{(1 + E_3)(1 + E_1)},$$

$$\frac{dV}{dV^{(0)}} - 1 = \sqrt{1 + 2J_1 + 4J_2 + 8J_3} - 1.\qquad(5.14.4)$$

Strain transformation law

$$\tilde{\gamma}_{mn} = \gamma_{rs} l_{r\tilde{m}} l_{s\tilde{n}}; \tag{5.14.5a}$$

$$\tilde{\gamma}_{11} = (l_{1\tilde{1}})^2 \gamma_{11} + (l_{2\tilde{1}})^2 \gamma_{22} + (l_{3\tilde{1}})^2 \gamma_{33}$$
$$+ 2(l_{1\tilde{1}} l_{2\tilde{1}} \gamma_{12} + l_{2\tilde{1}} l_{3\tilde{1}} \gamma_{23} + l_{3\tilde{1}} l_{1\tilde{1}} \gamma_{31}),$$

$$\tilde{\gamma}_{22} = (l_{1\tilde{2}})^2 \gamma_{11} + (l_{2\tilde{2}})^2 \gamma_{22} + (l_{3\tilde{2}})^2 \gamma_{33}$$
$$+ 2(l_{1\tilde{2}} l_{2\tilde{2}} \gamma_{12} + l_{2\tilde{2}} l_{3\tilde{2}} \gamma_{23} + l_{3\tilde{2}} l_{1\tilde{2}} \gamma_{31}),$$

$$\tilde{\gamma}_{33} = (l_{1\tilde{3}})^2 \gamma_{11} + (l_{2\tilde{3}})^2 \gamma_{22} + (l_{3\tilde{3}})^2 \gamma_{33}$$
$$+ 2(l_{1\tilde{3}} l_{2\tilde{3}} \gamma_{12} + l_{2\tilde{3}} l_{3\tilde{3}} \gamma_{23} + l_{3\tilde{3}} l_{1\tilde{3}} \gamma_{31}),$$

$$\tilde{\gamma}_{12} = l_{1\tilde{1}} l_{1\tilde{2}} \gamma_{11} + l_{2\tilde{1}} l_{2\tilde{2}} \gamma_{22} + l_{3\tilde{1}} l_{3\tilde{2}} \gamma_{33}$$
$$+ (l_{1\tilde{1}} l_{2\tilde{2}} + l_{2\tilde{1}} l_{1\tilde{2}}) \gamma_{12} + (l_{2\tilde{1}} l_{3\tilde{2}} + l_{3\tilde{1}} l_{2\tilde{2}}) \gamma_{23}$$
$$+ (l_{3\tilde{1}} l_{1\tilde{2}} + l_{1\tilde{1}} l_{3\tilde{2}}) \gamma_{31}, \tag{5.14.5b}$$

$$\tilde{\gamma}_{23} = l_{1\tilde{2}} l_{1\tilde{3}} \gamma_{11} + l_{2\tilde{2}} l_{2\tilde{3}} \gamma_{22} + l_{3\tilde{2}} l_{3\tilde{3}} \gamma_{33}$$
$$+ (l_{1\tilde{2}} l_{2\tilde{3}} + l_{2\tilde{2}} l_{1\tilde{3}}) \gamma_{12} + (l_{2\tilde{2}} l_{3\tilde{3}} + l_{3\tilde{2}} l_{2\tilde{3}}) \gamma_{23}$$
$$+ (l_{3\tilde{2}} l_{1\tilde{3}} + l_{1\tilde{2}} l_{3\tilde{3}}) \gamma_{31},$$

$$\tilde{\gamma}_{31} = l_{1\tilde{3}} l_{1\tilde{1}} \gamma_{11} + l_{2\tilde{3}} l_{2\tilde{1}} \gamma_{22} + l_{3\tilde{3}} l_{3\tilde{1}} \gamma_{33}$$
$$+ (l_{1\tilde{3}} l_{2\tilde{1}} + l_{2\tilde{3}} l_{1\tilde{1}}) \gamma_{12} + (l_{2\tilde{3}} l_{3\tilde{1}} + l_{3\tilde{3}} l_{2\tilde{1}}) \gamma_{23}$$
$$+ (l_{3\tilde{3}} l_{1\tilde{1}} + l_{1\tilde{3}} l_{3\tilde{1}}) \gamma_{31}.$$

Characteristic equation for principal strains

$$- (\gamma)^3 + J_1 (\gamma)^2 - J_2 (\gamma) + J_3 = 0. \tag{5.14.6}$$

Strain invariants

$$J_1 = \gamma_{11} + \gamma_{22} + \gamma_{33},$$

$$J_2 = \begin{vmatrix} \gamma_{11} & \gamma_{12} \\ \gamma_{21} & \gamma_{22} \end{vmatrix} + \begin{vmatrix} \gamma_{11} & \gamma_{13} \\ \gamma_{31} & \gamma_{33} \end{vmatrix} + \begin{vmatrix} \gamma_{22} & \gamma_{23} \\ \gamma_{32} & \gamma_{33} \end{vmatrix}, \tag{5.14.7}$$

$$J_3 = \begin{vmatrix} \gamma_{11} & \gamma_{12} & \gamma_{13} \\ \gamma_{21} & \gamma_{22} & \gamma_{23} \\ \gamma_{31} & \gamma_{32} & \gamma_{33} \end{vmatrix}.$$

Strain invariants in terms of principal strains

$$J_1 = \gamma_{\mathrm{I}} + \gamma_{\mathrm{II}} + \gamma_{\mathrm{III}},$$
$$J_2 = \gamma_{\mathrm{I}} \gamma_{\mathrm{II}} + \gamma_{\mathrm{II}} \gamma_{\mathrm{III}} + \gamma_{\mathrm{I}} \gamma_{\mathrm{III}}, \tag{5.14.8}$$
$$J_3 = \gamma_{\mathrm{I}} \gamma_{\mathrm{II}} \gamma_{\mathrm{III}}.$$

Equations for direction cosines of principal directions

$$[\gamma_{mn} - \gamma_{\mathrm{I}}\,\delta_{mn}]\lambda_n^{(\mathrm{I})} = 0,$$
$$[\gamma_{mn} - \gamma_{\mathrm{II}}\,\delta_{mn}]\lambda_n^{(\mathrm{II})} = 0, \qquad\qquad (5.14.9)$$
$$[\gamma_{mn} - \gamma_{\mathrm{III}}\,\delta_{mn}]\lambda_n^{(\mathrm{III})} = 0.$$

Small strain relations to elongations, angle changes and dilatation

$$E_1 \cong \gamma_{11}, \qquad \phi_{12} \cong 2\gamma_{12},$$
$$E_2 \cong \gamma_{22}, \qquad \phi_{23} \cong 2\gamma_{23}, \qquad \frac{dV}{dV^{(0)}} - 1 \cong J_1(\gamma_{mn}) \quad \text{(small strain)}.$$
$$E_3 \cong \gamma_{33}, \qquad \phi_{31} \cong 2\gamma_{31}, \qquad\qquad\qquad\qquad\qquad\qquad (5.14.10)$$

Since linear strain, by definition, is always a small strain, we also have

$$E_1 = \epsilon_{11}, \qquad \phi_{12} = 2\epsilon_{12},$$
$$E_2 = \epsilon_{22}, \qquad \phi_{23} = 2\epsilon_{23}, \qquad \frac{dV}{dV^{(0)}} - 1 = J_1(\epsilon_{mn}) \quad \text{(linear strain)}.$$
$$E_3 = \epsilon_{33}, \qquad \phi_{31} = 2\epsilon_{31}, \qquad\qquad\qquad\qquad\qquad\qquad (5.14.11)$$

Strain-displacement relations for linear strain

$$\epsilon_{mn} = \frac{1}{2}\left(\frac{\partial u_m}{\partial y_n} + \frac{\partial u_n}{\partial y_m}\right); \qquad\qquad (5.14.12a)$$

$$\epsilon_{11} = \frac{\partial u_1}{\partial y_1}, \qquad \epsilon_{12} = \frac{1}{2}\left(\frac{\partial u_1}{\partial y_2} + \frac{\partial u_2}{\partial y_1}\right),$$

$$\epsilon_{22} = \frac{\partial u_2}{\partial y_2}, \qquad \epsilon_{23} = \frac{1}{2}\left(\frac{\partial u_2}{\partial y_3} + \frac{\partial u_3}{\partial y_2}\right), \qquad\qquad (5.14.12b)$$

$$\epsilon_{33} = \frac{\partial u_3}{\partial y_3}, \qquad \epsilon_{31} = \frac{1}{2}\left(\frac{\partial u_3}{\partial y_1} + \frac{\partial u_1}{\partial y_3}\right).$$

Resolution of small strain tensor into deviator and spherical strain tensors

$$\gamma_{mn} = \hat{\gamma}_{mn} + \check{\gamma}_{mn}, \qquad\qquad (5.14.13)$$

where $\hat{\gamma}_{mn}$ = deviator strain tensor, and $\check{\gamma}_{mn}$ = spherical strain tensor.

Components of the deviator strain tensor

$$\hat{\gamma}_{mn} = \gamma_{mn} - \tfrac{1}{3}\delta_{mn}\gamma_{rr}; \qquad\qquad (5.14.14a)$$

$$\hat{\gamma}_{11} = \gamma_{11} - \tfrac{1}{3}(\gamma_{11} + \gamma_{22} + \gamma_{33}), \qquad \hat{\gamma}_{12} = \gamma_{12},$$
$$\hat{\gamma}_{22} = \gamma_{22} - \tfrac{1}{3}(\gamma_{11} + \gamma_{22} + \gamma_{33}), \qquad \hat{\gamma}_{23} = \gamma_{23}, \qquad (5.14.14b)$$
$$\hat{\gamma}_{33} = \gamma_{33} - \tfrac{1}{3}(\gamma_{11} + \gamma_{22} + \gamma_{33}), \qquad \hat{\gamma}_{31} = \gamma_{31}.$$

Components of the spherical strain tensor

$$\hat{\gamma}_{mn} = \tfrac{1}{3}\delta_{mn}\gamma_{rr}; \tag{5.14.15a}$$

$$\begin{aligned}
\hat{\gamma}_{11} &= \tfrac{1}{3}(\gamma_{11} + \gamma_{22} + \gamma_{33}), & \hat{\gamma}_{12} &= 0,\\
\hat{\gamma}_{22} &= \tfrac{1}{3}(\gamma_{11} + \gamma_{22} + \gamma_{33}), & \hat{\gamma}_{23} &= 0,\\
\hat{\gamma}_{33} &= \tfrac{1}{3}(\gamma_{11} + \gamma_{22} + \gamma_{33}), & \hat{\gamma}_{31} &= 0.
\end{aligned} \tag{5.14.15b}$$

Linear strain compatibility conditions

$$\frac{\partial^2 \epsilon_{nk}}{\partial y_m\,\partial y_l} + \frac{\partial^2 \epsilon_{ml}}{\partial y_n\,\partial y_k} + \frac{\partial^2 \epsilon_{nl}}{\partial y_m\,\partial y_k} - \frac{\partial^2 \epsilon_{mk}}{\partial y_n\,\partial y_l} = 0; \tag{5.14.16a}$$

$$\frac{\partial^2 \epsilon_{11}}{\partial y_2\,\partial y_2} + \frac{\partial^2 \epsilon_{22}}{\partial y_1\,\partial y_1} - 2\frac{\partial^2 \epsilon_{12}}{\partial y_1\,\partial y_2} = 0,$$

$$\frac{\partial^2 \epsilon_{22}}{\partial y_3\,\partial y_3} + \frac{\partial^2 \epsilon_{33}}{\partial y_2\,\partial y_2} - 2\frac{\partial^2 \epsilon_{23}}{\partial y_2\,\partial y_3} = 0,$$

$$\frac{\partial^2 \epsilon_{33}}{\partial y_1\,\partial y_1} + \frac{\partial^2 \epsilon_{11}}{\partial y_3\,\partial y_3} - 2\frac{\partial^2 \epsilon_{31}}{\partial y_3\partial\, y_1} = 0,$$

$$\frac{\partial^2 \epsilon_{11}}{\partial y_2\,\partial y_3} + \frac{\partial^2 \epsilon_{23}}{\partial y_1\,\partial y_1} - \frac{\partial^2 \epsilon_{31}}{\partial y_1\,\partial y_2} - \frac{\partial^2 \epsilon_{12}}{\partial y_1\,\partial y_3} = 0,$$

$$\frac{\partial^2 \epsilon_{22}}{\partial y_3\,\partial y_1} + \frac{\partial^2 \epsilon_{31}}{\partial y_2\,\partial y_2} - \frac{\partial^2 \epsilon_{12}}{\partial y_2\,\partial y_3} - \frac{\partial^2 \epsilon_{23}}{\partial y_2\,\partial y_1} = 0,$$

$$\frac{\partial^2 \epsilon_{33}}{\partial y_1\,\partial y_2} + \frac{\partial^2 \epsilon_{12}}{\partial y_3\,\partial y_3} - \frac{\partial^2 \epsilon_{23}}{\partial y_3\,\partial y_1} - \frac{\partial^2 \epsilon_{31}}{\partial y_3\,\partial y_2} = 0.$$

$$\tag{5.14.16b}$$

PROBLEMS

5.1   Expand Eq. (5.8.9) into six expressions for the individual strain components $\gamma_{11}, \gamma_{22}, \gamma_{33}, \gamma_{12}, \gamma_{23},$ and γ_{31}.

5.2   As a simple exercise in the application of the Lagrange multiplier method, find the extreme values of the function $f(x, y) = 4 - x^2 - y^2$, subject to the constraint $x^2 - y^2 = 9$. (Refer to the Appendix, Section A.16, for similar examples.)

5.3   Compute the direction cosines $l_{\bar{1}m}$ of the axis $\tilde{y}_1$ which is perpendicular to the face ABC of the tetrahedron shown in Fig. P.5.3.

5.4   In the y_1-, y_2-, y_3-coordinate system the components of the strain tensor are shown by the matrix

$$[\gamma_{mn}] = \begin{bmatrix} 0.01 & -0.005 & 0 \\ -0.005 & +0.02 & +0.01 \\ 0 & +0.01 & -0.02 \end{bmatrix}.$$

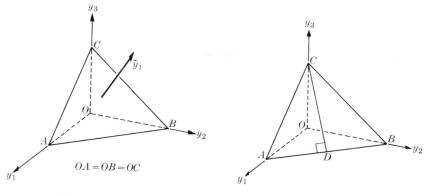

FIGURE P.5.3   FIGURE P.5.4

On the tetrahedron shown in Fig. P.5.4, where $OA = OB = OC$ (see Problem 5.3), what is the percentage elongation of the line AB, and what is the change in angle ADC which was 90° in the unstrained position?

5.5 At a point in a body the shear strain components γ_{13} and γ_{23} are zero with respect to the y_1-, y_2-, and y_3-coordinate system. In a new coordinate system $\tilde{y}_1$, $\tilde{y}_2$, and $\tilde{y}_3$ where $\tilde{y}_3$ and y_3 coincide (Fig. P.5.5), show that the following strain transformation relations hold:

$$\tilde{\gamma}_{11} = \frac{\gamma_{11} + \gamma_{22}}{2} + \frac{\gamma_{11} - \gamma_{22}}{2}\cos 2\theta + \gamma_{12}\sin 2\theta,$$

$$\tilde{\gamma}_{22} = \frac{\gamma_{11} + \gamma_{22}}{2} - \frac{\gamma_{11} - \gamma_{22}}{2}\cos 2\theta - \gamma_{12}\sin 2\theta,$$

$$\tilde{\gamma}_{12} = -\frac{\gamma_{11} - \gamma_{22}}{2}\sin 2\theta + \gamma_{12}\cos 2\theta,$$

$$\tilde{\gamma}_{23} = \tilde{\gamma}_{13} = 0,$$

where θ is the angle between the y_1-axis and the $\tilde{y}_1$-axis. *Note:* One can conclude that y_3 (hence also $\tilde{y}_3$) is one of the principal axes because the shear strains are zero along the principal directions.

5.6 The coordinates y_1, y_2, y_3 are located such that y_3 coincides with one of the principal axes, say y_{III}, and the angle from y_I to y_1 is θ, as shown in Fig. P.5.6(a). (Note that y_1, y_2, y_I, and y_{II} are all on the same plane.) The two principal axes are assigned such that $\gamma_I > \gamma_{II}$. Using the result in the preceding problem show that γ_{11} and γ_{12} can be determined graphically according to the following procedure. A circle (Fig. P.5.6b) called *Mohr's circle* is constructed with its center O located at $((\gamma_I + \gamma_{II})/2, O)$ and its radius equal to $(\gamma_I - \gamma_{II})/2$. A line OP is then drawn at an angle 2θ from the horizontal axis. [Both θ in Fig. 5.6(a) and 2θ in Fig. P.5.6(b) are measured counterclockwise.] The strain components γ_{11} and γ_{12} are then represented by the coordinates of point P. The abscissa of P is the normal strain γ_{11}, and the ordinate is the shear strain γ_{12}. Here γ_{11} is positive when P is located to the

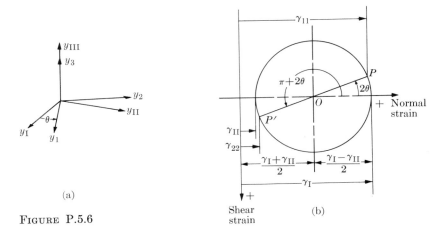

(a)

FIGURE P.5.6

right of the vertical axis, and γ_{12} is positive when P is located below the horizontal axis. Thus in Fig. P.5.6(b) γ_{11} is positive and γ_{12} is negative. Note that γ_{22} is the normal stress with respect to an axis at an angle $\pi/2 + \theta$ from y_I, and hence is represented by the abscissa of point P'. How do you interpret the fact that P' represents a shear strain equal in magnitude to γ_{12} but of opposite sign?

For a certain coordinate system y_1, y_2, y_3, the following strain components are given:

$$\gamma_{23} = \gamma_{13} = 0, \qquad \gamma_{11} = 0.005, \qquad \gamma_{22} = -0.001, \qquad \text{and} \qquad \gamma_{12} = 0.003.$$

Construct the corresponding Mohr circle. Determine γ_I and γ_{II}, and locate the two principal directions y_I and y_{II} with respect to the y_1- and y_2-axes.

5.7   Draw Mohr's circles for the following general states of strain:

$$\text{(a)} \quad \gamma_{11} > \gamma_{22} > 0, \qquad \gamma_{12} < 0;$$
$$\text{(b)} \quad \gamma_{22} > 0, \qquad \gamma_{11} < 0, \qquad \gamma_{12} > 0;$$
$$\text{(c)} \quad \gamma_{11} = \gamma_{22} > 0, \qquad \gamma_{12} < 0.$$

5.8   Let y_1 and y_2 be tangent to the surface of a solid and y_3, which is then perpendicular to the surface, be a principal direction. (In later chapters we shall show that for isotropic materials the normal direction to a surface which is free of stress is always a principal direction.) (a) Show that the strain components γ_{11}, γ_{12}, and γ_{22} can be calculated by measuring the normal strains E_A, E_B, E_C along any three different directions on the surface. (b) Let the three directions be given by $\theta_A = 0°$, $\theta_B = 45°$, $\theta_C = 90°$. Determine the principal strains γ_I and γ_{II} in terms of the three normal strain readings E_A, E_B, and E_C. What is the angle between y_1 and y_I? (c) Let the three directions be given by $\theta_A = 0°$, $\theta_B = 60°$, $\theta_C = 120°$. Determine γ_I and γ_{II} in terms of the three normal strain readings.

A device for measuring the normal strain on a surface is called a *strain gage*. The arrangement of three or more strain gages to determine the state of strain on a surface

Configuration (a)

Configuration (b)

FIGURE P.5.8

is called a *strain rosette*. In Fig. P.5.8, Configuration (a) is called a *rectangular or 45° rosette;* Configuration (b) is called a *delta rosette.*

5.9 By means of the Mohr circle show that the shear strain γ_{12} is given by

$$\gamma_{12} = \frac{E_A - E_B}{2},$$

where E_A and E_B are the normal strains along two mutually perpendicular directions A and B.

FIGURE P.5.9

5.10 (a) At a point O on the surface of a deformable body three strain gages were mounted as shown in the sketch. The angles between the y_1-axes and the $\tilde{y}_1$- and $\tilde{\tilde{y}}_1$-axes are 60°. Under a certain loading condition, the percentage elongations in these gages are as follows:

$$E_1 = -0.005,$$
$$\tilde{E}_1 = +0.005,$$
$$\tilde{\tilde{E}}_1 = +0.010.$$

Determine the strain components γ_{11}, γ_{12}, and γ_{22}.

(b) Consider now a deformable body made of rubber. Under a given loading condition the percentage elongations obtained by these strain gages are as follows:

$$E_1 = -0.5,$$
$$\tilde{E}_1 = +0.5,$$
$$\tilde{\tilde{E}}_1 = +1.0.$$

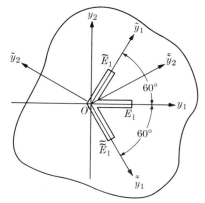

FIGURE P.5.10

What are the corresponding strain components γ_{11}, γ_{12}, and γ_{22}? Suppose that prior to loading, a 90° cross were inscribed to coincide with the y_1- and y_2-axes. What would the angle between the two lines be after deformation?

Note that in (a) E_1, $\frac{1}{2}\phi_{12}$, E_2 and $\tilde{E}_1$, $\frac{1}{2}\tilde{\phi}_{12}$, $\tilde{E}_2$ are related by the tensor transformation law, while in (b) they are no longer related by the tensor transformation law. Why?

5.11   An initial rectangular block 1 in. $\times$ 2 in. $\times$ 1 in. (see Fig. P.5.11) is deformed such that the displacement **u** of every point can be represented in the terms of the following equation

$$\mathbf{u}(y_1, y_2, y_3) = (3 - 0.5 \, y_3)\mathbf{i}_2 - 0.5 \, y_3\mathbf{i}_3.$$

(a) Sketch the deformed block.   (b) Determine the strains γ_{mn} (use strain-displacement relations).   (c) Determine the relative elongation E_m and angle changes.

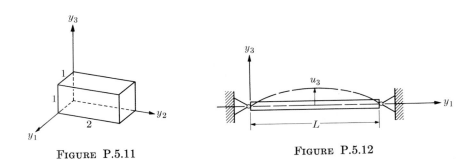

FIGURE P.5.11   FIGURE P.5.12

5.12   The beam shown in the sketch is deformed such that points lying on the undeformed axis of the beam do not experience any horizontal displacement (that is, $u_1 = 0$), but do experience a lateral displacement given by

$$u_3 = A\frac{y_1}{L}\left(1 - \frac{y_1}{L}\right),$$

where A is a constant.   Determine the distribution of the normal strain γ_{11} along the axis of the beam.   What are the consequences of employing the linear strain-displacement relations in the solution of the problem?

5.13   In the previous problem, assume that the normal strain γ_{11} is constant along the deformed axis, i.e., the displacement $u_1(y_1, 0)$ is not zero. Determine $u_1(y_1, 0)$ and $\gamma_{11}(y_1, 0)$.

5.14   Consider the displacement vector specified by

$$\mathbf{u}(y_1, y_2, y_3) = c(y_2 + y_3)\mathbf{i}_1.$$

(a) Sketch the final position and shape of a unit cube which has its nearest corner located at (1, 1, 1) and which was originally oriented with its edges parallel to the y_1-, y_2-, y_3-coordinates in the undeformed body.

(b) Determine the components of the strain tensor and the strain invariants in terms of the components of displacement.

(c) Find the components of the strain tensor for coordinates $\tilde{y}_1$, $\tilde{y}_2$, and $\tilde{y}_3$ which are related to the y_1-, y_2-, y_3-coordinates as follows:

$$y_1 = \tilde{y}_1, \qquad y_2 = \tilde{y}_1 \cos \frac{\pi}{4} - \tilde{y}_2 \cos \frac{\pi}{4}, \qquad y_3 = \tilde{y}_1 \cos \frac{\pi}{4} + \tilde{y}_2 \cos \frac{\pi}{4}.$$

5.15   Use the *Eulerian* representation, coordinates Y_1, Y_2, Y_3 (Fig. P.5.15), to determine the following: (a) the base vectors in a deformed and an undeformed system; (b) relations connecting the base vectors of the undeformed system to those of the deformed system, and the components of displacement $u_m(Y_1, Y_2, Y_3)$; (c) the fundamental metric tensor of the deformed system H_{mn} and of the undeformed system h_{mn}; and (d) the strain-displacement relations for the Eulerian strain tensor which is defined as $\eta_{mn} = \frac{1}{2}(H_{mn} - h_{mn})$.

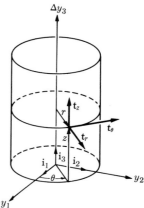

FIGURE P.5.15   FIGURE P.5.16

5.16   Strain problems for cylindrically shaped bodies are in general tackled most conveniently in terms of *cylindrical polar coordinates*. A cylindrical polar-coordinate system is shown in relation to the rectangular Cartesian system in Fig. P.5.16. The coordinate transformation between the two systems is given by

$$y_1 = r \cos \theta, \qquad y_2 = r \sin \theta, \qquad y_3 = z.$$

The set of unit tangent vectors (see Fig. P.5.16) associated with the cylindrical coordinates is related to the unit vectors i_1, i_2, i_3:

$$t_r = \cos \theta\, i_1 + \sin \theta\, i_2, \qquad t_\theta = -\sin \theta\, i_1 + \cos \theta\, i_2, \qquad t_z = i_3.$$

We can write the displacement vector as

$$u(r, \theta, z) = u t_r + v t_\theta + w t_z.$$

For cylindrical coordinates, the components of strain can be defined as follows (cf. Eq. 5.3.1):

$$\tfrac{1}{2}[(dS)^2 - (ds)^2] = \gamma_{rr}(dr)^2 + \gamma_{\theta\theta}(r\, d\theta)^2 + \gamma_{zz}(dz)^2$$
$$+ 2\gamma_{\theta r} r\, d\theta\, dr + 2\gamma_{\theta z} r\, d\theta\, dz + 2\gamma_{zr}\, dz\, dr.$$

Verify the following relations:

$$d\mathbf{R} = d\mathbf{r} + d\mathbf{u},$$

$$d\mathbf{r} = \mathbf{t}_r \, dr + r\mathbf{t}_\theta \, d\theta + \mathbf{t}_z \, dz,$$

$$d\mathbf{u} = \frac{\partial \mathbf{u}}{\partial r} \, dr + \frac{\partial \mathbf{u}}{\partial \theta} \, d\theta + \frac{\partial \mathbf{u}}{\partial z} \, dz,$$

where $\mathbf{R}$ and $\mathbf{r}$ are the position vectors to points in the deformed and undeformed body, respectively (see Section 5.8).

Next show that

$$\tfrac{1}{2}[(dS)^2 - (ds)^2] = d\mathbf{r} \cdot d\mathbf{u} + \tfrac{1}{2} d\mathbf{u} \cdot d\mathbf{u}$$

and (see Eq. 5.8.8)

$$\gamma_{rr} = \mathbf{t}_r \cdot \frac{\partial \mathbf{u}}{\partial r} + \frac{1}{2} \frac{\partial \mathbf{u}}{\partial r} \cdot \frac{\partial \mathbf{u}}{\partial r},$$

$$\gamma_{\theta\theta} = \frac{1}{r^2} \left\{ r\mathbf{t}_\theta \cdot \frac{\partial \mathbf{u}}{\partial \theta} + \frac{1}{2} \frac{\partial \mathbf{u}}{\partial \theta} \cdot \frac{\partial \mathbf{u}}{\partial \theta} \right\},$$

$$\gamma_{zz} = \mathbf{t}_z \cdot \frac{\partial \mathbf{u}}{\partial z} + \frac{1}{2} \frac{\partial \mathbf{u}}{\partial z} \cdot \frac{\partial \mathbf{u}}{\partial z},$$

$$\gamma_{r\theta} = \frac{1}{2r} \left\{ \mathbf{t}_r \cdot \frac{\partial \mathbf{u}}{\partial \theta} + r\mathbf{t}_\theta \cdot \frac{\partial \mathbf{u}}{\partial r} + \frac{\partial \mathbf{u}}{\partial r} \cdot \frac{\partial \mathbf{u}}{\partial \theta} \right\},$$

$$\gamma_{\theta z} = \frac{1}{2r} \left\{ r\mathbf{t}_\theta \cdot \frac{\partial \mathbf{u}}{\partial z} + \mathbf{t}_z \cdot \frac{\partial \mathbf{u}}{\partial \theta} + \frac{\partial \mathbf{u}}{\partial \theta} \cdot \frac{\partial \mathbf{u}}{\partial z} \right\},$$

$$\gamma_{zr} = \frac{1}{2} \left\{ \mathbf{t}_r \cdot \frac{\partial \mathbf{u}}{\partial z} + \mathbf{t}_z \cdot \frac{\partial \mathbf{u}}{\partial r} + \frac{\partial \mathbf{u}}{\partial z} \cdot \frac{\partial \mathbf{u}}{\partial r} \right\}.$$

Finally, verify the strain-displacement relations (compare with Eqs. 5.14.3b):

$$\gamma_{rr} = \frac{\partial u}{\partial r} + \frac{1}{2} \left[\left(\frac{\partial u}{\partial r} \right)^2 + \left(\frac{\partial v}{\partial r} \right)^2 + \left(\frac{\partial w}{\partial r} \right)^2 \right],$$

$$\gamma_{\theta\theta} = \frac{1}{r} \frac{\partial v}{\partial \theta} + \frac{u}{r} + \frac{1}{2} \left[\left(\frac{1}{r} \frac{\partial u}{\partial \theta} - \frac{v}{r} \right)^2 + \left(\frac{1}{r} \frac{\partial v}{\partial \theta} + \frac{u}{r} \right)^2 + \left(\frac{1}{r} \frac{\partial w}{\partial \theta} \right)^2 \right],$$

$$\gamma_{zz} = \frac{\partial u}{\partial z} + \frac{1}{2} \left[\left(\frac{\partial u}{\partial z} \right)^2 + \left(\frac{\partial v}{\partial z} \right)^2 + \left(\frac{\partial w}{\partial z} \right)^2 \right],$$

$$\gamma_{r\theta} = \frac{1}{2} \left\{ \frac{1}{r} \frac{\partial u}{\partial \theta} - \frac{v}{r} + \frac{\partial v}{\partial r} + \frac{\partial u}{\partial r} \left(\frac{1}{r} \frac{\partial u}{\partial \theta} - \frac{v}{r} \right) + \frac{\partial v}{\partial r} \left(\frac{1}{r} \frac{\partial v}{\partial \theta} + \frac{u}{r} \right) + \frac{\partial w}{\partial r} \frac{1}{r} \frac{\partial w}{\partial \theta} \right\},$$

$$\gamma_{\theta z} = \frac{1}{2} \left\{ \frac{\partial v}{\partial z} + \frac{1}{r} \frac{\partial w}{\partial \theta} + \frac{\partial u}{\partial z} \left(\frac{1}{r} \frac{\partial u}{\partial \theta} - \frac{v}{r} \right) + \frac{\partial v}{\partial z} \left(\frac{1}{r} \frac{\partial v}{\partial \theta} + \frac{u}{r} \right) + \frac{\partial w}{\partial z} \frac{1}{r} \frac{\partial w}{\partial \theta} \right\},$$

$$\gamma_{zr} = \frac{1}{2} \left\{ \frac{\partial u}{\partial z} + \frac{\partial w}{\partial r} + \frac{\partial u}{\partial r} \frac{\partial u}{\partial z} + \frac{\partial v}{\partial r} \frac{\partial v}{\partial z} + \frac{\partial w}{\partial r} \frac{\partial w}{\partial z} \right\}.$$

Note: The components of strain denoted in this problem as γ_{rr} $\gamma_{r\theta}$, $\gamma_{\theta\theta}$, etc., are dimensionless and hence are referred to as the *physical* components of the strain tensor. There are tensor methods of obtaining these results more elegant than the method of this problem. However, tensors in general curvilinear coordinates are beyond the scope of this introductory text. The reader who is interested can find such a treatment in Green and Zerna, *Theoretical Elasticity*. See Bibliography 5.4.

5.17. Strain problems for spherically shaped bodies are usually solved most easily in terms of *spherical coordinates*. A spherical coordinate system is shown in relation to the rectangular Cartesian system in Fig. P.5.17. The coordinate transformation between the two systems is given by

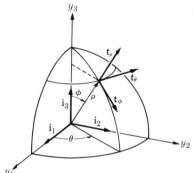

$$y_1 = \rho \sin \phi \cos \theta,$$
$$y_2 = \rho \sin \phi \sin \theta,$$
$$y_3 = \rho \cos \phi.$$

The set of unit tangent vectors (see Fig. P.5.17) associated with the spherical coordinates is related to the unit vectors $\mathbf{i}_1$, $\mathbf{i}_2$, $\mathbf{i}_3$:

$$\mathbf{t}_\rho = \sin \phi \cos \theta \mathbf{i}_1 + \sin \phi \sin \theta \mathbf{i}_2 + \cos \phi \mathbf{i}_3,$$
$$\mathbf{t}_\phi = \cos \phi \cos \theta \mathbf{i}_1 + \cos \phi \sin \theta \mathbf{i}_2 - \sin \phi \mathbf{i}_3,$$
$$\mathbf{t}_\theta = -\sin \theta \mathbf{i}_1 + \cos \theta \mathbf{i}_2.$$

FIGURE P.5.17

We can write the displacement vector in terms of components parallel to $\mathbf{t}_\rho$, $\mathbf{t}_\phi$, and $\mathbf{t}_\theta$, respectively:

$$\mathbf{u}(\rho, \phi, \theta) = w\mathbf{t}_\rho + u\mathbf{t}_\phi + v\mathbf{t}_\theta.$$

For spherical coordinates, the components of strain can be defined as follows (cf. Eq. 5.3.1):

$$\tfrac{1}{2}[(dS)^2 - (ds)^2] = \gamma_{\rho\rho}(d\rho)^2 + \gamma_{\phi\phi}(\rho d\phi)^2 + \gamma_{\theta\theta}(\rho \sin \phi \, d\theta)^2$$
$$+ 2\gamma_{\rho\phi} \, d\rho \, \rho d\phi + 2\gamma_{\phi\theta} \, \rho d\phi \, \rho \sin \phi \, d\theta$$
$$+ 2\gamma_{\theta\rho} \, \rho \sin \phi \, d\theta \, d\rho.$$

Verify the following relations:

$$d\mathbf{R} = d\mathbf{r} + d\mathbf{u},$$
$$d\mathbf{r} = \mathbf{t}_\rho \, d\rho + \mathbf{t}_\phi \, \rho \, d\phi + \mathbf{t}_\theta \, \rho \sin \phi \, d\theta,$$
$$d\mathbf{u} = \frac{\partial \mathbf{u}}{\partial \rho} \, d\rho + \frac{\partial \mathbf{u}}{\partial \phi} \, d\phi + \frac{\partial \mathbf{u}}{\partial \theta} \, d\theta,$$

where $\mathbf{R}$ and $\mathbf{r}$ are the position vectors to points in the deformed and undeformed body, respectively (see Section 5.8).

Next show that

$$\tfrac{1}{2}[(dS)^2 - (ds)^2] = d\mathbf{r} \cdot d\mathbf{u} + \tfrac{1}{2} d\mathbf{u} \cdot d\mathbf{u}$$

and that (see Eq. 5.8.8)

$$\gamma_{\rho\rho} = \mathbf{t}_\rho \cdot \frac{\partial \mathbf{u}}{\partial \rho} + \frac{1}{2} \frac{\partial \mathbf{u}}{\partial \rho} \cdot \frac{\partial \mathbf{u}}{\partial \rho},$$

$$\gamma_{\phi\phi} = \frac{1}{\rho^2} \left\{ \rho \mathbf{t}_\phi \cdot \frac{\partial \mathbf{u}}{\partial \phi} + \frac{1}{2} \frac{\partial \mathbf{u}}{\partial \phi} \cdot \frac{\partial \mathbf{u}}{\partial \phi} \right\},$$

$$\gamma_{\theta\theta} = \frac{1}{(\rho \sin \phi)^2} \left\{ \rho \sin \phi \, \mathbf{t}_\theta \cdot \frac{\partial \mathbf{u}}{\partial \theta} + \frac{1}{2} \frac{\partial \mathbf{u}}{\partial \theta} \cdot \frac{\partial \mathbf{u}}{\partial \theta} \right\}$$

$$\gamma_{\rho\phi} = \frac{1}{2\rho} \left\{ \mathbf{t}_\rho \cdot \frac{\partial \mathbf{u}}{\partial \phi} + \rho \, \mathbf{t}_\phi \cdot \frac{\partial \mathbf{u}}{\partial \rho} + \frac{\partial \mathbf{u}}{\partial \rho} \cdot \frac{\partial \mathbf{u}}{\partial \phi} \right\},$$

$$\gamma_{\phi\theta} = \frac{1}{2\rho^2 \sin \phi} \left\{ \rho \mathbf{t}_\phi \cdot \frac{\partial \mathbf{u}}{\partial \theta} + \rho \sin \phi \, \mathbf{t}_\theta \cdot \frac{\partial \mathbf{u}}{\partial \phi} + \frac{\partial \mathbf{u}}{\partial \phi} \cdot \frac{\partial \mathbf{u}}{\partial \theta} \right\},$$

$$\gamma_{\theta\rho} = \frac{1}{2\rho \sin \phi} \left\{ \rho \sin \phi \, \mathbf{t}_\theta \cdot \frac{\partial \mathbf{u}}{\partial \rho} + \mathbf{t}_\rho \cdot \frac{\partial \mathbf{u}}{\partial \theta} + \frac{\partial \mathbf{u}}{\partial \theta} \cdot \frac{\partial \mathbf{u}}{\partial \rho} \right\},$$

and also

$$\frac{\partial \mathbf{u}}{\partial \rho} = \frac{\partial w}{\partial \rho} \mathbf{t}_\rho + \frac{\partial u}{\partial \rho} \mathbf{t}_\phi + \frac{\partial v}{\partial \rho} \mathbf{t}_\theta,$$

$$\frac{\partial \mathbf{u}}{\partial \phi} = \left[\frac{\partial w}{\partial \phi} - u \right] \mathbf{t}_\rho + \left[\frac{\partial u}{\partial \phi} + w \right] \mathbf{t}_\phi + \left[\frac{\partial v}{\partial \phi} \right] \mathbf{t}_\theta,$$

$$\frac{\partial \mathbf{u}}{\partial \theta} = \left[\frac{\partial w}{\partial \theta} - v \sin \phi \right] \mathbf{t}_\rho + \left[\frac{\partial u}{\partial \theta} - v \cos \phi \right] \mathbf{t}_\phi + \left[\frac{\partial v}{\partial \theta} + w \sin \phi + u \cos \phi \right] \mathbf{t}_\theta.$$

Finally, verify the following strain-displacement relations (cf. Eq. 5.14.3b):

$$\gamma_{\rho\rho} = \frac{\partial w}{\partial \rho} + \frac{1}{2} \left[\left(\frac{\partial w}{\partial \rho} \right)^2 + \left(\frac{\partial u}{\partial \rho} \right)^2 + \left(\frac{\partial v}{\partial \rho} \right)^2 \right],$$

$$\gamma_{\phi\phi} = \frac{1}{\rho} \frac{\partial u}{\partial \phi} + \frac{w}{\rho} + \frac{1}{2} \left[\left(\frac{1}{\rho} \frac{\partial w}{\partial \phi} - \frac{u}{\rho} \right)^2 + \left(\frac{1}{\rho} \frac{\partial u}{\partial \phi} + \frac{w}{\rho} \right)^2 + \left(\frac{1}{\rho} \frac{\partial v}{\partial \phi} \right)^2 \right],$$

$$\gamma_{\theta\theta} = \frac{1}{\rho \sin \phi} \frac{\partial v}{\partial \theta} + \frac{w}{\rho} + \frac{u}{\rho} \cot \phi$$

$$+ \frac{1}{\sin^2 \phi} \left[\left(\frac{1}{\rho} \frac{\partial w}{\partial \theta} - \frac{v}{\rho} \sin \phi \right)^2 + \left(\frac{1}{\rho} \frac{\partial u}{\partial \theta} - \frac{v}{\rho} \cos \phi \right)^2 \right.$$

$$\left. + \left(\frac{1}{\rho} \frac{\partial v}{\partial \theta} + \frac{w}{\rho} \sin \phi + \frac{u}{\rho} \cos \phi \right)^2 \right],$$

$$\gamma_{\rho\phi} = \frac{1}{2} \left\{ \frac{1}{\rho} \frac{\partial w}{\partial \phi} - \frac{u}{\rho} + \frac{\partial u}{\partial \rho} + \left[\frac{\partial w}{\partial \rho} \left(\frac{1}{\rho} \frac{\partial w}{\partial \phi} - \frac{u}{\rho} \right) + \frac{\partial u}{\partial \rho} \left(\frac{1}{\rho} \frac{\partial u}{\partial \phi} + \frac{w}{\rho} \right) + \frac{\partial v}{\partial \rho} \frac{1}{\rho} \frac{\partial v}{\partial \phi} \right] \right\},$$

$$\gamma_{\phi\theta} = \frac{1}{2}\left\{\frac{1}{\rho\sin\phi}\frac{\partial u}{\partial\theta} - \cot\phi\frac{v}{\rho} + \frac{1}{\rho}\frac{\partial v}{\partial\phi} + \frac{1}{\sin\phi}\left[\left(\frac{1}{\rho}\frac{\partial w}{\partial\phi} - \frac{u}{\rho}\right)\left(\frac{1}{\rho}\frac{\partial w}{\partial\theta} - \sin\phi\frac{v}{\rho}\right)\right.\right.$$

$$\left.\left. + \left(\frac{1}{\rho}\frac{\partial u}{\partial\phi} + \frac{w}{\rho}\right)\left(\frac{1}{\rho}\frac{\partial u}{\partial\theta} - \cot\phi\frac{v}{\rho}\right) + \left(\frac{1}{\rho}\frac{\partial v}{\partial\phi}\right)\left(\frac{1}{\rho}\frac{\partial v}{\partial\theta} + \sin\phi\frac{w}{\rho} + \cos\phi\frac{u}{\rho}\right)\right]\right\},$$

$$\gamma_{\theta\rho} = \frac{1}{2}\left\{\frac{\partial v}{\partial\rho} + \frac{1}{\rho\sin\phi}\frac{\partial w}{\partial\theta} - \frac{v}{\rho} + \frac{1}{\sin\phi}\left[\left(\frac{\partial w}{\partial\rho}\right)\left(\frac{1}{\rho}\frac{\partial w}{\partial\theta} - \frac{v}{\rho}\sin\phi\right)\right.\right.$$

$$\left.\left. + \left(\frac{\partial u}{\partial\rho}\right)\left(\frac{1}{\rho}\frac{\partial u}{\partial\theta} - \frac{v}{\rho}\cos\phi\right) + \left(\frac{\partial v}{\partial\rho}\right)\left(\frac{1}{\rho}\frac{\partial v}{\partial\theta} + \frac{w}{\rho}\sin\phi + \frac{u}{\rho}\cos\phi\right)\right]\right\}.$$

[See note at end of Problem 5.16.]

5.18 Determine the dilatations (relative volume changes) for the following two states of strain:

(a)
$$[\gamma_{mn}] = \begin{bmatrix} -0.5 & 1 & 0 \\ 1 & 2 & 0.5 \\ 0 & 0.5 & 0 \end{bmatrix},$$

(b)
$$[\gamma_{mn}] = \begin{bmatrix} -0.005 & 0.01 & 0 \\ 0.01 & 0.02 & 0.005 \\ 0 & 0.005 & 0 \end{bmatrix}.$$

5.19 The body shown in Fig. P.5.19 is assumed to be in a state of strain given by:

$$\epsilon_{11} = 0.01(y_2)^2,$$
$$\epsilon_{12} = -0.01\, y_1 y_2,$$
all other $\epsilon_{mn} = 0.$

Using the compatibility relations check to see whether this strain state is possible for a continuous body. If so, find the displacements u_m corresponding to these strains. *Hint:* Note the boundary conditions on the edge $y_1 = 0$. Sketch the displacement components y_1, y_2 and y_3 (exaggerate the scale if necessary).

FIGURE P.5.19

5.20 With the aid of the ideas developed in Sections 5.4 and 5.5, prove that the components of strain γ_{rr}, $\gamma_{\theta\theta}$, γ_{zz}, and $\gamma_{r\theta}$, $\gamma_{\theta z}$, γ_{zr} derived in Problem 5.16 are the relative elongations and changes in angles for small strains. What are the strain-displacement relations for linear strain?

5.21 With the aid of the ideas developed in Sections 5.4 and 5.5, prove that the components of strain γ_{rr}, $\gamma_{\phi\phi}$, $\gamma_{\theta\theta}$ and $\gamma_{r\phi}$, $\gamma_{\phi\theta}$, $\gamma_{\theta r}$ derived in Problem 5.17 are the relative elongations and changes in angles for small strains. What are the strain-displacement relations for linear strain?

REFERENCES

(1) S. Timoshenko and J. N. Goodier. *Theory of Elasticity*, 2nd Ed., McGraw-Hill, New York, 1951.
(2) E. E. Sechler, *Elasticity in Engineering*, John Wiley and Sons, New York, 1952.
(3) W. Prager and P. G. Hodge, Jr., *Theory of Perfectly Plastic Solids*, John Wiley and Sons, New York, 1951.
(4) G. B. Thomas, *Calculus and Analytic Geometry*, Addison-Wesley, Reading, Mass., 1961.

6

Analysis of Stress

6.1 INTRODUCTION

The analysis of stress is concerned with a study of the cohesive forces, those which hold the structure together as an integral unit. On the scale of the individual atoms, these are the covalent, ionic, metallic, and van der Waals forces that bind the atoms together. In principle, stress analysis can proceed from such a viewpoint, but even the solid-state physicist is forced to idealize the discrete nature of the solid to a continuum and to adopt the ideas of continuum mechanics. The notion of stress which is adopted, therefore, is of an integrated effect of the atomic forces as seen from a macroscopic point of view. It is interesting to note that this continuum approach yields useful results down to a scale of dimension on the order of the spacing between atoms.

A structure or body is said to be "stress free" if the only internal forces present are those necessary to give the structure or body its desired shape in the absence of all external influences including gravitational attraction. Also specifically excluded are internal forces that might be generated during the process of manufacturing the material or of fabricating the specific configuration of the structure or body. Thus the stress-free structure is one in which all the atoms are arranged in their equilibrium interatomic positions. In the usage of solid mechanics, "stresses" will arise if the equilibrium interatomic spacings are disturbed. Thus the analysis of stress is actually concerned with the changes in atomic forces rather than with the absolute level of the atomic forces.

6.2 CONCEPT OF STRESS AT A POINT

The concept of stress at a point p in the interior of a body is introduced by visualizing an imaginary cut or slit of area ΔA surrounding point p (see Fig. 6.1). A pair of matching faces (i.e., surfaces) would be produced by the cut. According to the ideas of internal forces developed in Chapter 3, the detailed action of one face on the other can be represented by an equipollent

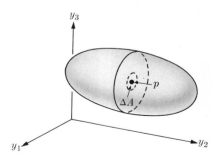

FIG. 6.1 Body cut by imaginary plane.

141

system consisting of a force vector **F** and moment vector **M**. These are shown on the left face produced by the cut in Fig. 6.2 on which the orientation of the element of area ΔA is specified by the outward unit normal vector **n**. The element of area ΔA is permitted to shrink in size toward zero, but in a manner such that point p always remains inside and **n** remains the normal vector. Then, from physical considerations, it is assumed that the following limits occur:

$$\lim_{\Delta A \to 0} \left(\frac{\Delta \mathbf{F}}{\Delta A}\right) = \frac{d\mathbf{F}}{dA} = \boldsymbol{\sigma}, \tag{6.2.1}$$

$$\lim_{\Delta A \to 0} \left(\frac{\Delta \mathbf{M}}{\Delta A}\right) = 0.^* \tag{6.2.2}$$

The vector denoted by $\boldsymbol{\sigma}$ is called the *stress vector* at point p with respect to an infinitesimal element of area dA which has an orientation specified by a unit normal, **n**, as illustrated in Fig. 6.3. Note that the dimensions of $\boldsymbol{\sigma}$ are force per unit area.

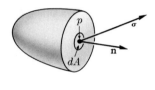

Fig. 6.2 Equipollent internal force system acting on Δa of isolated left half of body.

Fig. 6.3 Stress vector acting on dA of isolated left half of body.

6.3 THE STRESS TENSOR

If a structure is subjected to external loads, the stress-free shape of the structure will be changed. In the previous chapter, the deformations were analyzed in terms of the strain tensor and the displacement vector. As has been stated, stresses arise because the interatomic spacings are disturbed. If an element of volume in the form of a rectangular parallelepiped in the undeformed body is figuratively isolated (as in Fig. 5.3), then in the present context, there are no stresses acting on the exposed surfaces. There will be, however, stresses acting on the exposed surfaces of the deformed element of volume. The effect is illustrated in Fig. 6.4, which is based on Fig. 5.3.

In Fig. 6.4, the stresses that act on the surfaces of the deformed element of volume are summarized in the form of the stress vectors $\boldsymbol{\sigma}_1$, $\boldsymbol{\sigma}_2$, $\boldsymbol{\sigma}_3$ and their differential changes $d\boldsymbol{\sigma}_1$, $d\boldsymbol{\sigma}_2$, $d\boldsymbol{\sigma}_3$. The stress vectors have dimensions of force

---

* There also is a branch of elasticity which assumes this limit to be finite. The resulting quantity is called a *couple-stress vector*. See Cosserat [1] and Mindlin [2].

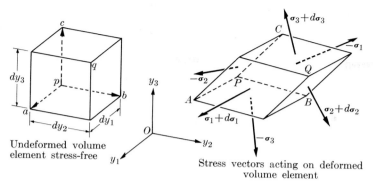

Fig. 6.4   Stress vectors acting on deformed volume element.

per unit area, and are assumed to act at the respective centers of each of the faces. Note carefully that Fig. 6.4 schematically represents the stress vectors, which act on the deformed element of volume, and not the force vectors. The latter are obtained by multiplying each stress vector by the appropriate surface area. It should also be observed that a stress vector is not, in general, oriented perpendicular to the surface on which it acts.

Fundamentally, the analysis of stress should proceed on the basis of the stress vectors acting on the deformed element of volume. This method would lead to certain geometrical difficulties best avoided at this stage in solid mechanics. Briefly, these difficulties arise because the element of volume in the deformed body (see Fig. 6.4) is not a rectangular parallelepiped. Its shape can only be described in terms of the displacements or strain tensor, and this means that the analysis of stress becomes inextricably entwined with the analysis of strain. In many of the modern problems confronting the men in structural research such an intertwining of stress and strain is unavoidable and, indeed, is the challenge. There is a restriction, however, which can be made to circumvent these difficulties. This restriction is embodied in the assumption of linear strains (see Section 5.9). It will be convenient in our discussion to adopt the assumption of linear strain for the analysis of stress. We will see later, however, that some of the results we are developing can also be applied to the general case of small strain.

It will be recalled that the assumption of linear strain implies that the edges of the deformed element of volume have undergone negligible rotations from their corresponding positions in the undeformed body (see Section 5.9). Additionally, the lengths of the edges in the deformed state were found to differ only by a negligible amount from their original lengths. Hence the surface areas of the faces differ only infinitesimally from the corresponding areas of the undeformed element of volume. All these factors contrive to make the deformed volume element indistinguishable from the undeformed volume element insofar as the analysis of stress is concerned. Thus the analysis of stress for linear

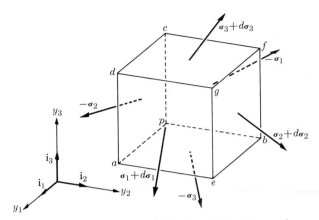

FIG. 6.5   Stress vectors neglecting body deformation.

strains can be based on an element of volume which is a rectangular parallelepiped and which can be assumed to be taken from the undeformed body (see Fig. 6.5).

The stress vectors σ_m are identified by a single subscript which denotes the direction of the unit normal vector of the surface on which the stress vector acts. For example, σ_2 acts on face $padc$ which is perpendicular to the unit vector i_2. Similarly, σ_1 acts on a face perpendicular to i_1, and σ_3 acts on a face perpendicular to i_3. The stress vectors are written in component form as

$$\sigma_1 = \sigma_{1m}i_m = \sigma_{11}i_1 + \sigma_{12}i_2 + \sigma_{13}i_3, \tag{6.3.1}$$

$$\sigma_2 = \sigma_{2m}i_m = \sigma_{21}i_1 + \sigma_{22}i_2 + \sigma_{23}i_3, \tag{6.3.2}$$

$$\sigma_3 = \sigma_{3m}i_m = \sigma_{31}i_1 + \sigma_{32}i_2 + \sigma_{33}i_3, \tag{6.3.3}$$

or in the compact tensor form as

$$\sigma_n = \sigma_{nm}i_m. \tag{6.3.4}$$

The stress tensor comprises the nine components σ_{nm} (it will presently be shown that the stress tensor has only six independent components). The one described above is the Cartesian stress tensor, since the definition is based on the use of rectangular Cartesian coordinates. It is observed that the first subscript in σ_{nm} coincides with the subscript in the stress vector σ_n, and that the second subscript coincides with the unit vector i_m. Thus the first subscript locates the plane on which σ_{nm} is acting, and the second subscript gives its direction. In this special case of rectangular Cartesian coordinates, the components of the stress tensor admit to a fairly simple interpretation. The components σ_{11}, σ_{22}, σ_{33} which have identical subscripts act perpendicular to the surface, and are usually referred to as the normal or extensional stresses. If

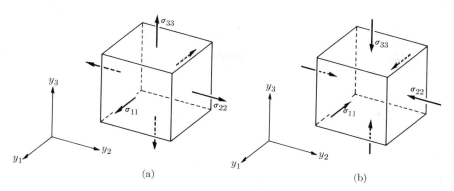

FIG. 6.6 Normal stress sign convention: (a) normal stresses in tension (positive); (b) normal stresses in compression (negative).

the sense of the normal stress is directed outward from the element of volume, the normal stress is referred to as *tensile* (or tension) and is assigned a positive number (see Fig. 6.6a). If the stress is directed inward toward the center of the element of volume, the normal stress is *compressive* (or compression) and is negative (see Fig. 6.6b).

The other six components which have different subscripts lie in the plane of the surface, and are called the *shear components*. It is a bit more involved to assign a positive or negative sign to the shear component than to the normal component. The explanation will be aided by referring to Fig. 6.7, which shows the shear components (in this figure the $d\boldsymbol{\sigma}_m$ have been set equal to zero for purposes of clarity). Two figures have been drawn. On both of these, the shear stresses as depicted are all positive. Negative shear stresses on any of the six faces of the rectangular parallelepiped point in directions opposite to those shown in Fig. 6.7. The first subscript in the shear stress, σ_{nm} $(m \neq n)$, coincides

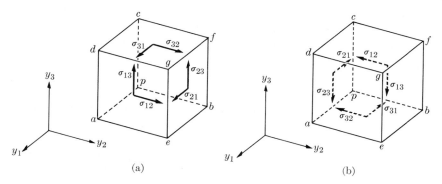

FIG. 6.7 Positive shear stress convention: (a) shear stress components on faces having positive, outward normals point in positive axis directions; (b) shear stress components on faces having negative, outward normals point in negative axis directions.

with the subscripts of the unit normal, i_n, which is perpendicular to the surface on which the shear stress acts. The second subscript coincides with the direction in which the line segment representing the shear stress is aligned. Thus the shear stress σ_{23} acts on surface *begf* whose normal is i_2, and is aligned in a direction parallel to the y_3-axis. Similarly, the shear stress σ_{32} acts on surface *cdgf* whose normal is i_3, and is aligned parallel to the y_2-axis. Each of the six faces of the rectangular parallelepiped can be identified by specifying the outward directed unit normal. Thus i_1 designates the face *aegd*, whereas the opposite face *pbfc* is designated by $-i_1$. The shear stress is positive if either (a) it acts on a face which has a positively directed outward normal and has a sense in the positive direction of the axis designated by the second subscript (Fig. 6.7a), or (b) it acts on a face which has a negatively directed outward normal and has a sense in the negative direction of the axis designated by the second subscript (Fig. 6.7b).

6.4 THE TRANSFORMATION OF STRESS

The Cartesian stress tensor has been defined with respect to an arbitrarily selected coordinate system, y_n (cf. Fig. 6.5). It is important to ascertain the components of the stress tensor if another coordinate system is chosen. This process is called the *transformation of stress*. Figure 6.8 shows a coordinate system, y_n, and another coordinate system, $\tilde{y}_n$. Both coordinate systems can be used to describe the state of stress at point p.

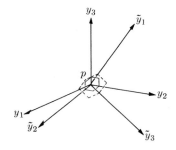

FIGURE 6.8

The law of transformation is arrived at by considering the equilibrium of a tetrahedron *pabc* formed by slicing the parallepiped of Fig. 6.5 by a fourth face perpendicular to $\tilde{y}_1$ (see Fig. 6.9). Face *abc*, which is canted to the axes y_n, is located by the unit normal vector j_1. The system of unit vectors j_n associated with the axes $\tilde{y}_n$ are fixed in the face *abc*, with j_1 perpendicular to, and j_2, j_3 lying in the canted face, *abc*. The vectors j_n can be expressed in terms of components relative to the axes y_n:

$$j_m = l_{\tilde{m}n} i_n, \qquad (6.4.1)$$

where the numbers designated by $l_{\tilde{m}n}$ are merely the direction cosines which connect the axes $\tilde{y}_n$ with y_n (see Appendix, Section A.12).

The stress vectors which act on the tetrahedron *pabc* are schematically represented in Fig. 6.10. The stress vectors σ_1, σ_2, σ_3 are the same as the ones shown in Fig. 6.5; σ_1 is the stress vector acting on the canted face *abc*. The vector $\mathbf{F}$ shown in Fig. 6.10 is a body force vector with dimensions of force per unit volume. The total body force for this element is $\frac{1}{2}\mathbf{F}\,dV$, and is assumed to act at the center of mass of the tetrahedron. Since the tetrahedron is assumed

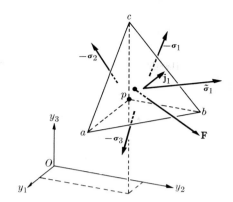

FIG. 6.9 System of unit vectors on canted face of infinitesimal tetrahedron at point p.

FIG. 6.10 Stresses and body force per unit volume acting on infinitesimal tetrahedron at point p.

to be in equilibrium, the following force equilibrium equation must be true:

$$\tfrac{1}{2}\tilde{\sigma}_1 \, d\tilde{A}_1 - \tfrac{1}{2}\sigma_1 \, dA_1 - \tfrac{1}{2}\sigma_2 \, dA_2 - \tfrac{1}{2}\sigma_3 \, dA_3 + \tfrac{1}{2}F \, dV = 0, \qquad (6.4.2)$$

where $\tfrac{1}{2} dA_1$ is the area of face pac which is a triangle, $\tfrac{1}{2} dA_2$ is the area of triangle pbc, $\tfrac{1}{2} dA_3$ is the area of triangle pab, $\tfrac{1}{2} d\tilde{A}_1$ is the area of triangle abc, and $\tfrac{1}{2} dV$ is the volume of the tetrahedron. The term containing the body force vector is of higher order and hence can be neglected. We have, then,

$$\tilde{\sigma}_1 \, d\tilde{A}_1 = \sigma_m \, dA_m. \qquad (6.4.3)$$

Before any further progress can be made, we must develop an expression connecting $d\tilde{A}_1$ and dA_m. We recall from vector analysis that the cross product of two vectors yields a vector whose magnitude is equal to the area of the parallelogram formed by the two vectors. Thus, with reference to Fig. 6.9,

$$\mathbf{ab} \times \mathbf{ac} = d\tilde{A}_1 \mathbf{j}_1, \qquad (6.4.4)$$

where $\mathbf{ab}$ and $\mathbf{ac}$ are vectors representing the edges of the canted face. It is easy to verify from Fig. 6.9 that

$$\mathbf{ab} = \mathbf{pb} - \mathbf{pa}, \qquad (6.4.5)$$

and

$$\mathbf{ac} = \mathbf{pc} - \mathbf{pa}, \qquad (6.4.6)$$

where $\mathbf{pa}$, $\mathbf{pb}$, and $\mathbf{pc}$ represent the edges of the tetrahedron. If we substitute these in Eq. (6.4.4), we find

$$\mathbf{pb} \times \mathbf{pc} - \mathbf{pa} \times \mathbf{pc} - \mathbf{pb} \times \mathbf{pa} = d\tilde{A}_1 \mathbf{j}_1. \qquad (6.4.7)$$

We make use of the following relations (see Fig. 6.9):

$$\mathbf{pb} \times \mathbf{pc} = dA_1\mathbf{i}_1, \tag{6.4.8}$$

$$\mathbf{pa} \times \mathbf{pc} = -dA_2\mathbf{i}_2, \tag{6.4.9}$$

$$\mathbf{pb} \times \mathbf{pa} = -dA_3\mathbf{i}_3. \tag{6.4.10}$$

When we substitute them in Eq. (6.4.7) we get

$$dA_1\mathbf{i}_1 + dA_2\mathbf{i}_2 + dA_3\mathbf{i}_3 = d\tilde{A}_1\mathbf{j}_1, \tag{6.4.11}$$

and hence the unit normal to the canted face has the component form [cf. Eqs. (6.4.7) and (6.4.1)]:

$$\mathbf{j}_1 = \frac{dA_m}{d\tilde{A}_1}\mathbf{i}_m. \tag{6.4.12}$$

If this latter expression is compared with Eq. (6.4.1), we see that

$$l_{\bar{1}m} = \frac{dA_m}{d\tilde{A}_1}, \tag{6.4.13}$$

that is, the ratios of the areas of the orthogonal faces of the tetrahedron to the area of the fourth face are also the direction cosines which the unit normal vector $\mathbf{j}_1$ makes with the y_n-axes. Thus Eq. (6.4.3) becomes

$$\tilde{\sigma}_1 = l_{\bar{1}m}\sigma_m. \tag{6.4.14}$$

In the coordinate system $\tilde{y}_n$, which is fixed in the canted face, the component form of $\tilde{\sigma}_1$ is written as

$$\tilde{\sigma}_1 = \tilde{\sigma}_{11}\mathbf{j}_1 + \tilde{\sigma}_{12}\mathbf{j}_2 + \tilde{\sigma}_{13}\mathbf{j}_3 = \tilde{\sigma}_{1m}\mathbf{j}_m, \tag{6.4.15}$$

where the components $\tilde{\sigma}_{nm}$ $(n = 1)$ in Eq. (6.4.15) are the sought-after representation of stress at p with respect to $\tilde{y}_n$. By substituting Eq. (6.4.15) into the left-hand side of Eq. (6.4.14), and Eq. (6.3.4) into the right-hand side, we find that the equilibrium equation of the tetrahedron becomes

$$\tilde{\sigma}_{1m}\mathbf{j}_m = l_{\bar{1}m}\sigma_{mn}\mathbf{i}_n. \tag{6.4.16}$$

This is a vector equation from which we can obtain three scalar equations by forming the scalar product with $\mathbf{j}_1$, $\mathbf{j}_2$, and $\mathbf{j}_3$, respectively. We note that

$$\mathbf{j}_m \cdot \mathbf{i}_n = l_{\bar{m}n}. \tag{6.4.17}$$

The scalar equations of equilibrium, which are the desired equations relating σ_{mn} to $\tilde{\sigma}_{mn}$, are summarized by

$$\tilde{\sigma}_{1r} = \sigma_{mn}l_{\bar{1}m}l_{\bar{r}n}. \tag{6.4.18}$$

These represent three of the transformation equations relating $\tilde{\sigma}_{mn}$ to σ_{mn}. The remaining equations are obtained by forming two other tetrahedrons in which the fourth faces are perpendicular to $\tilde{y}_2$ and $\tilde{y}_3$, respectively. By cyclically changing the 1 to a 2 and then to a 3, it is clear that the entire set of transformation equations is contained in the following:

$$\tilde{\sigma}_{rs}(\tilde{y}_1, \tilde{y}_2, \tilde{y}_3) = \sigma_{mn}(y_1, y_2, y_3)l_{\tilde{r}m}l_{\tilde{s}n}. \qquad (6.4.19)$$

It should be carefully noted again that the stress tensor σ_{mn} exists at a point, for example, at the point p with coordinates y_1, y_2, y_3. Limiting processes, whereby the element of volume is shrunk in size, have been tacitly assumed to occur; thus, in the limit, these results refer to a point in the body. Note that the transformation equation for the Cartesian stress tensor (Eq. 6.4.19) is of the same mathematical form as the transformation equation for the Cartesian strain tensor (Eq. 5.6.7).

6.5   THE SYMMETRY OF THE STRESS TENSOR: MOMENT EQUILIBRIUM

The stress tensor σ_{mn} is symmetric, that is,

$$\sigma_{mn} = \sigma_{nm}. \qquad (6.5.1)$$

This property of the stress tensor is a consequence of the moment equilibrium of the element of volume.† We can reproduce Fig. 6.5 for this special purpose, and to avoid cluttering the picture, show only two force vectors in Fig. 6.11.

First, let us recall that the moment of a force about a point p (see Chapter 3 and Appendix) can be calculated with the help of the vector product. Applying this process to the pair of force vectors shown in Fig. 6.11, we obtain for the

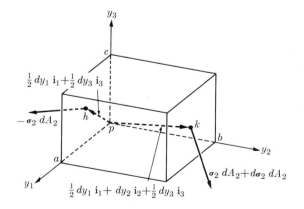

FIGURE 6.11

---

† It also depends on the absence of couple stresses, i.e., on the assumption made in Eq. (6.2.2). See footnote on p. 142.

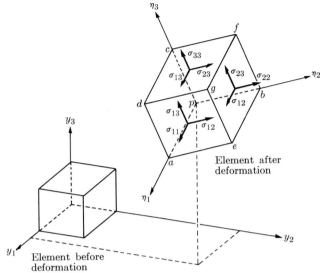

FIGURE 6.12

moment of these forces about point p,

$$- [\tfrac{1}{2} dy_1 \mathbf{i}_1 + \tfrac{1}{2} dy_3 \mathbf{i}_3] \times [\boldsymbol{\sigma}_2 \, dA_2]$$
$$+ [dy_2 \mathbf{i}_2 + \tfrac{1}{2} dy_1 \mathbf{i}_1 + \tfrac{1}{2} dy_3 \mathbf{i}_3] \times \left[\boldsymbol{\sigma}_2 \, dA_2 + \frac{\partial \boldsymbol{\sigma}_2}{\partial y_2} \, dA_2 \, dy_2 \right]$$
$$= (dy_2 \mathbf{i}_2) \times (\boldsymbol{\sigma}_2 \, dA_2) + \text{higher-order terms.} \qquad (6.5.2)$$

Similar equations can be obtained for the remaining two pairs of forces for which the subscripts are 1 and 3 respectively. Since the element of volume is in equilibrium, the sum of all contributing moments must be zero:

$$(dy_2 \mathbf{i}_2) \times (\boldsymbol{\sigma}_2 \, dA_2) + (dy_3 \mathbf{i}_3) \times (\boldsymbol{\sigma}_3 \, dA_3) + (dy_1 \mathbf{i}_1) \times (\boldsymbol{\sigma}_1 dA_1) = 0.$$
$$(6.5.3)$$

The body force vector does not contribute to the moment equilibrium equation since it contributes only a higher-order term. By canceling the common factor $dy_1 \, dy_2 \, dy_3$, Eq. (6.5.3) has the form

$$\mathbf{i}_m \times \boldsymbol{\sigma}_m = 0. \qquad (6.5.4)$$

This in turn becomes, with the introduction of the stress tensor,

$$\mathbf{i}_m \times (\sigma_{mn} \mathbf{i}_n) = 0, \quad \text{or} \quad \sigma_{mn} e_{mnr} \mathbf{i}_r = 0. \qquad (6.5.5)$$

The properties of the vector product of the unit orthogonal vectors reduce Eq. (6.5.5) to

$$(\sigma_{12} - \sigma_{21})\mathbf{i}_3 + (\sigma_{31} - \sigma_{13})\mathbf{i}_2 + (\sigma_{23} - \sigma_{32})\mathbf{i}_1 = 0. \qquad (6.5.6)$$

In order for the vector equation (6.5.6) to be satisfied, each component must independently vanish, that is, $\sigma_{12} = \sigma_{21}, \sigma_{31} = \sigma_{13}, \sigma_{23} = \sigma_{32}$ or, compactly,

$$\sigma_{mn} = \sigma_{nm}. \tag{6.5.7}$$

This result, then, demonstrates that the stress tensor is symmetric, and hence the stress tensor, σ_{mn}, consists of six independent components.

At this point it is worth while to extend the definition of the stress tensor to include the situation in which the strains are small but the rotations are not. In Fig. 6.12 *pabcdefg* represents the new location of an element that was originally a parallelepiped with all edges parallel to the Cartesian coordinates y_1, y_2, and y_3. Under the condition of finite rotation the edges *pa*, *pb*, and *pc* will not be parallel to the y_1-, y_2-, and y_3-axes, respectively. However, under the assumption of small strain, the changes in angles ϕ_{nm} (see Section 5.5) are negligible to the extent that the edges *pa*, *pb*, and *pc* may still be considered mutually orthogonal. Thus at the point p, another set of rectangular Cartesian coordinates η_1, η_2, and η_3 can be located as shown. This set can be used to define the components of the stress tensors σ_{mn} that are acting on the corresponding faces of the element in its deformed position. It is clear that the transformation laws and the symmetric properties of the stress tensor which have been derived are also applicable to the present extended definition.

6.6 THE DIFFERENTIAL EQUATIONS OF EQUILIBRIUM

The moment equilibrium of the element of volume is assured by the symmetry of the stress tensor. There is still the force equilibrium to be considered. By vectorially adding up all the forces which result from the stress vectors shown in Fig. 6.5 and a body force vector $\mathbf{F}$, we find that the force equilibrium equation is

$$dA_1 \, d\boldsymbol{\sigma}_1 + dA_2 \, d\boldsymbol{\sigma}_2 + dA_3 \, d\boldsymbol{\sigma}_3 + \mathbf{F} \, dV = 0. \tag{6.6.1}$$

Since the $d\boldsymbol{\sigma}_n$ shown in Fig. 6.5 represent changes only in the corresponding y_n-direction, then

$$d\boldsymbol{\sigma}_n = \frac{\partial \boldsymbol{\sigma}_n}{\partial y_n} \, dy_n \qquad \text{(no sum on } n\text{)}, \tag{6.6.2}$$

and the equation of force equilibrium becomes

$$\left(\frac{\partial \boldsymbol{\sigma}_1}{\partial y_1} + \frac{\partial \boldsymbol{\sigma}_2}{\partial y_2} + \frac{\partial \boldsymbol{\sigma}_3}{\partial y_3} + \mathbf{F} \right) dy_1 \, dy_2 \, dy_3 = 0. \tag{6.6.3}$$

If the stress tensor is introduced, and if the body force vector is written in component form as

$$\mathbf{F} = F_n \mathbf{i}_n, \tag{6.6.4}$$

then Eq. (6.6.3) assumes the form

$$\left(\frac{\partial \sigma_{mn}}{\partial y_m} + F_n\right) \mathbf{i}_n = 0, \tag{6.6.5}$$

where the common factor $dy_1 \, dy_2 \, dy_3$ has been canceled.

The scalar equations of equilibrium are obtained by forming the appropriate scalar products. Thus the scalar equations of equilibrium in the directions of the y_1-, y_2-, y_3-axes are obtained by forming the scalar product of Eq. (6.6.5) with $\mathbf{i}_1$, $\mathbf{i}_2$, and $\mathbf{i}_3$, respectively:

$$\frac{\partial \sigma_{11}}{\partial y_1} + \frac{\partial \sigma_{21}}{\partial y_2} + \frac{\partial \sigma_{31}}{\partial y_3} + F_1 = 0, \tag{6.6.6}$$

$$\frac{\partial \sigma_{12}}{\partial y_1} + \frac{\partial \sigma_{22}}{\partial y_2} + \frac{\partial \sigma_{32}}{\partial y_3} + F_2 = 0, \tag{6.6.7}$$

$$\frac{\partial \sigma_{13}}{\partial y_1} + \frac{\partial \sigma_{23}}{\partial y_2} + \frac{\partial \sigma_{33}}{\partial y_3} + F_3 = 0. \tag{6.6.8}$$

It is well to remember at this stage that the above set of equations of equilibrium has been derived on the assumption of linear strains. For the case of small strain but finite rotations, the stress components σ_{mn} are defined with respect to the rotated system of axes η_1, η_2, and η_3, and hence Eqs. (6.6.6), (6.6.7), and (6.6.8) are no longer the proper equations of equilibrium.

6.7 THE EQUATIONS OF EQUILIBRIUM ON THE SURFACE OF A BODY

The equations of equilibrium derived in the previous section are those which must hold in the interior of a body. There will be surface loads applied to some portion of the surface of a body. The intensity, i.e., the force per unit area, will be denoted as $\boldsymbol{\sigma}^*$ where the asterisk indicates that this is a prescribed quantity. Consider the body shown in Fig. 6.13. We imagine that the distribution of $\boldsymbol{\sigma}^*$ over some region of the surface is known. In particular, let us focus our attention on a triangular-shaped infinitesimal element of area at a point q. The orientation of the element of area is specified by the outward unit normal $\mathbf{n}$. Let us figuratively carve an infinitesimal tetrahedron out of the body at point q in such a manner that the element of area is the fourth face (see Fig. 6.14).

The three orthogonal faces of the tetrahedron are interior surfaces of the body and hence have the internal stress vectors $\boldsymbol{\sigma}_m$ acting on them. Figures 6.14 and 6.10 are identical except that one is located at the surface of the body and the other in the interior. The equilibrium of the tetrahedron of Fig. 6.14 is assumed, since the internal stresses at point q satisfy the relation (cf. Eq. 6.4.3),

$$\boldsymbol{\sigma}_m \, dA_m = \boldsymbol{\sigma}^* \, dA_s, \tag{6.7.1}$$

where dA_s is the triangular area on the surface. Let the unit normal **n** have components given by

$$\mathbf{n} = n_m \mathbf{i}_m. \qquad (6.7.2)$$

Then according to Eq. (6.4.13)

$$n_m = \frac{dA_m}{dA_s}. \qquad (6.7.3)$$

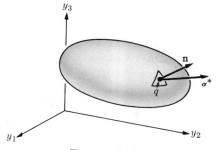

FIGURE 6.13

By introducing the stress tensor (Eq. 6.3.4) as well as Eq. (6.7.3) into Eq. (6.7.1) we obtain the desired equation of equilibrium at the surface of a body,

$$\sigma_{mn} n_m \mathbf{i}_n = \boldsymbol{\sigma}^*. \qquad (6.7.4)$$

The result summarized in Eq. (6.7.4) applies at the surface of a body; hence it is also the boundary condition for the stress tensor σ_{mn}. It relates the boundary values of σ_{mn}, that is, the values at the bounding surfaces, to the prescribed surface stresses $\boldsymbol{\sigma}^*$.

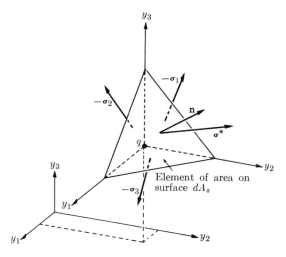

Element of area on surface dA_s

FIGURE 6.14

6.8 PRINCIPAL STRESSES AND PRINCIPAL DIRECTIONS

There are two questions which can be asked regarding the stresses at point p:

(1) At what orientation of plane abc (see Fig. 6.9) does the stress vector $\boldsymbol{\sigma}$ have no shear components; that is, when does $\boldsymbol{\sigma}$ consist only of a component normal to the plane abc?

(2) At what orientation of plane abc (see Fig. 6.9) is the normal component of $\boldsymbol{\sigma}$ a maximum or a minimum?

It will be demonstrated that the same set of planes answers both questions. These planes are called the *principal planes*, and the corresponding components of stress are called the *principal stresses*.

The answer to question (1) can be formulated by writing

$$\boldsymbol{\sigma} = \tau^* \mathbf{n}, \tag{6.8.1}$$

where τ^* is the magnitude of the normal component of $\boldsymbol{\sigma}$, and $\mathbf{n}$ is the unit normal to the plane on which τ^* acts (see Fig. 6.15).

If we combine Eqs. (6.8.1), (6.3.4), and (6.4.1), in which $\mathbf{n}$ takes on the role of $\mathbf{j}_1$, and n_m the role of $l_{\bar{1}m}$, with Eq. (6.4.14), where $\boldsymbol{\sigma}$ takes on the role of $\tilde{\boldsymbol{\sigma}}_1$, and n_m the role of $l_{\bar{1}m}$, we get the following result:

$$\sigma_{mn} \mathbf{i}_n n_m = \tau^* n_m \mathbf{i}_m, \tag{6.8.2}$$

wherein $\boldsymbol{\sigma}_m$ has been expressed in its component form (see Eq. 6.3.4). The scalar product of Eq. (6.8.2) with $\mathbf{i}_r$ yields

$$(\sigma_{mr} - \tau^* \delta_{mr}) n_m = 0. \tag{6.8.3}$$

Before analyzing Eq. (6.8.3), let us proceed to question (2).

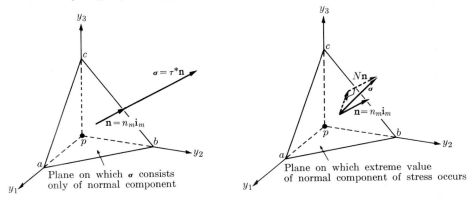

FIGURE 6.15   FIGURE 6.16

Let the normal component of $\boldsymbol{\sigma}$ be denoted by N (see Fig. 6.16). Then

$$N = \mathbf{n} \cdot \boldsymbol{\sigma}. \tag{6.8.4}$$

If we substitute Eqs. (6.3.4), (6.4.1), and (6.4.14), as we did in the development of Eq. (6.8.2), into Eq. (6.8.1), we may express the normal component N in terms of the stress tensor:

$$N = (n_r \mathbf{i}_r) \cdot (\sigma_{mn} \mathbf{i}_n n_m) = \sigma_{mn} n_m n_n. \tag{6.8.5}$$

Thus, given the stress tensor σ_{mn}, and the components n_m of the unit normal **n** which locates the plane on which $\boldsymbol{\sigma}$ acts, Eq. (6.8.5) is an explicit relation between the direction cosines of the plane abc and the normal component of the stress vector acting on abc. The maximum value of N is desired, and also the orientation of the plane on which it acts. This is again an extreme-value problem with a constraint (see Section 5.7 and Appendix, Section A.16), because the direction cosines n_m must satisfy the condition specified by

$$\delta_{mr} n_m n_r = 1. \tag{6.8.6}$$

If this equation of constraint is rewritten as

$$M = \delta_{mr} n_m n_r - 1 = 0, \tag{6.8.7}$$

then the necessary conditions for the existence of extreme values of N are embodied in the following set of partial differential equations (see Appendix, Section A.16):

$$\frac{\partial N}{\partial n_m} - \tau \frac{\partial M}{\partial n_m} = 0, \qquad \frac{\partial N}{\partial \tau} - M = 0, \tag{6.8.8}$$

where τ is the Lagrange multiplier. The first three of the necessary conditions result in a set of three simultaneous, homogeneous equations:

$$(\sigma_{mr} - \tau \delta_{mr}) n_r = 0, \tag{6.8.9}$$

and the last necessary condition reduces to the equation of constraint (6.8.7). Equations (6.8.9) have exactly the same form as Eqs. (6.8.3), and hence

$$\tau^* = \tau. \tag{6.8.10}$$

Thus the Lagrange multiplier is the normal component of stress, and the planes on which the maximum value of the normal component N occurs are also the planes on which the shearing components of $\boldsymbol{\sigma}$ are zero.

The necessary and sufficient condition that the homogeneous equations (6.8.9) have a solution is that the determinant formed by the coefficients of n_m vanish:

$$\begin{vmatrix} \sigma_{11} - \tau & \sigma_{12} & \sigma_{13} \\ \sigma_{21} & \sigma_{22} - \tau & \sigma_{23} \\ \sigma_{31} & \sigma_{32} & \sigma_{33} - \tau \end{vmatrix} = 0. \tag{6.8.11}$$

At this stage, the reader should observe the mathematical similarities between the search for principal strains and directions (see Section 5.7), and the search for principal stresses and directions.

The expansion of the determinant yields a cubic equation in τ. This can be written as

$$-(\tau)^3 + I_1(\tau)^2 - I_2(\tau) + I_3 = 0, \tag{6.8.12}$$

where the coefficients I_1, I_2, I_3 are called the first, second, and third stress invariants, respectively. When expressed in terms of the stress tensor with respect to y_n they can be expressed by

$$I_1 = \sigma_{11} + \sigma_{22} + \sigma_{33}, \tag{6.8.13}$$

$$I_2 = \begin{vmatrix} \sigma_{11} & \sigma_{12} \\ \sigma_{21} & \sigma_{22} \end{vmatrix} + \begin{vmatrix} \sigma_{22} & \sigma_{23} \\ \sigma_{32} & \sigma_{33} \end{vmatrix} + \begin{vmatrix} \sigma_{11} & \sigma_{13} \\ \sigma_{31} & \sigma_{33} \end{vmatrix}, \tag{6.8.14}$$

$$I_3 = \begin{vmatrix} \sigma_{11} & \sigma_{12} & \sigma_{13} \\ \sigma_{21} & \sigma_{22} & \sigma_{23} \\ \sigma_{31} & \sigma_{32} & \sigma_{33} \end{vmatrix}. \tag{6.8.15}$$

The three roots of Eq. (6.8.12) are the principal stresses, and will be designated by σ_{I}, σ_{II}, σ_{III} in an ordered fashion,

$$\sigma_{\mathrm{I}} > \sigma_{\mathrm{II}} > \sigma_{\mathrm{III}}. \tag{6.8.16}$$

The cubic equation can also be exhibited in factored form:

$$(\tau - \sigma_{\mathrm{I}})(\tau - \sigma_{\mathrm{II}})(\tau - \sigma_{\mathrm{III}}) = 0. \tag{6.8.17}$$

We find, therefore [compare the expanded forms of Eqs. (6.8.17) with (6.8.12)], that the stress invariants, if expressed in terms of the principal stresses, have the forms

$$I_1 = \sigma_{\mathrm{I}} + \sigma_{\mathrm{II}} + \sigma_{\mathrm{III}}, \tag{6.8.18}$$

$$I_2 = \sigma_{\mathrm{I}}\sigma_{\mathrm{II}} + \sigma_{\mathrm{II}}\sigma_{\mathrm{III}} + \sigma_{\mathrm{III}}\sigma_{\mathrm{I}}, \tag{6.8.19}$$

$$I_3 = \sigma_{\mathrm{I}}\sigma_{\mathrm{II}}\sigma_{\mathrm{III}}. \tag{6.8.20}$$

Since the principal stresses must be independent of the choice of the coordinate system of point p, the coefficients are invariant quantities, and hence are rightly called stress invariants.

In order to calculate the principal directions which correspond to the principal stresses, σ_{I}, σ_{II}, and σ_{III}, we must adopt a procedure similar to that used in determining the principal strain directions. The principal direction corresponding to σ_{I}, for example, is denoted by direction cosines labeled as $n_1^{(\mathrm{I})}$, $n_2^{(\mathrm{I})}$, and $n_3^{(\mathrm{I})}$. These three direction cosines must satisfy the set of homogeneous equations (6.8.9) in which τ is set equal to σ_{I}, and also the constraint equation (6.8.6). The three simultaneous equations to be solved for $n_m^{(\mathrm{I})}$ are

$$(\sigma_{11} - \sigma_{\mathrm{I}})n_1^{(\mathrm{I})} + \sigma_{12}n_2^{(\mathrm{I})} + \sigma_{13}n_3^{(\mathrm{I})} = 0, \tag{6.8.21}$$

$$\sigma_{21}n_1^{(\mathrm{I})} + (\sigma_{22} - \sigma_{\mathrm{I}})n_2^{(\mathrm{I})} + \sigma_{23}n_3^{(\mathrm{I})} = 0, \tag{6.8.22}$$

$$(n_1^{(\mathrm{I})})^2 + (n_2^{(\mathrm{I})})^2 + (n_3^{(\mathrm{I})})^2 = 1. \tag{6.8.23}$$

Actually, Eq. (6.8.9) represents three equations, but only two of them are independent, and the two exhibited in Eqs. (6.8.21) and (6.8.22) have been arbitrarily chosen.

We can also derive two other sets of equations of the form (6.8.21), (6.8.22), and (6.8.23) for σ_{II}, $n_m^{(II)}$, and σ_{III}, $n_m^{(III)}$.

6.9   THE EXTREME SHEAR STRESSES

Clearly, it is also pertinent to raise a question about the maximum and/or minimum values of the shear stress. This is most conveniently discussed by choosing the principal directions as the frame of reference and labeling the axes y_I, y_{II}, and y_{III}. (See Fig. 6.17.)

The stress transformation law with y_I, y_{II}, y_{III} as the axes assumes a particularly simple form because there are no shear stresses along the principal directions:

$$\tilde{\sigma}_{mn} = \sigma_I l_{\tilde{m}I} l_{\tilde{n}I} + \sigma_{II} l_{\tilde{m}II} l_{\tilde{n}II}$$
$$+ \sigma_{III} l_{\tilde{m}III} l_{\tilde{n}III}. \quad (6.9.1)$$

Let us choose as the object of our interest the shear stress $\tilde{\sigma}_{12}$. This does not entail any loss in generality since the orientation of $\tilde{y}_1$ and $\tilde{y}_2$ is arbitrary. For ease in writing we set

$$l_{\tilde{1}R} = n_R, \qquad R = I, II, III, \quad (6.9.2)$$

$$l_{\tilde{2}R} = \lambda_R, \qquad R = I, II, III, \quad (6.9.3)$$

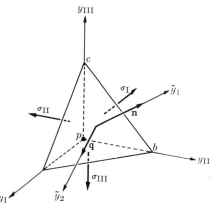

FIGURE 6.17

where n_R are the three direction cosines of the $\tilde{y}_1$-axis, and λ_R are the direction cosines of the $\tilde{y}_2$-axis (see Fig. 6.17). The transformation law for $\tilde{\sigma}_{12}$ is therefore written in the form

$$\tilde{\sigma}_{12} = \sigma_I n_I \lambda_I + \sigma_{II} n_{II} \lambda_{II} + \sigma_{III} n_{III} \lambda_{III}. \quad (6.9.4)$$

Our problem is now to find the extremum values of $\tilde{\sigma}_{12}$ subject to the constraints on the direction cosines:

$$C_1 = n_I \lambda_I + n_{II} \lambda_{II} + n_{III} \lambda_{III} = 0, \quad (6.9.5)$$

$$C_2 = (n_I)^2 + (n_{II})^2 + (n_{III})^2 - 1 = 0, \quad (6.9.6)$$

$$C_3 = (\lambda_I)^2 + (\lambda_{II})^2 + (\lambda_{III})^2 - 1 = 0. \quad (6.9.7)$$

Equation (6.9.5) is recognizable as the orthogonality condition between the $\tilde{y}_1$- and $\tilde{y}_2$-axes, whereas Eqs. (6.9.6) and (6.9.7) are the usual conditions on the direction cosines (see Eq. 6.8.6). We again use the Lagrange multiplier method and form the function

$$F = \tilde{\sigma}_{12} - \alpha C_1 - \beta C_2 - \gamma C_3, \qquad (6.9.8)$$

where α, β, and γ are the Lagrange multipliers. The extremum of F is found in the standard fashion:

$$\frac{\partial F}{\partial n_{\mathrm{I}}} = \sigma_{\mathrm{I}}\lambda_{\mathrm{I}} - \alpha\lambda_{\mathrm{I}} - 2\beta n_{\mathrm{I}} = 0, \qquad (6.9.9)$$

$$\frac{\partial F}{\partial n_{\mathrm{II}}} = \sigma_{\mathrm{II}}\lambda_{\mathrm{II}} - \alpha\lambda_{\mathrm{II}} - 2\beta n_{\mathrm{II}} = 0, \qquad (6.9.10)$$

$$\frac{\partial F}{\partial n_{\mathrm{III}}} = \sigma_{\mathrm{III}}\lambda_{\mathrm{III}} - \alpha\lambda_{\mathrm{III}} - 2\beta n_{\mathrm{III}} = 0, \qquad (6.9.11)$$

$$\frac{\partial F}{\partial \lambda_{\mathrm{I}}} = \sigma_{\mathrm{I}} n_{\mathrm{I}} - \alpha n_{\mathrm{I}} - 2\gamma\lambda_{\mathrm{I}} = 0, \qquad (6.9.12)$$

$$\frac{\partial F}{\partial \lambda_{\mathrm{II}}} = \sigma_{\mathrm{II}} n_{\mathrm{II}} - \alpha n_{\mathrm{II}} - 2\gamma\lambda_{\mathrm{II}} = 0, \qquad (6.9.13)$$

$$\frac{\partial F}{\partial \lambda_{\mathrm{III}}} = \sigma_{\mathrm{III}} n_{\mathrm{III}} - \alpha n_{\mathrm{III}} - 2\gamma\lambda_{\mathrm{III}} = 0, \qquad (6.9.14)$$

$$\frac{\partial F}{\partial \alpha} = -C_1 = 0, \qquad (6.9.15)$$

$$\frac{\partial F}{\partial \beta} = -C_2 = 0, \qquad (6.9.16)$$

$$\frac{\partial F}{\partial \gamma} = -C_3 = 0. \qquad (6.9.17)$$

These nine equations must be solved. We proceed by first determining the meaning of the Lagrange multipliers. If we multiply Eq. (6.9.9) by n_{I}, Eq. (6.9.10) by n_{II}, Eq. (6.9.11) by n_{III}, and then add, we get

$$2\beta = \tilde{\sigma}_{12}, \qquad (6.9.18)$$

where Eqs. (6.9.4), (6.9.5), and (6.9.6) have been used. In a similar fashion it can be shown that

$$2\gamma = \tilde{\sigma}_{12}, \qquad (6.9.19)$$

and

$$\alpha = \sigma_{\mathrm{I}}(n_{\mathrm{I}})^2 + \sigma_{\mathrm{II}}(n_{\mathrm{II}})^2 + \sigma_{\mathrm{III}}(n_{\mathrm{III}})^2. \qquad (6.9.20)$$

Next we note that Eqs. (6.9.9) and (6.9.12) are homogeneous equations for λ_{I} and n_{I}. Similarly, Eqs. (6.9.10) and (6.9.13) are homogeneous equations for λ_{II} and n_{II}, and Eqs. (6.9.11) and (6.9.14) are homogeneous equations for λ_{III} and n_{III}. There are two groups of solutions to these six equations. One group, representing what would generally be considered a trivial solution, leads to the following sets of direction cosines:

$$\text{(a)} \quad n_I = n_{II} = 0, \qquad n_{III} = \pm 1,$$

$$\text{(b)} \quad n_I = n_{III} = 0, \qquad n_{II} = \pm 1, \qquad (6.9.21)$$

$$\text{(c)} \quad n_{II} = n_{III} = 0, \qquad n_I = \pm 1.$$

This group does not provide any new information, since it merely locates the principal planes on which the shear is zero. The other group, representing the necessary condition for the existence of a nontrivial solution to Eqs. (6.9.9) to (6.9.14), is given by

$$\tilde{\sigma}_{12} = \pm[\sigma_I - \sigma_I(n_I)^2 - \sigma_{II}(n_{II})^2 - \sigma_{III}(n_{III})^2], \qquad (6.9.22)$$

$$\tilde{\sigma}_{12} = \pm[\sigma_{II} - \sigma_I(n_I)^2 - \sigma_{II}(n_{II})^2 - \sigma_{III}(n_{III})^2], \qquad (6.9.23)$$

$$\tilde{\sigma}_{12} = \pm[\sigma_{III} - \sigma_I(n_I)^2 - \sigma_{II}(n_{II})^2 - \sigma_{III}(n_{III})^2]. \qquad (6.9.24)$$

The only consistent sets of direction cosines which will satisfy Eqs. (6.9.22), (6.9.23), and (6.9.24) as well as Eqs. (6.9.5), (6.9.6), and (6.9.7) are the following:

$$\text{(a)} \quad n_{II}^{(a)} = 0, \qquad n_I^{(a)} = \pm \frac{1}{\sqrt{2}}, \qquad n_{III}^{(a)} = \pm \frac{1}{\sqrt{2}},$$

$$\text{(b)} \quad n_I^{(b)} = 0, \qquad n_{II}^{(b)} = \pm \frac{1}{\sqrt{2}}, \qquad n_{III}^{(b)} = \pm \frac{1}{\sqrt{2}}, \qquad (6.9.25)$$

$$\text{(c)} \quad n_{III}^{(c)} = 0, \qquad n_I^{(c)} = \pm \frac{1}{\sqrt{2}}, \qquad n_{II}^{(c)} = \pm \frac{1}{\sqrt{2}}.$$

Case (a) locates a plane parallel to the y_{II}-axis (see Fig. 6.18) and intersecting the y_Iy_{II}-plane at 45°. Similarly, case (b) locates a plane parallel to the y_I-axis and intersecting the y_Iy_{II}-plane at 45°. Case (c) is a plane parallel to the y_{III}-axis and intersecting the $y_{III}y_I$-plane at 45°. By substituting the direction cosines for each case into any of the three Eqs. (6.9.22), (6.9.23), or (6.9.24), the extreme values of the shear stresses can be obtained:

$$\tilde{\sigma}_{12} \equiv S_a = \pm\tfrac{1}{2}(\sigma_I - \sigma_{III}), \qquad (6.9.26)$$

$$\tilde{\sigma}_{12} \equiv S_b = \pm\tfrac{1}{2}(\sigma_{II} - \sigma_{III}), \qquad (6.9.27)$$

$$\tilde{\sigma}_{12} \equiv S_c = \pm\tfrac{1}{2}(\sigma_I - \sigma_{II}). \qquad (6.9.28)$$

Thus the maximum shear stress acts on the plane whose normal bisects the angle between the principal planes of the maximum and minimum principal stress, and has a magnitude equal to one-half the difference between these two principal stresses.

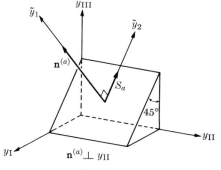

FIGURE 6.18

6.10   THE DEVIATOR AND SPHERICAL STRESS TENSORS

It will often be found convenient to express the stress tensor, σ_{mn}, as the sum of two other derived stress tensors called the *deviator* and *spherical stress tensors* (See Section 5.12). This is accomplished by writing

$$\sigma_{mn} = \hat{\sigma}_{mn} + \hat{\hat{\sigma}}_{mn}, \tag{6.10.1}$$

where

$$\hat{\sigma}_{mn} = \sigma_{mn} - \tfrac{1}{3}\delta_{mn}\sigma_{rr}, \tag{6.10.2}$$

$$\hat{\hat{\sigma}}_{mn} = \tfrac{1}{3}\delta_{mn}\sigma_{rr}. \tag{6.10.3}$$

The tensor, $\hat{\sigma}_{mn}$, is called the deviator stress tensor, and the other, $\hat{\hat{\sigma}}_{mn}$, is called the spherical stress tensor. If Eqs. (6.10.2) and (6.10.3) are substituted in Eq. (6.10.1), an identity will result. It should be observed that σ_{rr} is the first stress invariant (cf., Eq. 6.8.13). In detail, the components of these two derived stress tensors are related to σ_{mn} as follows:

$$\begin{aligned}
\hat{\sigma}_{11} &= \sigma_{11} - \tfrac{1}{3}(\sigma_{11} + \sigma_{22} + \sigma_{33}), & \hat{\sigma}_{12} &= \sigma_{12}, \\
\hat{\sigma}_{22} &= \sigma_{22} - \tfrac{1}{3}(\sigma_{11} + \sigma_{22} + \sigma_{33}), & \hat{\sigma}_{23} &= \sigma_{23}, \\
\hat{\sigma}_{33} &= \sigma_{33} - \tfrac{1}{3}(\sigma_{11} + \sigma_{22} + \sigma_{33}), & \hat{\sigma}_{31} &= \sigma_{31},
\end{aligned} \tag{6.10.4}$$

and

$$\begin{aligned}
\hat{\hat{\sigma}}_{11} &= \hat{\hat{\sigma}}_{22} = \hat{\hat{\sigma}}_{33} = \tfrac{1}{3}(\sigma_{11} + \sigma_{22} + \sigma_{33}), \\
\hat{\hat{\sigma}}_{12} &= \hat{\hat{\sigma}}_{23} = \hat{\hat{\sigma}}_{31} = 0.
\end{aligned} \tag{6.10.5}$$

The concept of the stress invariants can also be applied to the deviator and the spherical stress tensors. There results (see Section 5.12)

$$\hat{I}_1 = 0, \qquad \hat{I}_2 = I_2 - \tfrac{1}{3}(I_1)^2, \qquad \hat{I}_3 = I_3 - \tfrac{1}{3}(I_1 I_2) + \tfrac{2}{27}(I_1)^3, \tag{6.10.6}$$

and

$$\hat{\hat{I}}_1 = I_1, \qquad \hat{\hat{I}}_2 = \tfrac{1}{3}(I_1)^2, \qquad \hat{\hat{I}}_3 = \tfrac{1}{27}(I_1)^3. \tag{6.10.7}$$

6.11   SUMMARY

The stress equations derived in this chapter are summarized below in Cartesian coordinate form for convenient reference. The equations of equilibrium (6.11.3) and (6.11.4) are applicable only to linear strains. The other equations are applicable to general small strain conditions.

Stress transformation law

$$\tilde{\sigma}_{rs}(\tilde{y}_1, \tilde{y}_2, \tilde{y}_3) = \sigma_{mn}(y_1, y_2, y_3)l_{\tilde{r}m}l_{\tilde{s}n} \tag{6.11.1}$$

or

$$\tilde{\sigma}_{11} = \sigma_{11}(l_{\bar{1}1})^2 + \sigma_{22}(l_{\bar{1}2})^2 + \sigma_{33}(l_{\bar{1}3})^2$$
$$+ 2(\sigma_{12}l_{\bar{1}1}l_{\bar{1}2} + \sigma_{23}l_{\bar{1}2}l_{\bar{1}3} + \sigma_{31}l_{\bar{1}3}l_{\bar{1}1}),$$

$$\tilde{\sigma}_{22} = \sigma_{11}(l_{\bar{2}1})^2 + \sigma_{22}(l_{\bar{2}2})^2 + \sigma_{33}(l_{\bar{2}3})^2$$
$$+ 2(\sigma_{12}l_{\bar{2}1}l_{\bar{2}2} + \sigma_{23}l_{\bar{2}2}l_{\bar{2}3} + \sigma_{31}l_{\bar{2}3}l_{\bar{2}1}),$$

$$\tilde{\sigma}_{33} = \sigma_{11}(l_{\bar{3}1})^2 + \sigma_{22}(l_{\bar{3}2})^2 + \sigma_{33}(l_{\bar{3}3})^2$$
$$+ 2(\sigma_{12}l_{\bar{3}1}l_{\bar{3}2} + \sigma_{23}l_{\bar{3}2}l_{\bar{3}3} + \sigma_{31}l_{\bar{3}3}l_{\bar{3}1}),$$

$$\tilde{\sigma}_{12} = \sigma_{11}l_{\bar{1}1}l_{\bar{2}1} + \sigma_{22}l_{\bar{1}2}l_{\bar{2}2} + \sigma_{33}l_{\bar{1}3}l_{\bar{2}3} \qquad (6.11.2)$$
$$+ \sigma_{12}(l_{\bar{1}1}l_{\bar{2}2} + l_{\bar{1}2}l_{\bar{2}1}) + \sigma_{23}(l_{\bar{1}2}l_{\bar{2}3} + l_{\bar{1}3}l_{\bar{2}2})$$
$$+ \sigma_{31}(l_{\bar{1}3}l_{\bar{2}1} + l_{\bar{1}1}l_{\bar{2}3}),$$

$$\tilde{\sigma}_{23} = \sigma_{11}l_{\bar{2}1}l_{\bar{3}1} + \sigma_{22}l_{\bar{2}2}l_{\bar{3}2} + \sigma_{33}l_{\bar{2}3}l_{\bar{3}3} + \sigma_{12}(l_{\bar{2}1}l_{\bar{3}2} + l_{\bar{2}2}l_{\bar{3}1})$$
$$+ \sigma_{23}(l_{\bar{2}2}l_{\bar{3}3} + l_{\bar{2}3}l_{\bar{3}2}) + \sigma_{31}(l_{\bar{2}3}l_{\bar{3}1} + l_{\bar{2}1}l_{\bar{3}3}),$$

$$\tilde{\sigma}_{31} = \sigma_{11}l_{\bar{3}1}l_{\bar{1}1} + \sigma_{22}l_{\bar{3}2}l_{\bar{1}2} + \sigma_{33}l_{\bar{3}3}l_{\bar{1}3} + \sigma_{12}(l_{\bar{3}1}l_{\bar{1}2} + l_{\bar{3}2}l_{\bar{1}1})$$
$$+ \sigma_{23}(l_{\bar{3}2}l_{\bar{1}3} + l_{\bar{3}3}l_{\bar{1}2}) + \sigma_{31}(l_{\bar{3}3}l_{\bar{1}1} + l_{\bar{3}1}l_{\bar{1}3}).$$

Equations of equilibrium

$$\frac{\partial \sigma_{mn}}{\partial y_m} + F_n = 0 \qquad (6.11.3)$$

or

$$\frac{\partial \sigma_{11}}{\partial y_1} + \frac{\partial \sigma_{21}}{\partial y_2} + \frac{\partial \sigma_{31}}{\partial y_3} + F_1 = 0,$$

$$\frac{\partial \sigma_{12}}{\partial y_1} + \frac{\partial \sigma_{22}}{\partial y_2} + \frac{\partial \sigma_{32}}{\partial y_3} + F_2 = 0, \qquad (6.11.4)$$

$$\frac{\partial \sigma_{13}}{\partial y_1} + \frac{\partial \sigma_{23}}{\partial y_2} + \frac{\partial \sigma_{33}}{\partial y_3} + F_3 = 0.$$

Equations for determination of principle planes

$$(\sigma_{mr} - \sigma_I \delta_{mr})n_r^{(I)} = 0,$$
$$(\sigma_{mr} - \sigma_{II} \delta_{mr})n_r^{(II)} = 0, \qquad (6.11.5)$$
$$(\sigma_{mr} - \sigma_{III} \delta_{mr})n_r^{(III)} = 0.$$

The characteristic equation of the system (6.11.5) is

$$-(\tau)^3 + I_I(\tau)^2 - I_2\tau + I_3 = 0, \qquad (6.11.6)$$

where the roots of τ are $\tau = \sigma_I, \sigma_{II}, \sigma_{III}$.

Expressions for the stress invariants

$$I_1 = \sigma_{11} + \sigma_{22} + \sigma_{33} = \sigma_{\mathrm{I}} + \sigma_{\mathrm{II}} + \sigma_{\mathrm{III}}, \qquad (6.11.7)$$

$$I_2 = \begin{vmatrix} \sigma_{11} & \sigma_{12} \\ \sigma_{21} & \sigma_{22} \end{vmatrix} + \begin{vmatrix} \sigma_{22} & \sigma_{23} \\ \sigma_{32} & \sigma_{33} \end{vmatrix} + \begin{vmatrix} \sigma_{11} & \sigma_{13} \\ \sigma_{31} & \sigma_{33} \end{vmatrix} = \sigma_{\mathrm{I}}\sigma_{\mathrm{II}} + \sigma_{\mathrm{II}}\sigma_{\mathrm{III}} + \sigma_{\mathrm{III}}\sigma_{\mathrm{I}},$$

$$\qquad (6.11.8)$$

$$I_3 = \begin{vmatrix} \sigma_{11} & \sigma_{12} & \sigma_{13} \\ \sigma_{21} & \sigma_{22} & \sigma_{23} \\ \sigma_{31} & \sigma_{32} & \sigma_{33} \end{vmatrix} = \sigma_{\mathrm{I}}\sigma_{\mathrm{II}}\sigma_{\mathrm{III}}. \qquad (6.11.9)$$

Directions of normals to planes of extreme shear stresses

$$\begin{pmatrix} n_{\mathrm{I}}^{(a)} & n_{\mathrm{II}}^{(a)} & n_{\mathrm{III}}^{(a)} \\ n_{\mathrm{I}}^{(b)} & n_{\mathrm{II}}^{(b)} & n_{\mathrm{III}}^{(b)} \\ n_{\mathrm{I}}^{(c)} & n_{\mathrm{II}}^{(c)} & n_{\mathrm{III}}^{(c)} \end{pmatrix} = \begin{pmatrix} 0 & \pm 1/\sqrt{2} & \pm 1/\sqrt{2} \\ \pm 1/\sqrt{2} & 0 & \pm 1/\sqrt{2} \\ \pm 1/\sqrt{2} & \pm 1/\sqrt{2} & 0 \end{pmatrix}. \qquad (6.11.10)$$

(The above direction cosines refer to the principal axes.)

Values of extreme shear stresses

$$S_a = \pm \tfrac{1}{2}|\sigma_{\mathrm{II}} - \sigma_{\mathrm{III}}|, \qquad S_b = \pm \tfrac{1}{2}|\sigma_{\mathrm{III}} - \sigma_{\mathrm{I}}|, \qquad S_c = \pm \tfrac{1}{2}|\sigma_{\mathrm{I}} - \sigma_{\mathrm{II}}|.$$

$$\qquad (6.11.11)$$

Deviator components of stress

$$\hat{\sigma}_{mn} = \sigma_{mn} - \tfrac{1}{3}\delta_{mn}\sigma_{rr}, \qquad (6.11.12)$$

or

$$\begin{aligned} \hat{\sigma}_{11} &= \tfrac{2}{3}\sigma_{11} - \tfrac{1}{3}(\sigma_{22} + \sigma_{33}), & \hat{\sigma}_{12} &= \sigma_{12}, \\ \hat{\sigma}_{22} &= \tfrac{2}{3}\sigma_{22} - \tfrac{1}{3}(\sigma_{11} + \sigma_{33}), & \hat{\sigma}_{23} &= \sigma_{23}, \\ \hat{\sigma}_{33} &= \tfrac{2}{3}\sigma_{33} - \tfrac{1}{3}(\sigma_{11} + \sigma_{22}), & \hat{\sigma}_{31} &= \sigma_{31}. \end{aligned} \qquad (6.11.13)$$

Spherical components of stress

$$\hat{\hat{\sigma}}_{mn} = \tfrac{1}{3}\delta_{mn}\sigma_{rr}, \qquad (6.11.14)$$

or

$$\hat{\hat{\sigma}}_{11} = \hat{\hat{\sigma}}_{22} = \hat{\hat{\sigma}}_{33} = \tfrac{1}{3}(\sigma_{11} + \sigma_{22} + \sigma_{33}), \qquad (6.11.15)$$

$$\hat{\hat{\sigma}}_{12} = \hat{\hat{\sigma}}_{23} = \hat{\hat{\sigma}}_{31} = 0. \qquad (6.11.16)$$

Deviator stress invariants

$$\hat{I}_1 = 0, \qquad \hat{I}_2 = I_2 - \tfrac{1}{3}(I_1)^2, \qquad \hat{I}_3 = I_3 - \tfrac{1}{3}(I_1 I_2) + \tfrac{2}{27}(I_1)^3. \qquad (6.11.17)$$

Spherical stress invariants

$$\hat{\hat{I}}_1 = I_1, \qquad \hat{\hat{I}}_2 = \tfrac{1}{3}(I_1)^2, \qquad \hat{\hat{I}}_3 = \tfrac{1}{27}(I_1)^3. \qquad (6.11.18)$$

PROBLEMS

6.1   Expand the stress transformation law, Eq. (6.4.9)

$$\tilde{\sigma}_{rs}(\tilde{y}_1, \tilde{y}_2, \tilde{y}_3) = \sigma_{mn}(y_1, y_2, y_3)l_{\bar{r}m}l_{\bar{s}n}$$

for $\tilde{\sigma}_{11}$ and $\tilde{\sigma}_{23}$.

6.2   At a given point in a body, $\sigma_{11} = \sigma_{22} = \sigma_{33} = \sigma$, and $\sigma_{12} = \sigma_{13} = \sigma_{23} = 0$. (Note that the y_1-, y_2-, and y_3-axes are principal axes.) By means of the stress transformation law show that in any coordinate system $\tilde{y}_1$, $\tilde{y}_2$, and $\tilde{y}_3$, the normal stresses are equal to σ and the shear stresses are zero.

Such a state of stress, when σ is negative, is called *hydrostatic compression* (or pressure), and when σ is positive, *hydrostatic tension*.

6.3   At a given point in a body $\sigma_{11} = \sigma_{22} = \sigma$, and $\sigma_{12} = \sigma_{23} = \sigma_{13} = 0$. (Note that the y_1-, y_2-, and y_3-axes, are principal axes.) By means of the stress transformation law show that when the $\tilde{y}_1$- and $\tilde{y}_2$-axes are in the y_1y_2-plane, $\tilde{\sigma}_{11} = \tilde{\sigma}_{22} = \sigma$ and $\tilde{\sigma}_{12} = 0$. What is the value of the maximum shear stress (in terms of σ_{33}) when $\sigma = k\sigma_{33}$?

6.4   A state of plane stress is defined by the condition that three of the stress components are zero, for example, σ_{33}, σ_{13}, and σ_{23} are zero. Assume that the nonzero components are

$$\sigma_{11} = 10,000 \text{ psi,}$$
$$\sigma_{22} = -5,000 \text{ psi,}$$
$$\sigma_{12} = 5,000 \text{ psi.}$$

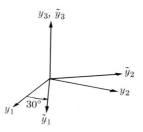

FIGURE P.6.4

Determine $\tilde{\sigma}_{11}$, $\tilde{\sigma}_{22}$, and $\tilde{\sigma}_{12}$ given that $\tilde{y}_1$ and $\tilde{y}_2$ are in the y_1y_2-plane and the angle between y_1 and $\tilde{y}_1$ is 30°. Determine the two principal stresses, $\sigma_{\rm I}$ and $\sigma_{\rm II}$. *Note* that the idea of Mohr's circle can be applied to the transformation of stress (see Problem 5.6).

6.5   Show that the state of stress at a stress-free surface is a plane stress state if the y_3-axis is normal to the surface, and y_1 and y_2 are tangent to the surface (Fig. P.6.5).

6.6   Figure P.6.6 illustrates the principal stresses acting on the principal planes of an infinitesimal cube surrounding a point p in a body. What is the maximum shear stress?

FIGURE P.6.5

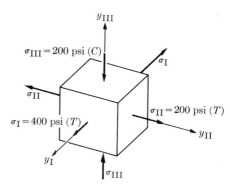

FIGURE P.6.6

6.7 A round bar is loaded as a tension specimen with an axial stress $\sigma_{11} = \sigma$. Then a radial pressure p is applied (by a fluid) so that $p = \sigma/4$. By what factor is the maximum shear stress increased with the application of this pressure?

6.8 An *octahedral plane* is a plane which intersects the principal axes at equal angles (Fig. P.6.8). (a) Show that the shear stress on this plane (called the *octahedral shear stress*) is given by

$$\sigma_{oct} = \tfrac{1}{3}\sqrt{(\sigma_I - \sigma_{II})^2 + (\sigma_{II} - \sigma_{III})^2 + (\sigma_{III} - \sigma_I)^2}.$$

(b) Show that the octahedral shear stress is related to the second deviator stress invariant by

$$\sigma_{oct} = \sqrt{-\tfrac{2}{3}\hat{I}_2}.$$

6.9 A pressure vessel is shown in Fig. P.6.9. If the circumferential normal stress (hoop stress) σ_{33} and the longitudinal normal stress σ_{11} are assumed uniform, while the normal stress σ_{22} along the radial direction varies linearly, we have

$$\sigma_{11} = pr/2t, \qquad \sigma_{22} = -p(1 - y_2/t), \qquad \sigma_{33} = pr/t,$$

where r is the radius of the vessel. In this case, the shear stresses corresponding to these axes are zero. Determine the location where the shear stress is maximum. Calculate the magnitude of this shear stress and indicate the plane where this maximum shear stress exists.

6.10 The components of a stress tensor at a point p are shown in the following matrix:

$$\sigma_{mn} = \begin{bmatrix} 12{,}000 & 4000 & 0 \\ 4000 & -8000 & 2000 \\ 0 & 2000 & -4000 \end{bmatrix}.$$

Determine the principal stresses, their directions, and the extremum value of each of the shear stresses.

6.11 (a) Verify that the equations of equilibrium (6.6.6) through (6.6.8) reduce to the form:

$$\frac{\partial \sigma_{11}}{\partial y_1} + \frac{\partial \sigma_{21}}{\partial y_2} + F_1 = 0, \qquad \frac{\partial \sigma_{12}}{\partial y_1} + \frac{\partial \sigma_{22}}{\partial y_2} + F_2 = 0,$$

for plane stress in the $y_1 y_2$-plane. (b) Verify that the function $\phi(y_1, y_2)$, defined by

$$\sigma_{11} = \frac{\partial^2 \phi}{\partial y_2^2}, \qquad \sigma_{22} = \frac{\partial^2 \phi}{\partial y_1^2}, \qquad \sigma_{12} = -\frac{\partial^2 \phi}{\partial y_1 \partial y_2},$$

satisfies the equations of equilibrium identically for plane stress with no body forces. The function $\phi(y_1, y_2)$ is called the *Airy stress function*.

6.12 The triangular plate shown in Fig. P.6.12 is in a state of plane stress under a certain set of boundary conditions. The Airy stress function which describes the stress distribution is given by $\phi(y_1, y_2) = A(\tfrac{1}{12}y_1^4 + \tfrac{1}{4}y_1^2 y_2^2 - \tfrac{1}{6}y_2^4)$, where A is a constant. (a) Show that this stress function is a possible solution of the problem, given that no

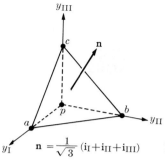

$$\mathbf{n} = \frac{1}{\sqrt{3}} (\mathbf{i}_\mathrm{I} + \mathbf{i}_\mathrm{II} + \mathbf{i}_\mathrm{III})$$ **FIGURE P.6.8**

FIGURE P.6.9

FIGURE P.6.12

body forces act on the plate. (b) Determine the stress distribution in the plate, and the distribution of the normal component of the boundary force along edge AB ("normal" component means normal to edge AB).

6.13   A thin slab hangs under the influence of gravity g as shown in Fig. P.6.13. It can be assumed here that the body is in a state of 2-dimensional *plane stress*, that is,

$$\sigma_{31} = \sigma_{32} = \sigma_{33} = 0, \quad \text{and} \quad \partial/\partial y_3 = 0.$$

Write out the appropriate equations of equilibrium for this stress state.   Show that a stress function $\Phi(y_1, y_2)$ defined as

$$\sigma_{11} = \frac{\partial^2 \Phi}{\partial y_2^2} - \rho g y_1,$$

$$\sigma_{22} = \frac{\partial^2 \Phi}{\partial y_1^2},$$

$$\sigma_{12} = -\frac{\partial^2 \Phi}{\partial y_1 \, \partial y_2}$$

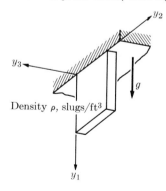

Density ρ, slugs/ft³

FIGURE P.6.13

satisfies these equilibrium equations identically.

6.14   Show that the conventional beam relations $dS/dy_1 = p$, $dM/dy_1 = S$, can be obtained by integrating the appropriate differential equations of force equilibrium, $\partial \sigma_{mn}/\partial y_m + F_n = 0$, over the thickness h and width b of a beam of rectangular cross-section. See Fig. P.6.14. The bending moment and shear are the equipollent of the normal stress σ_{11} and shear stress σ_{13} over the cross section of the beam:

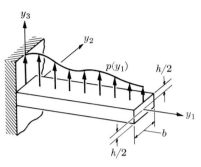

Bending moment:

$$M = -b \int_{-h/2}^{h/2} y_3 \sigma_{11} \, dy_3,$$

Shear force:

$$S = -b \int_{-h/2}^{h/2} \sigma_{13} \, dy_3.$$

FIGURE P.6.14

The lateral loading may be considered as a distributed traction σ_{33} acting on the upper face of the beam:

$$p = b\sigma_{33} \quad \text{at} \quad y_3 = h/2.$$

6.15 The nine components of stress for cylindrical polar coordinates are shown (Fig. P.6.15) acting on the appropriate element of volume which has edges of length $r d\theta$, dr, and dz.

(a) Show that the unit vectors $\mathbf{t}_r$, $\mathbf{t}_\theta$, and $\mathbf{t}_z$ in cylindrical coordinates are related to the unit vectors $\mathbf{i}_1$, $\mathbf{i}_2$, and $\mathbf{i}_3$ by

$$\mathbf{t}_r = \cos\theta \, \mathbf{i}_1 + \sin\theta \, \mathbf{i}_2, \qquad \mathbf{t}_\theta = -\sin\theta \, \mathbf{i}_1 + \cos\theta \, \mathbf{i}_2, \qquad \mathbf{t}_z = \mathbf{i}_3.$$

(b) Show that the force vectors acting on three of the faces of the element of volume are

$$\mathbf{S}_r = (\sigma_{rr}\mathbf{t}_r + \sigma_{r\theta}\mathbf{t}_\theta + \sigma_{rz}\mathbf{t}_z)r \, d\theta \, dz,$$
$$\mathbf{S}_\theta = (\sigma_{\theta r}\mathbf{t}_r + \sigma_{\theta\theta}\mathbf{t}_\theta + \sigma_{\theta z}\mathbf{t}_z) \, dr \, dz,$$
$$\mathbf{S}_z = (\sigma_{zr}\mathbf{t}_r + \sigma_{z\theta}\mathbf{t}_\theta + \sigma_{zz}\mathbf{t}_z)r \, d\theta \, dr.$$

(c) Let the body force vector per unit of volume acting on the element of volume be defined as $\mathbf{F} = F_r\mathbf{t}_r + F_\theta\mathbf{t}_\theta + F_z\mathbf{t}_z$. Show that the vector equation of force equilibrium is

$$\frac{\partial \mathbf{S}_r}{\partial r} dr + \frac{\partial \mathbf{S}_\theta}{\partial \theta} d\theta + \frac{\partial \mathbf{S}_z}{\partial z} dz + \mathbf{F} r \, dr \, d\theta \, dz = 0.$$

(d) Show that the components of stress are symmetric, i.e., show that $\sigma_{r\theta} = \sigma_{\theta r}$, $\sigma_{rz} = \sigma_{zr}$, $\sigma_{z\theta} = \sigma_{\theta z}$.

(e) From the results of part (c), show that the three scalar equations of equilibrium in cylindrical polar coordinates are

$$\frac{\partial \sigma_{rr}}{\partial r} + \frac{1}{r}\frac{\partial \sigma_{r\theta}}{\partial \theta} + \frac{\partial \sigma_{rz}}{\partial z} + \frac{1}{r}(\sigma_{rr} - \sigma_{\theta\theta}) + F_r = 0,$$

$$\frac{\partial \sigma_{\theta r}}{\partial r} + \frac{1}{r}\frac{\partial \sigma_{\theta\theta}}{\partial \theta} + \frac{\partial \sigma_{\theta z}}{\partial z} + \frac{2}{r}\sigma_{\theta r} + F_\theta = 0,$$

$$\frac{\partial \sigma_{zr}}{\partial r} + \frac{1}{r}\frac{\partial \sigma_{z\theta}}{\partial \theta} + \frac{\partial \sigma_{zz}}{\partial z} + \frac{1}{r}\sigma_{zr} + F_z = 0.$$

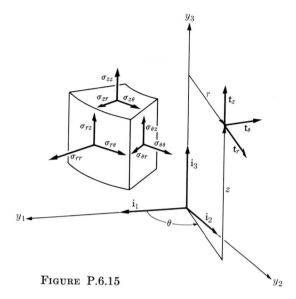

FIGURE P.6.15

Note: The components $\sigma_{\theta\theta}$, $\sigma_{\theta r}$, etc., used in this problem are the physical components of the stress tensors, and as such they all have dimensions of force per unit area. There are more elegant tensor methods for obtaining these equations of equilibrium. The interested reader is referred to Green and Zerna, Ref. 6.3 in the Bibliography.

6.16   Follow the steps outlined in Problem 6.15 and verify that the scalar equations of equilibrium in spherical polar coordinates ρ, ϕ, θ are given by (see Problem 5.17 for unit tangent vectors)

$$\frac{\partial \sigma_{\rho\rho}}{\partial \rho} + \frac{1}{\rho}\frac{\partial \sigma_{\rho\phi}}{\partial \phi} + \frac{1}{\rho \sin \phi}\frac{\partial \sigma_{\rho\theta}}{\partial \theta} + \frac{\cos \phi}{\rho \sin \phi}\sigma_{\rho\phi} + \frac{1}{\rho}\left[2\sigma_{\rho\rho} - \sigma_{\phi\phi} - \sigma_{\theta\theta}\right] + F_\rho = 0,$$

$$\frac{\partial \sigma_{\phi\rho}}{\partial \rho} + \frac{1}{\rho}\frac{\partial \sigma_{\phi\phi}}{\partial \phi} + \frac{1}{\rho \sin \phi}\frac{\partial \sigma_{\phi\theta}}{\partial \theta} + \frac{3}{\rho}\sigma_{\phi\rho} + \frac{\cos \phi}{\rho \sin \phi}(\sigma_{\phi\phi} - \sigma_{\theta\theta}) + F_\phi = 0,$$

$$\frac{\partial \sigma_{\theta\rho}}{\partial \rho} + \frac{1}{\rho}\frac{\partial \sigma_{\theta\phi}}{\partial \phi} + \frac{1}{\rho \sin \phi}\frac{\partial \sigma_{\theta\theta}}{\partial \theta} + \frac{3}{\rho}\sigma_{\theta\rho} + \frac{2\cos \phi}{\rho \sin \phi}\sigma_{\theta\phi} + F_\theta = 0.$$

See *note* at the end of Problem 6.15.

REFERENCES

(1) E. et F. Cosserat, *Théorie des Corps Déformables*, A. Hermann et Fils, Paris, 1909.
(2) R. D. Mindlin and H. F. Tiersten, "Effects of Couple Stresses in Linear Elasticity, *Archives for Rational Mechanics and Analysis*, **11**, 415–448 (1962).

Elasticity

7.1 INTRODUCTION

In Chapter 4 some simple examples were used to illustrate problems which require the simultaneous application of force equations and displacement equations. This necessitated the formulation of simple constitutive relations which connected force and displacement. Thus far, the study of strain in Chapter 5 and the study of stress in Chapter 6 have been pursued independently. Certain engineering problems can be solved without the need for relating stress to strain, problems analogous to those discussed in Chapters 2 and 3. However, many problems do require the simultaneous consideration of stress and strain, and hence the connection between stress and strain needs to be formalized. This chapter will be devoted to an exposition of the basic ideas governing an elementary class of constitutive relations known as the *elastic stress-strain relations*. With these relations, which will contain experimentally determined constants describing the material, the constants k used in Chapter 4 to relate force to displacement can be determined. Additionally, the concept of strain energy will be introduced. Finally, the complete set of the equations of elasticity will be summarized.

7.2 THE GENERALIZED HOOKE'S LAW—ANISOTROPY

It is an experimental fact that the relative elongations, E_n, and angular changes, ϕ_{nm}, are linearly proportional to applied stresses for most materials used for structural purposes providing the stresses are kept to reasonable magnitudes. Furthermore, if the applied stresses are removed, the relative elongations and angular changes vanish, and the body reverts to an unstrained state, i.e., there is no macroscopic evidence that the body has been subjected to loads. A body which exhibits this type of behavior is called a *linearly elastic body*.

The Cartesian strain tensor, γ_{mn}, and the Cartesian stress tensor, σ_{mn}, have been defined in previous chapters. We discovered in Chapter 5 that a rather complicated relationship exists between relative elongation and the extensional component of the strain tensor (see Section 5.4). The relationship between the angular changes and the shearing components of the strain tensor is equally complex. It will not be possible for us to express the connection between the general strain tensor and the stress tensor in a simple or meaningful manner. Fortunately, the operating range of strain for the vast majority of engineering materials is covered by the case which we have called "small" strain. We have seen in Chapter 5 that if the strains are small then the extensional components of strain are physically the relative elongations of an element, and the shearing components are the angular changes. The developments in this chapter concerning the constitutive relations will, therefore, be restricted to small strains which then will automatically also apply to linear strains.

The most general *linear* relationship which connects stress to strain is known as the *generalized Hooke's Law* and can be expressed mathematically as

$$\sigma_{mn} = E_{mnpr}\gamma_{pr}, \tag{7.2.1}$$

where the components of the fourth-order tensor E_{mnpr} are known as the *elastic constants*. It is seen that each stress component is related to all nine components of the strain tensor. For example, one of the nine equations collectively represented by Eq. (7.2.1) has the form

$$\begin{aligned}
\sigma_{13} = \; & E_{1311}\gamma_{11} + E_{1312}\gamma_{12} + E_{1313}\gamma_{13} \\
& + E_{1321}\gamma_{21} + E_{1322}\gamma_{22} + E_{1323}\gamma_{23} \\
& + E_{1331}\gamma_{31} + E_{1332}\gamma_{32} + E_{1333}\gamma_{33}.
\end{aligned} \tag{7.2.2}$$

There are 81 components of the tensor E_{mnpr}, but fortunately this tensor exhibits certain symmetry properties which reduce the total number of independent components to 21 for a material which does not have any axes of symmetry. Such a material is called *aeolotropic* or *anisotropic*.

If a body is in a state of strain such that the only strain components different from zero are γ_{12} and γ_{21}, then the stress-strain relations for this special situation would be written as

$$\sigma_{mn} = E^*_{mn12}\gamma_{12} + E^*_{mn21}\gamma_{21}. \tag{7.2.3}$$

However, the strain tensor is symmetric (see Section 5.3) and hence the above equation can be put into the form

$$\sigma_{mn} = (E^*_{mn12} + E^*_{mn21})\gamma_{12}. \tag{7.2.4}$$

We can now introduce a new fourth-order tensor,

$$E_{mn12} = \frac{E^*_{mn12} + E^*_{mn21}}{2}, \tag{7.2.5}$$

which is symmetric with respect to 1 and 2. Thus the stress-strain relation can be written as

$$\sigma_{mn} = E_{mn12}\gamma_{12} + E_{mn21}\gamma_{21}, \tag{7.2.6}$$

with

$$E_{mn12} = E_{mn21}. \tag{7.2.7}$$

In more general terms, we have

$$E_{mnpr} = E_{mnrp}. \tag{7.2.8}$$

Thus the tensor E_{mnpr} is unchanged when the last two indices are interchanged. This reduces the number of independent elastic constants by 27 to a total of 54.

If the state of strain in a body is such that the only nonzero component is γ_{11}, then the stress-strain relation becomes

$$\sigma_{mn} = E_{mn11}\gamma_{11}. \tag{7.2.9}$$

Two of the scalar equations contained in Eq. (7.2.9) are

$$\sigma_{12} = E_{1211}\gamma_{11}, \tag{7.2.10}$$

$$\sigma_{21} = E_{2111}\gamma_{11}. \tag{7.2.11}$$

In this case the symmetry of the stress tensor requires that

$$E_{1211} = E_{2111}, \tag{7.2.12}$$

or, in more general terms,

$$E_{mnpr} = E_{nmpr}. \tag{7.2.13}$$

Thus the tensor E_{mnpr} is unchanged if the first two indices are interchanged. This symmetry property reduces the number of independent elastic constants by 18 to a total of 36.

The further reduction of the number of independent constants to the final total of 21 can be accomplished only by thermodynamical considerations. Let us consider a unit cube of material which is in a state of stress and strain characterized by σ_{mn} and γ_{mn}. If we let the strain components increase by an amount $d\gamma_{mn}$, the work done by the stress components is given by

$$dU^* = \sigma_{mn}\, d\gamma_{mn}, \tag{7.2.14}$$

where U^* is called the *strain-energy density*. The validity of Eq. (7.2.14) can be ascertained by visualizing the deformation of a unit cube for each of the increases $d\gamma_{11}$, $d\gamma_{22}$, etc. Actually, Eq. (7.2.14) will not be fully appreciated until energy theorems are discussed in Chapter 9. However, its use is needed at this stage.

If the deformation process is isothermal and reversible, then according to the First Law of Thermodynamics, the work done is equal to the increase in the Helmholtz free energy, $d\psi$. This is stated as

$$d\psi = dU^* = \sigma_{mn}\, d\gamma_{mn}. \tag{7.2.15}$$

With the substitution of the generalized Hooke's law, Eq. (7.2.1), we have

$$d\psi = E_{mnpr}\gamma_{pr}\, d\gamma_{mn}. \tag{7.2.16}$$

Since the free energy is a function of γ_{mn}, the total differential $d\psi$ can also be written as

$$d\psi = \frac{\partial \psi}{\partial \gamma_{mn}}\, d\gamma_{mn}. \tag{7.2.17}$$

Comparing Eqs. (7.2.16) and (7.2.17), we find that

$$\frac{\partial \psi}{\partial \gamma_{mn}} = E_{mnpr}\gamma_{pr}. \tag{7.2.18}$$

The partial differentiation of Eq. (7.2.18) with respect to γ_{pr} yields

$$\frac{\partial}{\partial \gamma_{pr}}\left(\frac{\partial \psi}{\partial \gamma_{mn}}\right) = E_{mnpr}. \tag{7.2.19}$$

Interchanging the indices in Eq. (7.2.19), we obtain

$$\frac{\partial}{\partial \gamma_{mn}}\left(\frac{\partial \psi}{\partial \gamma_{pr}}\right) = E_{prmn}. \tag{7.2.20}$$

Since the order of partial differential is unimportant, that is,

$$\frac{\partial}{\partial \gamma_{pr}}\left(\frac{\partial \psi}{\partial \gamma_{mn}}\right) = \frac{\partial}{\partial \gamma_{mn}}\left(\frac{\partial \psi}{\partial \gamma_{pr}}\right), \tag{7.2.21}$$

it is clear that†

$$E_{mnpr} = E_{prmn}. \tag{7.2.22}$$

Thus the first pair of indices in the elasticity tensor can be interchanged with

---

† It can also be demonstrated that if the deformation process is adiabatic and reversible, the same conclusion is valid. Thus the assumptions of reversible isothermal or adiabatic processes are implicit in the use of a strain-energy function. Loads applied very slowly represent nearly isothermal conditions, and loads applied very rapidly, adiabatic conditions. The elastic constants $E_{mnpr} = \partial^2 U^*/\partial \gamma_{mn}\partial \gamma_{pr}$ are only slightly different for the two cases. For example, for steel in tension, the modulus of elasticity for adiabatic stretching is only 1 percent larger than for isothermal stretching.

the second pair without changing the values. This operation further reduces the number of independent elastic constants to a total of 21.†

Quite clearly, since the components both of the stress tensor and the strain tensor are functions of the orientation of the axis system, the elastic constants will also be functions of axis orientation. The transformation law for the elasticity tensor can be derived in a relatively simple fashion. If another coordinate system, $\tilde{y}_n$, is used then Eq. (7.2.1) is written as

$$\tilde{\sigma}_{kl}(\tilde{y}_n) = \widetilde{E}_{klst}(\tilde{y}_n)\tilde{\gamma}_{st}(\tilde{y}_n). \tag{7.2.23}$$

The tensor nature for both γ_{pr} and σ_{mn} has been established. Their transformation laws (see Eqs. 5.14.5a and 6.11.1) have been established:

$$\tilde{\sigma}_{kl} = \sigma_{mn}l_{\tilde{k}m}l_{\tilde{l}n}, \tag{7.2.24}$$

$$\gamma_{pr} = \tilde{\gamma}_{st}l_{p\tilde{s}}l_{r\tilde{l}}. \tag{7.2.25}$$

We can substitute Eq. (7.2.25) in Eq. (7.2.1), and the result into Eq. (7.2.24) to yield

$$\tilde{\sigma}_{kl} = E_{mnpr}\tilde{\gamma}_{st}l_{\tilde{k}m}l_{\tilde{l}n}l_{\tilde{s}p}l_{tr}, \tag{7.2.26}$$

where we have reversed the order of some of the subscripts in Eq. (7.2.25). This is permissible because $l_{p\tilde{s}}$ merely represents the cosine of the angle between y_p and $\tilde{y}_s$. Now, a comparison of Eqs. (7.2.23) and (7.2.26) reveals the transformation law for the elasticity tensor:

$$\widetilde{E}_{klst}(\tilde{y}_n) = E_{mnpr}(y_n)l_{\tilde{k}m}l_{\tilde{l}n}l_{\tilde{s}p}l_{\tilde{t}r}. \tag{7.2.27}$$

The preceding development would be considered superfluous in tensor analysis. Once the tensor natures of σ_{mn} and γ_{pr} have been established, the only permissible tensor connection between them is an equation of the form shown in Eq. (7.2.1); furthermore, the connecting function must obey the transformation law given by Eq. (7.2.27). However, since the complete tensor calculus has not been developed here, it is felt that the few additional equations would be informative and educational.

The generalized Hooke's law, in view of the fundamental symmetries which have been shown to exist, is most conveniently written as

$$\sigma_{11} = E_{1111}\gamma_{11} + E_{1122}\gamma_{22} + E_{1133}\gamma_{33} + 2(E_{1112}\gamma_{12} + E_{1113}\gamma_{13} + E_{1123}\gamma_{23}), \tag{7.2.28}$$

$$\sigma_{22} = E_{2211}\gamma_{11} + E_{2222}\gamma_{22} + E_{2233}\gamma_{33} + 2(E_{2212}\gamma_{12} + E_{2213}\gamma_{13} + E_{2233}\gamma_{23}), \tag{7.2.29}$$

---

† Historically, Cauchy thought that there were only 15 constants; Green, through energy considerations, arrived at the correct number of 21.

$$\sigma_{33} = E_{3311}\gamma_{11} + E_{3322}\gamma_{22} + E_{3333}\gamma_{33} + 2(E_{3312}\gamma_{12} + E_{3313}\gamma_{13} + E_{3323}\gamma_{23}),$$
$$(7.2.30)$$

$$\sigma_{12} = E_{1211}\gamma_{11} + E_{1222}\gamma_{22} + E_{1233}\gamma_{33} + 2(E_{1212}\gamma_{12} + E_{1213}\gamma_{13} + E_{1223}\gamma_{23}),$$
$$(7.2.31)$$

$$\sigma_{13} = E_{1311}\gamma_{11} + E_{1322}\gamma_{22} + E_{1333}\gamma_{33} + 2(E_{1312}\gamma_{12} + E_{1313}\gamma_{13} + E_{1323}\gamma_{23}),$$
$$(7.2.32)$$

$$\sigma_{23} = E_{2311}\gamma_{11} + E_{2322}\gamma_{22} + E_{2333}\gamma_{33} + 2(E_{2312}\gamma_{12} + E_{2313}\gamma_{13} + E_{2323}\gamma_{23}).$$
$$(7.2.33)$$

Note that there are three other relations which have not been displayed, since these are identical with Eqs. (7.2.31), (7.2.32), and (7.2.33). In addition, one should note the presence of the factor 2, which is due to the symmetries of the tensors.

For purposes of further discussion, it will be found convenient to exhibit the constants E_{mnpr} in a square array, or matrix form:

$$(E_{mnpr}) = \begin{pmatrix} E_{1111} & E_{1122} & E_{1133} & E_{1112} & E_{1113} & E_{1123} \\ E_{2211} & E_{2222} & E_{2233} & E_{2212} & E_{2213} & E_{2223} \\ E_{3311} & E_{3322} & E_{3333} & E_{3312} & E_{3313} & E_{3323} \\ E_{1211} & E_{1222} & E_{1233} & E_{1212} & E_{1213} & E_{1223} \\ E_{1311} & E_{1322} & E_{1333} & E_{1312} & E_{1313} & E_{1323} \\ E_{2311} & E_{2322} & E_{2333} & E_{2312} & E_{2313} & E_{2323} \end{pmatrix}, \qquad (7.2.34)\dagger$$

where $E_{mnpr} = E_{prmn}$.

The stress-strain relations given by Eq. (7.2.1) can be expressed in the inverted form

$$\gamma_{mn} = S_{mnpr}\sigma_{pr}, \qquad (7.2.35)$$

where S_{mnpr} is known as the *compliance tensor*. It should be evident, after just a few moments of thought, that S_{mnpr} has the same symmetry properties as E_{mnpr}, and the same type of transformation law. Furthermore, a set of equations analogous to Eqs. (7.2.28) through (7.2.33) can be written with the roles of σ_{mn} and γ_{mn} reversed, and the components of E_{mnpr} replaced by those of S_{mnpr} with the same arrangement of indices. In other words, an equation such as Eq. (7.2.34) can be exhibited for S_{mnpr} merely by replacing E by S.

---

† The reader who wants to write the stress-strain laws in matrix form is cautioned against using the 6×6 array shown in this equation. Read the sentence underneath Eq. (7.2.33).

The macroscopic structure of the material may introduce additional symmetries into the elasticity and compliance tensors. A tree, which grows by the
addition of rings, yields a material with elastic properties preferentially oriented
with and against the grain. A single crystal of silver, which is a face-centered
cubic material, has preferred axes along the crystal lattice. Most of the common metallic engineering materials, however, consist of the random orientation
of many single crystals. This randomness results in a material with properties
that are macroscopically independent of the orientation of the rectangular
Cartesian axes. It is an interesting exercise in the use of the transformation
laws to derive the number of independent elastic constants for the various
classes of materials.

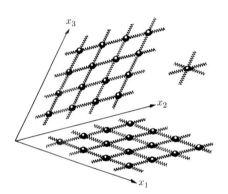

FIG. 7.1   Spring-ball model—three
oblique axes.

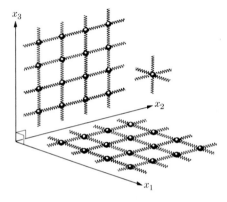

FIG. 7.2 Spring-ball model for monoclinic materials.

Before we proceed with the analysis of the symmetry relations, a few additional
remarks concerning the aeolotropic or anisotropic material may be helpful. Such
a material may be visualized on the atomic scale as one in which the atoms are
arranged along three oblique axes (see Fig. 7.1). In place of atoms, we may
consider rigid balls connected by springs with spring constants which are different along the three directions. The response of the material to impressed
forces is different along each of the axes. If one pushes along the x_1-direction,
changes in length as well as in angle will occur along and between all the axes.
There are no planes of symmetry, and 21 constants are required to express the
connection between stress and strain.

The following discussion will focus on the components of E_{mnpr}, but whatever
results are found to be true for the elasticity tensor will also be true for the
corresponding component of S_{mnpr}. For example, we will discover in the next
section that E_{1123} must be zero for a monoclinic material. Since this result will
be shown to depend upon the transformation law for E_{mnpr}, and since S_{mnpr} has
the same transformation law, then S_{1123} also is zero.

7.3 MONOCLINIC MATERIAL: THIRTEEN CONSTANTS

A *monoclinic* material exhibits symmetry of its elastic properties with respect to one plane which in this section will be taken as the y_1y_2-plane. If we apply the simple spring-ball model of Fig. 7.2, to a monoclinic material, its x_3-axis will be perpendicular to the other two which will intersect each other at an oblique angle. The spring constants will be different for each of the three directions, x_1, x_2, x_3. This symmetry is expressed by the requirement that the elastic constants do not change under the following coordinate transformation:

$$\tilde{y}_1 = y_1, \qquad \tilde{y}_2 = y_2, \qquad \tilde{y}_3 = -y_3. \qquad (7.3.1)$$

The direction cosines which correspond to this coordinate transformation can be expressed as follows:

	y_1	y_2	y_3
$\tilde{y}_1$	1	0	0
$\tilde{y}_2$	0	1	0
$\tilde{y}_3$	0	0	-1

$$(7.3.2)$$

Under the coordinate transformation given by Eq. (7.3.1), it is required that

$$\widetilde{E}_{mnpr}(\tilde{y}_1, \tilde{y}_2, \tilde{y}_3) = E_{mnpr}(y_1, y_2, y_3). \qquad (7.3.3)$$

Clearly, the additional symmetry must further reduce the number of independent constants from the 21 required to describe an aeolotropic material. The application of the transformation law for the elasticity tensor (Eq. 7.2.27) will determine the conditions necessary to satisfy Eq. (7.3.3). For example, let us determine the dependence of $\widetilde{E}_{1111}$ on E_{klst}:

$$\widetilde{E}_{1111} = E_{klst}l_{\bar{1}k}l_{\bar{1}l}l_{\bar{1}s}l_{\bar{1}t} = E_{1111}l_{\bar{1}1}l_{\bar{1}1}l_{\bar{1}1}l_{\bar{1}1} = E_{1111}. \qquad (7.3.4)$$

Since there are only three nonzero direction cosines (Eq. 7.3.2), the expansion of the transformation law is simplified. The result given by Eq. (7.3.4) states that Eq. (7.3.3) is satisfied for this one component. Similarly,

$$\widetilde{E}_{1123} = E_{1123}l_{\bar{1}1}l_{\bar{1}1}l_{\bar{2}2}l_{\bar{3}3} = -E_{1123}. \qquad (7.3.5)$$

The result stated in Eq. (7.3.5) is at odds with the invariance condition (Eq. 7.3.3); in order to meet the condition, the component E_{1123} is set equal to zero. It can be verified that of the 21 components of E_{mnpr} which must be tested against the transformation law, 7 others will yield a result similar to that given by Eq. (7.3.5). Thus a monoclinic material possesses only 13 nonzero independent elastic constants. Where the plane of symmetry is the y_1y_2-plane, the components which must be set equal to zero in order to satisfy Eq. (7.3.3) are:

$$E_{1123}, \quad E_{2233}, \quad E_{3323}, \quad E_{1131}, \quad E_{2231}, \quad E_{3331}, \quad E_{1223}, \quad E_{1231}. \qquad (7.3.6)$$

The array of elastic constants for a monoclinic material with symmetry about the y_1y_2-plane becomes

$$(E_{mnpr}) = \begin{pmatrix} E_{1111} & E_{1122} & E_{1133} & E_{1112} & 0 & 0 \\ E_{1122} & E_{2222} & E_{2233} & E_{2212} & 0 & 0 \\ E_{1133} & E_{2233} & E_{3333} & E_{3312} & 0 & 0 \\ E_{1112} & E_{2212} & E_{3312} & E_{1212} & 0 & 0 \\ 0 & 0 & 0 & 0 & E_{1313} & E_{1323} \\ 0 & 0 & 0 & 0 & E_{1323} & E_{2323} \end{pmatrix}. \qquad (7.3.7)$$

The physical meaning of the array shown in Eq. (7.3.7) is best appreciated by using the compliance tensor which, as we previously indicated, will have the same zero components as does E_{mnpr}. Thus, according to Eq. (7.3.7), the absence of S_{3313} means that a stress component σ_{33} will not cause any shearing strain γ_{13}. This can be seen by looking at the x_1x_3-plane of Fig. 7.2. Since x_1 is perpendicular to x_3, these axes also can be labeled as y_1, y_3. From Fig. 7.3 it can be seen that a negative stress σ_{33} will not cause the lines of action of the springs to alter their orthogonal relationship; this means that γ_{13} is zero.

Conversely, the nonzero component S_{1211} means that a stress σ_{11} will cause a shear. This is evident in Fig. 7.4, where we can see that σ_{11} will cause changes in the angles between the lines of action of the springs.

The compounds di-potassium tartrate, $K_2(C_4H_4O_6) \cdot \frac{1}{2}H_2O$, and sodium thiosulfate, $Na_2S_2O_3$, are monoclinic materials.

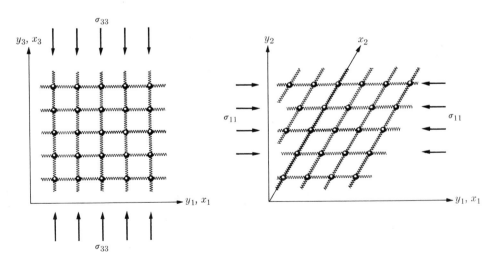

FIG. 7.3   Spring-ball model: x_1- and x_2-axes are perpendicular.

FIG. 7.4   Spring-ball model: x_1- and x_2-axes are not perpendicular.

7.4 ORTHOTROPIC MATERIAL: NINE CONSTANTS

An *orthotropic* material exhibits symmetry of its elastic properties with respect to two orthogonal planes, the y_1y_2- and y_2y_3-planes. (The spring-ball model shown in Fig. 7.5 now consists of axes which are mutually orthogonal, but which have different spring constants.) This symmetry is best expressed as an additional requirement, on a monoclinic material, that the constants of the previous section do not change under the following coordinate transformation:

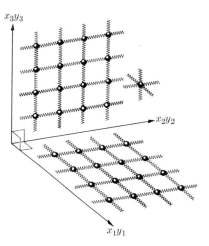

$$\tilde{y}_1 = -y_1,$$
$$\tilde{y}_2 = y_2, \qquad (7.4.1)$$
$$\tilde{y}_3 = y_3.$$

The direction cosines which correspond to Eq. (7.4.1) can be expressed as follows:

	y_1	y_2	y_3
$\tilde{y}_1$	-1	0	0
$\tilde{y}_2$	0	1	0
$\tilde{y}_3$	0	0	1

$(7.4.2)$

FIG. 7.5 Spring-ball model: x_1-, x_2-, and x_3-axes are mutually perpendicular.

As in Section 7.3, the application of the transformation law (Eq. 7.2.27) subject to the direction cosines given by Eq. (7.4.2) will lead to contradictions of the type shown in Eq. (7.3.5). These are resolved by setting the elastic constant equal to zero. For the orthotropic material, it is easily verified that the following constants, in addition to the ones shown in Eq. (7.3.6), must be zero:

$$E_{1112}, \quad E_{2212}, \quad E_{3312}, \quad E_{1323}. \qquad (7.4.3)$$

Thus an orthotropic material whose planes of symmetry are the y_1y_2- and y_2y_3-planes can be described by the following array of nine constants:

$$(E_{mnpr}) = \begin{pmatrix} E_{1111} & E_{1122} & E_{1133} & 0 & 0 & 0 \\ E_{1122} & E_{2222} & E_{2233} & 0 & 0 & 0 \\ E_{1133} & E_{2233} & E_{3333} & 0 & 0 & 0 \\ 0 & 0 & 0 & E_{1212} & 0 & 0 \\ 0 & 0 & 0 & 0 & E_{1313} & 0 \\ 0 & 0 & 0 & 0 & 0 & E_{2323} \end{pmatrix}. \qquad (7.4.4)$$

Note that since the y_n-axes coincide with the x_n-axes which are now orthogonal, normal stresses do not cause shearing strains, and shearing stresses do not cause extensional strains.

In the study of crystals, an orthotropic material is also called an ortho-rhombic material. An example of such a material is aragonite, $CaCO_3$, which has the following values for its elastic constants (in millions of pounds per square inch):

$$E_{1111} = 23.2, \qquad E_{1212} = 6.10, \qquad E_{1122} = 5.41,$$
$$E_{2222} = 12.6, \qquad E_{1313} = 3.71, \qquad E_{1133} = 0.25,$$
$$E_{3333} = 12.3, \qquad E_{2323} = 6.19, \qquad E_{2233} = 2.28.$$

Another example is topaz, $Al_2(F, OH)_2, SiO_4$:

$$E_{1111} = 40.1, \qquad E_{1212} = 15.7, \qquad E_{1122} = 18.3,$$
$$E_{2222} = 50.6, \qquad E_{1313} = 19.3, \qquad E_{1133} = 12.3,$$
$$E_{3333} = 42.8, \qquad E_{2323} = 19.0, \qquad E_{2233} = 12.8.$$

7.5   TETRAGONAL MATERIAL: SIX CONSTANTS

A *tetragonal* material is an orthotropic material which has the same properties along two of the axes but different properties along the third axis. For our purposes, the y_2- and y_3-axes will have the same properties. Then the additional requirement (beyond those needed for an orthotropic material) is that the elastic constants remain unchanged under a rotation of the y_2- and y_3-axes about the y_1-axis. This transformation is given by

$$\tilde{y}_1 = y_1, \qquad \tilde{y}_2 = y_3, \qquad \tilde{y}_3 = -y_2. \qquad (7.5.1)$$

The direction cosines may be expressed as

	y_1	y_2	y_3
$\tilde{y}_1$	1	0	0
$\tilde{y}_2$	0	0	1
$\tilde{y}_3$	0	-1	0

$$(7.5.2)$$

To preserve invariance under the transformation given by Eqs. (7.5.1), it is necessary to require that

$$E_{2222} = E_{3333}, \qquad\qquad\qquad (7.5.3)$$

$$E_{1122} = E_{1133}, \qquad\qquad\qquad (7.5.4)$$

$$E_{1212} = E_{1313}. \qquad\qquad\qquad (7.5.5)$$

Now there are only six independent constants:

$$(E_{mnpr}) = \begin{pmatrix} E_{1111} & E_{1122} & E_{1122} & 0 & 0 & 0 \\ E_{1122} & E_{2222} & E_{2233} & 0 & 0 & 0 \\ E_{1122} & E_{2233} & E_{2222} & 0 & 0 & 0 \\ 0 & 0 & 0 & E_{1212} & 0 & 0 \\ 0 & 0 & 0 & 0 & E_{1212} & 0 \\ 0 & 0 & 0 & 0 & 0 & E_{2323} \end{pmatrix}. \tag{7.5.6}$$

7.6 CUBIC MATERIAL: THREE CONSTANTS

The next step is to consider a material in which the properties are the same along three orthogonal directions. Such a material is known as a *cubic* material, and it can be considered as a tetragonal material with the additional constraint that invariance is preserved if the y_1- and y_2-axes are rotated 90° about the y_3-axis:

$$\tilde{y}_1 = y_2, \qquad \tilde{y}_2 = -y_1, \qquad \tilde{y}_3 = y_3. \tag{7.6.1}$$

The direction cosines are

	y_1	y_2	y_3
$\tilde{y}_1$	0	1	0
$\tilde{y}_2$	-1	0	0
$\tilde{y}_3$	0	0	1

$$\tag{7.6.2}$$

In order to preserve invariance under Eq. (7.6.1), it is necessary to require that

$$E_{1111} = E_{2222}, \tag{7.6.3}$$

$$E_{2233} = E_{1122}, \tag{7.6.4}$$

$$E_{2323} = E_{1212}. \tag{7.6.5}$$

Now there are only three independent constants:

$$(E_{mnpr}) = \begin{pmatrix} E_{1111} & E_{1122} & E_{1122} & 0 & 0 & 0 \\ E_{1122} & E_{1111} & E_{1122} & 0 & 0 & 0 \\ E_{1122} & E_{1122} & E_{1111} & 0 & 0 & 0 \\ 0 & 0 & 0 & E_{1212} & 0 & 0 \\ 0 & 0 & 0 & 0 & E_{1212} & 0 \\ 0 & 0 & 0 & 0 & 0 & E_{1212} \end{pmatrix}. \tag{7.6.6}$$

7.7 ISOTROPIC MATERIAL: TWO CONSTANTS

The simplest type of material is called an *isotropic* material; it possesses elastic properties independent of the orientation of the axes. If the cubic material is used as a starting point, then the additional constraint to show invariance is a rotation of the y_1- and y_2-axes through an angle of $45°$ about the y_3-axis. We arrive at the following equations:

$$\tilde{y}_1 = y_1 \cos 45° + y_2 \cos 45°,$$
$$\tilde{y}_2 = -y_1 \cos 45° + y_2 \cos 45°, \tag{7.7.1}$$
$$\tilde{y}_3 = y_3.$$

The direction cosines are

	y_1	y_2	y_3
$\tilde{y}_1$	$\sqrt{2}/2$	$\sqrt{2}/2$	0
$\tilde{y}_2$	$-\sqrt{2}/2$	$\sqrt{2}/2$	0
$\tilde{y}_3$	0	0	1

$$\tag{7.7.2}$$

The final requirement is found to be

$$E_{1212} = \tfrac{1}{2}(E_{1111} - E_{1122}). \tag{7.7.3}$$

It can now be verified that further coordinate transformations of any kind will not change the form of the stress-strain laws. Thus two constants are required to define the elasticity of an isotropic material.

The elastic constants for an isotropic material are usually written in the notation

$$E_{1122} = \lambda, \tag{7.7.4}$$
$$E_{1111} = \lambda + 2\mu, \tag{7.7.5}$$
$$E_{1212} = \mu. \tag{7.7.6}$$

The pair of constants λ and μ are called *Lamé's constants*, and μ is often referred to as the *shear modulus*.

The array of constants for an isotropic material is thus reduced to

$$(E_{mnpr}) = \begin{pmatrix} \lambda + 2\mu & \lambda & \lambda & 0 & 0 & 0 \\ \lambda & \lambda + 2\mu & \lambda & 0 & 0 & 0 \\ \lambda & \lambda & \lambda + 2\mu & 0 & 0 & 0 \\ 0 & 0 & 0 & \mu & 0 & 0 \\ 0 & 0 & 0 & 0 & \mu & 0 \\ 0 & 0 & 0 & 0 & 0 & \mu \end{pmatrix}. \tag{7.7.7}$$

The stress-strain relations for an isotropic material, when written out explicitly in terms of the elasticity tensor, have the following forms:

$$\sigma_{11} = 2\mu\gamma_{11} + \lambda(\gamma_{11} + \gamma_{22} + \gamma_{33}),\tag{7.7.8}$$

$$\sigma_{22} = 2\mu\gamma_{22} + \lambda(\gamma_{11} + \gamma_{22} + \gamma_{33}),\tag{7.7.9}$$

$$\sigma_{33} = 2\mu\gamma_{33} + \lambda(\gamma_{11} + \gamma_{22} + \gamma_{33}),\tag{7.7.10}$$

$$\sigma_{12} = 2\mu\gamma_{12},\tag{7.7.11}$$

$$\sigma_{13} = 2\mu\gamma_{13},\tag{7.7.12}$$

$$\sigma_{23} = 2\mu\gamma_{23}.\tag{7.7.13}$$

Note that these can be put into the compact tensor equation

$$\sigma_{mn} = 2\mu\gamma_{mn} + \lambda\delta_{mn}\gamma_{rr}.\tag{7.7.14}$$

The two independent elastic constants in the engineering terminology are E, *Young's modulus* or the *modulus of elasticity*, and ν, *Poisson's ratio*. Under uniaxial stress, say σ_{11}, the normal strain component γ_{11} is given by $\gamma_{11} = \sigma_{11}/E$, while the other two strain components, γ_{22} and γ_{33}, are given by

$$\gamma_{22} = -\nu\gamma_{11} = -\frac{\nu}{E}\sigma_{11},\tag{7.7.15}$$

$$\gamma_{33} = -\nu\gamma_{11} = -\frac{\nu}{E}\sigma_{11}.\tag{7.7.16}$$

The Poisson ratio thus is the ratio between the lateral contraction and the axial elongation under a uniaxial stress condition.

Under combined stresses σ_{11}, σ_{22}, and σ_{33} the three components of strain are given by superposition,

$$\gamma_{11} = \frac{1}{E}(\sigma_{11} - \nu\sigma_{22} - \nu\sigma_{33}),\tag{7.7.17}$$

$$\gamma_{22} = \frac{1}{E}(-\nu\sigma_{11} + \sigma_{22} - \nu\sigma_{33}),\tag{7.7.18}$$

$$\gamma_{33} = \frac{1}{E}(-\nu\sigma_{11} - \nu\sigma_{22} + \sigma_{33}).\tag{7.7.19}$$

These equations can be solved to yield expressions for stresses in terms of strains as follows:

$$\sigma_{11} = \frac{E}{(1+\nu)(1-2\nu)}[(1-\nu)\gamma_{11} + \nu\gamma_{22} + \nu\gamma_{33}],\tag{7.7.20}$$

$$\sigma_{22} = \frac{E}{(1+\nu)(1-2\nu)}[\nu\gamma_{11} + (1-\nu)\gamma_{22} + \nu\gamma_{33}],\tag{7.7.21}$$

$$\sigma_{33} = \frac{E}{(1+\nu)(1-2\nu)}[\nu\gamma_{11} + \nu\gamma_{22} + (1-\nu)\gamma_{33}].\tag{7.7.22}$$

By comparing the above expressions with Eqs. (7.7.8), (7.7.9), and (7.7.10) one can conclude that

$$\lambda = \frac{\nu E}{(1 + \nu)(1 - 2\nu)}, \tag{7.7.23}$$

and

$$\mu = \frac{E}{2(1 + \nu)}. \tag{7.7.24}$$

The relation between shear stress-strain relations can be written in terms of E and ν as follows:†

$$\gamma_{12} = \frac{1}{E}(1 + \nu)\sigma_{12}, \tag{7.7.25}$$

$$\gamma_{23} = \frac{1}{E}(1 + \nu)\sigma_{23}, \tag{7.7.26}$$

$$\gamma_{31} = \frac{1}{E}(1 + \nu)\sigma_{31}. \tag{7.7.27}$$

Note that Eqs. (7.7.20) through (7.7.22), and (7.7.25) through (7.7.27) can be put into the following compact form:

$$\gamma_{mn} = \frac{1}{E}[(1 + \nu)\sigma_{mn} - \nu\delta_{mn}\sigma_{rr}]. \tag{7.7.28}$$

Some forms of the stress-strain relations are of particular interest. Substituting the deviator and spherical tensors in Eq. (7.7.14) yields

$$\hat{\sigma}_{mn} + \hat{\sigma}_{mn} = \lambda\,\delta_{mn}(\hat{\gamma}_{rr} + \hat{\gamma}_{rr}) + 2\mu(\hat{\gamma}_{mn} + \hat{\gamma}_{mn}). \tag{7.7.29}$$

First (see Eq. 6.10.3), we find that the spherical stress $\hat{\sigma}_{mn}$ can be written as

$$\hat{\sigma}_{mn} = \tfrac{1}{3}\,\delta_{mn}\sigma_{rr}. \tag{7.7.30}$$

From Eqs. (7.7.8) through (7.7.10) we obtain

$$\sigma_{rr} = (2\mu + 3\lambda)\gamma_{rr}, \tag{7.7.31}$$

and from Eq. (5.12.3) we have

$$\tfrac{1}{3}\,\delta_{mn}\gamma_{rr} = \hat{\gamma}_{mn} \tag{7.7.32}$$

and

$$\gamma_{rr} = \hat{\gamma}_{rr}. \tag{7.7.33}$$

With these relations we can write Eq. (7.7.30) as

$$\hat{\sigma}_{mn} = \lambda\,\delta_{mn}\hat{\gamma}_{rr} + 2\mu\hat{\gamma}_{mn}. \tag{7.7.34}$$

---

† In conventional engineering notation (see Section 5.5) the shear stress-strain relations are usually expressed as $\gamma_{xy} = \tau_{xy}/G$, $\gamma_{yz} = \tau_{yz}/G$, $\gamma_{zz} = \tau_{zz}/G$, where G is called the shear modulus. The symbol τ is used to denote the shear stresses. It is seen that $G = E/2(1 + \nu) = \mu$.

It is now clear that Eq. (7.7.29) can be split into two equations, the one above, and the corresponding one for the deviator component,

$$\hat{\sigma}_{mn} = \lambda\, \delta_{mn} \hat{\gamma}_{rr} + 2\mu \hat{\gamma}_{mn}. \tag{7.7.35}$$

In Eq. (7.7.35) it is observed that the dilatation $\hat{\gamma}_{rr}$, associated with the deviator strain, is zero, and hence the relations between deviator stresses and strains become

$$\hat{\sigma}_{mn} = 2\mu \hat{\gamma}_{mn}. \tag{7.7.36}$$

The stress-strain relations, Eq. (7.7.34), between the spherical stress and strain tensors are in actuality only one relation because there is only one non-zero value of the spherical components [see Eqs. (5.14.15b) and (6.10.5)]. Thus, Eq. (7.7.34) can be replaced by

$$\hat{\sigma}_{rr} = 3K \hat{\gamma}_{rr}, \tag{7.7.37}$$

where the constant K is called the *bulk modulus*, and is related to the Lamé constants by

$$K = \frac{3\lambda + 2\mu}{3}. \tag{7.7.38}$$

The bulk modulus can be shown to be the ratio of a hydrostatic pressure, Δp, and the resulting dilatation,

$$K = -\frac{\Delta p}{(dV - dV^{(0)})/dV^{(0)}} = -\frac{\Delta p}{J_1}. \tag{7.7.39}$$

A special form of the stress-strain relations can be obtained by substituting the definitions for the deviator components [see Eqs. (5.12.2) and (6.10.2)] into Eq. (7.7.32). We obtain

$$\gamma_{mn} = \frac{1}{2\mu}[\sigma_{mn} - \tfrac{1}{3}\delta_{mn}\sigma_{rr}] + \frac{1}{9K}\delta_{mn}\sigma_{rr}. \tag{7.7.40}$$

7.8   THERMOELASTIC STRESS-STRAIN RELATION

Adding the effect of temperature changes to the stress-strain relations is accomplished in a straightforward fashion for a material that is thermodynamically as well as elastically isotropic. A thermodynamically isotropic material is one in which the expansion caused by a change in temperature is the same in all directions. It is an experimentally observed fact that a body which is stress free will experience relative elongations E_n, but no angular changes ϕ_{nm}, due to an increase or decrease in temperature. Let α signify the coefficient of thermal expansion with dimensions of $(T)^{-1}$, where T is temperature measured in any scale. For most materials the relative elongations are small compared to unity, even for temperature changes approaching the melting point. Thus we can write

$$\gamma_{mn}^{(T)} = \alpha\, \Delta T\, \delta_{mn}, \tag{7.8.1}$$

where $\gamma_{mn}^{(T)}$ represents the thermally induced strains and ΔT represents the change in temperature from some reference state. This thermally induced strain can be superimposed on the stress-induced strains provided the reference temperature is the temperature at which the body is stress free. In addition, we assume that the application of stress by itself will not cause appreciable changes in temperature. For thermoelastic problems, then, the constitutive relation of Eq. (7.7.28) is replaced by

$$\gamma_{mn} = \frac{1}{E}[(1 + \nu)\sigma_{mn} - \nu\,\delta_{mn}\sigma_{rr}] + \alpha\,\delta_{mn}\,\Delta T. \qquad (7.8.2)$$

The individual relations are

$$\gamma_{11} = \frac{1}{E}[\sigma_{11} - \nu(\sigma_{22} + \sigma_{33})] + \alpha\,\Delta T, \qquad (7.8.3)$$

$$\gamma_{22} = \frac{1}{E}[\sigma_{22} - \nu(\sigma_{33} + \sigma_{11})] + \alpha\,\Delta T, \qquad (7.8.4)$$

$$\gamma_{33} = \frac{1}{E}[\sigma_{33} - \nu(\sigma_{11} + \sigma_{22})] + \alpha\,\Delta T, \qquad (7.8.5)$$

$$\gamma_{12} = \frac{1}{E}(1 + \nu)\sigma_{12}, \qquad (7.8.6)$$

$$\gamma_{23} = \frac{1}{E}(1 + \nu)\sigma_{23}, \qquad (7.8.7)$$

$$\gamma_{31} = \frac{1}{E}(1 + \nu)\sigma_{31}. \qquad (7.8.8)$$

The inverse relationships are obtained by considering Eqs. (7.8.3) through (7.8.8) as a set of simultaneous equations for σ_{mn}. We obtain

$$\sigma_{mn} = 2\mu\gamma_{mn} + \lambda\,\delta_{mn}\gamma_{rr} - (3\lambda + 2\mu)\,\delta_{mn}\alpha\,\Delta T. \qquad (7.8.9)$$

The individual relations are

$$\sigma_{11} = 2\mu\gamma_{11} + \lambda(\gamma_{11} + \gamma_{22} + \gamma_{33}) - \frac{E}{1 - 2\nu}\alpha\,\Delta T, \qquad (7.8.10)$$

$$\sigma_{22} = 2\mu\gamma_{22} + \lambda(\gamma_{11} + \gamma_{22} + \gamma_{33}) - \frac{E}{1 - 2\nu}\alpha\,\Delta T, \qquad (7.8.11)$$

$$\sigma_{33} = 2\mu\gamma_{33} + \lambda(\gamma_{11} + \gamma_{22} + \gamma_{33}) - \frac{E}{1 - 2\nu}\alpha\,\Delta T, \qquad (7.8.12)$$

$$\sigma_{12} = 2\mu\gamma_{12}, \qquad (7.8.13)$$

$$\sigma_{23} = 2\mu\gamma_{23}, \qquad (7.8.14)$$

$$\sigma_{31} = 2\mu\gamma_{31}. \qquad (7.8.15)$$

We observe from an examination of Eqs. (7.8.10) through (7.8.15) that if a small cube of material, so restrained that changes in length are not possible, is heated uniformly to a temperature of $T + \Delta T$, the following thermal stresses will be induced:

$$\sigma_{11}^{(T)} = -\frac{E}{1 - 2\nu} \alpha \Delta T,$$ (7.8.16)

$$\sigma_{22}^{(T)} = -\frac{E}{1 - 2\nu} \alpha \Delta T,$$ (7.8.17)

$$\sigma_{33}^{(T)} = -\frac{E}{1 - 2\nu} \alpha \Delta T.$$ (7.8.18)

7.9 ELASTIC CONSTANTS FOR SOME MATERIALS OF ENGINEERING INTEREST

There are shown in Tables 7.1 and 7.2 the elastic constants of a few materials in their elemental single crystalline state. Some of the metals most useful to our civilization are included. Note that these are all members of the hexagonal or cubic crystal systems.

(a) Hexagonal system. Some common materials belong to the hexagonal class. Their elastic properties can be described by the following array of five constants:

$$(E_{mnpr}) = \begin{pmatrix} E_{1111} & E_{1122} & E_{1133} & 0 & 0 & 0 \\ E_{1122} & E_{1111} & E_{1133} & 0 & 0 & 0 \\ E_{1133} & E_{1133} & E_{3333} & 0 & 0 & 0 \\ 0 & 0 & 0 & \frac{1}{2}(E_{1111} - E_{1122}) & 0 & 0 \\ 0 & 0 & 0 & 0 & E_{1313} & 0 \\ 0 & 0 & 0 & 0 & 0 & E_{1313} \end{pmatrix}.$$

Table 7.1 lists the five constants for four of these materials.

TABLE 7.1 *Elastic Constants of Some Hexagonal Crystals*

Material[a]	E_{1111}	E_{3333}	E_{1122}	E_{1133}	E_{1313}
Beryllium	40.7	43.8	−3.62	–	22.5
Magnesium	8.66	8.95	3.80	3.14	2.38
Zinc	23.4	8.85	4.96	7.26	5.55
Ice	2.01	2.17	1.03	0.844	0.463

[a] Multiply values by 10^6 to obtain results in lb/in^2.

TABLE 7.2   *Elastic Constants of Some Cubic Crystals*

Material[a]	E_{1111}	E_{1122}	E_{1212}
Aluminum	15.7	8.89	4.13
Copper	24.4	17.6	10.9
Iron	29.0	15.7	16.8
Molybdenum	66.7	25.3	16.0
Nickel	35.7	21.4	18.1
Tungsten	72.7	28.7	22.0

[a] Multiply values by 10^6 to obtain results in lb/in^2.

TABLE 7.3   *Elementary Properties of Some Materials in Polycrystalline Form*

MATERIAL	$\alpha \times 10^6$ per °F	$E \times 10^{-6}$ psi	ρ lb/in³	$(E/\rho) \times 10^{-6}$ in.
Aluminum (2024–T3)	13.0	10.5	0.100	105
Beryllium	6.9	36.8	.066	558
Boron	8.3	55.0	.085	648
Brass[a]	10.6	13.1	.309	42.4
Bronze	11.1	14.5	.318	45.6
Chromium	3.8	36.0	.239	151
Concrete[b]	6.0	3.4	.090	37.8
Copper[a]	7.8	18.1	.321	56.4
Douglas fir[c]	3.0	1.9	.0208	91.4
Glass	4.0	9.4	.093	101
Gun metal	10.2	10.0	.317	31.6
Magnesium (AZ61A)	16.0	6.5	.065	100
Molybdenum	2.7	42.7	.326	131
Nickel	7.2	30.0	.316	95
Polyethylene	170	1.9	.033	57.6
Steel (SAE 4130)	6.5	29.0	.283	103
Titanium	6.0	17.0	.163	104
Tungsten	2.4	51.5	.680	75.8
Zinc[a]	14.7	13.1	.260	50.4

[a] Cold-rolled; [b] typical medium-strength concrete; [c] with the grain.

(b) Cubic system. Some other common materials belong to the cubic class. Their elastic properties are described by the array of constants in Section 7.6. Table 7.2 lists the three constants for six of these materials.

In order to obtain the values shown in Tables 7.1 and 7.2, single crystals of the material had to be grown. This is a laboratory process. In their useful form as found in structures, the metals are polycrystalline and on a macroscopic scale can be considered as isotropic materials. Shown in Table 7.3 are the isotropic elastic properties of a number of useful materials. Also shown are the coefficients of thermal expansion, the weight densities, and an elasticity efficiency factor E/ρ. This latter number is a measure of the weight of material required to attain a certain level of stiffness; the material with the larger number is deemed more efficient in this regard. Note that the common structural materials (aluminum, magnesium, steel and titanium) used in flight vehicles all have about the same value of E/ρ. The tantalizing promise of beryllium and boron are shown by their extremely large values. Of interest, also, is the fact that glass is the equal of most metals in this respect.

7.10 STRAIN ENERGY

The forces which are applied to a structure will perform work on the structure, since the points of application of the forces will undergo motion as the structure suffers distortions. In general, the change in temperature of most engineering materials due to deformation is negligibly small, and the assumption of isothermal behavior can be made. Then, the First Law of Thermodynamics states that the work done by the external forces results in an increase in the internal energy of the structure. In the theory of elasticity, the increase in internal energy is called the *strain energy*, and is denoted by U_i.

A simple example will suffice to reveal the mathematical form of the strain energy. Consider a member of length L which is in a uniaxial state of stress under the action of a total load P uniformly distributed over the free end (see Fig. 7.6). The state of stress in the bar is characterized by σ_{11} alone, and the state of deformation by γ_{11}, $\gamma_{22} = -\nu\gamma_{11}$ and $\gamma_{33} = -\nu\gamma_{11}$ (see Eqs. 7.7.15 and 7.7.16). As the load is gradually increased to its final magnitude of P, the end of the bar, which is the point of application of the load, will extend by the value of ΔL. A linear relationship (see Section 7.2) between stress and strain, and hence between load and deflection, is assumed. Thus the work done by the force P is

$$W = \tfrac{1}{2}P\,\Delta L. \tag{7.10.1}$$

An element of volume in the bar experiences an increase in the state of stress to a final value $\sigma_{11} = P/A$. On the planes which experience a stress, σ_{11}, there is a corresponding deformation characterized by γ_{11}. The relationship between σ_{11} and γ_{11} is linear, and is represented in Fig. 7.7. The strain energy due to

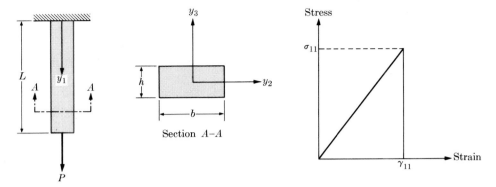

FIG. 7.6   Prismatic bar under uniaxial tension.   FIG. 7.7   Diagram of linear stress-strain relation.

this uniaxial state of stress is given by the following expression:

$$U = \int_0^L \int_{-b/2}^{b/2} \int_{-h/2}^{h/2} \tfrac{1}{2}\sigma_{11}\gamma_{11}\, dy_1\, dy_2\, dy_3. \qquad (7.10.2)$$

Thus the strain energy per unit of volume is proportional to the area under the stress-strain curve of Fig. 7.7.

In a similar fashion, the strain energy stored per unit of volume in a structure which experiences a general state of stress and strain is given by

$$U^* = \tfrac{1}{2}\sigma_{mn}\gamma_{mn}, \qquad (7.10.3)$$

where the * indicates that U^* is a strain-energy density. Note that there are nine terms in Eq. (7.10.3). The total strain energy in a body is

$$U = \iiint U^*\, dy_1\, dy_2\, dy_3 = \iiint \tfrac{1}{2}\sigma_{mn}\gamma_{mn}\, dy_1\, dy_2\, dy_3. \qquad (7.10.4)$$

There are several alternative forms of Eq. (7.10.3). The strain tensor γ_{mn} can be eliminated by substitution of the pertinent stress relation (see Eq. 7.7.28). The result is

$$U^* = (1/2E)[(1 + \nu)\sigma_{mn}\sigma_{mn} - \nu(\sigma_{rr})^2]. \qquad (7.10.5)$$

In explicit detail, Eq. (7.10.5) has the form

$$U^* = (1/2E)[(\sigma_{11}^2 + \sigma_{22}^2 + \sigma_{33}^2) - 2\nu(\sigma_{11}\sigma_{22} + \sigma_{22}\sigma_{33} + \sigma_{33}\sigma_{11})$$
$$+ 2(1 + \nu)(\sigma_{12}^2 + \sigma_{23}^2 + \sigma_{31}^2)]. \qquad (7.10.6)$$

The strain energy can also be expressed solely in terms of the strains. If Eq. (7.7.14) is employed as the stress-strain relation, we find that

$$U^* = \tfrac{1}{2}\lambda(\gamma_{rr})^2 + \mu\gamma_{mn}\gamma_{mn}. \qquad (7.10.7)$$

In explicit detail, Eq. (7.10.7) has the form

$$U^* = \tfrac{1}{2}\lambda(\gamma_{11} + \gamma_{22} + \gamma_{33})^2 + \mu(\gamma_{11}^2 + \gamma_{22}^2 + \gamma_{33}^2) + 2\mu(\gamma_{12}^2 + \gamma_{23}^2 + \gamma_{31}^2).$$

$$(7.10.8)$$

It is also of interest to present the strain-energy density in a form based on the stress-strain relation, Eq. (7.7.40). If we substitute this equation in Eq. (7.10.3), we get

$$U^* = \frac{1}{4\mu}\left[\sigma_{mn}\sigma_{mn} - \tfrac{1}{3}(\sigma_{rr})^2\right] + \frac{1}{18K}(\sigma_{rr})^2. \qquad (7.10.9)$$

We sometimes need to calculate the strain energies associated with the deviator and spherical components of the stress and strain tensors. The energy associated with the deviator components is called the *energy of distortion*, because there is no volume change associated with the deviator strains. The energy of distortion per unit volume is designated by $\hat{U}^*$, and is defined as

$$\hat{U}^* = \tfrac{1}{2}\hat{\sigma}_{mn}\hat{\gamma}_{mn}, \qquad (7.10.10)$$

and in terms of the stresses can be found by substituting Eqs. (5.12.2) and (6.10.2) into Eqs. (7.10.10):

$$\hat{U}^* = \frac{1}{4\mu}\left[\sigma_{mn}\sigma_{mn} - \tfrac{1}{3}(\sigma_{rr})^2\right]. \qquad (7.10.11)$$

Similarly, the energy associated with the spherical components is called the *energy of dilatation* because the entire volume change associated with a given state of infinitesimal strain is contained in the spherical component. The energy of dilatation per unit volume is designated by $\check{U}^*$, and is defined as

$$\check{U}^* = \tfrac{1}{2}\check{\sigma}_{mn}\check{\gamma}_{mn}. \qquad (7.10.12)$$

This equation can be put into the form

$$\check{U}^* = \frac{1}{18K}(\sigma_{rr})^2. \qquad (7.10.13)$$

It should be pointed out that the result,

$$U^* = \hat{U}^* + \check{U}^*, \qquad (7.10.14)$$

is a most convenient, albeit a totally unexpected one. In general, however,

$$U^*(\sigma) \neq U^*(\sigma_a) + U^*(\sigma_b), \qquad (7.10.15)$$

where

$$\dot{\sigma} = \sigma_a + \sigma_b. \qquad (7.10.16)$$

That is, the total strain energy associated with a stress σ is not the sum of the energies associated with an arbitrary partitioning of the stress.

7.11 SUMMARY: ISOTROPIC STRESS-STRAIN LAW AND ENERGY RELATIONS

The stress-strain laws derived in this chapter, as well as the energy relations, are restricted to the case of small strain. Nowhere has it been necessary to bring in the strain-displacement relations; hence the geometrical nonlinearities due to the presence of appreciable rotations have played no part in the formulation. Thus, in a certain sense, the stress-strain and energy relations are more general than the equilibrium equations derived in Chapter 6, since the latter are based on linear strain, i.e., on negligible rotations. It is, however, only a short step from the energy relations to equilibrium equations which do account for rotations, and that is the reason for not immediately going to the case of linear strain. At this stage of our study in solid mechanics, there is only a notational difference between the relations summarized in this section and those in the following section which will deal with linear elasticity.

We will not summarize all the various types of materials, but merely those pertaining to isotropic materials.

Stress-strain relations—elasticity tensor form

$$\sigma_{mn} = 2\mu\gamma_{mn} + \lambda\,\delta_{mn}\gamma_{rr} - (3\lambda + 2\mu)\,\delta_{mn}\alpha\,\Delta T, \tag{7.11.1}$$

$$\sigma_{11} = 2\mu\gamma_{11} + \lambda(\gamma_{11} + \gamma_{22} + \gamma_{33}) - \frac{E}{1 - 2\nu}\,\alpha\,\Delta T, \tag{7.11.2}$$

$$\sigma_{22} = 2\mu\gamma_{22} + \lambda(\gamma_{11} + \gamma_{22} + \gamma_{33}) - \frac{E}{1 - 2\nu}\,\alpha\,\Delta T, \tag{7.11.3}$$

$$\sigma_{33} = 2\mu\gamma_{33} + \lambda(\gamma_{11} + \gamma_{22} + \gamma_{33}) - \frac{E}{1 - 2\nu}\,\alpha\,\Delta T, \tag{7.11.4}$$

$$\sigma_{12} = 2\mu\gamma_{12}, \tag{7.11.5}$$

$$\sigma_{23} = 2\mu\gamma_{23}, \tag{7.11.6}$$

$$\sigma_{31} = 2\mu\gamma_{31}. \tag{7.11.7}$$

Stress-strain relations—compliance tensor form

$$\gamma_{mn} = (1/E)\,[(1 + \nu)\sigma_{mn} - \nu\,\delta_{mn}\sigma_{rr}] + \alpha\,\delta_{mn}\,\Delta T, \tag{7.11.8}$$

$$\gamma_{11} = (1/E)\,[\sigma_{11} - \nu\sigma_{22} - \nu\sigma_{33}] + \alpha\,\Delta T, \tag{7.11.9}$$

$$\gamma_{22} = (1/E)\,[-\nu\sigma_{11} + \sigma_{22} - \nu\sigma_{33}] + \alpha\,\Delta T, \tag{7.11.10}$$

$$\gamma_{33} = (1/E)\,[-\nu\sigma_{11} - \nu\sigma_{22} + \sigma_{33}] + \alpha\,\Delta T, \tag{7.11.11}$$

$$\gamma_{12} = \frac{1 + \nu}{E}\,\sigma_{12}, \tag{7.11.12}$$

$$\gamma_{23} = \frac{1 + \nu}{E}\,\sigma_{23}, \tag{7.11.13}$$

$$\gamma_{31} = \frac{1 + \nu}{E}\,\sigma_{31}. \tag{7.11.14}$$

Special forms for deviator and spherical components

$$\hat{\sigma}_{mn} = 2\mu\hat{\gamma}_{mn}, \tag{7.11.15}$$

$$\hat{\sigma}_{rr} = 3K\hat{\gamma}_{rr}. \tag{7.11.16}$$

Stress-strain relations in terms of μ and K

$$\gamma_{mn} = \frac{1}{2\mu}\left[\sigma_{mn} - \tfrac{1}{3}\,\delta_{mn}\sigma_{rr}\right] + \frac{1}{9K}\,\delta_{mn}\sigma_{rr}. \tag{7.11.17}$$

Relations between various elastic constants

$$\lambda = \frac{\nu E}{(1+\nu)(1-2\nu)}, \tag{7.11.18}$$

$$\mu = \frac{E}{2(1+\nu)}, \tag{7.11.19}$$

$$K = \frac{3\lambda + 2\mu}{3}, \tag{7.11.20}$$

$$3\lambda + 2\mu = \frac{E}{1-2\nu}. \tag{7.11.21}$$

Various forms of strain energy densities

$$U^* = \tfrac{1}{2}\sigma_{mn}\gamma_{mn}, \tag{7.11.22}$$

$$U^* = \frac{1}{2E}\left[(1+\nu)\sigma_{mn}\sigma_{mn} - \nu(\sigma_{rr})^2\right], \tag{7.11.23}$$

$$U^* = \frac{1}{2E}\left[(\sigma_{11}^2 + \sigma_{22}^2 + \sigma_{33}^2) - 2\nu(\sigma_{11}\sigma_{22} + \sigma_{22}\sigma_{33} + \sigma_{33}\sigma_{11})\right. $$
$$\left. + (1+\nu)(\sigma_{12}^2 + \sigma_{23}^2 + \sigma_{31}^2)\right], \tag{7.11.24}$$

$$U^* = \tfrac{1}{2}\lambda(\gamma_{rr})^2 + \mu\gamma_{mn}\gamma_{mn}, \tag{7.11.25}$$

$$U^* = \tfrac{1}{2}[\lambda(\gamma_{11} + \gamma_{22} + \gamma_{33})^2 + \mu(\gamma_{11}^2 + \gamma_{22}^2 + \gamma_{33}^2)$$
$$+ 2\mu(\gamma_{12}^2 + \gamma_{23}^2 + \gamma_{31}^2)], \tag{7.11.26}$$

$$U^* = \frac{1}{4\mu}\left[\sigma_{mn}\sigma_{mn} - \tfrac{1}{3}(\sigma_{rr})^2\right] + \frac{1}{18K}(\sigma_{rr})^2. \tag{7.11.27}$$

Distortion energy density

$$\hat{U}^* = \frac{1}{4\mu}\left[\sigma_{mn}\sigma_{mn} - \tfrac{1}{3}(\sigma_{rr})^2\right]. \tag{7.11.28}$$

Dilatation energy density

$$\hat{U}^* = \frac{1}{18K}(\sigma_{rr})^2. \tag{7.11.29}$$

7.12 SUMMARY: THE EQUATIONS OF LINEAR ELASTICITY

We are now in a position to summarize the equations of the linear theory of elasticity. The unknown quantities are the linear strain tensor, ϵ_{mn}, the displacement tensor, u_m, and the stress tensor, σ_{mn}. These tensors are a function of the coordinates y_1, y_2, y_3 of the structure. Their tensor properties are denoted by the following transformation laws:

$$\tilde{\epsilon}_{mn}(\tilde{y}_1, \tilde{y}_2, \tilde{y}_3) = \epsilon_{rs}(y_1, y_2, y_3) l_{r\tilde{m}} l_{s\tilde{n}}, \tag{7.12.1}$$

$$\tilde{u}_m(\tilde{y}_1, \tilde{y}_2, \tilde{y}_3) = u_r(y_1, y_2, y_3) l_{\tilde{m}r}, \tag{7.12.2}$$

$$\tilde{\sigma}_{mn}(\tilde{y}_1, \tilde{y}_2, \tilde{y}_3) = \sigma_{rs}(y_1, y_2, y_3) l_{\tilde{m}r} l_{\tilde{n}s}. \tag{7.12.3}$$

The objective of solid mechanics is the complete specification of these three tensors throughout any given structure under a prescribed loading condition and/or a geometrical boundary condition. The equations which govern the behavior of ϵ_{mn}, u_m, and σ_{mn} are as follows:

Linear strain-displacement relations

$$\epsilon_{mn} = \frac{1}{2}\left(\frac{\partial u_m}{\partial y_n} + \frac{\partial u_n}{\partial y_m}\right). \tag{7.12.4}$$

Force equilibrium equations for linear strains

$$\frac{\partial \sigma_{mn}}{\partial y_m} + F_n = 0. \tag{7.12.5}$$

Constitutive relations for anisotropic materials (without temperature changes)

$$\sigma_{mn} = E_{mnpr}\epsilon_{pr}, \tag{7.12.6}$$

$$\epsilon_{pr} = S_{mnpr}\sigma_{pr}. \tag{7.12.7}$$

These last relations, which are different forms of the generalized Hooke's law, introduce the elasticity tensor E_{mnpr} and the compliance tensor S_{mnpr}. The components of the elasticity tensor are a property of the material, and are determined experimentally. Since most of the high-strength engineering materials are isotropic, the bulk of the literature in solid mechanics is devoted to this class of materials. The number of independent components of the elasticity tensor reduces to two for isotropy, and Eqs. (7.12.6) and (7.12.7) become much simpler.

The *stress-strain relations* for isotropic materials with changes in temperature are

$$\epsilon_{mn} = \frac{1}{E}\left[(1 + \nu)\sigma_{mn} - \nu\,\delta_{mn}\sigma_{rr}\right] + \alpha\,\delta_{mn}\,\Delta T, \tag{7.12.8}$$

or alternatively,

$$\sigma_{mn} = 2\mu\epsilon_{mn} + \lambda\delta_{mn}\epsilon_{rr} - (3\lambda + 2\mu)\,\delta_{mn}\alpha\,\Delta T, \qquad (7.12.9)$$

where

$$\alpha = \text{Coefficient of thermal expansion,}$$
$$E = \text{Young's modulus,}$$
$$\nu = \text{Poisson's ratio,}$$

$$\mu = \frac{E}{2(1 + \nu)}, \qquad (7.12.10)$$

$$\lambda = \frac{\nu E}{(1 + \nu)(1 - 2\nu)}. \qquad (7.12.11)$$

The *boundary conditions* which Eqs. (7.12.4), (7.12.5), and either (7.12.8) or (7.12.9) must satisfy are of two types:

(a) *Geometric constraints on a region A_1 of the surface.* These mean the prescription of

$$\mathbf{u} = \mathbf{u}^*, \qquad (7.12.12)$$

where $\mathbf{u}^*$ is a prescribed displacement. At the points of support the boundary displacements are zero.

(b) *Applied surface loads on a region A_2 of the surface.* This specification means that the interior stresses in region A_2 must be in equilibrium with the externally applied surface loads. This restriction is expressed as

$$\sigma_{mn}n_m\mathbf{i}_n = \boldsymbol{\sigma}^*, \qquad (7.12.13)$$

where $\boldsymbol{\sigma}^*$ is the prescribed stress vector acting on region A_2.

We note that there are a total of fifteen unknowns, consisting of six components of the strain tensor, three components of the displacement tensor, and six components of the stress tensor. Balancing these unknowns are fifteen equations consisting of three equations of equilibrium, six strain-displacement relations, and six stress-strain relations. A remark should be made here concerning the six strain-displacement relations. We have shown in Section 5.13 that the six strain-displacement relations for linear strain also lead to a set of six compatibility relations between the components of the strain:

$$\frac{\partial^2 \epsilon_{nk}}{\partial y_m\,\partial y_l} + \frac{\partial^2 \epsilon_{ml}}{\partial y_n\,\partial y_k} - \frac{\partial^2 \epsilon_{nl}}{\partial y_m\,\partial y_k} - \frac{\partial^2 \epsilon_{mk}}{\partial y_n\,\partial y_l} = 0. \qquad (7.12.14)$$

Thus instead of using the strain-displacement relations one may verify the efficacy of a solution for the strain components by determining whether the compatibility equations are satisfied. However, Eqs. (7.12.4) must be employed in order to determine the displacements of the body.

The exact solution of the complete set of equations has not been accomplished except for a very few simple cases. The real challenge of solid mechanics to the engineer lies, then, in devising suitably accurate approximate solutions. Great ingenuity is required, first to construct a suitable mathematical model of the structure, and second, to solve the simplified equations which describe the mathematical model. Finally, engineering judgment is required to evaluate the validity of the analysis in the light of past experience and new experiments.

Our further studies in solid mechanics will be devoted to the solutions of the equations of elasticity. There are many different mathematical tools which can be used, and these range over a broad spectrum of mathematics from numerical analysis through the calculus of variations to the complex variable. The development of these analytical tools and their application to elasticity is a fascinating experience.

7.13 SIMPLE EXAMPLES OF SOLUTIONS FOR EQUATIONS OF ELASTICITY

As we have observed, for a solid of general geometry and arbitrary boundary conditions it is not possible to obtain a close solution of the fifteen equations of elasticity and the corresponding boundary conditions listed in the preceding section. For some important structural components of simplified geometry and loading, however, the number of equations can be reduced. Here for purposes of illustration we will present two simple examples for which the fifteen equations are satisfied. In addition we will derive the expressions of strain energy for the simple structural elements.

(a) Tension of a prismatic bar. Let us consider a uniform prismatic bar under uniform tension stress, as shown in Fig. 7.8. If body forces are not present, the equations of equilibrium (Eq. 7.12.5) are satisfied by the following components of stress:

$$\sigma_{11} = S = \text{Constant},$$
$$\sigma_{22} = \sigma_{33} = \sigma_{12} = \sigma_{23} = \sigma_{31} = 0. \tag{7.13.1}$$

It is seen that the lateral surface around the bar is free of stress. Since all stress

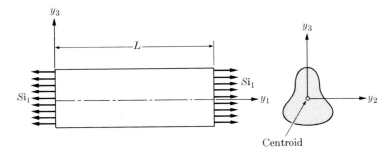

FIG. 7.8   Prismatic bar under uniaxial stress.

components except σ_{11} are zero, the boundary conditions given by Eq. (7.12.13) are satisfied. At the two ends, however, the boundary condition requires that the prescribed boundary stress vector $\boldsymbol{\sigma}^*$ be given by the normal stress $S i_1$.

Assuming that the material is isotropic, we can calculate the state of strain using Eq. (7.12.8). The result is

$$\epsilon_{11} = \sigma_{11}/E,$$
$$\epsilon_{22} = \epsilon_{33} = -\nu\sigma_{11}/E,$$
$$\epsilon_{12} = \epsilon_{23} = \epsilon_{31} = 0. \tag{7.13.2}$$

It is obvious that all the compatibility relations (7.12.14) are satisfied, since all strain components are constants. The strain-energy density U^* is simply [from Eq. (7.10.3)]

$$U^* = (1/2)\sigma_{11}\epsilon_{11}, \tag{7.13.3}$$

which can be written as either

$$U^* = (1/2E)\sigma_{11}^2, \tag{7.13.4}$$

or

$$U^* = (E/2)\epsilon_{11}^2. \tag{7.13.5}$$

For a bar of cross-sectional area A, length L, and total axial force P, we have

$$\sigma_{11} = P/A, \tag{7.13.6}$$

and hence the total strain energy in the bar is

$$U = \iiint U^* \, dV = P^2 L/2AE. \tag{7.13.7}$$

If the elongation of the bar is Δ, we have

$$\epsilon_{11} = \Delta/L, \tag{7.13.8}$$

and

$$U = AE\Delta^2/2L. \tag{7.13.9}$$

(b) Pure bending of a uniform beam. Consider a uniform beam bent in its plane of symmetry by two equal and opposite bending moments M, as shown in Fig. 7.9. Let the y_1-axis lie along the centroid of the cross section. The bending moment as shown is about the y_2-axis. According to elementary bending theory the stress components are given by

$$\sigma_{11} = Cy_3,$$
$$\sigma_{22} = \sigma_{33} = \sigma_{12} = \sigma_{23} = \sigma_{31} = 0, \tag{7.13.10}$$

where C is a constant.

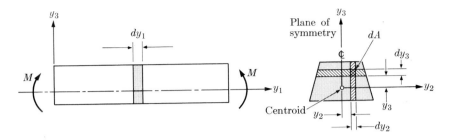

Fɪɢ. 7.9 Prismatic bar under pure bending.

We see that all the equations of equilibrium, Eq. (7.12.5), and the boundary conditions, Eq. (7.12.13), for the surface around the beam are satisfied. At the two ends of the beam the boundary condition requires that the prescribed boundary stress vector $\boldsymbol{\sigma}^*$ should consist only of normal stresses, $\sigma_{11}^* \mathbf{i}_1$. The variation of σ_{11}^* is also given by Cy_3, that is, it must be directly proportional to the distance from the y_2-axis. Since the prescribed boundary stresses σ_{11}^* must be equipollent to the applied bending moment M, we have

$$M = - \iint \sigma_{11}^* y_3 \, dA = - C \iint y_3^2 \, dA = -IC, \qquad (7.13.11)$$

where I is the cross-sectional moment of inertia with respect to the y_2-axis: $I = \iint y_3^2 \, dA$. In order to satisfy the other conditions of equilibrium we need to verify that the resulting axial force and moment about the y_3-axis are zero. This is indeed true:

$$\iint \sigma_{11}^* \, dA = C \iint y_3 \, dA = 0, \qquad (7.13.12)$$

and

$$\iint \sigma_{11}^* y_2 \, dy_2 \, dy_3 = C \iint y_2 y_3 \, dy_2 \, dy_3 = 0, \qquad (7.13.13)$$

because the y_2-axis passes through the centroid, and y_3 is the axis of symmetry of the cross section. We can now determine the constant C from Eq. (7.13.11),

$$C = -M/I, \qquad (7.13.14)$$

and substitute this value in Eq. (7.13.10).

$$\sigma_{11} = -My_3/I. \qquad (7.13.15)$$

For an isotropic material the strain components are given by

$$\epsilon_{11} = -My_3/EI, \qquad (7.13.16)$$

$$\epsilon_{22} = \epsilon_{33} = \nu My_3/EI, \qquad (7.13.17)$$

$$\epsilon_{12} = \epsilon_{23} = \epsilon_{31} = 0. \qquad (7.13.18)$$

The six compatibility equations are then satisfied, because the strain components are either zero or of only a first power in y_3.

Let us now consider the displacement of the beam under the condition of pure bending. The strain-displacement relations Eq. (7.12.4) yield the following differential equations:

$$\frac{\partial u_1}{\partial y_1} = \epsilon_{11} = -\frac{My_3}{EI},$$ (7.13.19)

$$\frac{\partial u_2}{\partial y_2} = \epsilon_{22} = \nu\frac{My_3}{EI},$$ (7.13.20)

$$\frac{\partial u_3}{\partial y_3} = \epsilon_{33} = \nu\frac{My_3}{EI},$$ (7.13.21)

$$\frac{1}{2}\left(\frac{\partial u_1}{\partial y_2} + \frac{\partial u_2}{\partial y_1}\right) = \epsilon_{12} = 0,$$ (7.13.22)

$$\frac{1}{2}\left(\frac{\partial u_2}{\partial y_3} + \frac{\partial u_3}{\partial y_2}\right) = \epsilon_{23} = 0,$$ (7.13.23)

$$\frac{1}{2}\left(\frac{\partial u_1}{\partial y_3} + \frac{\partial u_3}{\partial y_1}\right) = \epsilon_{31} = 0.$$ (7.13.24)

The displacements u_1, u_2, and u_3 can be obtained by integrating these equations when the geometrical conditions, i.e., the constraints of the bar are given. Let us now focus our attention on the lateral deflection of the beam, i.e., the component u_3. From Eq. (7.13.19) we obtain

$$u_1 = -\frac{My_1y_3}{EI} + \bar{u},$$ (7.13.25)

where $\bar{u}$ may be a function of y_2 and y_3. From Eq. (7.13.24) we obtain

$$\frac{\partial u_3}{\partial y_1} = -\frac{\partial u_1}{\partial y_3} = \frac{My_1}{EI} - \frac{\partial \bar{u}}{\partial y_3}.$$ (7.13.26)

Differentiation with respect to y_1 gives

$$\frac{\partial^2 u_3}{\partial y_1^2} = \frac{M}{EI}.$$ (7.13.27)

Since the bending moment is not a function of y_3, Eq. (7.13.27) yields the important result that the second derivative of lateral displacement for every longitudinal fiber of the beam is a constant. (A longitudinal fiber is an element of the beam with the same y_3-coordinate.) If we denote the lateral deflection of the axis of the beam by $w(y_1)$ instead of u_3, we have

$$\frac{d^2w}{dy_1^2} = \frac{M}{EI}.$$ (7.13.28)

We recall from calculus that the curvature of a given curve, $y = f(x)$, is given by

$$\frac{1}{R} = \frac{d^2f/dx^2}{[1 + (df/dx)^2]^{3/2}}, \qquad (7.13.29)$$

where R is the radius of curvature. For a very flat curve for which df/dx is very small in comparison to unity, the curvature may be represented simply by the second derivative of the curve, that is,

$$\frac{1}{R} = \frac{d^2f}{dx^2}. \qquad (7.13.30)$$

The deformed shapes of beams are such that the curvatures are small; thus d^2w/dy_1^2 is the curvature of the deformed beam. We also find that the normal strain ϵ_{11} is related to the curvature by

$$\epsilon_{11} = -y_3 \frac{d^2w}{dy_1^2}. \qquad (7.13.31)$$

We consider next the strain energy dU for an element dy_1 of the beam. Since the only stress component is σ_{11}, we have

$$dU = \left(\frac{1}{2} \iint \frac{\sigma_{11}^2}{E}\, dy_2\, dy_3\right) dy_1, \qquad (7.13.32)$$

or

$$dU = \left(\frac{1}{2} \iint E\epsilon_{11}^2\, dy_2\, dy_3\right) dy_1. \qquad (7.13.33)$$

Substituting Eq. (7.13.15) into Eq. (7.13.32), and Eq. (7.13.31) into Eq. (7.13.33), we obtain respectively

$$dU = \frac{M^2}{2EI}\, dy_1, \qquad (7.13.34)$$

and

$$dU = \frac{EI}{2}\left(\frac{d^2w}{dy_1^2}\right)^2 dy_1. \qquad (7.13.35)$$

7.14   ENGINEERING BEAM THEORY

At this point it is worth while to mention the so-called engineering beam theory which covers the nonuniform beam under general lateral loading conditions. In such a case, the bounding surface of the beam may not be free of stress, and/or the body force F_3 may not be zero. Also, in general, the shear force in each section is not zero, and hence the bending moment M is not constant along the beam. The engineering beam theory, however, also neglects the normal stresses σ_{22} and σ_{33}, because it can be shown that these components are of a much smaller order of magnitude than σ_{11}. The theory also assumes that for a beam, the deformation due to shear strain is negligible in comparison to that due to the normal strain ϵ_{11}. As a result, the normal stresses and strains may still be calculated using Eqs. (7.13.15) and (7.13.31), although the bending moment, curvature, and moment of inertia are no longer constant along y_1. This engineering beam theory also assumes that the moment-curvature relation, Eq. (7.13.28), will still hold, and that the strain energy of a complete beam can be calculated by integrating Eq. (7.13.35).

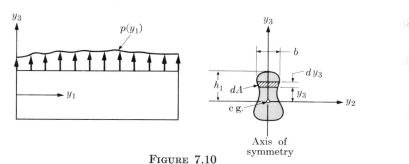

FIGURE 7.10

7.15 SUMMARY: ENGINEERING BEAM THEORY

The equations of engineering beam theory (see Figure 7.10 for coordinates and other nomenclature) are as follows:

Definition of equipollent transverse shear and bending moment

$$S = -\int_A \sigma_{13} \, dA, \tag{7.15.1}$$

$$M = -\int_A \sigma_{11} y_3 \, dA. \tag{7.15.2}$$

Displacements

$$u_3(y_1, y_2, y_3) = w(y_1), \tag{7.15.3}$$

$$u_1(y_1, y_2, y_3) = -y_3 \frac{dw}{dy_1}. \tag{7.15.4}$$

Strain-displacement relation

$$\epsilon_{11} = -y_3 \frac{d^2 w}{dy_1^2}. \tag{7.15.5}$$

Moment-curvature relation

$$\frac{d^2 w}{dy_1^2} = \frac{M}{EI}. \tag{7.15.6}$$

Force equilibrium

$$\frac{dS}{dy_1} = p. \tag{7.15.7}$$

Moment equilibrium

$$\frac{dM}{dy_1} = S. \tag{7.15.8}$$

Stress-strain relation

$$\sigma_{11} = E\epsilon_{11}. \tag{7.15.9}$$

Bending stress versus moment relation

$$\sigma_{11} = -\frac{My_3}{I}. \tag{7.15.10}$$

Shear stress versus transverse shear relation

$$\sigma_{13} = \frac{SQ}{bI}. \tag{7.15.11}$$

Cross-sectional moment of inertia

$$I = \iint y_3^2 \, dA. \tag{7.15.12}$$

Static moment

$$Q = \iint_{y_3}^{h_1} y_3 \, dA. \tag{7.15.13}$$

PROBLEMS

7.1 (a) Thin flat panels (Fig. P.7.1) with external forces acting in the y_1y_2-plane of the panel are said to be in a *state of plane stress*, that is, $\sigma_{33} = \sigma_{13} = \sigma_{23} = 0$ (see Problem 6.4). For an isotropic material verify the following expressions for γ_{11}, γ_{22}, and γ_{12} in terms of σ_{11}, σ_{22}, and σ_{12} and the elastic constants E and ν.

$$\gamma_{11} = \frac{1}{E}(\sigma_{11} - \nu\sigma_{22}), \qquad \gamma_{22} = \frac{1}{E}(\sigma_{22} - \nu\sigma_{11}), \qquad \gamma_{12} = \frac{1+\nu}{E}\sigma_{12}.$$

(b) Determine the following inverse stress-strain relations, i.e., the expression of σ_{11}, σ_{22}, and σ_{12} in terms of γ_{11}, γ_{22}, and γ_{12}:

$$\sigma_{11} = \frac{E}{1-\nu^2}(\gamma_{11} + \nu\gamma_{22}), \qquad \sigma_{22} = \frac{E}{1-\nu^2}(\gamma_{22} + \nu\gamma_{11}), \qquad \sigma_{12} = \frac{E}{1+\nu}\gamma_{12}.$$

How are the elastic constants related to the elasticity tensor E_{mnpr}?

7.2 The fibers of a reinforced plastic panel are evenly distributed along three different preferred directions, AA, BB, and CC, which are 60° apart. All are parallel to the face of the panel, as shown in Fig. P.7.2. One of these directions is along the

FIGURE P.7.1

FIGURE P.7.2   FIGURE P.7.4

y_1-axis. Show that the relation between stress and strain components in the y_1y_2-plane is governed by only two elastic constants, that is,

$$\gamma_{11} = S_1\sigma_{11} + S_2\sigma_{22}, \qquad \gamma_{22} = S_2\sigma_{11} + S_3\sigma_{22}, \qquad \gamma_{12} = S_4\sigma_{12},$$

where $S_3 = S_1$ and $S_4 = S_1 - S_2$. Thus the elastic properties are isotropic with respect to any direction normal to the y_3-axis. *Hint:* Prove $S_1 = S_3$ by considering the stress and strain components along the y_1y_2-coordinates for the case of uniaxial tension σ_{11}. Observe that the elastic constants for the y_1y_2-system and for $\tilde{y}_1\tilde{y}_2$-system are the same. Prove that $S_4 = S_1 - S_2$ by a similar consideration for the case of pure shear stress σ_{12}.

7.3 A hexagonal material has five independent elastic constants. (See Section 7.9 for example of hexagonal materials and the form of the elastic coefficient array.) Use symmetry arguments to reduce the elasticity matrix for orthotropic material (nine constants) to the one for hexagonal material.

7.4 Figure P.7.4 shows a panel made of orthotropic material with y_1-, y_2-, and y_3-axes parallel respectively to the axis of symmetry of the material. (a) Show that under plane stress conditions ($\sigma_{33} = \sigma_{13} = \sigma_{23} = 0$) the stress-strain relations for this panel can be reduced to the following matrix form which involves only four independent constants:

$$
\begin{bmatrix} \sigma_{11} \\ \sigma_{22} \\ \sigma_{12} \end{bmatrix} = \begin{bmatrix} G_{11} & G_{12} & 0 \\ G_{12} & G_{22} & 0 \\ 0 & 0 & H_{12} \end{bmatrix} \begin{bmatrix} \gamma_{11} \\ \gamma_{22} \\ \gamma_{12} \end{bmatrix}.
$$

(b) Derive expressions for G_{11}, G_{22}, G_{12}, and H_{12} in terms of the elasticity tensor E_{mnpr}.

(c) The inverse stress-strain relations may be written as

$$
\begin{bmatrix} \gamma_{11} \\ \gamma_{22} \\ \gamma_{12} \end{bmatrix} = \begin{bmatrix} \dfrac{1}{E_1} & -\dfrac{\nu_{12}}{E_1} & 0 \\ -\dfrac{\nu_{12}}{E_1} & \dfrac{1}{E_2} & 0 \\ 0 & 0 & \dfrac{1}{H_{12}} \end{bmatrix} \begin{bmatrix} \sigma_{11} \\ \sigma_{22} \\ \sigma_{12} \end{bmatrix}.
$$

Determine G_{11}, G_{22}, G_{12} in terms of E_1, E_2, and ν_{12}.

(d) Determine the stress-strain relations (strains in terms of stresses) for the $\tilde{y}_1$-, $\tilde{y}_2$-, $\tilde{y}_3$-coordinate system where $\tilde{y}_3$ and y_3 coincide and $\widehat{y_1\tilde{y}_1} = 30°$. Note that shear stress $\tilde{\sigma}_{12}$ will cause normal strains $\tilde{\gamma}_{11}$ and $\tilde{\gamma}_{22}$, and normal stress $\tilde{\sigma}_{11}$ or $\tilde{\sigma}_{22}$ will cause shear strain $\tilde{\gamma}_{12}$. Thus, for an orthotropic material the principal directions of stress and strain do not in general coincide. But for an isotropic material they always coincide.

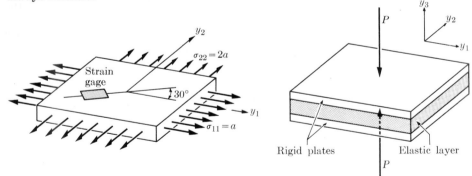

FIGURE P.7.5   FIGURE P.7.7

7.5 A rectangular plate of isotropic material is acted upon by boundary stresses $\sigma_{11} = a$, $\sigma_{22} = 2a$, $\sigma_{12} = 0$. The material properties are $E = 10^7$ psi, $\nu = 0.3$, and $\alpha = 10^{-6}/°F$. A strain gage is mounted at an angle of 30° from the y_1-axis, as shown in Fig. P.7.5. (a) What will the strain gage read under the above loading? (b) If the loading is kept constant and the temperature is raised 100°F, what will be the new reading of the strain gage?

7.6 The state in which the strain components γ_{33}, γ_{13}, and γ_{23} are zero is called the *plane strain state*. For an isotropic material in plane strain verify the following expressions of γ_{11}, γ_{22}, and γ_{12} in terms of σ_{11}, σ_{22}, and σ_{12} and the elastic constants E and ν.

$$\gamma_{11} = \frac{1+\nu}{E}[(1-\nu)\sigma_{11} - \nu\sigma_{22}],$$

$$\gamma_{22} = \frac{1+\nu}{E}[(1-\nu)\sigma_{22} - \nu\sigma_{11}],$$

$$\gamma_{12} = \frac{1+\nu}{E}\sigma_{12}.$$

7.7 An elastic layer is sandwiched between two rigid plates to which it is bonded, as shown in Fig. P.7.7. The layer is compressed, i.e., the normal stress σ_{33} is negative. Supposing that the bonding to the plates prevents any lateral strain ϵ_{11} or ϵ_{22}, find the ratio $\sigma_{33}/\epsilon_{33}$ in terms of E and ν of the elastic material.

7.8 A material has *equal* strength properties along two axes oblique to each other at an angle of 35°. The third axis is perpendicular to the plane of the other two axes, and properties along the third axis are different. How many elasticity components are required to describe the elastic behavior of this material?

7.9 (a) An isotropic panel of thickness h is in a state of plane stress. Derive the expression for the strain energy of an element of volume $dy_1\, dy_2$ in terms of the stress components σ_{11}, σ_{22}, and σ_{12}. (b) Derive the expression of the volume element for the strain energy in terms of the strain components γ_{11}, γ_{22}, and γ_{12}.

7.10 Derive the expression for the strain-energy density U^* in terms of σ_{11}, σ_{22}, and σ_{12} under the condition of plane strain (see Problem 7.6).

7.11 A long rectangular rod hangs under gravity in a pool of water as shown in Fig. P.7.11. The water exerts only a *normal* pressure $p = \rho_w g y_1$ on the surfaces of the rod. The rod itself has a density ρ_r and length l. (a) State the boundary conditions on *all* six faces of the rod (use an averaged boundary condition on the face $y_1 = 0$). (b) The assumed solution for the stress σ_{mn} given below satisfies all boundary conditions and the fifteen equations of elasticity. Evaluate the three unknowns C_1, C_0, and the end load P in terms of the given quantities ρ_w, ρ_r, l, b, h and g. (c) Determine the deflection u_1 everywhere in the rod. Assume that $u_1 = 0$ at $y_1 = 0$.

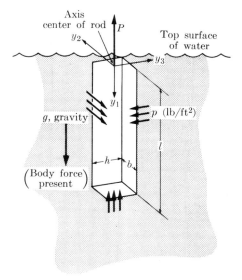

Assumed solution:

$$\sigma_{11} = C_1 y_1 + C_0, \qquad \sigma_{12} = 0,$$
$$\sigma_{22} = -\rho_w g y_1, \qquad \sigma_{23} = 0,$$
$$\sigma_{33} = -\rho_w g y_1, \qquad \sigma_{31} = 0,$$

FIGURE P.7.11

and C_1, C_0, P are constants.

$$\text{Density of water,} \quad \rho_w \text{ (slugs/ft}^3\text{)};$$
$$\text{Density of rod,} \quad \rho_r \text{ (slugs/ft}^3\text{)};$$
$$\text{Isotropic material,} \quad E, \nu.$$

7.12   Given a cantilever beam loaded by a tip load P (Fig. P.7.12). By integrating the moment curvature relation (that is, $M = EI \, (d^2w/dy_1^2)$ with the prescribed displacement boundary conditions, determine the vertical deflection $w(y_1)$ of the beam at any point, and the maximum deflection at the tip $w(a)$. What is the slope of the beam at $y_1 = a$? [Neglect the weight of the beam.]

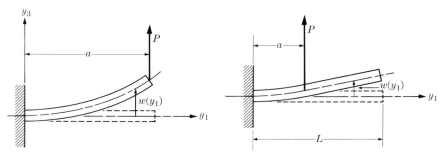

FIGURE P.7.12   FIGURE P.7.13

7.13   A cantilever beam of length L is loaded by a vertical load P at a distance a from the clamped end (Fig. P.7.13). Determine the tip deflection $w(L)$. *Hint:* Make use of the result of the previous problem. What is the curvature of the beam $y_1 > a$?

7.14   Many problems in plane stress are formulated in terms of the Airy stress function, which we encountered in Problem 6.11. We recall that the definition of the Airy stress function,

$$\sigma_{11} = \frac{\partial^2 \phi}{\partial y_2^2}, \qquad \sigma_{22} = \frac{\partial^2 \phi}{\partial y_1^2}, \qquad \sigma_{12} = -\frac{\partial^2 \phi}{\partial y_1 \, \partial y_2},$$

ensures that the equations of equilibrium will be satisfied. To complete the formulation it is necessary to replace all the equations of plane elasticity by a single equation in ϕ alone. The equations of plane elasticity are summarized as follows:

Equations of equilibrium,

$$\frac{\partial \sigma_{11}}{\partial y_1} + \frac{\partial \sigma_{21}}{\partial y_2} = 0, \qquad \frac{\partial \sigma_{12}}{\partial y_1} + \frac{\partial \sigma_{22}}{\partial y_2} = 0.$$

Strain-displacement relations,

$$\epsilon_{11} = \frac{\partial u_1}{\partial y_1}, \qquad \epsilon_{22} = \frac{\partial u_2}{\partial y_2}, \qquad \epsilon_{12} = \frac{1}{2}\left(\frac{\partial u_1}{\partial y_2} + \frac{\partial u_2}{\partial y_1}\right).$$

Stress-strain relations,

$$\epsilon_{11} = \frac{1}{E}(\sigma_{11} - \nu\sigma_{22}), \qquad \epsilon_{22} = \frac{1}{E}(\sigma_{22} - \nu\sigma_{11}), \qquad \epsilon_{12} = \frac{1+\nu}{E}\sigma_{12}.$$

(a) Show that combination of the stress-strain relations, the definition of ϕ, and the strain-displacement relations (in the form of a compatibility condition) leads to the biharmonic equation of plane elasticity,

$$\frac{\partial^2 \phi}{\partial y_1^4} + 2\frac{\partial^4 \phi}{\partial y_1^2 \partial y_2^2} + \frac{\partial^4 \phi}{\partial y_2^4} = 0.$$

(b) A certain problem in plane stress is solved via the biharmonic equation, and it is found that

$$\phi(y_1, y_2) = k(y_1^4 - 6y_1^2 y_2^2 + y_2^4),$$

where k is a constant. Calculate the components of stress and strain in the structure, including the strain ϵ_{zz}.

7.15   Derive a formula for the strain-energy density in terms of the stress function ϕ of the structure under the condition of plane stress.

8

Plastic Behavior of Solids

8.1 INTRODUCTION

In Chapter 7 the simplest kind of constitutive relation was described and formulated, namely, that of a linear elastic stress-strain relation. However, the engineering use of materials requires not only a knowledge of elastic behavior, but also of inelastic or plastic behavior. For example, plastic deformations in structures are usually permitted under emergency or sometimes even under normal operating conditions. In fact, the metal-forming processes involve essentially a plastic flow of materials. For the former problem the plastic strains are usually small; for the latter, the plastic strains may be of the order of several hundred percent. Thus, in some cases, the elastic strain may be completely neglected. In this chapter we shall consider the relations between stress and strain in the range of small plastic strain.

Much knowledge has been gained during the past two decades about how structural defects in the orderly arrangement of the atoms cause the observed mechanical behavior of materials. Much further research must be done before all portions of the ordinary stress-strain curve can be predicted or explained. Notwithstanding its humble nature, the ordinary stress-strain curve of the common engineering materials is amazingly reproducible, and contains most of the material data necessary for design. The response of materials to stress and strain from a microscopic and atomistic point of view is a fascinating study and the subject of many recent books. In this first course on solid mechanics, however, we shall adopt a phenomenological point of view and content ourselves with an engineering approach to plasticity. However, we must be aware of those developments in the field of physical metallurgy and solid-state physics which will aid our engineering approach.

8.2 STRESS-STRAIN RELATIONS UNDER UNIAXIAL LOADING CONDITIONS

The simplest description of the plastic behavior of solids is the stress-strain curve under the condition of uniaxial stress. This curve is usually obtained by a simple tensile test which involves a slender specimen pulled in a direction parallel to its axis. Figure 8.1 shows a narrow strip cut from a thin sheet. The center part of the strip was machined so that a uniform cross-sectional area could be maintained. When the specimen is pulled apart, the elongation between previously indented gage marks is measured. The ratio between the elongation Δl and the original gage length l is the strain in the axial direction; the applied load divided by the original area of the specimen yields the uniaxial stress. Figure 8.2 shows stress-strain curves for several typical engineering materials. It is worth while to discuss briefly some of the mechanical properties defined by the tensile stress-strain curves.

FIG. 8.1   Tension specimen.

The ultimate tensile stress is defined by the maximum load the specimen can sustain divided by the original area of the cross section. For the brittle material shown in Fig. 8.2(c), the ultimate tensile stress is actually the fracture stress of the material. For a ductile material, the ultimate tensile stress is the stress at which local necking of a specimen occurs. Thus, although the so-called engineering stress (i.e., load divided by the original area) decreases after necking begins, the true stress (defined by the tensile load divided by the instantaneous minimum area) actually increases. The specimen finally fractures at a maximum value of true stress.

In Fig. 8.2(a) and (b) the stress-strain curves corresponding to the necking region are drawn as dashed lines. For this part of the curve, the cross section of the specimen is no longer uniform between the two gage points. Consequently, the strain is nonuniform, and indeed for some materials the regions of large strain are concentrated in small bands. The average value of strain obtained by dividing the elongation by the original gage length thus loses its value as a description of the process of deformation. It is obvious that this value will be different when the original gage length is different.

The yielding, or the onset of plastic flow, for certain ductile materials such as low carbon steel, can be clearly identified as shown in Fig. 8.2(a). In fact, for this case upper and lower yield points exist. The upper yield point exists because interstitial solute atoms serve as obstacles to the movement of dislocations. When the stress becomes sufficiently high to tear the obstacles loose, the dislocations can move at a lower value of applied stress. For a low carbon steel this lower yield stress remains constant for a certain range of strain until the phenomenon of strain hardening becomes significant.

For most ductile materials strain hardening follows plastic flow immediately, hence there is no clear-cut indication of the onset of plastic flow. We normally define the yield stress as the stress which produces a very small, but easily measurable, amount of plastic deformation. The most commonly used yield

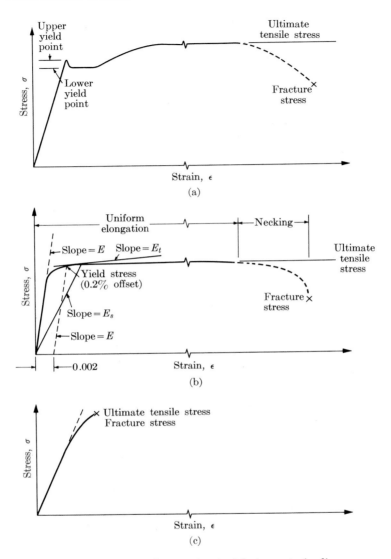

Fɪɢ. 8.2   The nomenclature of uniaxial stress-strain diagrams.

stress is defined by the intersection of a line which passes through the strain axis at a strain of 0.002, and is parallel to the elastic line, as shown in Fig. 8.2(b). When a tensile specimen is loaded up to this stress and then is unloaded, the unloading curve is, in general, parallel to the initial straight portion of the stress-strain curve. Thus, when the stress has returned to zero, there will remain a 0.2% permanent strain, which is often called the *permanent offset*. The above arbitrary definition of yield stress is often called 0.2% *offset yield stress*.

The *proportional limit* is the stress at which strain ceases to be proportional to stress. This limit is very difficult to obtain experimentally. In fact, the more precise the technique of measurement, the lower the proportional limit will be found. It is thus customary to adopt an arbitrary definition by taking the proportional limit as the stress which would produce a plastic strain of 0.0001 in./in.

The *modulus of elasticity (or Young's modulus)* is the slope of the initial straight-line portion of the stress-strain curve. At high stresses, when the relation between stress and strain ceases to be linear, two moduli are often used. They are: (1) the tangent modulus, E_t, defined by the slope of the tangent to the stress-strain curve, $E_t = d\sigma/d\epsilon$; and (2) the secant modulus, E_s, defined by the slope of a line from the origin to a point on the stress-strain curve, $E_s = \sigma/\epsilon$. (see Fig. 8.2b)

For most materials the available stress-strain data are limited to tensile properties because of the simplicity of conducting a tensile test. However, it should be mentioned that the stress-strain curve for compression is generally not the same as that for tension. Figure 8.3 shows typical stress-strain curves of a 2024-T3 aluminum alloy sheet. The curves show clearly that there is an appreciable difference between the curves in tension and in compression. This figure also shows that although Young's modulus for the rolled aluminum alloy sheet remains the same both for the direction with the grain and across the grain, the properties in the plastic range are certainly nonisotropic.

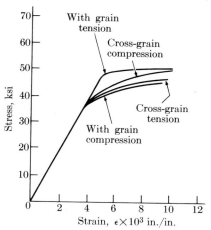

Fig. 8.3 Uniaxial stress-strain diagrams for 2024-T3 aluminum alloy (rolled sheet).

For many structural materials it has been found that the experimental stress-strain curve can be closely fitted over a fairly large range by the following relatively simple polynomial relations known as the *Ramberg-Osgood* relations (Ref. 8.1):

$$\epsilon = \frac{\sigma}{E} + \left(\frac{\sigma}{B}\right)^n. \tag{8.2.1}$$

The first term on the right-hand side represents the elastic strain, and the second term represents the plastic strain. Typical values for the three constants E, B, and n for various materials are given in Table 8.1.

It should be remarked that for materials with clearly defined yield points, such as low carbon steel (Fig. 8.2a), the effect of the slight rise of the upper yield point may be neglected. Thus for the range of small plastic strains, the stress remains practically constant. In this case, the stress-strain curve may be

TABLE 8.1   *Typical Stress-Strain Constants (Approximate)*

Material	Ultimate tensile stress, psi	E, psi $(\times 10^6)$	B, psi	n
Alloy steel	100,000	29	122,400	25
Alloy steel	180,000	29	202,000	30
Aluminum alloy 2024-T3	65,000	10.5	72,300	10
Aluminum alloy 7075-T6	83,000	10.5	101,200	20
Magnesium alloy	39,000	6.5	47,500	10

idealized by two straight lines, one with a slope of E, representing the elastic range, the other with zero slope representing the plastic range (Fig. 8.4a). This idealized model is often called the elastic perfectly plastic material. It is interesting to point out that in applying Eq. (8.2.1) to this limiting case, the constant n should approach infinity while the constant B is equal to the yield stress of the material.

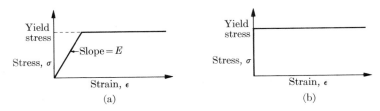

FIG. 8.4   Idealized uniaxial stress-strain diagrams: (a) elastic perfectly plastic material; (b) rigid perfectly plastic material.

Another idealized model is called the rigid perfectly plastic material (Fig. 8.4b). For a problem in which the plastic strain is much larger than the elastic strain, it is justifiable to neglect the latter. In this case, the solid will be considered as rigid when the applied stress is less than the yield stress, and the material will flow whenever the yield stress is reached.

8.3   YIELD CONDITION UNDER GENERAL STATE OF STRESS FOR ISOTROPIC MATERIALS

In the previous section we discussed the plastic behavior of a slender bar under uniaxial loading. For materials such as low carbon steel it was shown that plastic flow will occur when the normal stress reaches the yield stress, or yield point, of the material. In fact, for all materials plastic strain begins to appear when the uniaxial stress reaches a certain value. The question now arises as to what is the condition under which plastic deformation or yielding occurs under a general state of combined stress, i.e., two-dimensional or three-dimensional stress. To be more specific, the yield condition under combined stress can be expressed as a certain function of the stress components. When the value of this function reaches a certain level, plastic flow will occur. In the present discussion we shall limit ourselves to isotropic materials.

The plastic deformations of crystalline materials are the result of slip along atomic planes or of twin-glide displacement. In either case, the deformation does not involve permanent changes in the distance between atomic lattice planes. In fact, in both cases the deformation is the result of shearing action. It can thus be concluded that there will be no volume change in the solid due to plastic deformation, and that a state of stress which involves no shear component will not cause plastic deformation, no matter how high the stress magnitude may be. Examples of this type of stress state are *hydrostatic pressure,* for which the three principal stresses are of equal magnitude in compression, and the so-called *hydrostatic tension,* for which the three principal stresses are of equal magnitude in tension.

Since plastic deformation is directly associated with shearing action, it is logical to assume that the material will yield when the maximum shear stress reaches a critical value. This critical value is the maximum shear stress corresponding to the yielding of a simple tensile specimen; hence we speak of the *maximum shear-stress criterion for yielding.* This criterion is also called the *Tresca yield condition.*

Under a uniaxial stress condition, the maximum shear stress $\tau_{\max}$ is equal to half the applied normal stress:

$$(\tau_{\max})_{\text{yield}} = \frac{\sigma_0}{2}, \tag{8.3.1}$$

where $\sigma_0 =$ yield stress in simple tension. Under a three-dimensional stress condition, the maximum shear stresses are given by (see Section 6.9)

$$\tfrac{1}{2}|\sigma_{\mathrm{I}} - \sigma_{\mathrm{II}}|, \qquad \tfrac{1}{2}|\sigma_{\mathrm{II}} - \sigma_{\mathrm{III}}|, \qquad \tfrac{1}{2}|\sigma_{\mathrm{III}} - \sigma_{\mathrm{I}}|,$$

where σ_{I}, σ_{II}, and σ_{III} are the three principal stresses. The maximum shear stress to be used in Eq. (8.3.1) is the largest of these three values. If, for example, we assume that $\sigma_{\mathrm{I}} < \sigma_{\mathrm{II}} < \sigma_{\mathrm{III}}$, then the Tresca yield condition is written as

$$\sigma_{\mathrm{III}} - \sigma_{\mathrm{I}} = \sigma_0. \tag{8.3.2}$$

A complete description of the Tresca yield condition is given in Table 8.2.

The yield condition under three given principal stresses is represented by a surface in three-dimensional space with the principal stresses as the coordinates. The yield surface under the maximum shear-stress criterion is the continuous

TABLE 8.2

Stress state	Tresca condition
$\sigma_I < \sigma_{II} < \sigma_{III}$	$\sigma_{III} - \sigma_I = \sigma_0$
$\sigma_{III} < \sigma_{II} < \sigma_I$	$\sigma_I - \sigma_{III} = \sigma_0$
$\sigma_I < \sigma_{III} < \sigma_{II}$	$\sigma_{II} - \sigma_I = \sigma_0$
$\sigma_{II} < \sigma_{III} < \sigma_I$	$\sigma_I - \sigma_{II} = \sigma_0$
$\sigma_{II} < \sigma_I < \sigma_{III}$	$\sigma_{III} - \sigma_{II} = \sigma_0$
$\sigma_{III} < \sigma_I < \sigma_{II}$	$\sigma_{II} - \sigma_{III} = \sigma_0$

surface formed by the six planes given by the equations of Table 8.2. It can be seen that the first two planes are parallel to the σ_{II}-axis and inclined at a 45° angle to the $\sigma_I\sigma_{III}$-plane, the third and fourth planes are parallel to the σ_{III}-axis and inclined at a 45° angle to the $\sigma_I\sigma_{II}$-plane, and the last two planes are parallel to the σ_I-axis and inclined at a 45° angle to the $\sigma_{II}\sigma_{III}$-plane. These six planes form a hexagonal prism which is extended to infinity in both directions, as shown in Fig. 8.5. The axis of this prism intersects the three coordinate axes at the same angle. The surface of this prism is the Tresca yield surface. When a point which represents the three principal stresses falls within this surface, the material is in the elastic range, and when the point lies on this surface, yielding will occur.

Another logical criterion for yielding is associated with the strain-energy content of the material at yielding. We have just pointed out that hydrostatic pressure or tension, which causes only volume change without distortion, will not produce any plastic deformation. This implies that the yield condition will depend only on the distortion energy and be independent of the dilatation energy. The distortion-energy criterion for yielding can thus be described by the following

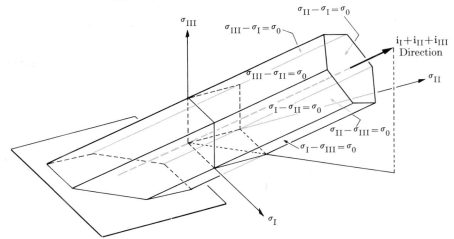

FIG. 8.5 Representation of the Tresca criterion as a surface in principal stress space.

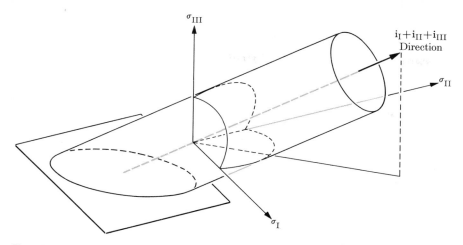

FIG. 8.6   The Mises-Hencky criterion shown as a surface in principal stress space.

statement: *Plastic flow will occur when the distortion-energy density in the material reaches the value corresponding to the yielding of a simple tensile specimen.* This criterion is often called the *Huber-von Mises-Hencky** or *Mises-Hencky Theory.*

The distortion-energy density under three-dimensional stress was given in Section 7.10:

$$U^* = \frac{1}{12G} [(\sigma_I - \sigma_{II})^2 + (\sigma_{II} - \sigma_{III})^2 + (\sigma_{III} - \sigma_I)^2].$$

Under uniaxial stress conditions the distortion energy becomes

$$U^* = \frac{1}{6G} (\sigma_0)^2.$$

The distortion-energy criterion can thus be stated as

$$\frac{1}{12G} [(\sigma_I - \sigma_{II})^2 + (\sigma_{II} - \sigma_{III})^2 + (\sigma_{III} - \sigma_I)^2] = \frac{1}{6G} (\sigma_0)^2,$$

or

$$(\sigma_I - \sigma_{II})^2 + (\sigma_{II} - \sigma_{III})^2 + (\sigma_{III} - \sigma_I)^2 = 2(\sigma_0)^2. \qquad (8.3.3)$$

We can see that, if the three principal stresses are chosen as the coordinate axes, the Mises-Hencky yield condition will be represented by a circular cylindrical surface whose axis coincides with the line which intersects the origin at equal angles with the three coordinate axes. The radius of this cylinder is equal to $\sqrt{2/3}\,\sigma_0$. This yield surface extends to infinity in both directions, (see Fig. 8.6).

* The maximum distortion energy criterion was discussed in two German articles by von Mises (Ref. 7) and Hencky (Ref. 8) in 1913 and 1925 respectively; the same yield condition had been suggested by Huber (Ref. 9) in 1904 in a Polish publication but did not attract general attention until nearly twenty years later.

Let us now discuss an important physical picture given by the two yield surfaces. The axis for either the hexagonal prism or the circular cylinder makes equal angles with the three principal stress axes. Hence it represents the state of hydrostatic tension or hydrostatic pressure. Thus both yield conditions are in agreement with our previous conclusion that hydrostatic tension or pressure, no matter how large in magnitude, will not produce yielding. Another way of interpreting this is by considering two points a and a' (Fig. 8.6) which are on a line parallel to the axis of the yield surface. Point a' represents the superposition of a hydrostatic pressure on the state of stress given by point a. If point a is not on the yield surface, a superposition of a hydrostatic pressure on this state of stress should not produce yielding in the solid. This fact has been verified by Bridgeman by conducting tension tests under very high hydrostatic pressures (Ref. 8.2).

Next let us consider the mathematical interpretations of the two yield conditions developed above. We have seen that a yield condition can be expressed in terms of stress components. For an isotropic material it should be independent of the choice of reference axes. Thus, we should expect the yield condition to be a function of the stress invariants. In fact, since it is not affected by the hydrostatic component of stress, we expect it to be dependent only on the deviatoric stress invariants $\hat{I}_2$ and $\hat{I}_3$. The yield condition hence will take the general form

$$f(\hat{I}_2, \hat{I}_3) = 0. \tag{8.3.4}$$

By referring to Eqs. (6.8.18), (6.8.19) and (6.10.6) we see that we can write

$$\hat{I}_2 = -\tfrac{1}{6}[(\sigma_I - \sigma_{II})^2 + (\sigma_{II} - \sigma_{III})^2 + (\sigma_{III} - \sigma_I)^2].$$

The Mises-Hencky criterion then becomes

$$\hat{I}_2 + \frac{(\sigma_0)^2}{3} = 0. \tag{8.3.5}$$

The Tresca yield condition given by Table 8.2 can be represented by the following equation:

$$[(\sigma_I - \sigma_{II})^2 - (\sigma_0)^2][(\sigma_{II} - \sigma_{III})^2 - (\sigma_0)^2][(\sigma_{III} - \sigma_I)^2 - (\sigma_0)^2] = 0. \tag{8.3.6}$$

In terms of the deviatoric stress invariants this equation becomes

$$4\hat{I}_2^3 - 27\hat{I}_3^2 - 9(\sigma_0)^2\hat{I}_2^2 + 6(\sigma_0)^4\hat{I}_2 - (\sigma_0)^6 = 0. \tag{8.3.7}$$

Another way of interpreting the Mises-Hencky criterion is to associate the yield condition with the octahedral shear stress τ_{oct}. We showed in Chapter 6 (see Problem 6.8) that

$$\tau_{\text{oct}} = \tfrac{1}{3}\sqrt{(\sigma_I - \sigma_{II})^2 + (\sigma_{II} - \sigma_{III})^2 + (\sigma_{III} - \sigma_I)^2} = \sqrt{-(\tfrac{2}{3})\hat{I}_2}.$$
(8.3.8)

Thus the Mises-Hencky criterion given by $\hat{I}_2 = $ const can also be written as $\tau_{\text{oct}} = $ const. This interpretation was given by Nadai (Ref. 8.3).

For convenience, the yield condition under combined stress is usually defined by an equivalent stress $\bar{\sigma}$. When the equivalent stress $\bar{\sigma}$ is equal to σ_0, the yield stress under uniaxial stress conditions, plastic flow will begin. Thus under the maximum shear-stress criterion, $\bar{\sigma}$ is equal to twice the maximum shear stress. Under the distortion energy criterion, we have

$$\bar{\sigma} = \sqrt{\tfrac{1}{2}[(\sigma_I - \sigma_{II})^2 + (\sigma_{II} - \sigma_{III})^2 + (\sigma_{III} - \sigma_I)^2]}.$$
(8.3.9)

Experimental verifications of the yield criteria have been conducted by many researchers during the last several decades (see Ref. 3, Chap. 17). Most of these studies were concerned with two-dimensional states of stress obtained by testing thin-walled tubes under combined internal pressure and axial load, or under combined torsion and tension.

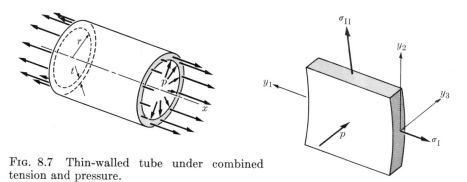

FIG. 8.7   Thin-walled tube under combined tension and pressure.

Let us consider a thin-walled tube under internal pressure and axial tension or compression loads, as shown in Fig. 8.7. The three principal stresses for an element shown in the lower half of the figure are σ_I, the axial stress; σ_{II}, the circumferential stress; and σ_{III}, the radial stress. It can be seen that the radial stress σ_{III} varies from $-p$ to 0 from the inner surface to the outer surface, while the circumferential stress resulting from hoop tension is equal to pr/t. For thin-walled tubes where r/t is much larger than unity, the radial stress can be ignored, and the problem may be considered a two-dimensional problem with the principal stress $\sigma_{III} = 0$.

In applying the maximum shear criterion to this case, we see that when both σ_I and σ_{II} are positive, the yield condition is determined by

$$\sigma_I - \sigma_{III} = \sigma_I = \sigma_0, \quad \text{when} \quad \sigma_I > \sigma_{II};$$

or

$$\sigma_{II} - \sigma_{III} = \sigma_{II} = \sigma_0, \quad \text{when} \quad \sigma_{II} > \sigma_I.$$

These equations are represented by the vertical line AB and the horizontal line CB in Fig. 8.8. When both σ_I and σ_{II} are negative, the yield condition will be given by

$$-\sigma_I = \sigma_0, \quad \text{when } \sigma_I < \sigma_{II};$$
$$-\sigma_{II} = \sigma_0, \quad \text{when } \sigma_{II} < \sigma_I.$$

These equations are represented by lines DE and EF, respectively. However, when σ_I and σ_{II} are of opposite sign, the yield condition must be determined by

$$\sigma_I - \sigma_{II} = \pm\sigma_0.$$

These equations are represented by the lines AF and CD. The complete Tresca yield condition is thus given by the closed hexagon in Fig. 8.8.

FIG. 8.8   Yield conditions, under biaxial stress.

In applying the distortion energy criterion to this case we see that Eq. (8.3.3) is reduced to

$$(\sigma_I)^2 - 2\sigma_I\sigma_{II} + (\sigma_{II})^2 + (\sigma_I)^2 + (\sigma_{II})^2 = 2(\sigma_0)^2,$$

or

$$(\sigma_I)^2 - \sigma_I\sigma_{II} + (\sigma_{II})^2 = (\sigma_0)^2. \tag{8.3.10}$$

This equation represents an ellipse which passes through points A, B, C, D, E, and F as shown in Fig. 8.8.

Experimental results by Lode (Ref. 4) and by Ros and Eichinger (Ref. 5) are illustrated in Fig. 8.9. The materials used in these experiments included copper, nickel, and steel. It can be seen that the experimental results correlate better with the distortion-energy theory.

When a thin-walled tube is acted on by combined tension and twisting, the principal stresses σ_I and σ_{II} can be obtained by using the Mohr circle for stress:

$$\sigma_I = \sigma/2 + \sqrt{(\sigma/2)^2 + (\tau)^2}, \quad \sigma_{II} = \sigma/2 - \sqrt{(\sigma/2)^2 + (\tau)^2},$$

where $\sigma = $ the axial tensile stress, and $\tau = $ shear stress due to torsion. When we apply the maximum shear-stress theory, we substitute the above equations into $\sigma_I - \sigma_{II} = \sigma_0$, from which we obtain

$$2\sqrt{(\sigma/2)^2 + (\tau)^2} = \sigma_0$$

or

$$(\sigma)^2 + 4(\tau)^2 = (\sigma_0)^2. \qquad (8.3.11)$$

When we apply the distortion-energy theory, we substitute the same equations into

$$(\sigma_1)^2 - (\sigma_I \sigma_{II}) + (\sigma_{II})^2 = (\sigma_0)^2,$$

and obtain

$$(\sigma)^2 + 3(\tau)^2 = (\sigma_0)^2. \qquad (8.3.12)$$

Equations (8.3.11) and (8.3.12) represent the two ellipses shown in Fig. 8.10. Experimental results obtained by Taylor and Quinney (Ref. 8.6) using copper, aluminum, and mild steel tubes are plotted for comparison. In their experiments they first strain-hardened each tube by tension load, and then after partially removing the load they applied a gradually increas-

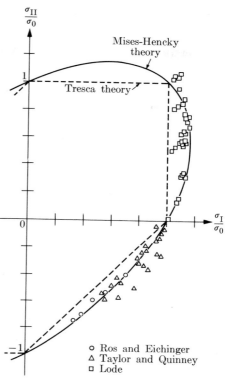

FIGURE 8.9

ing torque until yielding occurred. Thus for these tests the onset of plastic flow could be distinctly observed in these materials, although in their virgin states there had been no clear-cut indication of such phenomena. Taylor and Quinney's results again substantiate the distortion-energy yield criterion.

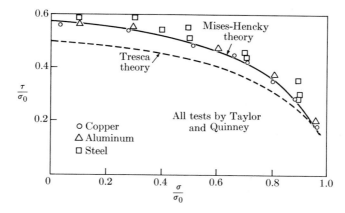

FIGURE 8.10

8.4 PLASTIC STRESS-STRAIN RELATIONS

In the previous section we discussed only the state of combined stress that would cause a material to begin to deform plastically. For an elastic perfectly plastic material, if the equivalent stress $\bar{\sigma}$ reaches the yield stress, the material will flow. But the problem is, "How will the material flow and what are the magnitudes of the various strain components when the material does flow?" For a uniaxial loading condition, the value of plastic strain for a perfectly plastic material is indeterminate. Thus in the case of a combined loading condition, if the equivalent stress is maintained at the yield stress, the magnitudes of the plastic strain components are also indeterminate. However, it is possible to determine the relations among the various components of strain. This problem on the plastic flow of elastic plastic material may also be approached in the following way: "What are the various components of stress when an elastic perfectly plastic material is deformed into the plastic range with known components of strain?"

For materials deformed beyond the elastic range, it is convenient to express the total strain ϵ in terms of two components, the elastic strain ϵ^e and the plastic strain ϵ^p, such that

$$\epsilon_{mn} = \epsilon_{mn}^e + \epsilon_{mn}^p. \tag{8.4.1}$$

The elastic-strain components can be related to the components of stress by means of Eq. (7.7.28). For the plastic-strain part, we note that the volume remains unchanged during plastic deformation, that is,

$$\epsilon_{ii}^p = 0. \tag{8.4.2}$$

From Eq. (5.11.2) we conclude that the total plastic-strain tensor ϵ_{ij}^p is identical to the deviatoric plastic-strain tensor $\hat{\epsilon}_{ij}^p$.

A simple theory for plastic flow consistent with the Mises-Hencky yield condition is that the ratio of the increment of each plastic strain component to its corresponding deviatoric stress component remains constant, that is,

$$d\epsilon_{ij}^p / \hat{\sigma}_{ij} = d\lambda, \tag{8.4.3}$$

where $d\lambda$ is a positive scalar factor of proportionality.

To illustrate this relation, let us consider several two-dimensional stress problems, each of which involves a thin-walled tube under combined axial and torsional loading (Fig. 8.11). The material is assumed to be elastic perfectly plastic. In the first case, let the tubing be loaded up to yield by a pure torsional moment, so that the shear stress at that instant is equal to the yielding shear stress, while the tensile stress is zero. The tube is then stretched in the axial direction by a gradually increasing tensile stress. According to Eq. (8.4.3), we find that at the initial instant the plastic tensile strain must also be zero, and

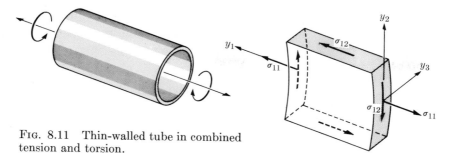

FIG. 8.11   Thin-walled tube in combined tension and torsion.

the initial tensile strain will consist of only an elastic component. The initial slope of the tensile stress-strain curve must then remain equal to the elastic modulus E. In the second case, let the yield condition be reached by combined shear and tensile stresses. When the tube is stretched beyond yielding both elastic and plastic strains will occur, and the slope of the tensile stress-strain curve must be less than E. In the limiting case where the initial yielding was the result of pure tension, the slope of the tensile stress-strain curve beyond this point will certainly be zero, because no further tensile stress can be added beyond this point.

We can extend this example further by calculating the complete tensile stress-strain relation of the thin-walled tube for the period preceding the initial yielding. Let us consider the case for which the yielding has been attained by pure shear, and the twisting angle is maintained constant while the tensile strain is applied.

The increments in total shear strain and total tensile strain are, respectively,

$$d\epsilon_{12} = d\epsilon_{12}^e + d\epsilon_{12}^p, \tag{8.4.4}$$

$$d\epsilon_{11} = d\epsilon_{11}^e + d\epsilon_{11}^p. \tag{8.4.5}$$

Substituting the relations

$$d\epsilon_{12}^e = d\sigma_{12}/2G, \tag{8.4.6}$$

$$d\epsilon_{11}^e = d\sigma_{11}/E, \tag{8.4.7}$$

$$d\epsilon_{12}^p = \hat{\sigma}_{12}\,d\lambda = \sigma_{12}\,d\lambda, \tag{8.4.8}$$

$$d\epsilon_{11}^p = \hat{\sigma}_{11}\,d\lambda = \tfrac{2}{3}\sigma_{11}\,d\lambda, \tag{8.4.9}$$

into Eqs. (8.4.4) and (8.4.5), we obtain

$$d\epsilon_{12} = \frac{d\sigma_{12}}{2G} + \sigma_{12}\,d\lambda, \tag{8.4.10}$$

$$d\epsilon_{11} = \tfrac{2}{3}\sigma_{11}\,d\lambda + \frac{d\sigma_{11}}{E}. \tag{8.4.11}$$

We see that $d\lambda$ can be eliminated from these equations. By substituting $d\epsilon_{12} = 0$ for our present problem and introducing the yield condition (Eq. 8.3.12),

$$(\sigma_{11})^2 + 3(\sigma_{12})^2 = (\sigma_0)^2, \qquad (8.4.12)$$

we obtain the following relation between ϵ_{11} and σ_{11}:

$$d\epsilon_{11} = \frac{(E/3 - G)(\sigma_{11})^2 + G(\sigma_0)^2}{EG[(\sigma_0)^2 - (\sigma_{11})^2]} d\sigma_{11}. \qquad (8.4.13)$$

Integrating, we obtain

$$\epsilon_{11} = \int_0^{\epsilon_{11}} d\epsilon_{11} = \int_0^{\sigma_{11}} \frac{(E/3 - G)(\sigma_{11})^2 + G(\sigma_0)^2}{EG[(\sigma_0)^2 - (\sigma_{11})^2]} d\sigma_{11}, \quad (8.4.14)$$

or

$$\epsilon_{11} = \frac{G - (E/3)}{EG} \sigma_{11} + \frac{\sigma_0}{6G} \ln\left(\frac{\sigma_0 + \sigma_{11}}{\sigma_0 - \sigma_{11}}\right). \qquad (8.4.15)$$

For a typical engineering material the stress-strain relation given by Eq. (8.4.15) is shown in Fig. 8.12. It is seen that the initial slope of this curve is equal to E.

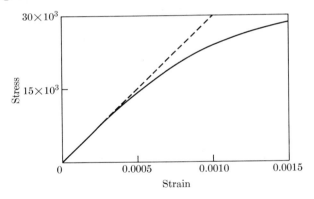

FIG. 8.12 A plot of Eq. (8.4.4) for steel.

The next problem to be considered is the plastic stress-strain relation for materials which are characterized by strain-hardening in the plastic range. Suppose we conduct a simple tensile test and load the specimen into the plastic range to a point a, as shown in Fig. 8.13. If we then release the load and reload again, we find that the yield stress has increased to the value σ_a because of the previous plastic deformation.

We now raise the question, "If, after the release of the tensile load, a combined loading is applied, what will be the yield condition?" According to a

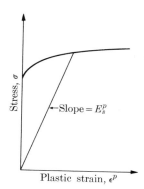

FIG. 8.13   The plastic secant modulus.

simple theory of isotropic strain-hardening, yielding will occur when the equivalent stress $\bar{\sigma}$ determined by, say, the distortion energy theory, has reached the value σ_a. The question to be answered next is, "What is the relation between the plastic strain and the equivalent stress?" In this case we are also interested in the relations among the various strain components. Of course, the latter relations are the same as those for the perfectly plastic material, given by Eq. (8.4.3), i.e., the ratio between each incremental plastic strain and the corresponding deviatoric stress remains a constant value $d\lambda$. However, for materials which are characterized by strain hardening the value $d\lambda$ can be uniquely determined if the stress-strain ($\bar{\sigma}$ vs. $\bar{\epsilon}$) curve under uniaxial loading is given. Under uniaxial tension, the incremental plastic strain is $d\bar{\epsilon}^p$ while the deviatoric stress is $\frac{2}{3}\bar{\sigma}$. Thus

$$d\lambda = \frac{3}{2}\frac{d\bar{\epsilon}^p}{\bar{\sigma}}.$$

(8.4.16)

Substituting this equation into Eq. (8.4.3), we obtain

$$d\epsilon_{11}^p = [\sigma_{11} - \tfrac{1}{2}(\sigma_{22} + \sigma_{33})]\frac{d\bar{\epsilon}^p}{\bar{\sigma}}, \qquad d\epsilon_{12}^p = \tfrac{3}{2}\sigma_{12}\frac{d\bar{\epsilon}^p}{\bar{\sigma}},$$

$$d\epsilon_{22}^p = [\sigma_{22} - \tfrac{1}{2}(\sigma_{11} + \sigma_{33})]\frac{d\bar{\epsilon}^p}{\bar{\sigma}}, \qquad d\epsilon_{23}^p = \tfrac{3}{2}\sigma_{23}\frac{d\bar{\epsilon}^p}{\bar{\sigma}},$$

$$d\epsilon_{33}^p = [\sigma_{33} - \tfrac{1}{2}(\sigma_{11} + \sigma_{22})]\frac{d\bar{\epsilon}^p}{\bar{\sigma}}, \qquad d\epsilon_{31}^p = \tfrac{3}{2}\sigma_{31}\frac{d\bar{\epsilon}^p}{\bar{\sigma}};$$

(8.4.17)

or

$$d\epsilon_{ij}^p = \tfrac{3}{2}\hat{\sigma}_{ij}\frac{d\bar{\epsilon}^p}{\bar{\sigma}}.$$

(8.4.18)

We can eliminate stresses from the above equation. For example, if the reference axes are the principal axes, we have

$$d\epsilon_I^p = [\sigma_I - \tfrac{1}{2}(\sigma_{II} + \sigma_{III})]\frac{d\bar{\epsilon}^p}{\bar{\sigma}}, \qquad d\epsilon_{II}^p = [\sigma_{II} - \tfrac{1}{2}(\sigma_I + \sigma_{III})]\frac{d\bar{\epsilon}^p}{\bar{\sigma}},$$

$$d\epsilon_{III}^p = [\sigma_{III} - \tfrac{1}{2}(\sigma_I + \sigma_{II})]\frac{d\bar{\epsilon}^p}{\bar{\sigma}}. \tag{8.4.19}$$

From the above we obtain

$$(d\epsilon_I^p - d\epsilon_{II}^p)^2 + (d\epsilon_{II}^p - d\epsilon_{III}^p)^2 + (d\epsilon_{III}^p - d\epsilon_I^p)^2$$

$$= \tfrac{9}{4}[(\sigma_I - \sigma_{II})^2 + (\sigma_{II} - \sigma_{III})^2 + (\sigma_{III} - \sigma_I)^2]\left(\frac{d\bar{\epsilon}^p}{\bar{\sigma}}\right)^2 \tag{8.4.20}$$

$$= \tfrac{3}{2}(d\bar{\epsilon}^p)^2,$$

or

$$d\bar{\epsilon}^p = \sqrt{\tfrac{2}{9}[(d\epsilon_I^p - d\epsilon_{II}^p)^2 + (d\epsilon_{II}^p - d\epsilon_{III}^p)^2 + (d\epsilon_{III}^p - d\epsilon_I^p)^2]}. \tag{8.4.21}$$

Knowing the incremental values $d\bar{\epsilon}^p$, we can determine by integration the total equivalent plastic strain $\bar{\epsilon}^p$.

Under the present theory, which is often called the *incremental strain theory* or *flow theory*, the equivalent stress $\bar{\sigma}$ and equivalent strain $\bar{\epsilon}$ are related in the *same* manner *as* the tensile stress-strain curve of the material. It should be noted that the individual strain components such as ϵ_I^p, ϵ_{II}^p, and ϵ_{III}^p, which are obtainable by integration, are usually not unique functions of the stress components. Under the incremental strain theory the final state of strain is a function of the loading path. Thus if the same state of strain is reached through two different paths, the resulting states of stress will be different.

We shall consider now a particular type of combined loading under which the proportions of the various stress components remain the same. This means that the ratio $\hat{\sigma}_{ij}/\bar{\sigma}$ remains constant. We can thus integrate Eq. (8.4.18) and write

$$\epsilon_{ij}^p = \frac{3}{2}\frac{\hat{\sigma}_{ij}}{\bar{\sigma}}\bar{\epsilon}^p, \tag{8.4.22}$$

or

$$\epsilon_{ij}^p = \frac{3}{2}\frac{\hat{\sigma}_{ij}}{E_s^p}, \tag{8.4.23}$$

where E_s^p is the secant modulus referred to the plastic component of strain, as shown in Fig. 8.13. It is seen that this stress-strain relation is expressed in terms of final strain. Thus the stress-strain relation given by Eq. (8.4.12) is often referred to as the total strain or deformation theory of plasticity. In a strict sense, this theory is applicable only under proportional loading conditions.

Illustrative Examples

(a) Shear stress-strain relations. The stress-strain curve obtained by a simple tensile test of an isotropic material can be expressed as

$$\epsilon = \frac{\sigma}{E} + \left(\frac{\sigma}{B}\right)^n.$$ (8.4.24)

It is required to determine the shear stress-shear strain relation for the same material. The shear modulus in the elastic range is G.

For the shear stress and strain we use the engineering notation τ and γ (see Sections 5.5 and 7.7). We have

$$\gamma = \frac{\tau}{G} + \gamma^p,$$ (8.4.25)

$$\frac{\gamma^p/2}{\tau} = \frac{3}{2}\frac{1}{E_s^p},$$ (8.4.26)

$$E_s^p = \frac{\bar{\sigma}}{\bar{\epsilon}^p} = \frac{\bar{\sigma}}{(\bar{\sigma}/B)^n}.$$ (8.4.27)

Under pure shear the equivalent stress given by the distortion-energy theory is

$$\bar{\sigma} = \sqrt{3}\,\tau.$$ (8.4.28)

Thus, by combining the above equations, we obtain

$$\gamma = \frac{\tau}{G} + 3^{(n+1)/2}\,B^{-n}\tau^n.$$ (8.4.29)

We can then write

$$\gamma = \frac{\tau}{G} + \left(\frac{\tau}{A}\right)^n,$$ (8.4.30)

where

$$A = \frac{B}{3^{(1/2+1/2n)}}.$$ (8.4.31)

(b) Plate under varying biaxial stresses. Consider a thin plate under biaxial tension stresses σ_I and σ_{II}, as shown in Fig. 8.14. The material is isotropic, and its plastic behavior may be idealized as rigid-plastic with linear strain-hardening. Under uniaxial tension the stress-strain diagram is as shown in Fig. 8.15. The tangent modulus E_t is a constant. Now let the principal stresses σ_I and σ_{II} be varying with respect to time. We represent this condition as

$$\sigma_I = f(t),$$ (8.4.32)

and

$$\sigma_{II} = g(t).$$ (8.4.33)

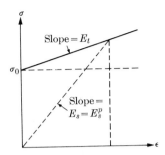

FIG. 8.14 Thin plate under biaxial tension stresses.

FIG. 8.15 Stress-strain diagram: rigid-plastic with linear strain-hardening.

Our objective is to calculate the time history of the three principal strains ϵ_I, ϵ_{II}, and ϵ_{III}, based on the incremental strain theory.

Since the material is rigid-plastic, the total strains ϵ_I, ϵ_{II}, and ϵ_{III} are the same as the plastic strains. Thus, based on Eq. (8.4.19), the increments of the principal strains can be expressed as

$$d\epsilon_I = d\epsilon_I^p = (\sigma_I - \tfrac{1}{2}\sigma_{II})\frac{d\bar{\epsilon}^p}{\bar{\sigma}}, \tag{8.4.34}$$

$$d\epsilon_{II} = d\epsilon_{II}^p = (\sigma_{II} - \tfrac{1}{2}\sigma_I)\frac{d\bar{\epsilon}^p}{\bar{\sigma}}, \tag{8.4.35}$$

$$d\epsilon_{III} = d\epsilon_{III}^p = -\tfrac{1}{2}(\sigma_I + \sigma_{II})\frac{d\bar{\epsilon}^p}{\bar{\sigma}}, \tag{8.4.36}$$

where the equivalent stress $\bar{\sigma}$ is given by

$$\bar{\sigma} = (\sigma_I^2 - \sigma_I\sigma_{II} + \sigma_{II}^2)^{1/2} = (f^2 - fg + g^2)^{1/2}. \tag{8.4.37}$$

For the present linear strain-hardening behavior,

$$\frac{d\bar{\epsilon}^p}{d\bar{\sigma}} = \frac{1}{E_t} = \text{const.} \tag{8.4.38}$$

Let us rewrite Eq. (8.4.34) in the form

$$d\epsilon_I = \frac{(\sigma_I - (1/2)\sigma_{II})}{\bar{\sigma}}\frac{d\bar{\epsilon}^p}{d\bar{\sigma}}\,d\bar{\sigma}. \tag{8.4.39}$$

By substituting Eqs. (8.4.32), (8.4.33), (8.4.37), (8.4.38), and the following one,

$$d\bar{\sigma} = \tfrac{1}{2}(f^2 - fg + g^2)^{-1/2}[f'(2f - g) + g'(2g - f)], \tag{8.4.40}$$

into Eq. (8.4.39), we obtain

$$d\epsilon_I = \frac{1}{4E_t} \frac{(2f-g)[f'(2f-g) + g'(2g-f)]}{f^2 - fg + g^2} dt. \qquad (8.4.41)$$

Thus

$$\epsilon_I = \frac{1}{4E_t} \int_{t_0}^{t} \frac{(2f-g)[f'(2f-g) + g'(2g-f)]}{f^2 - fg + g^2} dt, \qquad (8.4.42)$$

where t_0 is the instant of time when the material begins to yield under biaxial stresses, i.e., when

$$[f(t)]^2 - f(t)g(t) + [g(t)]^2 = \sigma_0^2. \qquad (8.4.43)$$

Similarly, for the other two principal strains, we obtain

$$\epsilon_{II} = \frac{1}{4E_t} \int_{t_0}^{t} \frac{(2g-f)[f'(2f-g) + g'(2g-f)]}{f^2 - fg + g^2} dt \qquad (8.4.44)$$

and

$$\epsilon_{III} = -\frac{1}{4E_t} \int_{t_0}^{t} \frac{(f+g)[f'(2f-g) + g'(2g-f)]}{f^2 - fg + g^2} dt. \qquad (8.4.45)$$

Thus based on the incremental strain theory, the state of strain is a function of the complete loading history.

It is of interest to note that under the deformation theory the state of strain at a given instant of time is given by Eqs. (8.4.23):

$$\epsilon_I = \epsilon_I^p = \frac{\sigma_I - \frac{1}{2}\sigma_{II}}{E_s^p}, \qquad \epsilon_{II} = \epsilon_{II}^p = \frac{\sigma_{II} - \frac{1}{2}\sigma_I}{E_s^p},$$

$$\epsilon_{III} = \epsilon_{III}^p = -\frac{1}{2}\left(\frac{\sigma_I + \sigma_{II}}{E_s^p}\right), \qquad (8.4.46)$$

where for a given value of the equivalent stress $\bar{\sigma}$ the secant modulus is

$$E_s^p = \frac{\bar{\sigma} E_t}{\bar{\sigma} - \sigma_0}. \qquad (8.4.47)$$

Under the deformation theory the state of strain is only a function of the instantaneous state of stress.

8.5 SUMMARY

This chapter presents the two most important considerations in defining the plastic behavior of materials, the state of combined stresses which will cause the material to yield, and the multiaxial stress-strain relations in the plastic range. For simplicity this discussion has been limited to isotropic materials.

Yield conditions

   The Tresca or maximum shear-stress condition. Yielding occurs whenever the maximum shear stress is equal to one-half the yield stress in simple tension. Under the state of biaxial stress when $\sigma_{\text{III}} = 0$, the yield boundary is a closed hexagon defined by the following lines:

$$\sigma_{\text{I}} = \pm\sigma_0,$$

$$\sigma_{\text{II}} = \pm\sigma_0, \tag{8.5.1}$$

and

$$\sigma_{\text{I}} - \sigma_{\text{II}} = \pm\sigma_0.$$

   The Mises-Hencky or distortion-energy criterion: yielding occurs whenever the distortion energy is equal to $(1/6G)\sigma_0^2$ or when the following condition for the principal stresses is satisfied:

$$(\sigma_{\text{I}} - \sigma_{\text{II}})^2 + (\sigma_{\text{II}} - \sigma_{\text{III}})^2 + (\sigma_{\text{I}} - \sigma_{\text{III}})^2 = 2\sigma_0^2. \tag{8.5.2}$$

   The biaxial stress yield condition is given by an ellipse:

$$\sigma_{\text{I}}^2 - \sigma_{\text{I}}\sigma_{\text{II}} + \sigma_{\text{II}}^2 = \sigma_0^2. \tag{8.5.3}$$

   Plastic stress-strain relations for elastic perfectly plastic materials

$$\epsilon_{mn} = \epsilon_{mn}^e + \epsilon_{mn}^p. \tag{8.5.4}$$

The elastic-strain components are related to the stress components by the generalized Hooke's law:

$$\epsilon_{mn}^e = (1/E)[(1 + \nu)\sigma_{mn} - \nu\,\delta_{mn}\sigma_{rr}]. \tag{8.5.5}$$

The plastic strain components are characterized by

$$\epsilon_{rr}^p = 0 \quad \text{and} \quad \frac{d\epsilon_{mn}^p}{\hat{\sigma}_{mn}} = d\lambda, \tag{8.5.6}$$

where $d\lambda$ is an indication of plastic flow.

   Plastic stress-strain relation for materials which are characterized by strain hardening. The plastic behavior is governed by an equivalent stress $\bar{\sigma}$ and equivalent plastic strain $\bar{\epsilon}^p$, where $\bar{\sigma}$ is defined by

$$\bar{\sigma} = \sqrt{\tfrac{1}{2}[(\sigma_{\text{I}} - \sigma_{\text{II}})^2 + (\sigma_{\text{II}} - \sigma_{\text{III}})^2 + (\sigma_{\text{I}} - \sigma_{\text{III}})^2]} \tag{8.5.7}$$

and $\bar{\epsilon}^p$ is the integral of $d\bar{\epsilon}^p$ defined by

$$d\bar{\epsilon}^p = \sqrt{\tfrac{2}{9}[(d\epsilon_{\text{I}}^p - d\epsilon_{\text{II}}^p)^2 + (d\epsilon_{\text{II}}^p - d\epsilon_{\text{III}}^p)^2 + (d\epsilon_{\text{I}}^p - d\epsilon_{\text{III}}^p)^2]},$$

$$\tag{8.5.8}$$

where

$$d\epsilon^p_I = \frac{[\sigma_I - \frac{1}{2}(\sigma_{II} + \sigma_{III})] \, d\bar{\epsilon}^p}{\bar{\sigma}},$$

$$d\epsilon^p_{II} = \frac{[\sigma_{II} - \frac{1}{2}(\sigma_I + \sigma_{III})] \, d\bar{\epsilon}^p}{\bar{\sigma}}, \qquad (8.5.9)$$

$$d\epsilon^p_{III} = \frac{[\sigma_{III} - \frac{1}{2}(\sigma_I + \sigma_{II})] \, d\bar{\epsilon}^p}{\bar{\sigma}}.$$

PROBLEMS

8.1 (a) Plot stress-strain diagrams for the following materials: steel alloy, $\sigma_{ult} = 180{,}000$ psi; aluminum alloy, 2024-T3; and magnesium alloy. Use the data given in Table 8.1. (b) Find graphically the 0.2% offset yield stress for each of the above materials. (c) From the graphs obtained in part (a), draw graphs of the tangent and secant moduli versus total strain for each material.

8.2 The following analytical expression has been used to describe the stress-strain relation of a certain material:

$$\epsilon = \frac{\sigma}{B} + \frac{\sigma}{\sigma_{ult} - \sigma},$$

where B and σ_{ult} are constants. From a uniaxial tensile test of this material the following test data were obtained:

σ (psi)	500	1000	10,000
ϵ (in./in.)	0.0051	0.0104	0.1500

(a) Determine the values of B, σ_{ult}, and the elastic modulus E. (b) Let σ_0 be the 0.2% offset yield stress. Calculate the numerical value of σ_0 from the given test data. (c) Derive an expression for the relation between shear stress and engineering strain for the material, using (i) the distortion energy theory, and (ii) the maximum shear stress theory.

8.3 A two-material bar is built into rigid walls at both ends, as shown in Fig. P.8.3(a). Both bars have the same cross-sectional area and coefficient of thermal expansion, $\alpha = 10^{-4}/°\text{F}$. Bar A may be treated as a rigid perfectly plastic material, and bar B as elastic and linear strain-hardening. Figure P.8.3(b) illustrates the material properties

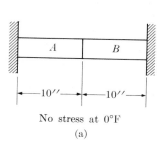

No stress at 0°F

(a)

FIGURE P.8.3

(b)

of bars A and B. It is assumed that the material properties are independent of temperature. (a) Describe the deformation of the system as the temperature is increased. (b) Calculate the temperature at which materials A and B start to yield. Neglect three-dimensional effects by assuming that $\nu = 0$ in both the elastic and the plastic ranges. Describe the deformation and stress histories of the system as the temperature is increased further.

8.4 A sheet of material having a yield stress $\sigma_0 = 50{,}000$ psi is loaded in a state of plane stress by the stresses $\sigma_{11} = 200{,}000$ psi, $\sigma_{22} = -20{,}000$ psi, and σ_{12}. Compute the value of σ_{12} which is required to cause the material to yield under the assumptions of (a) the Tresca Theory and (b) the Distortion-Energy Theory.

8.5 A thin plate is in the state of uniform plane stress (Fig. P.8.5). The stress components are in the following proportions:

$$\sigma_{11} : \sigma_{22} : \sigma_{12} = 1 : +\tfrac{1}{2} : +\tfrac{1}{2}.$$

Determine the plane along which slip will occur when the stress is increasing proportionally. Assume slip will occur along planes of maximum shear stress.

FIGURE P.8.5   FIGURE P.8.6

8.6 The rectangular plate shown in Fig. P.8.6 is constrained against deformation in the y_2-direction by rigid tracks at the edges AB and CD. The material is elastic perfectly plastic, with $E = 10{,}000{,}000$ psi, $\nu = 0.3$, and $\sigma_0 = 50{,}000$ psi for uniaxial tension. Using (a) the Mises-Hencky criterion, and (b) the Tresca criterion, calculate the values of σ_{11} and ϵ_{11} at which the constrained plate begins to yield.

8.7 A square plate is subjected to uniform tension in both the y_1- and y_2-directions, such that σ_{11} is always twice the value of σ_{22} (see Fig. P.8.7a). The material is isotropic and can be idealized as elastic and linear strain-hardening, as shown in Fig. P.8.7(b). Poisson's ratio is equal to $\tfrac{1}{3}$ in the elastic range. Calculate and plot the strains ϵ_{11} and ϵ_{22} as functions of σ_{11} for the range $0 \leq \sigma_{11} \leq 2\sigma_0$.

8.8 For the plate in the previous problem, if the value of σ_{22} remains always $\tfrac{1}{2}\sigma_0$ while σ_{11} increases gradually from zero, calculate and plot the strains ϵ_{11} and ϵ_{22} as functions of σ_{11} for the range $0 \leq \sigma_{11} \leq 2\sigma_0$.

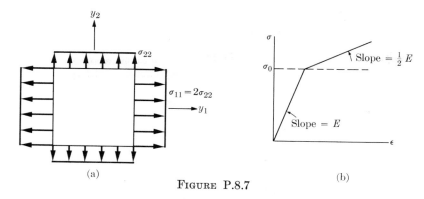

(a)

(b)

FIGURE P.8.7

8.9   The plate illustrated by Figs. 8.14 and 8.15 is strained by biaxial tension. The time histories of the two principal strains are given by $\epsilon_I = F(t)$ and $\epsilon_{II} = G(t)$. Develop the equations which are required for determining the time histories of the two principal stresses.

8.10   A thin-wall tube with closed ends as shown in Fig. P.8.10 is acted upon by a constant torque of 12,560 in -lb. The shear stress σ_{12} due to T is given by $\sigma_{12} = T/2\pi r^2 t$, where t = thickness of the tube = 0.05 in. and r = radius of the tube = 2 in. As shown in the sketch, y_1, y_2, and y_3 are along the longitudinal, circumferential, and radial directions, respectively.

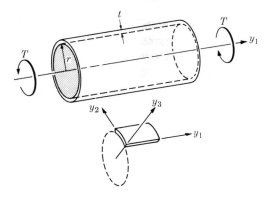

FIGURE P.8.10

The torque is kept constant while the internal pressure is gradually increased. Express the percentage increase in tube diameter as a function of the internal pressure p for each of the following sets of material properties:

(a) elastic linear strain-hardening with elastic modulus = $E = 10^7$ psi, yield stress under uniaxial tension = $\sigma_0 = 40,000$ psi, tangent modulus = $E_t = 2 \times 10^6$ psi;

(b) stress-strain relation in tension given by

$$\epsilon = \frac{\sigma}{10^7} + \left(\frac{\sigma}{10^6}\right)^2.$$

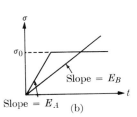

FIGURE P.8.11

8.11   The wall of a long closed-end tube consists of two layers as shown in Fig. P.8.11(a). The thickness for each layer is h which is small in comparison to the diameter d of the tube. The elastic moduli for the two materials A and B are E_A and E_B, respectively, and Poisson's ratio for both materials is ν. Material A becomes perfectly plastic at σ_0, while material B has a very high elastic limit (see Fig. P.8.11b). Derive the equations required for evaluating the elastic and plastic deformation of the tube under increasing internal pressure.

REFERENCES

(1) W. RAMBERG and W. R. OSGOOD, "Description of Stress-Strain Curves by Three Parameters," *NACA TN* 902 (July 1943).

(2) P. W. BRIDGEMAN, "Effects of High Hydrostatic Pressure on the Plastic Properties of Metals," *Reviews of Modern Physics* **17**, 3 (Jan. 1945).

(3) A. NADAI, *Theory of Flow and Fracture of Solids*, 2nd Ed., Vol. I, McGraw-Hill, New York, 1950.

(4) W. LODE, "Versuche über den Einfluss der Mittleren Hauptspannung auf das Fliessen der Metalle Eisen, Kupfer, und Nickel," *Zeitschrift für Physik* **36**, 913–939 (1926).

(5) M. ROS and A. EICHINGER, *Proc. 2nd International Congress for Applied Mechanics*, Zurich, Switzerland, p. 315, 1926.

(6) G. I. TAYLOR and H. QUINNEY, "The Plastic Distortion of Metals," *Philosophical Transactions of the Royal Society*, London, Ser. A. **230**, 323–362 (1931).

(7) R. VON MISES, "Mechanik der festen Körper im plastischen Deformationzustand", *Göttinger Nachrichten, math.-phys. Klasse*, 582–592 (1913).

(8) H. HENCKY, "Über das Wesen der plastischen Verformung," *Z. Verendeut. Ing.* **69**, 695 (1925).

(9) M. T. HUBER, "The Work of Deformation as a Proper Measure of Material Failure" (in Polish), *Czasopismò technicznè*, Lwov (Lemberg) **22**, 81 (1904).

Energy Principles in
Solid Continuum

9.1 INTRODUCTION

The preceding seven chapters have laid the foundation for the statics of deformable bodies. We have seen that equations of static equilibrium, consistent deformation, and constitutive relationships are required for solving many problems. These equations for linearly elastic problems form a system of fifteen partial differential equations. The prospect of tackling these equations head on is somewhat frightening, and the chances of success are not very bright. Further along in our study of statics we shall discuss the possibility of reducing the general equations of three-dimensional elasticity to a considerably simplified form for problems involving the bending and twisting of beams and the bending of plates, and for problems which involve only two of the three space coordinates. We shall also discuss the direct approach of finding solutions to the simplified equations.

The direct approach of finding solutions to these fifteen equations is often difficult. An alternative method derives from considering the energy of the structural system. This direct approach may be loosely classified as a "vector" method, whereas the energy approach is often described as "scalar." The vector method examines in detail the stress vectors and displacement vectors along predetermined directions. Energy is an invariant, i.e., the energy is independent of the coordinate system used to describe the structure. The application of the energy approach, in general, obviates the task of writing some vector equations—a task often very difficult to accomplish.

This chapter will derive the various energy theorems for a general solid continuum. However, applications of these theorems will be confined to simple structural forms such as cables, rods, beams, and trusses. Applications of the energy methods to more complex structural forms will be investigated at a later time.

We must keep in mind that the various energy approaches represent alternative methods of solving the elasticity equations. For example, some energy approaches may be interpreted as a replacement of the equations of static equilibrium, while others can be used to derive the conditions of consistent deformation. There are many names attached to these theorems. The theorems are all related, as indeed they must be, since they are based on the same set of equations, i.e., the equations of elasticity. The various energy theorems merely attack the problem from different quarters. Some are better adapted for the calculation of deflections, others for the calculation of stresses. With slightly different re-interpretations, the same theorem can handle a variety of problems. The cardinal feature, however, is that the energy theorems enable us to circumvent a frontal attack on the fifteen partial differential equations of elasticity.

9.2   WORK AND INTERNAL ENERGY

In Chapter 7 we stated, on the basis of the First Law of Thermodynamics, that the work performed by the loads applied externally to a structure is equal to the energy stored in the structure by the internal stresses and strains, if we neglect the very small temperature changes which occur. Let us elaborate on this theme in order to develop a terminology and methodology which we can use in developing the energy theorems.

Consider a deformable structure which is fixed in space. Such a structure may be schematically represented in Fig. 9.1 as a planar body supported at points A and B, although the results to be derived will be applicable to three-dimensional bodies. The structure is acted upon by a system of Q-forces, as shown in the figure. There are N such forces. Note that Q_1 shown acting at point 1 is a force in the usual sense of the word, but that Q_3 shown acting at point 3 is a couple

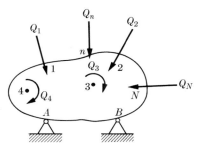

FIG. 9.1   Body loaded at N points.

force or moment. The term "generalized forces" is used to include both forces and moments; henceforth, unless specifically stated otherwise, the symbol Q_n will represent a *generalized force*.

There is defined at each of the N points a *generalized displacement*, q_n, representing the deformation of the body at that point. For Q_2, the generalized displacement is a linear deflection along the line of action of Q_2, and for the couple force (moment) Q_3, it is an angular rotation about a line perpendicular to the plane of the couple force Q_3. These two typical generalized displacements are shown in Fig. 9.2, where the generalized force Q_3 is depicted as a couple force in order to indicate more clearly the angular rotation nature of q_3. Thus q_3 represents the rotation of a small line segment at point 3 as the body is deformed. In general, therefore, the product of a generalized force and its associated

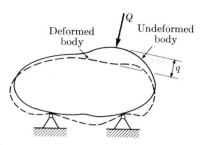

FIG. 9.2   Two types of generalized forces and generalized displacements.

FIG. 9.3   Body under a single force.

generalized displacement represents work. The positive sense of the generalized displacement is the same as that of the corresponding force.

In order to develop some fundamental concepts, let us focus our attention on a body which is acted upon by a single generalized force (see Fig. 9.3). The dashed line represents to an exaggerated degree the deformed shape of the body after Q has reached its final magnitude. The relationship between the force Q and the displacement q is shown as a force-displacement curve in Fig. 9.4. Note that we have not as yet postulated a linear relationship. For an infinitesimal increment in q, the increment in work done by Q is

$$dW = Q \, dq, \qquad (9.2.1)$$

which is the crosshatched area in Fig. 9.4. By applying the First Law of Thermodynamics (neglecting temperature changes), we find that the work done by Q is stored as internal energy in the structure, provided the supports are unyielding. This may be expressed as

$$dU = dW, \qquad (9.2.2)$$

where U denotes the strain energy (see Chapter 7). The total strain energy is given by the integral

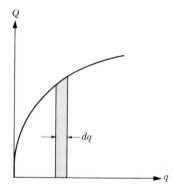

FIG. 9.4   General force-displacement relationship.

$$U = \int_0^q Q' \, dq', \qquad (9.2.3)$$

where Q and q represent the final values, and the primes merely indicate dummy integration variables.

Let us also define at this time the complementary strain energy or, as it is usually called, the *complementary energy*. It is given by a relation which is conjugate to Eq. (9.2.3),

$$U_c = \int_0^Q q' \, dQ', \qquad (9.2.4)$$

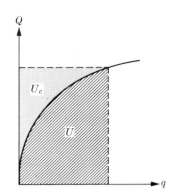

FIG. 9.5   Definition of complementary   FIG. 9.6   Strain energy and complemen-
energy.   tary energy.

and is represented by the crosshatched area in Fig. 9.5. If Eq. (9.2.4) is integrated
by parts, we get

$$U_c = Qq - U, \qquad (9.2.5)$$

a result geometrically verified by Fig. 9.6, in which the product Qq is seen to be
the area of a rectangle. The relation given by Eq. (9.2.5) is sometimes known
as *Friederich's Theorem*.

9.3   RELATIONS FOR LINEARLY ELASTIC SYSTEMS

The force-displacement curve for a linearly elastic structure is a straight line
(see Fig. 9.7). The constant slope of the curve, denoted by K, is called the
stiffness coefficient. We can write

$$Q = Kq. \qquad (9.3.1)$$

Note that if Q is a force, then K has the dimensions of force per unit length,
whereas if Q is a moment (couple force) then K has the units of force-length per
radian (or just force-length, since the radian measure of an angle is dimensionless). The determination of K, as we discovered in Chapters 4 and 7, requires
the solution of the equations of elasticity. For the present we will assume that
the value of K is known.

With the linear relation of Eq. (9.3.1), the strain energy given by Eq. (9.2.3)
becomes

$$U = \int_0^q Kq' \, dq' = \tfrac{1}{2}Kq^2. \qquad (9.3.2)$$

If the final value of the force is factored out of Eq. (9.3.2), we find that

$$U = \tfrac{1}{2}Qq. \qquad (9.3.3)$$

FIG. 9.7 Stiffness (K) and compliance (C) coefficients.

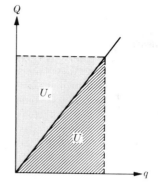

FIG. 9.8 Strain energy and complementary energy—linear system.

The preceding formula which states that the strain energy is equal to one-half the product of the force and the corresponding displacement is known as *Clapeyron's Law*. Geometrically, Eq. (9.3.3) is the area of the shaded triangle in Fig. 9.7. We will state Clapeyron's Law more rigorously at a later stage (cf. Eq. 9.3.21).

The relation conjugate to Eq. (9.3.1) is

$$q = CQ, \tag{9.3.4}$$

where C is called the *flexibility* or *compliance coefficient*. It has the dimensions of length per unit force if q is a linear displacement, and radian per unit force-length if q is an angular displacement.

By substituting Eq. (9.3.4) into Eq. (9.2.4), we obtain the complementary energy of an elastic system,

$$U_c = \int CQ' \, dQ' = \tfrac{1}{2}CQ^2. \tag{9.3.5}$$

However, it is an obvious but very useful fact that for a *linearly elastic system* the complementary energy is numerically equal to the strain energy (see Fig. 9.8), or

$$U = U_c. \tag{9.3.6}$$

For this illustrative example in which only a single force is acting on the body, we see that

$$C = K^{-1}, \tag{9.3.7}$$

that is, the compliance or flexibility coefficient is equal to the inverse of the stiffness coefficient.

Let us extend these results to a linearly elastic structure which is acted upon by a system of N (a specific number) generalized forces. Then the increment in strain energy is given by

$$dU = \sum_{m=1}^{N} Q_m \, dq_m. \qquad (9.3.8)$$

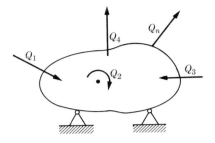

It is evident, for example, that the force Q_3 (see Fig. 9.9) will cause deformations throughout the body and specifically at the N points of particular interest. Thus the displacement at point n, for instance, is due not only to the load at

FIG. 9.9   Body loaded at N points.

point n, but to all the other $N-1$ generalized forces. We may therefore write

$$q_n = q_n(Q_1, Q_2, \ldots, Q_N), \qquad (9.3.9)$$

to indicate that q_n is a function of all the generalized forces which are acting on the structure. The total differential of q_n is

$$dq_n = \frac{\partial q_n}{\partial Q_1} dQ_1 + \frac{\partial q_n}{\partial Q_2} dQ_2 + \cdots + \frac{\partial q_n}{\partial Q_N} dQ_N. \qquad (9.3.10)$$

Since the structure is linearly elastic, the partial derivatives are constants. We will call them the flexibility or compliance influence coefficients:

$$C_{nm} = \frac{\partial q_n}{\partial Q_m}. \qquad (9.3.11)$$

It is seen that C_{nm} is the generalized displacement at point n in the structure, caused by a unit value of the generalized force at point m. This is illustrated in Fig. 9.10 by means of a cantilever beam. We will later prove that the flexibility influence coefficients are symmetric, that is,

$$C_{nm} = C_{mn}. \qquad (9.3.12)$$

The linear nature of the problem permits us to integrate Eq. (9.3.10) to obtain

$$q_n = \sum_{m=1}^{N} C_{nm}Q_m, \qquad n = 1, 2, \ldots, N. \qquad (9.3.13)$$

We will assume that the relation given by Eq. (9.3.9) can be inverted to yield

$$Q_n = Q_n(q_1, q_2, \ldots, q_N). \qquad (9.3.14)$$

By a line of reasoning parallel to that used for C_{nm} we can develop the equation

$$Q_m = \sum_{n=1}^{N} K_{mn}q_n, \qquad (9.3.15)$$

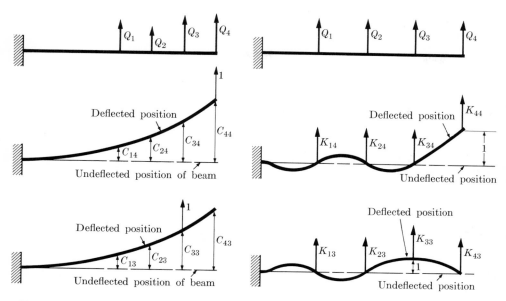

FIG. 9.10 Illustration of flexibility influence coefficients.

FIG. 9.11 Illustration of stiffness influence coefficients.

where the K_{mn}, called the *stiffness influence coefficients*, are given by

$$K_{mn} = \frac{\partial Q_m}{\partial q_n}.\qquad(9.3.16)$$

The stiffness influence coefficients are somewhat more difficult to visualize. The coefficient K_{nm} is the generalized force Q_n required at point n when the generalized displacement q_m has a unit value while all the other generalized displacements are zero. We again use a cantilever beam (shown in Fig. 9.11) to illustrate the meaning of the stiffness influence coefficient. We will later show that the stiffness influence coefficients are also symmetric, that is,

$$K_{nm} = K_{mn}.\qquad(9.3.17)$$

In order to evaluate the total strain energy by integrating Eq. (9.3.8), we must become cognizant of the conservative nature of our linearly elastic system. The strain energy stored in the body is dependent only on the final state of the forces and displacements, and not on the process whereby the final state is attained. This means that the sequence of load applications, that is, Q_1 first, then Q_2, etc., or any order whatever, is unimportant. Mathematically, it is said that the "path" of integration is unimportant. In evaluating the strain energy it is therefore permissible and helpful in the integration process to assume that the generalized displacements q_n maintain the same proportion at all times, that is,

$$q_n = B_n q, \tag{9.3.18}$$

where the B_n's are factors of proportionality and q is a function varying from 0 to 1. The generalized force Q_m is then given by

$$Q_m = \sum_{n=1}^{N} K_{mn} q_n = \sum_{n=1}^{N} K_{mn} B_n q. \tag{9.3.19}$$

With this intermediate result, Eq. (9.3.8) can be integrated to yield

$$U = \frac{1}{2} \sum_{m=1}^{N} \sum_{n=1}^{N} K_{mn} B_m B_n q^2 = \frac{1}{2} \sum_{m=1}^{N} \sum_{n=1}^{N} K_{mn} q_m q_n. \tag{9.3.20}$$

The factoring of Eq. (9.3.15) from Eq. (9.3.20) results in

$$U = \frac{1}{2} \sum_{n=1}^{N} Q_n q_n. \tag{9.3.21}$$

This formula is Clapeyron's Law which can be stated as follows:

The work done by a system of forces acting on a linearly elastic structure is in-dependent of the rate at which the forces increase and of the order in which the forces are applied. The work done, which is stored as strain energy, is equal to one-half the product of the final magnitudes of the generalized force and its corresponding generalized displacement. The structure must be initially stress free and not subjected to temperature changes.

By using an argument similar to that used for U, the complementary energy relation can be derived:

$$U_c = \frac{1}{2} \sum_{m=1}^{N} \sum_{n=1}^{N} C_{mn} Q_m Q_n. \tag{9.3.22}$$

The relationship between the flexibility influence coefficients and the stiffness influence coefficients can be derived from Eqs. (9.3.13) and (9.3.15), which are two sets of simultaneous linear algebraic equations. They can be written in matrix notation (see Appendix, Section A-20):

$$
\begin{bmatrix} q_1 \\ q_2 \\ \vdots \\ q_N \end{bmatrix}
=
\begin{bmatrix}
C_{11} & C_{12} & \cdots & C_{1N} \\
C_{21} & \cdots & \cdots & C_{2N} \\
\vdots & & & \vdots \\
C_{N1} & \cdots & \cdots & C_{NN}
\end{bmatrix}
\begin{bmatrix} Q_1 \\ Q_2 \\ \vdots \\ Q_N \end{bmatrix}, \tag{9.3.23}
$$

and

$$
\begin{bmatrix} Q_1 \\ Q_2 \\ \vdots \\ Q_N \end{bmatrix} = \begin{bmatrix} K_{11} & K_{12} & \ldots & K_{1N} \\ K_{21} & \ldots & \ldots & K_{2N} \\ \vdots & & & \vdots \\ K_{N1} & \ldots & \ldots & K_{NN} \end{bmatrix} \begin{bmatrix} q_1 \\ q_2 \\ \vdots \\ q_N \end{bmatrix}.
\tag{9.3.24}
$$

These may be written compactly as

$$
\{q\} = [C]\{Q\}
\tag{9.3.25}
$$

and

$$
\{Q\} = [K]\{q\},
\tag{9.3.26}
$$

where $[C]$ and $[K]$ are, respectively, the matrices of flexibility and stiffness influence coefficients. By premultiplying Eq. (9.3.25) by $[C]^{-1}$, the inverse of the matrix of the flexibility influence coefficients (see Appendix, Section A–26), we obtain

$$
[C]^{-1}\{q\} = [C]^{-1}[C]\{Q\} = \{Q\}.
\tag{9.3.27}
$$

Comparing with Eq. (9.3.26) we can conclude that

$$
[K] = [C]^{-1}.
\tag{9.3.28}
$$

This says that the matrix of stiffness influence coefficients is the inverse of the matrix of flexibility influence coefficients. We can also show that

$$
[C] = [K]^{-1}.
\tag{9.3.29}
$$

9.4 PRINCIPLE OF VIRTUAL WORK

We are now in position to develop the Principle of Virtual Work. This energy principle will be used as the foundation for other energy principles and theorems. It is simply stated, but the many different possible interpretations not only lead to new theorems, but give the principle a great deal of versatility.

Let us consider again a structure acted on by a system of generalized forces Q_m (see Fig. 9.12). The generalized forces induce stresses and deformations which satisfy the differential equations of equilibrium (Eq. 7.12.5), strain-displacement relations (Eq. 7.12.4), and the stress-strain relations. The last relations are not necessarily elastic. We can gain information about the behavior of this particular structure by deliberately perturbing (or provoking) the structure. The cause of the perturbations will, in general, be entirely unrelated to the Q forces already acting on the body, and will depend on the type of information desired. For example, the virtual deformations may be caused by another system of forces acting on the body or by a temperature change. In the development of the principle our only concern is that the perturbations

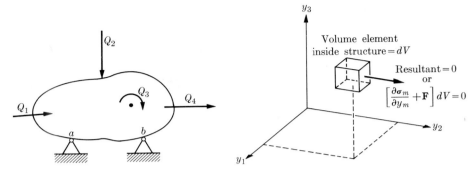

Fɪɢ. 9.12   Body under a system of generalized forces.

Fɪɢ. 9.13   Equilibrium of an elementary volume.

manifest themselves in what will be called a virtual distortion of the body. The word "virtual" is used to signify that the distortion is independent of the Q-forces. In the interior of the structure the virtual distortion will be denoted by the vector $\delta \mathbf{u}$ (y_1, y_2, y_3), and at the points of application of the Q forces, by δq_m. The virtual displacement $\delta \mathbf{u}$ must be consistent with the geometrical constraints of the structure, e.g., in Fig. 9.12, we know that $\delta \mathbf{u}$ must be zero at points a and b. Additionally, the virtual displacement cannot affect the equilibrium of the Q-force system. Consequently, the magnitudes of $\delta \mathbf{u}$ are usually such that the lines of action of the Q-forces and the Q-induced internal stresses can be assumed to be unaffected by the distortion.

The Principle of Virtual Work is stated mathematically as

$$\delta U = Q_m \, \delta q_m, \tag{9.4.1}$$

where δU represents the work done internally by the Q-induced stresses under the strains engendered by the virtual deformation $\delta \mathbf{u}$. In words, the Principle may be stated as follows:

If a body is in equilibrium and remains in equilibrium while it is subjected to a virtual distortion compatible with the geometrical constraints, the virtual work done by the external forces is equal to the virtual work done by the internal stresses.

Let us now present a formal proof of Eq. (9.4.1). The resultant force acting on a volume element is given by Eq. (6.6.3), and because the volume element is in equilibrium, this resultant force must be zero. These results are shown schematically in Fig. 9.13. The point of application of the force vector shown in this figure is subjected to the small virtual displacement $\delta \mathbf{u}$, and hence, although work is done by each of the components, the net result is zero. We write this as the integral of the scalar product of force and displacement:

$$\iiint \left\{ \left(\frac{\partial \boldsymbol{\sigma}_m}{\partial y_m} + \mathbf{F} \right) \cdot \delta \mathbf{u} \right\} dV = 0. \tag{9.4.2}$$

A slight rearrangement of Eq. (9.4.2) leads to the form

$$\iiint \left\{ \frac{\partial(\boldsymbol{\sigma}_m \cdot \delta \mathbf{u})}{\partial y_m} + \mathbf{F} \cdot \delta \mathbf{u} \right\} dV = \iiint \left\{ \boldsymbol{\sigma}_m \cdot \frac{\partial(\delta \mathbf{u})}{\partial y_m} \right\} dV. \qquad (9.4.3)$$

With the aid of the Divergence Theorem, or Green's Theorem (see Section A-19), the first term on the left-hand side of the preceding equation can be converted to a surface integral:

$$\iiint \frac{\partial(\boldsymbol{\sigma}_m \cdot \delta \mathbf{u})}{\partial y_m} \, dV = \iint \boldsymbol{\sigma}_m \cdot \delta \mathbf{u} \, n_m \, dA, \qquad (9.4.4)$$

where the n_m are the components of the unit outward normal vector which locates the orientation of the element of area dA on the surface of the body (see Chapter 6).

The surface integral in Eq. (9.4.4) is recognizable as the virtual work of the externally applied surface forces, since $\boldsymbol{\sigma}_m$ will be zero except at those places where forces are applied. Thus, if only discrete forces are applied to the surface of the structure as in Fig. (9.12), then

$$Q_n \, \delta q_n = \iint \{ \boldsymbol{\sigma}_m \cdot \delta \mathbf{u} \, n_m \, dA \}. \qquad (9.4.5)$$

The right-hand side of Eq. (9.4.3) can also be simplified and interpreted in a meaningful fashion. By introducing Eq. (6.3.4) we can change the integral into the form

$$\boldsymbol{\sigma}_m \cdot \frac{\partial(\delta \mathbf{u})}{\partial y_m} = \sigma_{mn} \mathbf{i}_n \cdot \frac{\partial(\delta \mathbf{u})}{\partial y_m}. \qquad (9.4.6)$$

Since the stress tensor σ_{mn} is symmetric, the terms can be further rearranged:

$$\sigma_{mn} \mathbf{i}_n \cdot \frac{\partial(\delta \mathbf{u})}{\partial y_m} = \sigma_{mn} \left\{ \frac{1}{2} \left[\mathbf{i}_n \cdot \frac{\partial(\delta \mathbf{u})}{\partial y_m} + \mathbf{i}_m \cdot \frac{\partial(\delta \mathbf{u})}{\partial y_n} \right] \right\}. \qquad (9.4.7)$$

The geometrical meaning of the expression inside the braces is recognized as the virtual strain tensor (compare with Eq. 5.9.1):

$$\delta \epsilon_{mn} = \frac{1}{2} \left[\mathbf{i}_n \cdot \frac{\partial(\delta \mathbf{u})}{\partial y_m} + \mathbf{i}_m \cdot \frac{\partial(\delta \mathbf{u})}{\partial y_n} \right]. \qquad (9.4.8)$$

If we write the virtual displacement in component form,

$$\delta \mathbf{u} = \delta u_m \mathbf{i}_m, \qquad (9.4.9)$$

then

$$\delta \epsilon_{mn} = \frac{1}{2} \left[\frac{\partial \delta u_m}{\partial y_n} + \frac{\partial \delta u_n}{\partial y_m} \right]. \qquad (9.4.10)$$

All these expressions [Eqs. (9.4.8) through (9.4.10)] are of the same form as those used in Chapter 5. The only difference is that instead of using $\mathbf{u}$ to describe the deformation of the structure we are now using $\delta\mathbf{u}$ to describe the virtual deformation.

The virtual-work equation which started out as Eq. (9.4.2) now assumes a form which can be directly applied to structural problems:

$$\iint \boldsymbol{\sigma}_m \cdot \delta\mathbf{u}n_m \, dA + \iiint \mathbf{F} \cdot \delta\mathbf{u} \, dV = \iiint \sigma_{mn} \, \delta\epsilon_{mn} \, dV. \qquad (9.4.11)$$

The left-hand side has a physical interpretation as the virtual work of the external forces, and the right-hand side is the virtual work of the internal stresses (Eq. 9.4.1). It will be helpful to write Eq. (9.4.11) as

$$\delta W = \delta U, \qquad (9.4.12)$$

with

$$\delta W = \iint \boldsymbol{\sigma}_m \cdot \delta\mathbf{u}n_m \, dA + \iiint \mathbf{F} \cdot \delta\mathbf{u} \, dV, \qquad (9.4.13)$$

and

$$\delta U = \iiint \sigma_{mn} \, \delta\epsilon_{mn} \, dV. \qquad (9.4.14)$$

If, as has already been remarked, the external forces consist only of generalized forces of a discrete nature, then Eq. (9.4.12) has the special form given by Eq. (9.4.1). The semantics of the word "external" may be a little troublesome since the force $\mathbf{F}$ is a volume force and appears in the interior of the body. However, "external" is used to mean the applied loads or the cause of the stresses and strains.

Let us present several examples to illustrate the application of the Principle of Virtual Work.

(a) Some simple examples for δU. The virtual work of the internal stresses takes on simple forms for the simpler types of structures. For a member in a state of uniaxial stress (such as a rod or the members of a truss) there is only one stress component and one strain component. Let us consider the situation shown in Fig. 9.14. A rod of uniform cross-sectional area A and length L is loaded at its free end by a load Q. If we let the virtual deformation of the rod be represented by the end elongation δq, the virtual strain $\delta\epsilon$ in the rod is given by $\delta q/L$. The axial stress caused by Q is

$$\sigma^{(Q)} = Q/A. \qquad (9.4.15)$$

Hence the virtual work of the internal stress is

$$\delta U = \int_{\text{vol}} \sigma^{(Q)} \, \delta\epsilon \, dV = Q \, \delta q. \qquad (9.4.16)$$

(a)

(b)

FIG. 9.14 Prismatic bar under uniaxial   FIG. 9.15 Cantilever beam under two
tension.   systems of loading.

If we consider the virtual deformation as that caused by a load P (Fig. 9.14b)
we have

$$\delta q = PL/AE, \tag{9.4.17}$$

and

$$\delta U = QPL/AE. \tag{9.4.18}$$

Consider next a cantilever beam as shown in Fig. 9.15. The stresses caused by
Q (see Section 7.13) are

$$\sigma^{(Q)} = -\frac{M^{(Q)}(x)z}{I}, \tag{9.4.19}$$

where I is the cross-sectional moment of inertia and $M^{(Q)}(x)$ is the bending-
moment function caused by the Q-forces. We shall now consider the virtual
deformation as that due to a uniformly distributed load p. Again, according
to Chapter 7, the virtual strain distribution in the beam corresponding to this
virtual deformation is given by

$$\delta\epsilon = -\frac{M^{(p)}(x)z}{EI}, \tag{9.4.20}$$

where $M^{(p)}(x)$ is the bending-moment function caused by the distributed load p
on the beam. The virtual work of the internal stresses for the bending of a
beam is

$$\delta U = \int_{\text{vol}} \sigma^{(Q)}\,\delta\epsilon\,dV = \int_0^L \frac{M^{(Q)}(x)M^{(p)}(x)}{EI}\,dx. \tag{9.4.21}$$

Note the similarity in form of Eqs. (9.4.18) and (9.4.21): one represents the
internal virtual work of a rod (which could be a truss member) and the other,
the internal virtual work of a beam. Nevertheless, both contain a product of
two generalized forces, one of which is associated with the Q-force and the other
with the forces which cause distortion.

(b) Solution for simple statically indeterminate trusses. Let us consider next the problem of a plane truss with three members acted on by a single load Q, as shown in Fig. 9.16. This statically indeterminate problem was treated previously in Chapter 4 by solving simultaneously the equations of equilibrium, the equations of consistent deformation, and the constitutive equations. The solutions for the three member forces were given in Eqs. (4.4.8) and (4.4.9).

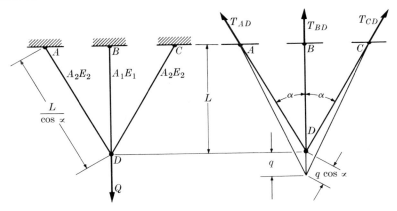

Fig. 9.16   Statically indeterminate planar truss.

For the present problem the only external force is Q. If we let the vertical displacement at the point D be denoted by q, then the elongation of the member BD is q, while for geometrical compatibility the elongation of member AD or CD is $q \cos \alpha$. The internal forces and elongation of the truss members are given by the constitutive relations as follows:

$$T_{BD} = qA_1E_1/L, \qquad (9.4.22)$$

$$T_{AD} = T_{CD} = qA_2E_2 \cos^2 \alpha/L. \qquad (9.4.23)$$

Let us now prescribe a virtual distortion such that the vertical deflection at D is δq. This means that the elongation of BD is δq, while the geometric compatibility requires that the elongation of AD or BD be $\delta q \cos \alpha$. According to Eq. (9.4.16), the work done internally by the Q-induced stresses under this prescribed virtual displacement is

$$\delta U = \frac{qA_1E_1 \, \delta q}{L} + \frac{2qA_2E_2 \cos^3 \alpha}{L} \, \delta q. \qquad (9.4.24)$$

According to the principle of virtual work we have

$$\delta U = Q \, \delta q. \qquad (9.4.25)$$

Substituting δU from Eq. (9.4.24) and simplifying, we obtain

$$q = \frac{QL}{A_1 E_1 [1 + 2(A_2 E_2/A_1 E_1) \cos^3 \alpha]} . \tag{9.4.26}$$

Substituting into Eqs. (9.4.22) and (9.4.23), we find that

$$T_{BD} = \frac{Q}{1 + 2A_2 E_2 \cos^3 \alpha / A_1 E_1} , \tag{9.4.27}$$

$$T_{AD} = T_{CD} = \frac{Q \sec \alpha}{2 + A_1 E_1 / A_2 E_2 \cos^3 \alpha} . \tag{9.4.28}$$

These agree with the result obtained previously in Chapter 4. It is seen that in evaluating the change in strain energy the geometrical compatibility condition for the elongation of the three bars was used. However, the vector equation of equilibrium was not introduced. The conditions of equilibrium are thus implied in the energy principle.

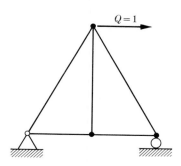

FIG. 9.17   Statically determinate planar truss.

FIG. 9.18   Planar truss under a dummy load.

(c) Virtual Work applied to deflection of a truss. The Principle of Virtual Work is well suited to the calculation of deflections. Consider a simple truss loaded as shown in Fig. 9.17. We wish to calculate the horizontal deflection of joint A caused by the system of P-forces. This can be accomplished by an adroit choice of a Q-force system consisting of a unit horizontal load applied to joint A (see Fig. 9.18). When the deformation by the system of P-forces is considered as the virtual deformation, the virtual work equation becomes

$$Q \, \delta q = (1) \, \Delta_h = \delta U, \tag{9.4.29}$$

where Δ_h is the desired horizontal displacement of joint A. Each bar of a truss is in a state of uniaxial stress, and so for each bar there is an expression for the virtual work of the internal stresses in the form given by Eq. (9.4.18). We can represent this calculation as

$$(1)\ \Delta_h = \sum \frac{F_i^{(Q)}F_iL_i}{A_iE_i}, \tag{9.4.30}$$

where $F_i^{(Q)}$ and F_i are the axial loads in the ith member due to, respectively, the unit load Q and the P-forces. Here L_i, A_i, and E_i are, respectively, the length, area, and elastic modulus of the ith member. Thus we have obtained the deflection of a truss by a clever choice of the Q-force system and by a calculation of the virtual work of the internal strain energy. Note that the cause of distortion, namely the P-forces, is the major item of interest, and that the Q-force system is merely a vehicle to the desired result. The deflection calculation is reduced to two stress analyses, one under the P-forces and the other under the single Q-force. Hence the integration of strain-displacement relations has been circumvented.

(d) Virtual Work applied to deflection of a beam. Consider the cantilever beam loaded in some arbitrary manner (see Fig. 9.19). It is desired to determine the deflection at the tip of the beam. As for the truss, we choose as the Q-force system a unit load on the point at which, and in the direction along which, the deflection is desired. The virtual work equation becomes, with the aid of Eq. (9.4.21),

$$(1)\ \Delta_z = \int_0^L \frac{M^{(Q)}(x)M(x)}{EI}\,dx, \tag{9.4.31}$$

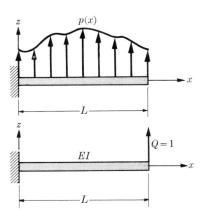

where $M(x)$ is the bending moment due to the distributed load $p(x)$, $M^{(Q)}(x)$ is the bending moment due to the unit load, and Δ_z is the desired displacement. We are able to calculate the deflection at a point of a beam merely by calculating the bending-moment function for the cause of distortion, and using a specially chosen Q-force system. Again the integration of strain-displacement relations has been avoided.

FIG. 9.19   Cantilever beam under two systems of loading.

Because the approach we have used in these examples involves the introduction of a unit load at the point where the structure deflection is required, it is sometimes called the *unit load method*. In the latter part of this chapter we will see that the equation obtained by the unit load method is identical with that developed by the dummy load method which is derived from the Principle of Minimum Complementary Energy (see Section 9.10).

9.5   BETTI'S LAW AND MAXWELL'S LAW

The Principle of Virtual Work can be used to formulate *Betti's Law*. Let us consider our all-purpose example structure which will be loaded in turn by two different systems of generalized forces. One system will be called the Q- and the other the P-system (see Fig. 9.20). The structure is assumed to be linearly elastic. There are L number of Q-forces, and K number of P-forces. Let the displacements of the points of application of the Q-forces caused by the P-forces be denoted by $\Delta_l^{(P)}$. Similarly the deflections of the points of application of the P-forces caused by the Q-forces will be denoted by $\Delta_k^{(Q)}$.

The virtual work of the Q-system of forces and the internal stresses, $\sigma_{mn}^{(Q)}$ under the displacements caused by the P-forces is given by

$$\sum_{l=1}^{L} Q_l \, \Delta_l^{(P)} = \iiint \sigma_{mn}^{(Q)} \, \delta\epsilon_{mn}^{(P)} \, dV, \tag{9.5.1}$$

where $\delta\epsilon_{mn}^{(P)}$ are the internal virtual strains caused by the P-forces. Similarly, the virtual work of the P-system of forces and internal stresses $\sigma_{mn}^{(P)}$ under the displacements caused by the Q-forces is given by

$$\sum_{k=1}^{K} P_k \, \Delta_k^{(Q)} = \iiint \sigma_{mn}^{(P)} \, \delta\epsilon_{mn}^{(Q)} \, dV. \tag{9.5.2}$$

The virtual strains $\delta\epsilon_{mn}^{(P)}$ are caused by the P-induced stresses $\sigma_{mn}^{(P)}$. Thus for a linearly elastic body we can write (see Eq. 7.2.35)

$$\delta\epsilon_{mn}^{(P)} = S_{mnrs}\sigma_{rs}^{(P)}. \tag{9.5.3}$$

Similarly,

$$\delta\epsilon_{mn}^{(Q)} = S_{mnrs}\sigma_{rs}^{(Q)}. \tag{9.5.4}$$

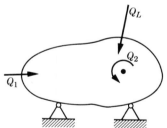

The two virtual-work equations, (9.5.1) and (9.5.2), become

$$\sum_{l=1}^{L} Q_l \, \Delta_l^{(P)} = \iiint \sigma_{mn}^{(Q)} \, S_{mnrs}\sigma_{rs}^{(P)} \, dV, \tag{9.5.5}$$

$$\sum_{k=1}^{K} P_k \, \Delta_k^{(Q)} = \iiint \sigma_{mn}^{(P)} \, S_{mnrs}\sigma_{rs}^{(Q)} \, dV. \tag{9.5.6}$$

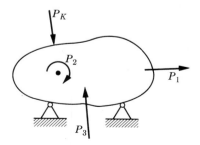

It is observed that the integrands are the same because of the symmetry property

Fig. 9.20   Body under two systems of generalized forces.

$S_{mnrs} = S_{rsmn}$. We obtain

$$\sum_{l=1}^{L} Q_l \,\Delta_l^{(P)} = \sum_{k=1}^{K} P_k \,\Delta_k^{(Q)}, \qquad (9.5.7)$$

which is the mathematical statement of Betti's Law:

In any structure which is linearly elastic, the virtual work done by a system of Q-forces under a distortion caused by a system of P-forces is equal to the virtual work done by the system of P-forces under a distortion caused by the system of Q-forces.

Maxwell's Law of Reciprocal Deflections fol-lows directly from, and is a special case of Betti's Law. We consider just one Q-force and one P-force which are *numerically* equal (see Fig. 9.21). Then according to Betti's Law, we have

$$Q \,\Delta_1^{(P)} = Q \,\Delta_2^{(Q)}. \qquad (9.5.8)$$

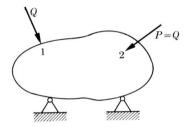

FIG. 9.21 Body under two numerically equal forces.

Further, let us denote the deflection at point m caused by a load at point n by Δ_{mn}, and the de-flection at point n caused by the same magni-tude of load at point m, by Δ_{nm}. Then Eq. (9.5.8) reads, in general terms,

$$\Delta_{mn} = \Delta_{nm}, \qquad (9.5.9)$$

which is a general formula for Maxwell's Law of Reciprocal Deflections:

In any structure which is linearly elastic the generalized deflection at point m caused by a generalized load Q at point n is numerically equal to the generalized deflection at point n caused by the same magnitude of generalized force Q at point m.

It is a small step from Eq. (9.5.9) to prove Eq. (9.3.12), which states that the flexibility-influence coefficients, previously defined, are symmetric.

9.6 PRINCIPLE OF MINIMUM POTENTIAL ENERGY

The Principle of Minimum Potential Energy may be looked upon as a specialization of the Principle of Virtual Work. We now use the symbol δ (in Eqs. 9.4.13 and 9.4.14) to mean the variation of a function according to the Calculus of Variations (see Section A.18). At a given point (y_1, y_2, y_3) of a body, the state of stress and strain is represented by σ_{mn} and ϵ_{mn}. Then $\delta\epsilon_{mn}$ represents any small change of the function $\epsilon_{mn}(y_1, y_2, y_3)$, subject to the condition that the compatibility equations and boundary constraints be satisfied. As shown in Section A-18, the use of the symbol δ is in many respects analogous to the use of the differential symbol.

For linear isotropic elastic behavior, the stress-strain relation and the expression of the strain-energy density U^* are given by Eqs. (7.7.14) and (7.10.7), respectively. These are rewritten by replacing γ_{mn} by ϵ_{mn} as follows:

$$\sigma_{mn} = 2\mu\epsilon_{mn} + \lambda\,\delta_{mn}\epsilon_{rr}, \tag{9.6.1}$$

and

$$U^* = \mu\epsilon_{mn}\epsilon_{mn} + \tfrac{1}{2}\lambda(\epsilon_{rr})^2. \tag{9.6.2}$$

It is seen that the variation in internal strain energy U is†

$$\delta U = \delta \iiint [\mu\epsilon_{mn}\epsilon_{mn} + \tfrac{1}{2}\lambda(\epsilon_{rr})^2]\,dV$$

$$= \iiint [2\mu\epsilon_{mn} + \lambda\,\delta_{mn}\epsilon_{rr}]\,\delta\epsilon_{mn}\,dV. \tag{9.6.3}$$

By substituting Eq. (9.6.1) into Eq. (9.6.3), we obtain

$$\delta U = \iiint \sigma_{mn}\,\delta\epsilon_{mn}\,dV. \tag{9.6.4}$$

We see that, according to the Principle of Virtual Work, we may now treat δU in Eq. (9.4.1) as the variation in the internal strain energy.

The stage is now set to rewrite the Principle of Virtual Work in the form

$$\delta\pi_p = 0, \tag{9.6.5}$$

where

$$\pi_p = U(\epsilon_{mn}) - W, \tag{9.6.6}$$

$$U = \iiint \tfrac{1}{2}[2\mu\epsilon_{mn}\epsilon_{mn} + \lambda(\epsilon_{rr})^2]\,dV, \tag{9.6.7}$$

and

$$W = \iint \sigma_m \cdot \mathbf{u}\,n_m\,dA + \iiint \mathbf{F} \cdot \mathbf{u}\,dV. \tag{9.6.8}$$

The scalar π_p is called the *total potential energy* (or just potential energy) of the structural system, and W, as before, is the work done by the applied body and surface forces.

It should be carefully noted that in order to satisfy the condition of continuity of displacements over the entire body, the function ϵ_{mn} must first be

---

† Care should be exercised in applying the δ- or d-operation to equations written in summation notation. The best approach is to write out first the equations in explicit form and then to perform the desired operation.

expressed in terms of the displacement functions u_m by

$$\epsilon_{mn} = \frac{1}{2}\left(\frac{\partial u_m}{\partial y_n} + \frac{\partial u_n}{\partial y_m}\right),\tag{9.6.9}$$

and the variation of the strain energy U must then be carried out with respect to the displacement functions.

The result, succinctly summarized by Eq. (9.6.5) and subject to Eqs. (9.6.6), (9.6.7), (9.6.8), and (9.6.9), is known as the Principle of Minimum Potential Energy and is stated as follows:

Among all the geometrically possible states of displacement, the correct state of displacement is that which makes the potential energy a minimum.

From a physical argument one can conclude that for a stable equilibrium condition the total potential energy of a system must be a minimum. The fact that π_p is a minimum can also be proved more rigorously by comparing the potential energy π_p at the equilibrium state with that at a neighboring state, π_p'. The state at π_p' is characterized by strains, $\epsilon_{mn} + \delta\epsilon_{mn}$, and the corresponding displacements, $\mathbf{u} + \delta\mathbf{u}$. We find that

$$\pi_p' = \iiint \{\tfrac{1}{2}[2\mu(\epsilon_{mn} + \delta\epsilon_{mn})(\epsilon_{mn} + \delta\epsilon_{mn}) + \lambda(\epsilon_{rr} + \delta\epsilon_{rr})^2]$$
$$-\mathbf{F}\cdot(\mathbf{u} + \delta\mathbf{u})\} \, dV - \int \sigma_m \cdot (\mathbf{u} + \delta\mathbf{u})n_m \, dA.\tag{9.6.10}$$

The right-hand side of this equation can be regrouped so that

$$\pi_p' = \iiint \{\tfrac{1}{2}[2\mu\epsilon_{mn}\epsilon_{mn} + \lambda(\epsilon_{rr})^2] - \mathbf{F}\cdot\mathbf{u}\} \, dV - \int \sigma_m \cdot \mathbf{u} \, n_m \, dA$$
$$+ \iiint \{(2\mu\epsilon_{mn} + \lambda \, \delta_{mn}\epsilon_{rr}) \, \delta\epsilon_{mn} - \mathbf{F}\cdot\delta\mathbf{u}\} \, dV - \int \sigma_m \cdot \delta\mathbf{u} \, n_m \, dA$$
$$+ \iiint [2\mu(\delta\epsilon_{mn})(\delta\epsilon_{mn}) + \lambda(\delta\epsilon_{rr})(\delta\epsilon_{rr})] \, dV.\tag{9.6.11}$$

It is seen that the first group of terms is π_p, while the second group is $\delta\pi_p$ and hence is zero according to Eq. (9.6.5). The last group is a positive quadratic in $\delta\epsilon_{mn}$, and is therefore nonnegative for any arbitrary variation of ϵ_{mn}. We have thus shown $\pi_p' - \pi_p$ to be always nonnegative. This means that for stable equilibrium the potential energy must be a minimum.

A remark should be made here that the strain energy U is also a characteristic of materials which exhibit nonlinear elastic behavior. For example, in the simple case of the uniform bar under uniformly distributed stress shown in Fig. 9.22, the uniaxial stress-strain relation can be represented by

$$\sigma = f(\epsilon).\tag{9.6.12}$$

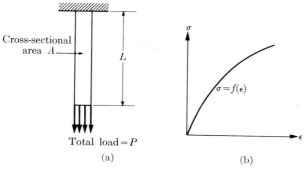

FIG. 9.22 Strain energy of a prismatic bar—nonlinear stress-strain relation.

The strain energy in the bar is

$$U = \iiint \left[\int_0^{\epsilon} \sigma \, d\epsilon \right] dV, \tag{9.6.13}$$

or

$$U = AL \int_0^{\epsilon} f(\epsilon) \, d\epsilon, \tag{9.6.14}$$

where A is the cross-sectional area and L is the length of the bar. The variation
in strain energy is thus

$$\delta U = AL f(\epsilon) \, \delta\epsilon = \iiint \sigma \, \delta\epsilon \, dV, \tag{9.6.15}$$

which is the work done by the internal stresses due to the virtual deformation $\delta\epsilon$.

The Principle of Minimum Potential Energy is most advantageously used in
conjunction with the calculus of variation. We will more fully exploit this
principle at a later time. At this point we will be content to make a few quali-
tative observations. The statement of the principle contains the words "the
correct state," and "correct" as used in this context means that the rigorous
application of $\delta\pi_p = 0$ would lead back to the three differential equations of
force equilibrium. However, the words "the correct state" can be changed to
mean "the most nearly correct state" or "the best state" if we are willing to
accept approximate solutions. Herein lies the greatest utility of the Principle
of Minimum Potential Energy, namely, the development of approximate
equations of equilibrium to replace the three coupled partial differential equations.

9.7 CASTIGLIANO'S FIRST THEOREM

The Principle of Minimum Potential Energy leads naturally and easily to
another theorem adapted for structures which are loaded discretely. Let us
again consider a structure which is acted upon by a system of generalized

forces Q_m. Since the body forces are zero, the work expression, Eq. (9.6.8), becomes simply

$$W = \sum_{m=1}^{N} Q_m q_m, \tag{9.7.1}$$

where q_m are the displacements of the points of application of the generalized forces. Then the potential energy of the system is written as

$$\pi_p = U(q_m) - \sum_{m=1}^{N} Q_m q_m, \tag{9.7.2}$$

where the internal energy is expressed in terms of the generalized displacements. The Principle of Minimum Potential Energy requires that

$$\delta \pi_p = \sum_{m=1}^{N} \frac{\partial \pi_p}{\partial q_m} \delta q_m = 0, \tag{9.7.3}$$

and since the set of displacements q_m is independent, we have

$$\frac{\partial \pi_p}{\partial q_m} = 0, \tag{9.7.4}$$

or, from Eq. (9.7.2),

$$Q_m = \frac{\partial U}{\partial q_m}. \tag{9.7.5}$$

This result which relates Q_m to the rate of change of strain energy with respect to the corresponding displacement is known as Castigliano's First Theorem. Let us consider several simple applications of Eqs. (9.7.5).

(a) Verification of Eq. (9.3.15). The strain energy U is expressed in terms of the stiffness influence coefficients K_{mn} in Eq. (9.3.20). We see that the application of Eq. (9.7.5) to Eq. (9.3.20) leads to

$$Q_m = \sum_{n=1}^{N} K_{mn} q_n, \tag{9.7.6}$$

which is a verification of Eq. (9.3.15).

(b) Statically indeterminate plane truss. Let us consider again the statically indeterminate truss shown in Fig. 9.16. The strain energy in the three members can be expressed in terms of the vertical displacement q at D as

$$\begin{aligned}
U &= \frac{1}{2} \frac{A_1 E_1}{L} q^2 + 2 \cdot \frac{1}{2} \frac{A_2 E_2}{L/\cos \alpha} (q \cos \alpha)^2 \\
&= \frac{1}{2} \frac{A_1 E_1}{L} q^2 \left(1 + \frac{2 A_2 E_2}{A_1 E_1} \cos^3 \alpha \right).
\end{aligned} \tag{9.7.7}$$

By means of Eq. (9.7.5) we obtain

$$Q = \frac{dU}{dq} = \frac{A_1 E_1}{L}\left(1 + \frac{2A_2 E_2}{A_1 E_1} \cos^3 \alpha\right) q, \tag{9.7.8}$$

which agrees with the result previously derived in Eq. (9.4.26).

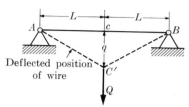

FIG. 9.23   Wire under a single load.

Wire area $= A$
Elastic modulus $= E$

(c) Deflection of a wire. In the two previous examples the resulting force-displacement relations are linear. Let us now consider an example in which the resulting force displacement relation is nonlinear. Figure 9.23 shows a wire which is held fixed at both ends, and is acted on by a downward force Q at the mid-span point. The deformed shape of the wire is shown by the dashed line. The strain energy stored in the stretched wire is given by

$$U = 2 \cdot \frac{1}{2} \frac{EA}{L} \Delta^2, \tag{9.7.9}$$

where E is the elastic modulus, A the cross-sectional area, and Δ the elongation of the segment AC. The original length of the wire is $2L$. We have

$$\Delta = (L^2 + q^2)^{1/2} - L, \tag{9.7.10}$$

where q is the deflection at mid-span. When we restrict our discussion to small deflections, (i.e. such that q is small in comparison to L), we obtain

$$\Delta = L\left[1 + \frac{(q/L)^2}{2} + \cdots\right] - L,$$

or approximately,

$$\Delta = \frac{q^2}{2L}. \tag{9.7.11}$$

Thus the strain energy is

$$U = EAq^4/4L^3, \tag{9.7.12}$$

and, from Castigliano's First Theorem,

$$Q = \partial U/\partial q = EAq^3/L^3. \tag{9.7.13}$$

(d) Deflection of a simply supported beam. As a final example, let us calculate the deflection of a simply supported uniform beam acted upon by a uniformly distributed load (see Fig. 9.24). We will first integrate the differential equations of beam theory to obtain a close form solution, and then we will use the Principle of Minimum Potential Energy to obtain an approximate solution of those same beam equations. Let us derive the differential equation governing w, the deflection of the beam. We have from Eq. (7.13.28)

$$\frac{d^2 w}{dy_1^2} = \frac{M}{EI},$$

$$\tag{9.7.14}$$

where I is the cross-sectional moment of inertia, and E is the elastic modulus of the beam. We also have the relation between the bending moment and the distributed load p (see Chapter 3):

$$\frac{dS}{dy_1} = -p, \qquad \tag{9.7.15}$$

$$\frac{dM}{dy_1} = -S. \qquad \tag{9.7.16}$$

Equations (9.7.15) and (9.7.16) can be combined to yield

$$\frac{d^2 M}{dy_1^2} = p. \qquad \tag{9.7.17}$$

FIG. 9.24   Simply supported beam under uniform lateral loading.

By differentiating Eq. (9.7.14) twice and substituting into Eq. (9.7.17), we obtain

$$EI \frac{d^4 w}{dy_1^4} = p. \tag{9.7.18}$$

This is a fourth-order differential equation with four boundary conditions as follows:

$$w(0) = 0, \tag{9.7.19}$$

$$w(L) = 0, \tag{9.7.20}$$

$$M(0) = EI \frac{d^2 w}{dy_1^2}\bigg|_{y_1=0} = 0, \quad \text{or} \quad \frac{d^2 w}{dy_1^2}\bigg|_{y_1=0} = 0, \tag{9.7.21}$$

$$M(L) = 0, \quad \text{or} \quad \frac{d^2 w}{dy_1^2}\bigg|_{y_1=L} = 0. \tag{9.7.22}$$

The solution is

$$w(y_1) = \frac{py_1}{24EI}(y_1^3 - 2Ly_1^2 + L^3),$$
(9.7.23)

and the maximum deflection which occurs at mid-span is

$$w_{max} = w\left(\frac{L}{2}\right) = \frac{5}{384}\frac{pL^4}{EI} = 0.013020\,\frac{pL^4}{EI}.$$
(9.7.24)

The results shown in Eqs. (9.7.23) and (9.7.29) are considered as exact within the framework of the engineering theory of beams. Now let us proceed to an approximate solution by applying the Principle of Minimum Potential Energy. We assume that the deflection $w(y_1)$ can be represented by a Fourier series,

$$w(y_1) = \sum_{i=1}^{\infty} w_i \sin\frac{i\pi y_1}{L}.$$
(9.7.25)

It is seen that in each term the deflections at the two ends are zero. The assumed deflection $w(y_1)$ thus satisfies the displacement boundary conditions.† The strain energy in the beam is given by Eq. (7.13.35):

$$U = \frac{1}{2}\int_0^L EI\left(\frac{d^2w}{dy_1^2}\right)^2 dy_1$$

$$= \frac{EI}{2}\int_0^L\left[\sum_{i=1}^{\infty}\left(\frac{i\pi}{L}\right)^2 w_i \sin\frac{i\pi y_1}{L}\right]^2 dy_1.$$
(9.7.26)

Introducing the orthogonality property of the Fourier series, that is,

$$\int_0^L \sin\frac{i\pi y_1}{L}\sin\frac{j\pi y_1}{L}\,dy_1 = \begin{cases} 0, & i \neq j, \\ \frac{L}{2}, & i = j, \end{cases}$$
(9.7.27)

we obtain

$$U = \tfrac{1}{4}EIL\sum_{i=1}^{\infty}\left(\frac{i\pi}{L}\right)^4 w_i^2.$$
(9.7.28)

The potential energy due to the distributed load is

$$-W = \int_0^L(-pw)\,dy_1 = -p\int_0^L\sum_{i=1}^{\infty} w_i\sin\frac{i\pi y_1}{L}\,dy_1 = -p\sum_{i=1,3,5,\ldots}^{\infty}\frac{2}{\pi}\frac{w_i}{i}.$$
(9.7.29)

---

† In the present case it happens the moment boundary conditions are also satisfied in each term. This is, however, not required in the application of the Principle of Minimum Potential Energy.

Thus

$$\pi_p = \tfrac{1}{4}EI \sum_{i=1}^{\infty} \frac{(i\pi)^4}{L^3} w_i^2 - p \sum_{i=1,3,5,\ldots}^{\infty} \frac{2}{\pi} \frac{w_i}{i}. \tag{9.7.30}$$

Here π_p is expressed in terms of w_i. For π_p to be a minimum we must set

$$\frac{\partial \pi_p}{\partial w_i} = 0 \qquad i = 1, 2, \ldots, \infty,$$

which yields

$$\frac{\partial \pi_p}{\partial w_1} = 0; \qquad \tfrac{1}{2}EI \left(\frac{\pi}{L}\right)^4 w_1 = \frac{2}{\pi} p, \qquad \text{or} \qquad w_1 = \frac{4pL^4}{\pi^5 EI};$$

$$\frac{\partial \pi_p}{\partial w_2} = 0; \qquad \tfrac{1}{2}EI(16) \left(\frac{\pi}{L}\right)^4 w_2 = 0, \qquad \text{or} \qquad w_2 = 0; \tag{9.7.31}$$

$$\frac{\partial \pi_p}{\partial w_3} = 0; \qquad \tfrac{1}{2}EI(81) \left(\frac{\pi}{L}\right)^4 w_3 = \frac{2}{\pi} \frac{p}{3}, \qquad \text{or} \qquad w_3 = \frac{4pL^4}{\pi^5 EI} \frac{1}{(81)(3)};$$

$$\vdots$$

Substituting the values of w_i into Eq. (9.7.25), we obtain

$$w(y_1) = \frac{4}{\pi^5} \frac{pL^4}{EI} \sum_{i=1,3,5,\ldots}^{\infty} \frac{1}{i^5} \sin \frac{i\pi y_1}{L}. \tag{9.7.32}$$

It can be shown that this is the Fourier expansion for the deflection shape given by Eq. (9.7.23). The infinite series can, of course, be considered also as a close form solution. However, its utility lies in the fact that approximate results of acceptable accuracy can be obtained with only a few terms. For example, if we use only the leading term of the series (see Eq. 9.7.25), we obtain

$$w_1 = \frac{4}{\pi^5} \frac{pL^4}{EI}. \tag{9.7.33}$$

Thus the maximum deflection of the beam is

$$w\left(\frac{L}{2}\right) = w_1 = 0.013071 \frac{pL^4}{EI}. \tag{9.7.34}$$

It differs from the exact solution, Eq. (9.7.24), by only 0.04 percent.

9.8 PRINCIPLE OF VIRTUAL COMPLEMENTARY WORK

In the earlier sections of this chapter, the notions of strain energy and complementary energy were developed. There was seen to be a certain duality or conjugate nature between many of the ideas. We will pursue this duality by developing the Principle of Virtual Complementary Work which can, in a certain sense, be considered a dual or conjugate to the Principle of Virtual Work. Instead of considering a virtual deformation, let us consider a virtual change $\delta\sigma_{mn}$ in the stress tensor. These changes in stresses are to satisfy the equations of equilibrium,

$$\frac{\partial}{\partial y_m}(\delta\sigma_{mn}) = 0. \tag{9.8.1}$$

From Eq. (9.8.1) we conclude that the following integral also vanishes:

$$\iiint \frac{\partial \delta\sigma_{mn}}{\partial y_m} u_n \, dV = 0, \tag{9.8.2}$$

where u_m is the displacement caused by the stresses σ_{mn}. Equation (9.8.2) can also be written in terms of vector quantities,

$$\iiint \frac{\partial \delta\boldsymbol{\sigma}_m}{\partial y_m} \cdot \mathbf{u} \, dV = 0 \tag{9.8.3}$$

when the following vector relations are recognized:

$$\delta\boldsymbol{\sigma}_m = \delta\sigma_{mn}\mathbf{i}_n, \tag{9.8.4}$$

and

$$\mathbf{u} = u_n\mathbf{i}_n. \tag{9.8.5}$$

Equation (9.8.3) can be rearranged to read

$$\iiint \frac{\partial}{\partial y_m}(\delta\boldsymbol{\sigma}_m \cdot \mathbf{u}) \, dV = \iiint \delta\boldsymbol{\sigma}_m \cdot \frac{\partial \mathbf{u}}{\partial y_m} \, dV. \tag{9.8.6}$$

By making use of the Divergence Theorem, we can convert the left-hand side of Eq. (9.8.6) to a surface integral:

$$\iiint \frac{\partial}{\partial y_m}(\delta\boldsymbol{\sigma}_m \cdot \mathbf{u}) \, dV = \iint (\delta\boldsymbol{\sigma}_m \cdot \mathbf{u})n_m \, dA. \tag{9.8.7}$$

This integral represents the work done by the virtual surface stresses $\delta\sigma_m^* n_m$, which obviously must be consistent with the changes in internal stress $\delta\sigma_{mn}$.

By making use of Eqs. (9.8.6) and (5.9.1) and the fact that σ_{mn} is symmetric, we can express the right-hand side of Eq. (9.8.6) as

$$\iiint \delta\boldsymbol{\sigma}_m \cdot \frac{\partial \mathbf{u}}{\partial y_m} \, dV = \iiint \epsilon_{mn} \, \delta\sigma_{mn} \, dV. \tag{9.8.8}$$

This is clearly the internal complementary work done under the actual state of strain ϵ_{mn}, and a virtual change $\delta\sigma_{mn}$ of the stress tensor. Equation (9.8.6) thus becomes

$$\iiint \epsilon_{mn} \, \delta\sigma_{mn} \, dV = \iint [\delta\boldsymbol{\sigma}_m \cdot \mathbf{u}]n_m \, dA. \tag{9.8.9}$$

This is the mathematical summary of the Principle of Virtual Complementary Work, which may be stated as follows:

> *The virtual complementary work done under the actual state of strain and virtual stress change $\delta\sigma_{mn}$, which satisfies the differential equations of equilibrium, is equal to the complementary work done by the virtual surface forces.*

More advanced study will show that a rigorous solution of the variational problem represented by Eq. (9.8.9) leads to the strain-displacement relations and the displacement-boundary conditions at the surface of the body. At this stage, however, there is no restriction on the type of stress-strain relation, i.e., these may be nonlinear. The principle summarized by Eq. (9.8.9) is complementary to the Principle of Virtual Work given by Eq. (9.4.11). Each represents an alternative approach to the small-deflection equations of elasticity. The application of these principles to the same problem will yield the same answer if the problem can be solved exactly, but if approximate answers are desired, the different approaches will, in many instances, yield slightly different answers.

9.9 PRINCIPLE OF MINIMUM COMPLEMENTARY ENERGY

The Principle of Minimum Complementary Energy represents a specialization of the principle derived in the previous section. As in the development of the Principle of Minimum Potential Energy (Section 9.6), we again consider the virtual stress change $\delta\sigma_{mn}$ as a variation of the stress σ_{mn}. The meaning of the integral $\iiint \epsilon_{mn}\,\delta\sigma_{mn}\,dV$ is, thus, clearly the change in complementary energy δU_c.

For a linearly elastic and isotropic material the relation between the strain and stress tensors has been given by Eq. (7.7.24). By replacing γ_{mn} by ϵ_{mn} the equation is rewritten in the following way:

$$\epsilon_{mn} = (1/E)[(1 + \nu)\sigma_{mn} - \nu\,\delta_{mn}\sigma_{rr}]. \tag{9.9.1}$$

For a linearly elastic material the value of strain energy U is identical to that of the complementary energy U_c. The expression of the strain energy density, U^*, in terms of stresses was presented previously in Eq. (7.10.5). Thus we may also write the complementary energy as

$$U_c = \iiint (1/2E)[(1 + \nu)\sigma_{mn}\sigma_{mn} - \nu(\sigma_{rr})^2]\,dV. \tag{9.9.2}$$

Clearly, the variation in internal complementary strain energy δU_c can be written as

$$\delta U_c = \delta\iiint (1/2E)[(1 + \nu)\sigma_{mn}\sigma_{mn} - \nu(\sigma_{rr})^2]\,dV$$

$$= \iiint (1/E)[(1 + \nu)\sigma_{mn} - \nu\,\delta_{mn}\sigma_{rr}]\delta\sigma_{mn}\,dV,$$

or

$$\delta U_c = \iiint \epsilon_{mn}\,\delta\sigma_{mn}\,dV. \tag{9.9.3}$$

If the total complementary energy is now defined as

$$\pi_c = U_c - \iint [\boldsymbol{\sigma}_m \cdot \mathbf{u}] n_m \, dA, \tag{9.9.4}$$

then the Principle of Virtual Complementary Work becomes the Principle of Minimum Complementary Energy:

$$\delta \pi_c = 0, \tag{9.9.5}$$

which may be stated as follows:

Of all the states of stress which satisfy the equations of equilibrium, the actual state of stress is that which makes the complementary energy a minimum.

It should be emphasized again that in the application of this principle the quantities to be varied are the internal stresses σ_{mn} and the surface stresses $\sigma_m n_m$. This should be contrasted with the Principle of Minimum Potential Energy.

We shall discuss the application of the Principle of Minimum Complementary Energy in the following two sections which are concerned with Castigliano's Second Theorem and the Theorem of Least Work. Both theorems can be derived from the Principle of Minimum Complementary Energy.

9.10 CASTIGLIANO'S SECOND THEOREM

Let us consider again our all-purpose body as it is acted upon by a system of N generalized forces Q_m, and assume that the internal stresses have been explicitly expressed in terms of these generalized forces. Then for a structure whose material is linearly elastic the total complementary energy can be written as

$$\pi_c = U(Q_1, Q_2, \ldots, Q_N) - \sum_{m=1}^{N} q_m Q_m, \tag{9.10.1}$$

where q_m is the generalized displacement corresponding to Q_m. The Principle of Minimum Complementary Energy can thus be expressed as

$$\delta \pi_c(Q_1, Q_2, \ldots, Q_N) = 0. \tag{9.10.2}$$

This equation can be expanded to yield

$$\sum_{m=1}^{N} \frac{\partial \pi_c}{\partial Q_m} \delta Q_m = 0. \tag{9.10.3}$$

Each of the variations δQ_m is independent of the others; hence the condition set forth by Eq. (9.10.3) yields N independent equations

$$\frac{\partial \pi_c}{\partial Q_m} = 0, \qquad m = 1, 2, \ldots, N. \tag{9.10.4}$$

The application of Eq. (9.10.4) to Eq. (9.10.1) leads to the result known as Castigliano's Second Theorem,

$$q_m = \frac{\partial U}{\partial Q_m}. \tag{9.10.5}$$

In words, the result shown in Eq. (9.10.5) states:

In a linearly elastic structure, the partial derivative of the strain energy with respect to an externally applied generalized force is equal to the displacement corresponding to that force.

Castigliano's Second Theorem can be applied in calculating the deflections of structures. Illustrative examples are given in the following subsections.

(a) Deflections in terms of flexibility—influence coefficients. The complementary energy U has been expressed in terms of the flexibility influence coefficients C_{mn} in Eq. (9.3.22). Castigliano's Second Theorem (since $U = U_c$) then yields

$$q_m = \sum_{n=1}^{N} C_{mn}Q_n, \tag{9.10.6}$$

a result shown in Eq. (9.3.13) which was obtained by another argument.

(b) Deflection of a truss at a loading point. Let us consider the simple statically determinate truss which is reproduced here in Fig. 9.25 with specific information about the dimensions and loadings. The cross-sectional areas for members AD and AB are 2 in^2, while those for members DC, CB, and AC are $\frac{1}{2}$ in^2. All bars are made of aluminum alloy whose modulus of elasticity is 10^7 psi. A single downward load P of 10,000 lb is acting at the joint C. It is required to determine the vertical deflection at C.

Through the application of equations of statics, the axial loads in all members can be calculated in terms of the applied load Q. These loads are listed in Table 9.1. This table also contains the calculation of the total strain energy U, which is given by

$$U = \frac{1}{2}\sum \frac{F_i^2 L_i}{A_i E_i}, \tag{9.10.7}$$

where L_i, A_i, E_i are respectively the length, area, and elastic modulus of the ith member, and F_i is the axial force in the ith member due to given applied loads. In the present problem only a single load Q is involved. As shown in the calculation given in Table 9.1,

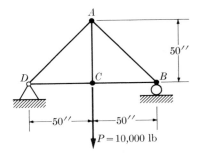

FIG. 9.25 Statically determinate planar truss.

TABLE 9.1 *Calculation of Truss Deflection*

Member	AB	AD	AC	DC	CB	Σ
Area (in^2) A_i	2	2	$\frac{1}{2}$	$\frac{1}{2}$	$\frac{1}{2}$	—
Length (in.) L_i	$50\sqrt{2}$	$50\sqrt{2}$	50	50	50	—
Member load due to Q (Fig. 9.25): F_i	$-(\sqrt{2}/2)P$	$-(\sqrt{2}/2)P$	$+P$	$+P/2$	$+P/2$	—
$\dfrac{F_i^2 L_i}{A_i E_i}$	$12.5\sqrt{2}P^2/E$	$12.5\sqrt{2}P^2/E$	$100P^2/E$	$25P^2/E$	$25P^2/E$	$185.4P^2/E$
Member load due to $Y = 1$ (Fig. 9.26): f_i	$-\sqrt{2}/2$	$+\sqrt{2}/2$	0	$+\frac{1}{2}$	$+\frac{1}{2}$	—
$\dfrac{F_i f_i L_i}{A_i E_i}$	$12.5\sqrt{2}P/E$	$-12.5\sqrt{2}P/E$	0	$25P/E$	$25P/E$	$50P/E$

the strain energy is

$$U = \frac{185.4}{2}\frac{P^2}{E}.$$

Hence the deflection at C is

$$q = \frac{\partial U}{\partial P} = 185.4\frac{P}{E} = 0.1854 \text{ in.}$$

(c) Calculation of structural deflection by Dummy Load method. As another example, let us suppose that we wish to compute the deflection of a truss at any joint which may or may not have an external load. In such a case we place a dummy load Y at the joint pointing toward the direction of the deflection to be determined. The strain energy of the truss due to the given applied loads Q_i and the dummy load Y is

$$U = \frac{1}{2}\sum \frac{(F_i + f_i Y)^2 L_i}{A_i E_i}, \qquad (9.10.8)$$

where F_i, as before, is the load in the ith member of the truss due to the applied loads, while f_i is the load in the ith member due to a unit dummy load ($Y = 1$). According to Castigliano's Second Theorem, the deflection at this joint is

$\partial U/\partial Y$. Here, since Y is only a fictitious load, this deflection can be written as

$$\Delta = \lim_{Y \to 0} \left(\frac{\partial U}{\partial Y}\right) = \lim_{Y \to 0} \sum \frac{(F_i + f_i Y)f_i L_i}{A_i E_i},$$

or

$$\Delta = \sum \frac{F_i f_i L_i}{A_i E_i}. \qquad (9.10.9)$$

This equation is the same as Eq. (9.4.30) which was obtained from the consideration of virtual work (with a slight change in notation: $f_i \equiv F_i^{(Q)}$).

FIG. 9.26 Statically determinate planar truss under a dummy load.

FIG. 9.27 Statically determinate beam under external loads and a dummy load.

Let us refer again to the truss shown in Fig. 9.25. This time, however, it is required to determine the horizontal deflection at the joint A. In using the dummy load method a unit horizontal load is applied at A as shown in Fig. 9.26. The loads f_i in all members are then calculated by equations of statics. The last two rows in Table 9.1 also list the calculations for the horizontal deflection at A, that is,

$$\Delta = 50\frac{P}{E} = 0.05 \text{ in.}$$

(d) Deflection of a simple beam. The dummy load method for deflection analysis can be applied to other structures in general. For example, it is required to compute the vertical deflection at A for a simple beam (Fig. 9.27) under a number of external forces $Q_1, \ldots, Q_n$, or a continuously distributed load $p(x)$. At A we apply a dummy vertical load Y. We see that the internal bending-moment distribution can be expressed in terms of the external forces and the dummy force Y. Let

$$M(x) = \text{bending moment due to } Q_1, \ldots, Q_n,$$
$$m(x) = \text{bending moment due to a unit load at } A.$$

We can then write the internal strain energy as

$$U = \frac{1}{2} \int_0^l \frac{(M + Ym)^2}{EI} \, dx. \tag{9.10.10}$$

According to Castigliano's Second Theorem, the vertical deflection at A is

$$\Delta_A = \lim_{Y \to 0} \frac{dU}{dY} = \lim_{Y \to 0} \int_0^l \frac{(M + Ym)m}{EI} \, dx = \int_0^l \frac{Mm}{EI} \, dx. \tag{9.10.11}$$

This equation is the same as Eq. (9.4.31), which was obtained previously from a different consideration (with a slight change in notation: $m \equiv M^{(Q)}$).

9.11 THEOREM OF LEAST WORK

The strain energy, U, for a statically indeterminate structure cannot be immediately written only in terms of the prescribed external forces. However, the strain energy can be expressed in terms of the applied external forces and a number of redundant internal forces or reactions. For example, the three-bar truss shown in Fig. 9.16 is a statically indeterminate structure, i.e., the member axial loads T_{AD} and T_{BD} cannot be determined by the equations of statics alone. However, if we let one of these, say T_{BD}, be the redundant force, we can express the other axial force T_{AD} in terms of T_{BD} and Q by applying the condition of equilibrium of internal forces at joint D.

In general, let a structure contain N independent redundant forces,

$$X_1, X_2, \ldots, X_N.$$

They are either internal forces or reactions forces. The latter are, of course, forces at the boundary; their corresponding generalized displacements, however, are zero. The expression for the complementary energy is

$$\pi_c = U(Q_1, Q_2, \ldots, Q_M, X_1, X_2, \ldots, X_N) - Q_m q_m, \tag{9.11.1}$$

where Q_1, Q_2, and Q_M are the prescribed external forces. The Principle of Minimum Complementary Energy thus consists of two groups of terms:

$$\partial \pi_c / \partial Q_m = 0, \tag{9.11.2}$$

and

$$\partial \pi_c / \partial X_n = 0. \tag{9.11.3}$$

The first set of equations again yields Castigliano's Second Theorem (Eq. 9.10.4); the second set, since the X_n redundants appear only in U, yields

$$\partial U / \partial X_n = 0. \tag{9.11.4}$$

This equation is referred to as the Theorem of Least Work, which may be stated in words as follows:

> *For a linear statically indeterminate structure, the derivative of the strain energy with respect to any redundant internal force or redundant reaction must be zero.*

It can be concluded from Eq. (9.11.4) only that the redundant quantities are chosen such as to make the strain energy of the system either a maximum or a minimum. However, by calculating the second derivatives and showing that they are always positive for a stable system, it can be proved that the strain energy must be a minimum. Thus the theorem embracing Eq. (9.11.4) is known as the Theorem of Least Work.

It should be carefully observed that, whereas the Theorem of Minimum Complementary Energy applies to nonlinear as well as to linear systems, Castigliano's Theorem and the Theorem of Least Work apply only to systems in which the principle of superposition is valid, that is, to linear systems.

We shall consider several examples to illustrate the application of the Theorem of Least Work.

(a) Simple statically indeterminate truss. In the three-bar truss (Fig. 9.16), the strain energy is given by

$$U = \frac{1}{2}\frac{l}{A_1E_1}T_{BD}^2 + \frac{l}{A_2E_2\cos\alpha}T_{AD}^2. \tag{9.11.5}$$

Here T_{BD} and T_{AD} are related by the condition of equilibrium at joint D, that is,

$$T_{BD} + 2T_{AD}\cos\alpha = Q. \tag{9.11.6}$$

Let T_{BD} be the redundant internal force. We can write

$$T_{AD} = \frac{Q - T_{BD}}{2\cos\alpha}. \tag{9.11.7}$$

Substitution into Eq. (9.11.5) yields

$$U = \frac{1}{2}\frac{l}{A_1E_1}T_{BD}^2 + \frac{l}{A_2E_2\cos\alpha}\left(\frac{Q - T_{BD}}{2\cos\alpha}\right)^2. \tag{9.11.8}$$

Application of the Theorem of Least Work thus leads to

$$\frac{\partial U}{\partial T_{BD}} = \frac{l}{A_1E_1}T_{BD} + \frac{2l}{A_2E_2\cos\alpha}\left(\frac{Q - T_{BD}}{2\cos\alpha}\right)\left(-\frac{1}{2\cos\alpha}\right) = 0. \tag{9.11.9}$$

This equation can be solved for T_{BD}. The result is

$$T_{BD} = \frac{Q}{(1 + 2A_2E_2\cos^3\alpha)/A_1E_1}. \tag{9.11.10}$$

FIG. 9.28   Statically indeterminate beam.

(b) Statically indeterminate beam. Let us consider the beam shown in Fig. 9.28. There are five unknown reactions, but only three equilibrium equations of statics. The problem hence has two redundant forces. Of the five reactions, $R_1^{(A)}$ is found to be zero when the condition of force summation along the y_1-direction is imposed. However, any two of the remaining reactions may be used as the redundant forces. For example, if we let

$$X_1 = R_3^{(A)}, \qquad X_2 = M_3^{(A)}, \tag{9.11.11}$$

we can write

$$R_3^{(B)} + R_3^{(C)} = -p(L_1 + L_2) - X_1,$$

and

$$L_1 R_3^{(B)} + (L_1 + L_2)R_3^{(C)} = -p\frac{(L_1 + L_2)^2}{2} + X_2. \tag{9.11.12}$$

These two equations can be solved to obtain $R_3^{(B)}$ and $R_3^{(C)}$ in terms of X_1 and X_2.

We may also assign the redundant forces in the following manner: By figuratively cutting the beam apart at any station D (between stations A and B) and replacing the internal stresses by the equipollent shear force $S^{(D)}$ and bending moment $M^{(D)}$, we obtain two separate structures as shown in Fig. 9.29. It is clear that if $M^{(D)}$ and $S^{(D)}$ are assigned respectively as the two redundant forces X_1 and X_2, the bending-moment distribution in each part of the beam can be written in terms of X_1, X_2, and p. Thus, in turn, the strain energy U of the complete beam can be written as

$$U = U(X_1, X_2). \tag{9.11.13}$$

The two redundant forces can then be calculated by solving the two equations given by

$$\partial U/\partial X_1 = 0, \quad \text{and} \quad \partial U/\partial X_2 = 0. \tag{9.11.14}$$

FIG. 9.29   Statically indeterminate beam and choice of redundant forces.

The Theorem of Least Work may also be interpreted as the result of Castigliano's Second Theorem. In order for the two parts illustrated in Fig. 9.29 to behave like the complete structure, the deformations at point D must be consistent, i.e., point D of the left portion must displace in exactly the same fashion as point D of the right portion. For example, Castigliano's Second Theorem can be applied to the bending moment $M^{(D)}$ acting on the left portion, yielding an angular displacement

$$\theta_{\text{left}} = \frac{\partial U_{\text{left}}}{\partial M^{(D)}}, \tag{9.11.15}$$

and also to the right portion yielding

$$\theta_{\text{right}} = \frac{\partial U_{\text{right}}}{\partial M^{(D)}}, \tag{9.11.16}$$

where θ is the rotation corresponding to the bending moment $M^{(D)}$. The relative rotation must be zero in order to satisfy the requirement of consistent deformations, that is,

$$\theta_{\text{left}} + \theta_{\text{right}} = 0, \tag{9.11.17}$$

or

$$\partial U / \partial M^{(D)} \equiv \partial U / \partial X_1 = 0, \tag{9.11.18}$$

because

$$U = U_{\text{left}} + U_{\text{right}}. \tag{9.11.19}$$

By an analogous treatment we can also obtain

$$\partial U / \partial S^{(D)} \equiv \partial U / \partial X_2 = 0. \tag{9.11.20}$$

When the results given by Eqs. (9.11.18) and (9.11.20) are interpreted in terms of the complete structure, they state that the relative generalized displacement of a pair of equal and opposite internal generalized forces is equal to zero. Such a result is the same as that derived from the Theorem of Least Work.

9.12   SUMMARY

The following energy theorems have been derived and illustrated:

Clapeyron's Law

The work done by a system of generalized forces Q_n acting on a linearly elastic structure is stored as strain energy and is equal to

$$U = \tfrac{1}{2} \sum_{n=1}^{N} Q_n q_n, \tag{9.12.1}$$

where q_n is the generalized displacement corresponding to Q_n.

Principle of Virtual Work

If a body is in equilibrium and remains in equilibrium while it is subjected to a virtual distortion compatible with the geometrical constraints, the virtual work done by the external forces is equal to the virtual work done by the internal stresses.

Betti's Law

In any structure which is linearly elastic, the virtual work done by a system of Q-forces under a distortion caused by a system of P-forces is equal to the virtual work done by the system of P-forces under a distortion caused by the system of Q-forces.

Maxwell's Law of Reciprocal Deflections

In any structure which is linearly elastic the generalized deflection at point m caused by a generalized load Q at point n is numerically equal to the generalized deflection at point n caused by the same magnitude of generalized force Q at point m.

Principle of Minimum Potential Energy

Among all the geometrically possible states of displacement, the correct state of displacement is that which makes the potential energy π_p a minimum, where $\pi_p = U - W$.

Castigliano's First Theorem

When the strain energy U can be expressed in terms of a system of generalized displacement q_m, then the generalized force is given by

$$Q_m = \frac{\partial U}{\partial q_m}.$$ (9.12.2)

Principle of Virtual Complementary Work

Due to virtual stress changes $\delta\sigma_{mn}$, which satisfy the differential equations of equilibrium, the virtual complementary work under the actual state of strain is equal to the work done by the virtual external forces.

Principle of Minimum Complementary Energy

Of all the states of stress which satisfy the equations of equilibrium, the actual state of stress is that which makes the complementary energy π_c a minimum, where $\pi_c = U_c - W$.

Castigliano's Second Theorem

For a linearly elastic structure, if the strain energy U can be expressed in terms of a system of generalized forces Q_m, then the generalized displacement is given by

$$q_m = \frac{\partial U}{\partial Q_m}.$$ (9.12.3)

Theorem of Least Work

For a linear statically indeterminate structure, the derivative of the strain energy with respect to any redundant internal force or redundant reaction must be zero.

PROBLEMS

9.1   A thin uniform rod with two concentrated masses is rotating about one of its ends at a constant velocity ω (Fig. P.9.1a). The cross-sectional area of the rod is A. The mass of the rod is negligibly small in comparison to that of the concentrated masses; hence the two centrifugal forces Q_1 and Q_2 are the generalized forces.

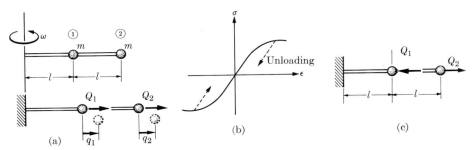

FIGURE P.9.1

(a) Let the rod be made of elastic material of Young's modulus E. Determine the strain energy stored in the rod by $U = \frac{1}{2} \int \epsilon \sigma \, dV$. Verify the strain energy expression by calculating the work done by the two concentrated forces. Will the order of application of the two forces affect your answer?

(b) Consider the rod strained into the plastic range. Let the stress-strain relation of the material be given by Fig. P.9.1(b). Determine the strain energy stored in the rod. Will the order of application of the two forces affect your answer?

(c) Now consider the problem illustrated by Fig. P.9.1(c). The forces Q_1 and Q_2 are in *opposite* directions, and $Q_2 = 4Q_1$. Will the order of application of the two forces affect the strain energy stored when the plastic behavior of the material is taken into consideration?

9.2   A truss is subject to the loading shown in Fig. P.9.2. Determine the bar forces and thereby determine the displacement of point d, at the mid-span, using the Principle of Virtual Work.

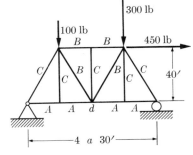

FIGURE P.9.2

Bar	Area
A	5 in^2
B	20 in^2
C	10 in^2

$E = 30 \times 10^6$ psi

9.3   A beam is subjected to a uniformly distributed load as shown in Fig. P.9.3. Determine by the Principle of Virtual Work, the displacement of a relative to the displacement of b. By a proper choice of a Q-force system, the solution can be obtained directly.

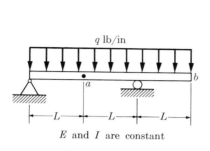

q lb/in

a

b

L ── L ── L

E and I are constant

FIGURE P.9.3

y_3

$\dfrac{KL^3}{EI} = 2$

M

y_1

K lb/in.

$\dfrac{L}{2}$ $\dfrac{L}{2}$

FIGURE P.9.5

9.4 Solve Problem 4.1 by the Principle of Minimum Potential Energy.

9.5 An elastic cantilever beam is restrained by a linear spring of spring constant k, and is acted upon by a couple M at the mid-span point (Fig. P.9.5). E and I are constant. By means of the Principle of Minimum Potential Energy determine approximately the vertical deflection at the end of the beam. Assume the beam has the following deflection shape,

$$w(y_1) = q_1 y_1^2 + q_2 y_1^3,$$

where q_1 and q_2 are the generalized displacements to be determined. Take $kL^3/EI = 2$.

9.6 Compute the forces in the bars of the system shown by Fig. P.9.6. All bars are of the same length, cross-sectional area, and material.

9.7 A beam of length $2l$, and bending stiffness EI is acted upon by a concentrated load P at the mid-span and is supported at three points A, B, and C by three springs each of which has a spring constant k lb/in. (Fig. P.9.7). Determine the deflection at the mid-span point B.

P

P

FIGURE P.9.6

P

A B C

l l

FIGURE P.9.7

9.8 The beam AB is clamped at A and supported by a ball at B which is the end of another cantilever beam CB (Fig. P.9.8). Both beams have the same bending stiffness EI. The lengths are $2l$ and l, respectively. A vertical load P is acting at the mid-span of AB. Determine the vertical deflection at B.

9.9 Solve Problems 4.7 and 4.9 by an energy method.

FIGURE P.9.8

FIGURE P.9.10

9.10   The cantilever beam shown in Fig. P.9.10 has a variable-section moment of inertia given by the following expression,

$$I(x) = I_0L/(L + x),$$

where I_0 is the value at the clamped end. A concentrated load is acting at the midspan point.   Determine the deflection curve by means of Castigliano's Second Theorem.

9.11   A truss is subjected to the loading as shown in Fig. P.9.11. For bars AE, BE, BD, and CD the area is 1 in^2. For bars AB, BC, and ED, the area is $\frac{1}{2}$ in^2. Determine the bar forces and the vertical deflection at B by Castigliano's Second Theorem. All the bars are constructed of the same material.

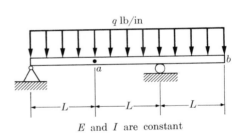

FIGURE P.9.11

FIGURE P.9.12

9.12   A beam is subjected to a uniformly distributed load as shown in Fig. P.9.12. Determine the deflections at points a and b. (a) Use Castigliano's Second Theorem to obtain the exact solution. (b) Assume any reasonable deflection function and use the Principle of Minimum Potential Energy. Compare the result with that of (a).

9.13   Wire RS has a cross-sectional area A and modulus of elasticity E (Fig. P.9.13). A uniform load w lb/in. acts on the entire length of the beam PR which is also supported by a spring QT at mid-span and by a hinge at point P. The spring has a spring constant k lb/in. Calculate the deflection of point R, given that (a) the beam PR is a rigid body, (b) the beam PR has a bending stiffness EI.

9.14   The beam ABC is *clamped* at A and supported by a light truss for which the points $ABCD$ and E are *hinge joints*. The weight of the beam is 1 lb/in. of span, the cross-section moment of inertia is 10 in^4, and cross-sectional area is 5 in^2. The modulus

FIGURE P.9.13

FIGURE P.9.14

of elasticity is $E_{\text{beam}} = 3 \times 10^7$ psi. The cross-sectional area of all the members of the truss is 0.1 in² and the modulus of elasticity is $E_{\text{truss member}} = 10^7$ psi. Determine the bending-moment distribution along the beam and the stresses in the truss members.

9.15 Determine the bending-moment distribution of the statically indeterminate beam shown in Fig. P.9.15. Determine the slope at the end of the beam and the deflection at $x = L/2$, using Castigliano's Second Theorem. Check your result with the approximate solution obtained in Problem 9.5.

FIGURE P.9.15

FIGURE P.9.16

9.16 The cross-sectional area for each member of the given truss (Fig. P.9.16) is 1 in², and the modulus is $E = 10^7$ psi. The turnbuckle T along AC is tightened such that the ends of the two bars at the turnbuckle are brought 0.2 in. closer to each other. Determine the stresses induced by this operation.

9.17 A frame composed of members rigidly joined together is acted upon by a uniform lateral load of 10 lb/in. along the vertical member CD as shown in Fig. P.9.17. The term "rigidly joined together at B" is used to denote the physical condition that the B-ends of members AB and BC undergo the same displacement and rotation under loads. Each member has a square cross section of dimensions 6 in. × 6 in. Determine the bending-moment distributions in

FIGURE P.9.17

the three members, and the horizontal deflection of the point C. (Neglect the strain energy due to axial loads in each member.) After solving the problem, calculate the strain energy due to axial loads and compare this result with the strain energy due to bending moment.

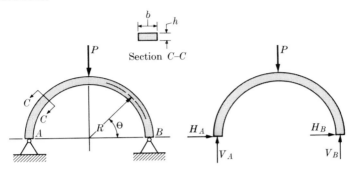

FIGURE P.9.18

9.18 The strain energy for a curved beam, with radius of curvature R much larger than its thickness h, can be obtained according to slender-beam analysis, i.e., according to the ordinary beam theory discussed in previous chapters. For example, if $M(\theta)$ represents the bending-moment distribution of the half-ring shown in Fig. P.9.18, then the total strain energy is

$$U = \int_0^\pi \frac{[M(\theta)]^2}{2EI} R \, d\theta.$$

The half-ring is acted upon by a concentrated load P as shown. Determine the bending moment at the section where the load P is applied. What is the deflection at this point? *Hint:* Remove the supports and replace with a shear force H and an axial force V, as shown. Note that because of symmetry, $H_A = -H_B$ and $V_A = V_B$.

Appendix

Mathematical Themes

A.1 INTRODUCTION

Many of the difficulties in the field of solid mechanics lie not in the basic ideas but arise, rather, as a result of the geometrical descriptions which must be made. Many variables must be sorted, and many equations derived. The sorting of the variables, i.e., the "cataloging" aspects will be minimized by adopting the summation and indicial conventions of tensor analysis. The derivation of the equations will become clearer and simplified by the use of ordinary vector analysis. In addition, the use of matrices will prove to be invaluable.

We will summarize in this Appendix some of the uses of mathematics which heretofore have not been presented in a first course in solid mechanics. Some of the topics included are covered in the first three semesters of calculus. The remaining topics are considered to be material for advanced calculus because of time limitations in the first courses, not because a great deal of mathematical sophistication is required.

A.2 THE SUMMATION AND INDICIAL NOTATION [1]*

The three-dimensional Euclidean space of solid mechanics will be described by the rectangular Cartesian coordinates y_1, y_2, and y_3, which are to be arranged in a right-handed system. A linear homogeneous function of the coordinates is usually written in the form

$$a_1y_1 + a_2y_2 + a_3y_3 \equiv \sum_{m=1}^{3} a_m y_m, \qquad (A.2.1)$$

where a_1, a_2, and a_3 are constants.

A great deal of writing and space can be saved by eliminating the $\sum$-sign with the adoption of the following two conventions:

(1) A lower-case subscript which is repeated in a term replaces the $\sum$-sign, i.e., a repeated lower-case subscript is to be summed from 1 to 3.

(2) A free, i.e., an unrepeated, lower-case subscript is to have the range of values 1, 2, and 3 unless otherwise noted.

---

* Numbers in brackets refer to references at the end of the Appendix.

Thus, Eq. (A.2.1) will now read

$$a_m y_m \equiv a_1 y_1 + a_2 y_2 + a_3 y_3. \qquad \text{(A.2.2)}$$

A homogeneous quadratic function of the variables y_1, y_2, y_3 can be compactly written as

$$
\begin{aligned}
a_{mn} y_m y_n \equiv\ & a_{11}(y_1)^2 + a_{12} y_1 y_2 + a_{13} y_1 y_3 \\
& + a_{21} y_2 y_1 + a_{22}(y_2)^2 + a_{23} y_2 y_3 \\
& + a_{31} y_3 y_1 + a_{32} y_3 y_2 + a_{33}(y_3)^2,
\end{aligned}
\qquad \text{(A.2.3)}
$$

where the a_{mn}'s are again constants.

The repeated index is often called the "dummy" index because it is immaterial which index is used. Thus

$$a_m y_m \equiv a_r y_r, \qquad a_{mn} y_m y_n \equiv a_{rs} y_r y_s. \qquad \text{(A.2.4)}$$

The system of linear equations

$$
\begin{aligned}
b_1 &= a_{11} y_1 + a_{12} y_2 + a_{13} y_3, \\
b_2 &= a_{21} y_1 + a_{22} y_2 + a_{23} y_3, \\
b_3 &= a_{31} y_1 + a_{32} y_2 + a_{33} y_3,
\end{aligned}
\qquad \text{(A.2.5)}
$$

is written in the form

$$b_r = a_{rs} y_s, \qquad \text{(A.2.6)}$$

where the index r is called the free index since it is not repeated in any single term. The appearance of a free index, by convention (2), means that Eq. (A.2.6) represents a system of three simultaneous equations. The same index cannot be used more than twice in the same term.

Equation (A.2.6) may be called a "tensor" equation. At the outset of this course of study, the quantities to be studied will be restricted to that part of tensor analysis commonly known as Cartesian tensors. This means that the frame of reference to be used is restricted to rectangular Cartesian coordinates. If a completely general curvilinear coordinate frame of reference is used, then the concepts of covariant and contravariant tensors become necessary. The power and usefulness of tensor analysis lie in the extreme ease with which equations formulated in rectangular Cartesian coordinates can be transformed to any kind of coordinate system.

A.3 THE e-SYMBOL AND THE KRONECKER DELTA [1], [2]

A symbol, which will prove very useful in dealing with determinants, is the completely skew-symmetric system of the third order, which is denoted by e_{rst}. The components of this system by definition have only the following three definite numerical values:

(a)   0 when any two of the indices are equal,
(b) +1 when rst is an even permutation of 1, 2, 3,
(c) −1 when rst is an odd permutation of 1, 2, 3.

The permutation of the three numbers 1, 2, 3 is accomplished by a finite number of interchanges of any pair of the numbers, and hence the number of interchanges required to bring about a given sequence of the numbers from the initial arrangement of 1, 2, 3 will be either odd or even. Thus the arrangement 312 requires two interchanges, whereas 132 requires only one interchange. Hence $e_{312} = 1$, and $e_{132} = -1$.

The Kronecker delta can be generated from the e-symbol with the aid of the indicial and summation notation

$$\delta_{rm} = \tfrac{1}{2} e_{rsp} e_{msp}. \tag{A.3.1}$$

This symbol δ_{rm}, called the Kronecker delta (a bit of trivia on which to attach a great man's name), has the following numerical values:

(a)   1 if the two indices are equal,
(b)   0 if the two indices are unequal.

A.4   COORDINATE TRANSFORMATIONS AND DETERMINANTS [1] [2]

Let Oy_1, Oy_2, Oy_3 and $O\tilde{y}_1$, $O\tilde{y}_2$, $O\tilde{y}_3$ be two rectangular Cartesian coordinate systems with a common origin O. The angles between Oy_1 and $O\tilde{y}_2$, for example, will be denoted by $\widehat{y_1\tilde{y}_2}$ or $\widehat{\tilde{y}_2 y_1}$. Similarly, the angle between Oy_n and $O\tilde{y}_m$ will be denoted by $\widehat{y_n\tilde{y}_m}$ or $\widehat{\tilde{y}_m y_n}$. Figure A.1 shows the angles which axis $O\tilde{y}_2$ makes with axes Oy_1, Oy_2, and Oy_3. A point p with coordinates y_1, y_2, y_3 in the first coordinate frame will have coordinates in the other frame given by

$$\tilde{y}_1 = y_1 \cos \widehat{\tilde{y}_1 y_1} + y_2 \cos \widehat{\tilde{y}_1 y_2} + y_3 \cos \widehat{\tilde{y}_1 y_3} = y_n l_{\tilde{1}n},$$
$$\tilde{y}_2 = y_1 \cos \widehat{\tilde{y}_2 y_1} + y_2 \cos \widehat{\tilde{y}_2 y_2} + y_3 \cos \widehat{\tilde{y}_2 y_3} = y_n l_{\tilde{2}n}, \tag{A.4.1}$$
$$\tilde{y}_3 = y_1 \cos \widehat{\tilde{y}_3 y_1} + y_2 \cos \widehat{\tilde{y}_3 y_2} + y_3 \cos \widehat{\tilde{y}_3 y_3} = y_n l_{\tilde{3}n},$$

where $l_{\tilde{r}n}$ is called the direction cosine and is the cosine of the angle between axes $\tilde{y}_r$ and y_n. This can be compactly written as

$$\tilde{y}_m = y_n l_{\tilde{m}n}. \tag{A.4.2}$$

In this special case of Fig. A.1 it is obvious that the coordinate transformation given by Eq. (A.4.2) is reversible, that is, Eq. (A.4.2) can be solved to yield

$$y_n = \tilde{y}_m l_{n\tilde{m}}. \tag{A.4.3}$$

More formally, Eq. (A.4.2) can be solved only if the determinant of the coefficients of y_1, y_2, y_3 is not zero. The determinant will be denoted by θ, and is represented by

$$\theta = |l_{\tilde{m}n}| = \begin{vmatrix} l_{\tilde{1}1} & l_{\tilde{1}2} & l_{\tilde{1}3} \\ l_{\tilde{2}1} & l_{\tilde{2}2} & l_{\tilde{2}3} \\ l_{\tilde{3}1} & l_{\tilde{3}2} & l_{\tilde{3}3} \end{vmatrix}. \tag{A.4.4}$$

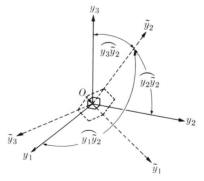

Fɪɢ. A.1   Two sets of rectangular Cartesian coordinate systems.

It can be verified through expansion of the determinant by rows that the value of the determinant is given by

$$\theta = |l_{\tilde{m}n}| = e_{mnp}l_{\tilde{1}m}l_{\tilde{2}n}l_{\tilde{3}p}. \tag{A.4.5}$$

If the cofactor of the term $l_{\tilde{m}n}$ in the determinant (Eq. A.4.4) is denoted by $\Theta_{\tilde{m}n}$, the expansion in terms of the rth column is given by

$$\delta_{mr}\theta = \Theta_{\tilde{n}m}l_{\tilde{n}r}, \tag{A.4.6}$$

and in terms of the sth row, by

$$\delta_{ms}\theta = \Theta_{\tilde{s}n}l_{\tilde{m}n}. \tag{A.4.7}$$

A.5   CURVILINEAR COORDINATES

The ideas in the preceding section can be easily extended to general curvilinear coordinates, x_m. These may be cylindrical, spherical, elliptical, or even more exotic frames. But all can be considered as a case of the general functional transformation

$$x_m = x_m(y_1, y_2, y_3), \tag{A.5.1}$$

where

y_m are the rectangular Cartesian coordinates,

x_m are general curvilinear coordinates,

$x_m(y_1, y_2, y_3)$ are single-valued functions of y_1, y_2, y_3.

For the transformation to be reversible, the determinant

$$\left|\frac{\partial x_m}{\partial y_s}\right| = e_{mnp}\frac{\partial x_1}{\partial y_m}\frac{\partial x_2}{\partial y_n}\frac{\partial x_3}{\partial y_p} \tag{A.5.2}$$

must be different from zero.   Then Eq. (A.5.2) can be solved to yield

$$y_m = y_m(x_1, x_2, x_3). \tag{A.5.3}$$

The surfaces x_m = const are called the coordinate surfaces, and the intersections of these coordinate surfaces are called the coordinate curves.   Through each point in a Euclidean space there pass three coordinate curves.   The intersections of the two surfaces x_2 = const and x_3 = const are curves along which only x_1 varies.   Thus the x_m coordinate curves are those points in space for which only x_m is changing.   In general, these curves are not straight lines, which is the justification for the name "curvilinear coordinates."

Similar relations must hold if another curvilinear system, $\tilde{x}_r$, is introduced.   The functional transformations can be written as

$$\tilde{x}_r = \tilde{x}_r(x_1, x_2, x_3), \tag{A.5.4}$$

and

$$x_r = x_r(\tilde{x}_1, \tilde{x}_2, \tilde{x}_3). \tag{A.5.5}$$

If Eq. (A.5.4) is substituted into Eq. (A.5.5), we obtain

$$x_r = x_r[\tilde{x}_1(x_1, x_2, x_3), \tilde{x}_2(x_1, x_2, x_3), \tilde{x}_3(x_1, x_2, x_3)]. \tag{A.5.6}$$

The partial derivative of this last equation yields

$$\frac{\partial x_r}{\partial x_s} = \frac{\partial x_r}{\partial \tilde{x}_m} \frac{\partial \tilde{x}_m}{\partial x_s}. \tag{A.5.7}$$

Since the curvilinear coordinates x_1, x_2, x_3 are independent, then if $r \neq s$, the left-hand side of Eq. (A.5.7) is zero. If $r = s$, then the left-hand side has the value "unity." This means that the left-hand side of Eq. (A.5.7) can be replaced by the Kronecker delta, that is,

$$\delta_{rs} = \frac{\partial x_r}{\partial \tilde{x}_m} \frac{\partial \tilde{x}_m}{\partial x_s}. \tag{A.5.8}$$

In a similar manner we find that

$$\delta_{rs} = \frac{\partial \tilde{x}_r}{\partial x_m} \frac{\partial x_m}{\partial \tilde{x}_s}. \tag{A.5.9}$$

If these results are applied to the pair of rectangular Cartesian frames, shown in Fig. A.1, we obtain

$$\delta_{rs} = l_{\tilde{m}r} l_{\tilde{m}s}. \tag{A.5.10}$$

One of these equations is the result,

$$(l_{\tilde{1}1})^2 + (l_{\tilde{2}1})^2 + (l_{\tilde{3}1})^2 = 1, \tag{A.5.11}$$

which is the familiar statement that the sum of the squares of the direction cosines of a line (in this example the line is the axis Oy_1) with respect to a rectangular frame $(O\tilde{y}_1, O\tilde{y}_2, O\tilde{y}_3)$ is equal to unity.

Another result contained in Eq. (A.5.10) is

$$l_{\tilde{1}1} l_{\tilde{1}2} + l_{\tilde{2}1} l_{\tilde{2}2} + l_{\tilde{3}1} l_{\tilde{3}2} = 0, \tag{A.5.12}$$

which can be recognized as the orthogonality condition for axes $O\tilde{y}_1$ and $O\tilde{y}_2$.

There are two other relations of the form given by Eq. (A.5.11) and two others of the form given by Eq. (A.5.12).

A.6 INVARIANTS, VECTORS, AND TENSORS [1], [2], [3]

The field of solid mechanics is intimately concerned with sets of quantities in relation to a system of coordinate frames. It is of prime importance to understand the manner in which these sets of quantities change if the original coordinate frame is transformed to another coordinate frame.

The simplest set of quantities is a single number which is usually referred to as a *scalar*. Such a quantity has the same value regardless of the coordinate frame which is used. Thus, if $f(x_1, x_2, x_3)$ denotes its value in one coordinate frame and $g(\tilde{x}_1, \tilde{x}_2, \tilde{x}_3)$ its value in another, then

$$f(x_1, x_2, x_3) = g(\tilde{x}_1, \tilde{x}_2, \tilde{x}_3) \tag{A.6.1}$$

defines what is variously referred to as a scalar, or an invariant, or a tensor of zero order. The labels "scalar," "invariant," or "tensor of zero order" have the same meaning. Familiar invariants are energy, the speed of light, and the length of a line element.

A familiar tensor of order one is the set of differentials dy_1, dy_2, dy_3. In another rectangular Cartesian frame $\tilde{y}_1$, $\tilde{y}_2$, $\tilde{y}_3$, the differentials are related to those in the first frame by

$$d\tilde{y}_m = \frac{\partial \tilde{y}_m}{\partial y_r} dy_r. \tag{A.6.2}$$

Note that the partial derivative $\partial \tilde{y}_m / \partial y_r$ is the direction cosine $l_{\tilde{m}r}$ (see Eq. A.4.1). Functions, such as the differentials, which transform in this manner are called tensors of order one, or vectors. If u_1, u_2, u_3 are the components of a first-order tensor, then under a transformation of coordinates, the tensor behaves according to the relation

$$\tilde{u}_m(\tilde{y}_1, \tilde{y}_2, \tilde{y}_3) = \frac{\partial \tilde{y}_m}{\partial y_r} u_r(y_1, y_2, y_3). \tag{A.6.3}$$

If Eq. (A.6.3) is multiplied by $\partial y_n / \partial \tilde{y}_m$, and summed on m from 1 to 3, we derive

$$\frac{\partial y_n}{\partial \tilde{y}_m} \tilde{u}_m = \frac{\partial y_n}{\partial \tilde{y}_m} \frac{\partial \tilde{y}_m}{\partial y_r} u_r = \delta_{nr} u_r = u_n,$$

through the use of Eq. (A.5.8). This result is the inverse transformation

$$u_n(y_1, y_2, y_3) = \frac{\partial y_n}{\partial \tilde{y}_m} \tilde{u}_m(\tilde{y}_1, \tilde{y}_2, \tilde{y}_3). \tag{A.6.4}$$

It should be observed that Eq. (A.6.4) has the same structure as Eq. (A.6.3).

A simple way to introduce tensors of the second order is to multiply two first-order tensors. Thus the second-order tensor w_{mn} can be formed by multiplying the tensors u_m and v_n:

$$w_{mn} = u_m v_n. \tag{A.6.5}$$

In general, a second-order tensor has nine independent components. If the coordinates are changed, then, since u_m and v_n obey the tensor transformation law, Eq. (A.6.3) or (A.6.4), we find that

$$\tilde{u}_m(\tilde{y}_1, \tilde{y}_2, \tilde{y}_3)\tilde{v}_n(\tilde{y}_1, \tilde{y}_2, \tilde{y}_3) = \frac{\partial \tilde{y}_m}{\partial y_r} \frac{\partial \tilde{y}_n}{\partial y_s} u_r(y_1, y_2, y_3)v_s(y_1, y_2, y_3). \tag{A.6.6}$$

Upon the introduction of Eq. (A.6.5), we obtain the transformation law for second-order tensors,

$$\tilde{w}_{mn}(\tilde{y}_1, \tilde{y}_2, \tilde{y}_3) = \frac{\partial \tilde{y}_m}{\partial y_r} \frac{\partial \tilde{y}_n}{\partial y_s} w_{rs}(y_1, y_2, y_3). \tag{A.6.7}$$

Systems of second-order quantities which transform according to Eq. (A.6.7) are called tensors of the second order. Familiar examples which will be studied in detail are the Cartesian strain and stress tensors.

The pattern for the transformation law of higher-order tensors can be seen by examining Eqs. (A.6.3) and (A.6.7). Thus a third-order tensor obeys the transformation law

$$\widetilde{w}_{mnp}(\tilde{y}_1, \tilde{y}_2, \tilde{y}_3) = \frac{\partial \tilde{y}_m}{\partial y_r} \frac{\partial \tilde{y}_n}{\partial y_s} \frac{\partial \tilde{y}_p}{\partial y_t} w_{rst}(y_1, y_2, y_3). \tag{A.6.8}$$

It should be noted that the components of a tensor in the new variables $\tilde{y}_r$, are linear combinations of the components in the old variables y_m. Consequently, if all the components of a tensor vanish in any coordinate frame, the components are zero in all coordinate frames. Or, if all the components are zero at some particular point in space, then all the components are zero at this point for all coordinate systems. These are extremely important properties of tensors.

One other tensor operation needs to be discussed, an operation called *contraction*. A second-order tensor has been defined as one which obeys the transformation law, Eq. (A.6.7). If, in the second-order tensor w_{mn}, the components w_{11}, w_{22}, and w_{33} are summed or added, the resulting quantity is represented by

$$w_{mm} = w_{11} + w_{22} + w_{33} \tag{A.6.9}$$

in accordance with the indicial and summation convention. Note carefully that w_{mm} does not contain any free indices, that is, w_{mm} is obtained by setting $m = n$ in w_{mn}; hence m becomes a dummy index. This process whereby two indices are set equal to each other in order to obtain a new quantity is called "contraction." In general, contraction reduces the order of the original tensor. Thus, a third-order tensor if contracted becomes a first-order tensor. Further, if the contraction process is carried to the point where there are no longer any free indices, then the resulting tensor is one of zero order, i.e., the resulting quantity is an invariant. For example, w_{mm} is an invariant, as can be demonstrated by setting $m = n$ in Eq. (A.6.7). Then

$$\widetilde{w}_{mm} = \frac{\partial \tilde{y}_m}{\partial y_r} \frac{\partial \tilde{y}_m}{\partial y_s} w_{rs} = w_{rs} l_{\widetilde{m}r} l_{\widetilde{m}s}, \tag{A.6.10}$$

and with the introduction of Eq. (A.5.10) this becomes

$$\widetilde{w}_{mm} = \delta_{rs} w_{rs} = w_{rr}. \tag{A.6.11}$$

Thus it has been demonstrated that $\widetilde{w}_{mm}$ in the coordinate system $\tilde{y}_1, \tilde{y}_2, \tilde{y}_3$ has the same value as w_{rr} in the coordinate system y_1, y_2, y_3; hence $\widetilde{w}_{mm}$ is an invariant.

A.7   VECTOR ANALYSIS [3], [4], [5]

In the previous section we defined a first-order tensor or vector in terms of its behavior under a transformation of coordinates. The branch of mathematics which deals with first-order tensors is called *vector analysis*. Many of the physical quantities encountered in mechanics, such as the displacement of a point, the velocity of a particle or a mechanical force, are vectors and require both magnitude and direction for complete specification. Thus a vector is any physical quantity which can be represented by a directed line segment. The following seven sections will define the essential operations of vector analysis. Vectors will be denoted by bold face letters, for example, **a**.

A.8 VECTOR ADDITION

Two vectors **a** and **b** are defined as equal if they are parallel, have the same sense, and are of equal length (see Fig. A.2). Equality is shown by writing

$$\mathbf{a} = \mathbf{b}. \tag{A.8.1}$$

Note that two vectors which are equal do not have to occupy the same points in space. The length or absolute magnitude is denoted by $|\mathbf{a}|$, and is always taken as positive.

Let **a** and **b** represent two vectors (see Fig. A.3). Then vector addition is defined as the geometrical sum of **a** and **b** and is written as

$$\mathbf{c} = \mathbf{a} + \mathbf{b}. \tag{A.8.2}$$

From Fig. A.3 we see that (1) the addition of vectors produces another vector, and (2) the order of addition is unimportant, i.e., vector addition is commutative:

$$\mathbf{a} + \mathbf{b} = \mathbf{b} + \mathbf{a}. \tag{A.8.3}$$

The process of addition can be extended to three or more vectors. Vector addition is also associative:

$$(\mathbf{a} + \mathbf{b}) + \mathbf{c} = \mathbf{a} + (\mathbf{b} + \mathbf{c}). \tag{A.8.4}$$

To complete the definition of vector addition, it is necessary to define a null vector which is represented by 0. If

$$\mathbf{a} + \mathbf{b} = 0, \tag{A.8.5}$$

then

$$\mathbf{b} = -\mathbf{a}, \tag{A.8.6}$$

which means that **b** is a vector parallel to **a** and of the same length but of opposite sense. The process of vector subtraction, for example $\mathbf{a} - \mathbf{b}$, means the addition of $(-\mathbf{b})$ to **a** (see Fig. A.4).

FIG. A.2 Equality of vectors.

FIG. A.3 Addition of two vectors.

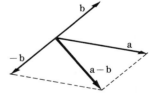

FIG. A.4 Subtraction of two vectors.

A.9 SCALAR MULTIPLICATION

The multiplication of a vector **a** by a real number m is defined to result in a vector **c** parallel to **a**, and m times as long, with a sense the same as **a** or opposite, according to whether m is positive or negative. Scalar multiplication is symbolized by

$$\mathbf{c} = m\mathbf{a}, \tag{A.9.1}$$

and obeys the commutative, associative, and distributive laws:

$$m\mathbf{a} = \mathbf{a}m, \quad (mn)\mathbf{a} = m(n\mathbf{a}), \quad (m + n)\mathbf{a} = m\mathbf{a} + n\mathbf{a}. \tag{A.9.2}$$

A.10 UNIT VECTORS

A unit vector is one which has unit length or magnitude. The most important set of unit vectors comprises those which are oriented along the axes of a rectangular Cartesian coordinate system. They will be denoted by i_1, i_2, and i_3, and are referred to as the base vectors associated with the rectangular Cartesian coordinate system.

A.11 CARTESIAN REPRESENTATION OF A VECTOR

The components of a vector **a** are any vectors whose sum is equal to **a**. The most convenient components are those parallel to a rectangular Cartesian coordinate system. Let **a** be a vector with its tail at point O, the origin of y_1, y_2, y_3 (see Fig. A.5). Then **a** is completely determined by specifying its components a_1, a_2, a_3 on the axes y_1, y_2, y_3. This is symbolized by writing

$$\mathbf{a} = a_n i_n = a_1 i_1 + a_2 i_2 + a_3 i_3. \tag{A.11.1}$$

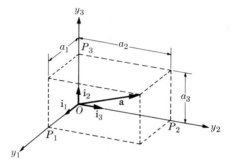

In this figure vector **a** is represented by the directed line segment $\overrightarrow{OP}$ and the three rectangular components of **a** are represented by $\overrightarrow{OP}_1$, $\overrightarrow{OP}_2$, and $\overrightarrow{OP}_3$, respectively. Let $\widehat{ay_1}$, $\widehat{ay_2}$, $\widehat{ay_3}$ represent the angles between OP and the axes y_1, y_2, y_3. Then the three components are obtained by multiplying the length of **a** by the corresponding direction cosines:

$$OP_1 = a_1 = |\mathbf{a}| \cos \widehat{ay_1}, \tag{A.11.2}$$

$$OP_2 = a_2 = |\mathbf{a}| \cos \widehat{ay_2}, \tag{A.11.3}$$

$$OP_3 = a_3 = |\mathbf{a}| \cos \widehat{ay_3}. \tag{A.11.4}$$

FIG. A.5   Rectangular Cartesian components of a vector.

The application of the Pythagorean Theorem gives the length of **a** in terms of its components; thus

$$(OP)^2 = (OP_1)^2 + (OP_2)^2 + (OP_3)^2, \quad \text{or} \quad |\mathbf{a}|^2 = (a_1)^2 + (a_2)^2 + (a_3)^2. \tag{A.11.5}$$

By substituting Eqs. (A.11.2), (A.11.3), and (A.11.4) into Eq. (A.11.5) we obtain

$$(\cos \widehat{ay_1})^2 + (\cos \widehat{ay_2})^2 + (\cos \widehat{ay_3})^2 = 1, \tag{A.11.6}$$

a result previously derived (cf. Eq. A.5.11).

The notion of the rectangular components of a vector can be generalized to represent the rectangular components of any point Q. Let y_1, y_2, y_3 be the rectangular Cartesian coordinates of point Q, and let **r** denote the line segment called the position vector, which connects the origin of the axis system, O, to Q. Then

$$\mathbf{r} = y_n i_n = y_1 i_1 + y_2 i_2 + y_3 i_3. \tag{A.11.7}$$

In this manner a position vector can be attached to all points in space.

A.12   THE SCALAR PRODUCT

The processes of vector addition and multiplication by a scalar have been defined to yield new quantities. Another vector operation, which involves just two vectors, is called the *scalar product*. The scalar product of two vectors **a** and **b** is defined as the scalar quantity formed by the product of the lengths of these vectors and the cosine of the angle between them:

$$\mathbf{a} \cdot \mathbf{b} = |\mathbf{a}||\mathbf{b}| \cos \widehat{\mathbf{ab}}, \qquad (A.12.1a)$$

where $\widehat{\mathbf{ab}}$ represents the angle between **a** and **b**. The scalar product may be interpreted geometrically as

$$\mathbf{a} \cdot \mathbf{b} = |\mathbf{a}| \text{ (component of } \mathbf{b} \text{ on } \mathbf{a}),$$

or

$$\mathbf{a} \cdot \mathbf{b} = |\mathbf{b}| \text{ (component of } \mathbf{a} \text{ on } \mathbf{b}),$$

$$(A.12.1b)$$

as illustrated in Fig. A.6. The scalar product is, therefore, a number which is positive, zero, or negative depending on whether the angle between the two vectors is acute, right, or obtuse, providing neither vector is a null vector. Hence, if neither vector is a null vector, then the equation

$$\mathbf{a} \cdot \mathbf{b} = 0 \qquad (A.12.2)$$

means that vector **a** is perpendicular to vector **b**.

It can be seen from Eqs. (A.12.1b) that scalar multiplication obeys the commutative law,

$$\mathbf{a} \cdot \mathbf{b} = \mathbf{b} \cdot \mathbf{a}. \qquad (A.12.3)$$

In addition, the geometrical interpretation shown in Fig. A.7 indicates that

$$|\mathbf{a}| \text{ (component of } (\mathbf{b} + \mathbf{c}) \text{ on } \mathbf{a}) = |\mathbf{a}| \text{ (component of } \mathbf{b} \text{ on } \mathbf{a})$$
$$+ |\mathbf{a}| \text{ (component of } \mathbf{c} \text{ on } \mathbf{a}), \qquad (A.12.4a)$$

or

$$\mathbf{a} \cdot (\mathbf{b} + \mathbf{c}) = \mathbf{a} \cdot \mathbf{b} + \mathbf{a} \cdot \mathbf{c}, \qquad (A.12.4b)$$

which is the distributive law of scalar multiplication.

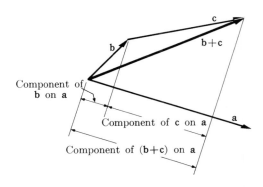

FIG. A.6 Geometrical representation of scalar product.

FIG. A.7 Geometrical representation of distributive law.

Let two vectors **a** and **b** be written in component form:

$$\mathbf{a} = a_n \mathbf{i}_n, \tag{A.12.5}$$

$$\mathbf{b} = b_n \mathbf{i}_n. \tag{A.12.6}$$

Then by virtue of the distributive law of multiplication the scalar product of two vectors is equal to the sum of the products of their corresponding rectangular components:

$$\mathbf{a} \cdot \mathbf{b} = (a_n \mathbf{i}_n) \cdot (b_m \mathbf{i}_m) = a_n b_m \delta_{nm} = a_n b_n. \tag{A.12.7}$$

In obtaining the result shown by Eq. (A.12.7), we have utilized the special property of scalar products of the base vectors, $\mathbf{i}_1$, $\mathbf{i}_2$, $\mathbf{i}_3$:

$$\mathbf{i}_n \cdot \mathbf{i}_m = \delta_{nm}. \tag{A.12.8}$$

Also, if $\mathbf{i}_n$ and $\mathbf{j}_r$ are unit vectors along the y_n- and $\tilde{y}_r$-axes, respectively, we have from Eq. (A.12.1)

$$\mathbf{i}_n \cdot \mathbf{j}_r = \mathbf{j}_r \cdot \mathbf{i}_n = l_{\bar{r}n}, \tag{A.12.9}$$

where $l_{\bar{r}n} = \cos(\widehat{\tilde{y}_r y_n})$ is the cosine of the angle between the y_n and $\tilde{y}_r$ axes.

The scalar product is useful in determining the angle between two vectors. Thus

$$\cos \widehat{\mathbf{ab}} = \frac{a_n b_n}{|\mathbf{a}||\mathbf{b}|}. \tag{A.12.10}$$

It is also useful in determining the length of a vector because the scalar product of a vector by itself yields

$$|\mathbf{a}|^2 = \mathbf{a} \cdot \mathbf{a} = a_n a_m \delta_{nm} = a_n b_n. \tag{A.12.11}$$

A.13   THE VECTOR PRODUCT

Scalar multiplication has been shown to yield a scalar. The *vector product*, which also involves only two vectors, of **a** and **b** is symbolized as **a** × **b** (read as **a** cross **b**), and is defined to yield a new vector:

$$\mathbf{a} \times \mathbf{b} = |\mathbf{a}||\mathbf{b}|\mathbf{n} \sin \widehat{\mathbf{ab}}, \tag{A.13.1}$$

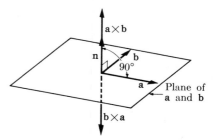

FIG. A.8 Geometrical representation of vector product.

where **n** is a unit vector perpendicular to both **a** and **b**, with a sense such that **a**, **b**, and **n** form a right-handed system. The meaning of this definition can be seen from Fig. A.8.

If neither **a** nor **b** is a null vector, then the equation

$$\mathbf{a} \times \mathbf{b} = 0 \tag{A.13.2}$$

means that vector **a** is parallel to vector **b**.

The requirement that the new vector **a** × **b** form a right-handed system with **a** and **b** in that particular order means that vector multiplication is not commutative, but instead:

$$\mathbf{a} \times \mathbf{b} = -\mathbf{b} \times \mathbf{a}. \tag{A.13.3}$$

The process of vector multiplication applied to the unit vectors i_1, i_2, i_3 yields

$$i_1 \times i_2 = i_3, \tag{A.13.4}$$

$$i_2 \times i_3 = i_1, \tag{A.13.5}$$

$$i_3 \times i_1 = i_2, \tag{A.13.6}$$

$$i_1 \times i_1 = i_2 \times i_2 = i_3 \times i_3 = 0, \tag{A.13.7}$$

or in a more compact form

$$i_m \times i_n = e_{mnp} i_p. \tag{A.13.8}$$

The vector product can also be cast into component form as follows:

$$\mathbf{a} \times \mathbf{b} = (a_m i_m) \times (b_n i_n),$$
$$\mathbf{a} \times \mathbf{b} = (a_2 b_3 - a_3 b_2) i_1 + (a_3 b_1 - a_1 b_3) i_2 + (a_1 b_2 - a_2 b_1) i_3. \tag{A.13.9}$$

A useful device to help in the calculation of the components of $\mathbf{a} \times \mathbf{b}$ is to write

$$\mathbf{a} \times \mathbf{b} = \begin{vmatrix} i_1 & i_2 & i_3 \\ a_1 & a_2 & a_3 \\ b_1 & b_2 & b_3 \end{vmatrix}. \tag{A.13.10}$$

It is seen from a comparison of Eqs. (A.13.9) and (A.13.10) that the components of $\mathbf{a} \times \mathbf{b}$ are the cofactors of i_1, i_2, i_3 in the expansion of the determinant. In summation notation the vector product $\mathbf{a} \times \mathbf{b}$ is written as

$$\mathbf{a} \times \mathbf{b} = e_{mnr} a_m b_n i_r. \tag{A.13.11}$$

It is now a simple task to prove that vector multiplication is distributive:

$$\mathbf{a} \times (\mathbf{b} + \mathbf{c}) = \mathbf{a} \times \mathbf{b} + \mathbf{a} \times \mathbf{c}, \tag{A.13.12}$$

or, in component form,

$$\mathbf{a} \times (\mathbf{b} + \mathbf{c}) = a_m i_m \times (b_n + c_n) i_n. \tag{A.13.13}$$

By making use of Eq. (A.13.9) we find that

$$\mathbf{a} \times (\mathbf{b} + \mathbf{c}) = a_m (b_n + c_n) i_m \times i_n$$
$$= a_m b_n e_{mnp} i_p + a_m c_n e_{mnp} i_p. \tag{A.13.14}$$

The right-hand side according to Eq. (A.13.11) is seen to be

$$\mathbf{a} \times \mathbf{b} + \mathbf{a} \times \mathbf{c}.$$

Thus the distributive law is proved.

Some additional relations concerning vector multiplication can be included here. If m and n are two scalar quantities, then

$$(m\mathbf{a}) \times (n\mathbf{b}) = (mn)\mathbf{a} \times \mathbf{b}. \tag{A.13.15}$$

By repeated application of the distributive law, the vector product of two vector sums can be expanded as in ordinary algebra, provided the order of the factors is not altered. Thus, for example,

$$(\mathbf{a} + \mathbf{b}) \times (\mathbf{c} + \mathbf{d}) = \mathbf{a} \times \mathbf{c} + \mathbf{a} \times \mathbf{d} + \mathbf{b} \times \mathbf{c} + \mathbf{b} \times \mathbf{d}. \quad \text{(A.13.16)}$$

If vector $\mathbf{c}$ is not a null vector, then the equation

$$\mathbf{a} \times \mathbf{c} = \mathbf{b} \times \mathbf{c}, \quad \text{(A.13.17)}$$

which can be rearranged to read

$$(\mathbf{a} - \mathbf{b}) \times \mathbf{c} = 0, \quad \text{(A.13.18)}$$

means that either $\mathbf{a} - \mathbf{b}$ is a null vector, or $\mathbf{a} - \mathbf{b}$ and $\mathbf{c}$ are parallel. It is seen that the process of cancellation cannot be applied to vector $\mathbf{c}$ in Eq. (A.13.7).

A.14 THE TRIPLE SCALAR PRODUCT

The scalar product of the vector $\mathbf{a} \times \mathbf{b}$ and a third vector $\mathbf{c}$ is symbolized as $(\mathbf{a} \times \mathbf{b}) \cdot \mathbf{c}$ or sometimes as $[\mathbf{abc}]$. It is easily demonstrated (see Fig. A.9) that the triple scalar product is numerically equal to the volume of a parallelepiped having the vectors $\mathbf{a}, \mathbf{b}, \mathbf{c}$ as concurrent edges. Its sign is positive or negative depending on whether the three vectors form a right-handed or left-handed set. If none of the three vectors is a null vector, then the equation

$$(\mathbf{a} \times \mathbf{b}) \cdot \mathbf{c} = 0 \quad \text{(A.14.1)}$$

means that the three vectors are coplanar.

In terms of the rectangular components, the triple scalar product can be obtained from the expansion of the determinant formed by the components:

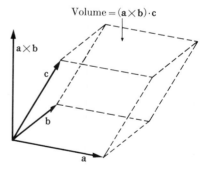

FIG. A.9 Geometrical representation of triple scalar product.

$$(\mathbf{a} \times \mathbf{b}) \cdot \mathbf{c} = \begin{vmatrix} a_1 & a_2 & a_3 \\ b_1 & b_2 & b_3 \\ c_1 & c_2 & c_3 \end{vmatrix}. \quad \text{(A.14.2)}$$

The product of two triple scalar products can be shown (albeit not easily) to be given by

$$[\mathbf{uvw}][\mathbf{abc}] = \begin{vmatrix} \mathbf{u} \cdot \mathbf{a} & \mathbf{u} \cdot \mathbf{b} & \mathbf{u} \cdot \mathbf{c} \\ \mathbf{v} \cdot \mathbf{a} & \mathbf{v} \cdot \mathbf{b} & \mathbf{v} \cdot \mathbf{c} \\ \mathbf{w} \cdot \mathbf{a} & \mathbf{w} \cdot \mathbf{b} & \mathbf{w} \cdot \mathbf{c} \end{vmatrix}. \quad \text{(A.14.3)}$$

(See Ref. A.3, Section 24.)

A.15   EXTREME-VALUE PROBLEMS IN DIFFERENTIAL CALCULUS [4]

In developing some of the basic equations in solid mechanics, we become involved in the subsidiary problem of having to maximize or minimize a function of many variables. For example, we might begin with a set of general expressions for all the components of stress acting on an element of a body. Our task might be to find the maximum value of a particular component σ_{mn}, and the direction cosines of the plane on which $\sigma_{mn(\text{max})}$ acts.

We apply elementary partial differential calculus to the function of many variables in a manner analogous to the procedure used to find the local maxima and minima of a function of one variable. If $f(x_1, x_2, \ldots, x_n)$ is a function of n independent variables, we say that an *extreme value* of f is defined by

$$\frac{\partial f}{\partial x_i} = 0, \qquad i = 1, 2, \ldots, n. \tag{A.15.1}$$

That is, an extreme value of f occurs at any point where the rates of change of f with respect to each of the independent variables simultaneously vanish, as expressed by the set of n simultaneous equations (A.15.1).

As an example, consider the function of two independent variables:

$$f(x, y) = 4 - x^2 - y^2. \tag{A.15.2}$$

Its extreme values are found in a straightforward manner by solving the conditions (A.15.1) for the values $(x, y)_{\text{ext}}$, and introducing these back into f. Thus

$$\begin{aligned}
\partial f/\partial x &= -2x = 0, \qquad \partial f/\partial y = -2y = 0, \\
(x, y)_{\text{ext}} &= (0, 0), \qquad f_{\text{ext}}(0, 0) = 4.
\end{aligned} \tag{A.15.3}$$

Since f is a function of only two independent variables, we can plot f on an axis perpendicular to the xy-plane, as illustrated by Fig. A.10. We can easily visualize the general function of two variables as a surface of "hills," "valleys," and "saddle points,"

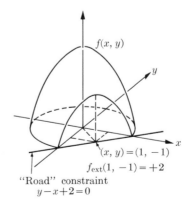

FIG. A.10   A surface representing a function $f(x, y)$.

FIG. A.11   Intersection of $f(x, y)$ and a plane perpendicular to the xy-plane.

where the crest of a hill, the bottom of a valley, and the seat of a saddle point correspond to max-max, min-min, and max-min or min-max extreme values of the function. The function

$$f(x, y) = 4 - x^2 - y^2$$

is an inverted parabolic cone, and it may be thought of as a single "hill" with a crest 4 units above the xy-plane and directly above $(0, 0)$. The "hill-and-valley" concept will be useful in the ensuing discussion of more complicated extreme-value problems.

A.16 SOME EXAMPLES OF EXTREME-VALUE PROBLEMS WITH SIMPLE CONSTRAINTS

Suppose we add a condition to the simple extreme-value problem. We desire the locations $(x_1, \ldots, x_n)$ of the extreme values of $f(x_1, x_2, \ldots, x_n)$, *subject to the constraint that these locations also satisfy the equation*

$$g(x_1, x_2, \ldots, x_n) = 0. \tag{A.16.1}$$

We can think of the constraint expressed by Eq. (A.16.1) as some sort of hypersurface in the n-dimensional space of the problem. Satisfying the constraint is then equivalent to making a plot of the values of $f(x_1, \ldots, x_n)$ at locations (x_i) of the intersection of the surfaces defined by f and g. The extreme values of $f(x_i)$ on this intersection may be altogether different from the values we found when we were allowed to roam freely over all points on f.

As an example, let it be required to find the extreme values of

$$f(x, y) = 4 - x^2 - y^2$$

subject to the constraint   (A.16.2)

$$g(x, y) = y - x + 2 = 0.$$

Returning to the "hill-and-valley" analogy, we again visualize $f(x, y)$ as the parabolic "hill" shown in Fig. A.10. The constraint may be solved to yield

$$y = x - 2, \tag{A.16.3}$$

which is the equation of a straight line in the xy-plane, passing through the points $(0, -2)$ and $(2, 0)$. If we visualize the constraint as a "road" which follows the xy-plane and the part of $f(x, y)$ above the xy-plane, we can immediately make the general conclusion that we shall find a new extreme value for $f(x, y)$ in this case.

Figure A.11 shows the "hill" with the "road" constraint superimposed. For clarity, we have created a vertical "cliff" on the hill between the road and the observer. It is evident from the figure that the constraint is a surface, a plane perpendicular to the xy-plane. The constraint plane does not pass through the extreme values of the surface,

$$f_{\text{ext}}(0, 0) = 4,$$

found in the previous section.

To obtain the constrained extreme value of $f(x, y)$, we must satisfy the equation $g(x, y) = 0$ before applying the extremalizing conditions $\partial f/\partial x = 0$ and $\partial f/\partial y = 0$.

Equation (A.16.3) may be introduced directly into the first of Eqs. (A.16.2) to yield

$$f(x, y)|_g = 4 - x^2 - (x - 2)^2, \tag{A.16.4}$$

where the symbol $|_g$ after $f(x, y)$ indicates that the expression for f which follows has been constrained to $g(x, y) = 0$. We observe that $f|_g$ is a function of the single independent variable x; thus the extremalizing conditions reduce to

$$\frac{df}{dx} = 0 = -2x - 2(x - 2),$$

which yields

$$x_{\text{ext}} = +1, \qquad y_{\text{ext}} = x - 2 = -1, \tag{A.16.5}$$

as the location of the constrained extreme value of $f(x, y)$. The value itself is obtained by introducing Eqs. (A.16.5) back into $f(x, y)$:

$$f_{\text{ext}}(1, -1) = 4 - 1 - 1 = 2. \tag{A.16.6}$$

A.17   THE LAGRANGE MULTIPLIER METHOD [4]

Let us consider again the parabolic "hill" which we examined in the previous section. This time we are asked to find the extreme values of

$$f(x, y) = 4 - x^2 - y^2$$

subject to the constraint

$$g(x, y) = xy + 1 = 0. \tag{A.17.1}$$

It is possible to solve Eqs. (A.17.1) for the constrained extreme value of f by the procedure developed in Section A.16. However, let us instead add λ times $g(x, y)$ to $f(x, y)$, where λ has the properties of an independent variable:

$$F(x, y) = f(x, y) + \lambda g(x, y), \tag{A.17.2}$$

or

$$F(x, y) = 4 - x^2 - y^2 + \lambda(xy + 1). \tag{A.17.3}$$

We now apply the extremalizing formulas of elementary partial differential calculus to Eq. (A.17.3), considering x, y, and λ as independent variables:

$$\frac{\partial F}{\partial x} = 0, \qquad \frac{\partial F}{\partial y} = 0, \qquad \frac{\partial F}{\partial \lambda} = 0. \tag{A.17.4}$$

The results of the calculations are:

$$\text{(a)} \quad \frac{\partial F}{\partial x} = -2x + \lambda y = 0,$$

$$\text{(b)} \quad \frac{\partial F}{\partial y} = -2y + \lambda x = 0, \tag{A.17.5}$$

$$\text{(c)} \quad \frac{\partial F}{\partial \lambda} = xy + 1 = 0.$$

We can now solve Eqs. (A.17.5) for x, y, and λ:

$$\text{from (c),} \quad x = -\frac{1}{y};$$

$$\text{from (a),} \quad \frac{2}{y} + \lambda y = 0 \Rightarrow \lambda = -\frac{2}{y^2};$$

$$\text{from (b),} \quad -2y + \frac{2}{y^2}\left(\frac{1}{y}\right) = 0 \Rightarrow y^4 = 1.$$

The real solutions thus become

$$x = -1, +1, \quad y = +1, -1, \quad \lambda = -2, +2. \tag{A.17.6}$$

Introduction of the values $(x, y) = (-1, +1)$ or $(+1, -1)$ into $f(x, y)$ yields the solution

$$f_{\text{ext}}(x, y)\big|_g = +2 \quad \text{at} \quad \begin{cases} (+1, -1), \\ (-1, +1). \end{cases} \tag{A.17.7}$$

Figure A.12 illustrates the intersection of the constraint surface (a hyperbolic cylinder) with the portion of $f(x, y)$ which lies above the xy-plane. Calculation of $f_{\text{ext}}|_g$ by the method of Section A.16 will yield the answer in Eq. (A.17.7).

In the above method of solution, we began by creating an extra (and apparently useless) variable, λ, called a Lagrange multiplier. The normal procedure of first eliminating as many independent variables as possible (Section A.16) is more efficient when the problem to be solved is simple. However, the advantages of the systematic Lagrange multiplier method will become apparent in problems having many independent variables and multiple nonlinear constraints.

We shall first consider a quite general extreme-value problem. Let

$$f = f(x_1, x_2, \ldots, x_n)$$

be a given function of the n independent variables $\{x_i\}$, and let

$$g_1 = g_1(x_1, x_2, \ldots, x_n) = 0,$$
$$g_2 = \quad \cdots \quad = 0,$$
$$\vdots \qquad \qquad \vdots \tag{A.17.8}$$
$$g_m = g_m(x_1, x_2, \ldots, x_n) = 0$$

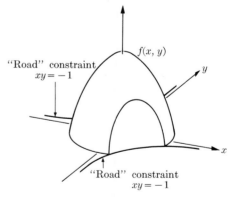

FIG. A.12 Intersection of $f(x, y)$ and a hyperbolic cylinder.

be given equations of constraint. We are required to find the extreme values of f subject simultaneously to all m of the constraints, $g_j = 0$. We observe that the problem is trivial if $m = n$, since the constraint equations will then confine the examination to one point in the n-space. If $m > n$, the problem is overconstrained, i.e., there may be no points of f which will satisfy all the constraints. Thus we can restrict our consideration to problems in which $m < n$ without losing any generality.

In the previous section, we saw that extreme-value problems of the type outlined above can be solved, in theory, by straightforward elimination by substitution of each of the constraint equations before the extremalizing conditions are applied. In practice, the number and complexity of the constraint equations may be such that it is not possible to make the substitutions in a systematic manner. We then turn to the Lagrange multiplier method, which provides the systematic approach for the general extreme-value problem.

The steps in the Lagrange method (outlined here without proof) are as follows (see Ref. A.4, Sections 3.10 and 3.11):

(a) Multiply each constraint by an undetermined parameter, called a Lagrange multiplier.

(b) Form the sum of the products of constraints and multipliers by summing over all the constraints.

(c) Add the above sum to the function f, which is to be extremalized, and call this sum F.

(d) Apply the extremalizing conditions by setting equal to zero the partial derivatives of F with respect to each independent variable *and each Lagrange multiplier*.

(e) Solve the resulting equations for the locations and values of the extreme values of f.

Example. Let it be required to find the extreme values of

$$f(x_1, x_2, x_3, x_4) = (x_1)^2 + 2(x_2)^2 + 3(x_3)^2 + 4(x_4)^2 \tag{A.17.9}$$

subject to the constraints

$$\begin{aligned} g_1 &= x_1 + x_2 - 3 = 0, \\ g_2 &= x_2 + x_3 - 5 = 0, \\ g_3 &= x_3 + x_4 - 7 = 0. \end{aligned} \tag{A.17.10}$$

Solution: We must define three Lagrange multipliers λ_1, λ_2, and λ_3 to form

$$\lambda_1 g_1 + \lambda_2 g_2 + \lambda_3 g_3.$$

The function $F(x_1, x_2, x_3, x_4)$ then becomes

$$F = f + \sum_{i=1}^{3} \lambda_i g_i,$$

or

$$\begin{aligned} F = (x_1)^2 + 2(x_2)^2 + 3(x_3)^2 + 4(x_4)^2 + \lambda_1(x_1 + x_2 - 3) \\ + \lambda_2(x_2 + x_3 - 5) + \lambda_3(x_3 + x_4 - 7). \end{aligned} \tag{A.17.11}$$

Applying the extremalizing conditions, we find four equations by setting $\partial F/\partial x_i = 0$:

$$\frac{\partial F}{\partial x_1} = 2x_1 + \lambda_1 = 0, \qquad \frac{\partial F}{\partial x_2} = 4x_2 + \lambda_1 + \lambda_2 = 0,$$

$$\frac{\partial F}{\partial x_3} = 6x_3 + \lambda_2 + \lambda_3 = 0, \qquad \frac{\partial F}{\partial x_4} = 8x_4 + \lambda_3 = 0,$$

$$\tag{A.17.12}$$

and three additional equations by setting $\partial F/\partial \lambda_i = 0$:

$$\frac{\partial F}{\partial \lambda_1} = x_1 + x_2 - 3 = 0,$$

$$\frac{\partial F}{\partial \lambda_2} = x_2 + x_3 - 5 = 0, \qquad \text{(A.17.13)}$$

$$\frac{\partial F}{\partial \lambda_3} = x_3 + x_4 - 7 = 0.$$

Comparison of Eqs. (A.17.13) with Eqs. (A.17.10) shows that by taking $\partial F/\partial \lambda_i = 0$, we have obtained the constraint equations again.

The seven Eqs. (A.17.12) and (A.17.13) may be solved systematically by first eliminating the λ_i from Eqs. (A.17.12). We find that

$$\lambda_1 = -2x_1, \qquad \lambda_2 = 2x_1 - 4x_2,$$
$$\lambda_3 = -6x_3 - 2x_1 + 4x_2, \qquad \lambda_3 = -8x_4. \qquad \text{(A.17.14)}$$

The third and fourth of Eqs. (A.17.14) can now be combined with Eqs. (A.17.13) to get a set of four simultaneous equations in the x_i:

$$\begin{aligned} x_1 - 2x_2 + 3x_3 - 4x_4 &= 0, \\ x_1 + x_2 &= 3, \\ x_2 + x_3 &= 5, \\ x_3 + x_4 &= 7. \end{aligned} \qquad \text{(A.17.15)}$$

Solution of Eqs. (A.17.15) by the methods of ordinary algebra yields the location of a single extreme value of f:

$$x_1 = 2, \qquad x_2 = 1, \qquad x_3 = 4, \qquad x_4 = 3, \qquad \text{(A.17.16)}$$

and introduction of Eqs. (A.17.16) into Eq. (A.17.9) for f yields

$$f_{\text{ext}}(2, 1, 4, 3) = +90. \qquad \text{(A.17.17)}$$

A.18   ELEMENTS OF THE CALCULUS OF VARIATIONS [6]

We are all familiar with the problem of finding a maximum or a minimum of a simple function $y(x)$. Graphically, such a function is shown in Fig. A.13. For a relative maximum or minimum to occur, the slope dy/dx must be zero.

Let us now consider the problem of determining a function $y(x)$ which makes the integral

$$I = \int_a^b F(x, y, y')\, dx \qquad \text{(A.18.1)}$$

an extremum, i.e., stationary, and which satisfies the prescribed end conditions,

$$y(a) = y_a \qquad \text{and} \qquad y(b) = y_b. \qquad \text{(A.18.2)}$$

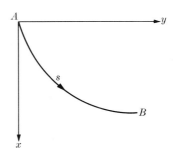

FIG. A.13 Maximum and minimum of a function $y(x)$.

FIG. A.14 Coordinate system for the brachistochrone problem.

The integrand $F(x, y, y')$ is a function of x, y, and the first derivative dy/dx, which for convenience will be denoted by y'.

As an example of F, let us consider the famous problem of the brachistochrone which Johann Bernoulli formulated in 1696. Imagine a particle constrained to slide without friction along a certain curve joining a point A to a lower point B. Along which curve will the time required for the descent be the least if this particle is allowed to fall under the influence of gravity?

Let s be the length of the curve measured from A (see Fig. A.14), v the velocity, and t the time. We wish to determine the curve which will make the total time T of descent from A to B a minimum. The arc length is calculable from

$$ds = v \, dt, \tag{A.18.3}$$

$$ds = \sqrt{dx^2 + dy^2} = \sqrt{1 + y'^2} \, dx. \tag{A.18.4}$$

A freely falling body gains velocity according to

$$v = 2gx, \tag{A.18.5}$$

where g is the acceleration due to gravity. Then from the preceding three equations,

$$dt = \frac{ds}{v} = \frac{\sqrt{1 + y'^2}}{\sqrt{2gx}} \, dx. \tag{A.18.6}$$

The total time is the integral of Eq. (A.18.6),

$$I = \frac{1}{\sqrt{2g}} \int_{x=0}^{x=x_B} \frac{\sqrt{1 + y'^2}}{\sqrt{x}} \, dx. \tag{A.18.7}$$

By comparing Eq. (A.18.7) with Eq. (A.18.1), we find that the functional of interest in the brachistochrone problem is

$$F = \frac{\sqrt{1 + y'^2}}{\sqrt{x}}. \tag{A.18.8}$$

We want to develop the ideas which will enable us to solve this particular problem as well as many others.

Let us suppose that $y(x)$ is the actual minimizing function. This is schematically illustrated in Fig. A.15. The method of attack will be to investigate what happens to the integral I when neighboring functions are used in F. These functions are constructed by adding to $y(x)$ a function $\epsilon\eta(x)$, where ϵ is a constant which can take on different quantitative values, and $\eta(x)$ is an arbitrary function of x which vanishes at $x = a$ and $x = b$, that is,

$$\eta(a) = 0, \quad \text{and} \quad \eta(b) = 0. \quad (A.18.9)$$

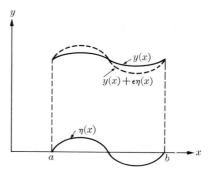

Thus $y(x) + \epsilon\eta(x)$ will satisfy the end conditions. A neighboring function is shown as a dashed curve in Fig. A.15. The integral I which is obtained by replacing y by $y + \epsilon\eta$ is then a function of ϵ once η is chosen, since y is the actual minimizing function. We take note of this dependence on ϵ by writing

$$I(\epsilon) = \int_a^b F(x, y + \epsilon\eta, y' + \epsilon\eta') \, dx. \quad (A.18.10)$$

FIG. A.15   Function $y(x)$ and a neighboring function.

This integral takes on its minimum value when ϵ is zero, but this is possible only if

$$\frac{dI(\epsilon)}{d\epsilon} = 0 \quad \text{when} \quad \epsilon = 0. \quad (A.18.11)$$

Our manipulations will become a bit easier if we set

$$F_e = F(x, y + \epsilon\eta, y' + \epsilon\eta') \quad (A.18.12)$$

and

$$Y(x) = y(x) + \epsilon\eta(x). \quad (A.18.13)$$

Then the differential of Y with respect to x is

$$Y' = y'(x) + \epsilon\eta'(x). \quad (A.18.14)$$

Next we differentiate F_e with respect to ϵ to obtain

$$\frac{dF_e}{d\epsilon} = \frac{\partial F_e}{\partial Y}\frac{\partial Y}{\partial \epsilon} + \frac{\partial F}{\partial Y'}\frac{\partial Y'}{\partial \epsilon}. \quad (A.18.15)$$

Note that F_e is treated as a composite function of Y and Y'. From Eqs. (A.18.13) and (A.18.14) we find that

$$\frac{\partial Y}{\partial \epsilon} = \eta(x), \quad (A.18.16)$$

$$\frac{\partial Y'}{\partial \epsilon} = \eta'(x), \quad (A.18.17)$$

so that Eq. (A.18.17) takes on the form

$$\frac{dF_e}{d\epsilon} = \frac{\partial F_e}{\partial Y}\,\eta(x) + \frac{\partial F_e}{\partial Y'}\,\eta'(x). \tag{A.18.18}$$

It follows that

$$\frac{dI}{d\epsilon} = \int_a^b \left\{ \frac{\partial F_e}{\partial Y}\,\eta(x) + \frac{\partial F_e}{\partial Y'}\,\eta'(x) \right\} dx = 0. \tag{A.18.19}$$

The second term can be transformed through integration by parts:

$$\int_a^b \frac{\partial F_e}{\partial Y'}\,\eta'(x)\,dx = \frac{\partial F_e}{\partial Y'}\,\eta(x)\bigg]_a^b - \int_a^b \frac{d}{dx}\left(\frac{\partial F_e}{\partial Y'}\right)\eta(x)\,dx. \tag{A.18.20}$$

Since $\eta(a) = 0$ and $\eta(b) = 0$, the integrated term vanished. Thus

$$\int_a^b \left\{ \frac{\partial F_e}{\partial Y}\,\eta(x) - \frac{d}{dx}\left(\frac{\partial F_e}{\partial Y'}\right)\eta(x) \right\} dx = 0. \tag{A.18.21}$$

This derivative must vanish when ϵ approaches 0. But as ϵ approaches 0, F_e approaches F, Y approaches y, and Y' approaches y'. Hence, Eq. (A.18.21) becomes

$$\int_a^b \left\{ \frac{\partial F}{\partial y} - \frac{d}{dx}\left(\frac{\partial F}{\partial y'}\right) \right\}\eta(x)\,dx = 0. \tag{A.18.22}$$

There is a lemma called the Fundamental Lemma of the Calculus of Variations which says that if $\eta(x)$ is well behaved, then for the integral to be zero,

$$\frac{\partial F}{\partial y} - \frac{d}{dx}\left(\frac{\partial F}{\partial y'}\right) = 0. \tag{A.18.23}$$

This is called *Euler's* equation, and is a necessary condition for $y(x)$ to make I a minimum or maximum. We remind ourselves that the partial derivatives have been taken by assuming that x, y, and y' are three independent variables. But in computing d/dx we must recall that y and y' are functions of x. The last term can be expanded as follows:

$$\frac{d}{dx}\left(\frac{\partial F}{\partial y'}\right) = \frac{\partial^2 F}{\partial x\,\partial y'} + \frac{\partial^2 F}{\partial y\,\partial y'}\frac{dy}{dx} + \frac{\partial^2 F}{\partial y'^2}\frac{d^2 y}{dx^2}. \tag{A.18.24}$$

Euler's equation becomes

$$\frac{\partial F}{\partial y} - \frac{\partial^2 F}{\partial x\,\partial y'} - \frac{\partial^2 F}{\partial y\,\partial y'}\frac{dy}{dx} - \frac{\partial^2 F}{\partial y'^2}\frac{d^2 y}{dx^2} = 0. \tag{A.18.25}$$

This is a second-order differential equation, and hence its solution contains two arbitrary constants. These are to be determined by the requirement that the curve pass through the end-points A and B.

In the *brachistochrone* problem,

$$F = \frac{\sqrt{1 + y'^2}}{\sqrt{x}}.$$
(A.18.26)

Hence

$$\frac{\partial F}{\partial y} = 0,$$
(A.18.27)

$$\frac{\partial F}{\partial y'} = \frac{y'}{\sqrt{x(1 + y'^2)}}.$$
(A.18.28)

Euler's equation becomes

$$-\frac{d}{dx}\left(\frac{y'}{\sqrt{x(1 + y'^2)}}\right) = 0.$$
(A.18.29)

The solution is a curve called the brachistochrone.

The variational procedure can be formalized by introducing the variational notation. In our treatment of the simplest case, we were seeking a function $y(x)$ which makes a certain integral I an extremum. The function

$$Y = y(x) + \epsilon\eta(x)$$

was formed. This can be rewritten as

$$\epsilon\eta(x) = Y - y.$$
(A.18.30)

The quantity $\epsilon\eta(x)$ is called the variation of y and will be denoted by δy, that is,

$$\delta y \equiv \epsilon\eta(x).$$
(A.18.31)

Similarly, we can write

$$\epsilon\eta' = Y' - y'.$$
(A.18.32)

This is the variation of y' and will be denoted by $\delta y'$, that is,

$$\delta y' \equiv \epsilon\eta'.$$
(A.18.33)

It follows from these definitions that

$$\frac{d}{dx}(\delta y) = \delta\left(\frac{dy}{dx}\right).$$
(A.18.34)

That is, the operators δ and d/dx are commutative.

The integrand we considered previously was $F = F(x, y, y')$. This integrand for a *fixed* value of x depends only upon the function $y(x)$ and its derivative $y'(x)$. Note that y is the dependent variable, and x is the independent variable. Now when $y(x)$ and $y'(x)$ are varied, F will also vary. We denote the variation of F by δF. Since F

for a fixed value of x depends on $y(x)$ and $y'(x)$, the variation of F can be written as

$$\delta F = \frac{\partial F}{\partial y} \delta y + \frac{\partial F}{\partial y'} \delta y'. \tag{A.18.35}$$

It can be shown that the laws governing the variation are the same as those governing differentiation. For example,

$$\delta(F_1 F_2) = F_1 \delta F_2 + F_2 \delta F_1, \tag{A.18.36}$$

$$\delta \left(\frac{F_1}{F_2} \right) = \frac{F_2 \delta F_1 - F_1 \delta F_2}{F_2^2}, \tag{A.18.37}$$

where F_1 and F_2 are two different functions of x, y, and y'.

For the integral I, the variation has the following meaning:

$$\delta I = \delta \int_a^b F(x, y, y') \, dx = \int_a^b \delta F \, dx. \tag{A.18.38}$$

A necessary condition that the integral I be stationary is that its first variation vanish, that is,

$$\delta I = \int_a^b \delta F(x, y, y') \, dx = 0. \tag{A.18.39}$$

We can easily show this by writing

$$\int_a^b \delta F \, dx = \int_a^b \left[\frac{\partial F}{\partial y} \delta y + \frac{\partial F}{\partial y'} \delta y' \right] dx = 0. \tag{A.18.40}$$

Integrating the second term by parts, we have

$$\int_a^b \frac{\partial F}{\partial y'} \delta \left(\frac{dy}{dx} \right) dx = \int_a^b \frac{\partial F}{\partial y'} \frac{d}{dx} (\delta y) \, dx = \frac{\partial F}{\partial y'} \delta y \bigg]_a^b - \int_a^b \frac{d}{dx} \left(\frac{\partial F}{\partial y'} \right) \delta y \, dx. \tag{A.18.41}$$

Thus

$$\int_a^b \delta F \, dx = \int_a^b \left[\frac{\partial F}{\partial y} - \frac{d}{dx} \frac{\partial F}{\partial y'} \right] \delta y \, dx + \frac{\partial F}{\partial y'} \delta y \bigg]_a^b = 0. \tag{A.18.42}$$

This is precisely what we had previously (see Eqs. A.18.20 and A.18.22).

Let us consider next a more general case in which the integral is of the form

$$I = \iint_R F(x, y, u, v, u_x, u_y, v_x, v_y) \, dx \, dy, \tag{A.18.43}$$

where the subscripts indicate differentiation, that is, $u_x = \partial u / \partial x$. Here x, y are the independent variables, the region R could be a body in a state of plane stress, and u and v would be the displacements. Then the derivatives u_x, u_y, etc., are related to the components of strain. The condition for an extremum is again

$$\delta I = 0. \tag{A.18.44}$$

This becomes

$$\delta I = \iint \delta F \, dx \, dy = \iint_R \left\{ \left(\frac{\partial F}{\partial u} \delta u + \frac{\partial F}{\partial u_x} \delta u_x + \frac{\partial F}{\partial u_y} \delta u_y \right) \right.$$

$$\left. + \left(\frac{\partial F}{\partial v} \delta v + \frac{\partial F}{\partial v_x} \delta v_x + \frac{\partial F}{\partial v_y} \delta v_y \right) \right\} dx \, dy = 0. \qquad \text{(A.18.45)}$$

The terms involving δu_x, δu_y, δv_x, and δv_y must be integrated by parts. We obtain

$$\delta I = \iint_R \left\{ \left[\frac{\partial F}{\partial u} - \frac{\partial}{\partial x} \left(\frac{\partial F}{\partial u_x} \right) - \frac{\partial}{\partial y} \left(\frac{\partial F}{\partial u_y} \right) \right] \delta u \right.$$

$$+ \left[\frac{\partial F}{\partial v} - \frac{\partial}{\partial x} \left(\frac{\partial F}{\partial v_x} \right) - \frac{\partial}{\partial y} \left(\frac{\partial F}{\partial v_y} \right) \right] \delta v \right\} dx \, dy$$

$$+ \int \frac{\partial F}{\partial u_x} \delta u \, dy \Big]_c^d + \int \frac{\partial F}{\partial u_y} \delta u \, dx \Big]_a^b + \int \frac{\partial F}{\partial v_x} \delta v \, dy \Big]_c^d$$

$$+ \int \frac{\partial F}{\partial v_y} \delta v \, dx \Big]_a^b = 0. \qquad \text{(A.18.46)}$$

The necessary conditions (i.e. Euler equations) become, since δu and δv are independent,

$$\frac{\partial F}{\partial u} - \frac{\partial}{\partial x} \left(\frac{\partial F}{\partial u_x} \right) - \frac{\partial}{\partial y} \left(\frac{\partial F}{\partial u_y} \right) = 0, \qquad \text{(A.18.47)}$$

$$\frac{\partial F}{\partial v} - \frac{\partial}{\partial x} \left(\frac{\partial F}{\partial v_x} \right) - \frac{\partial}{\partial y} \left(\frac{\partial F}{\partial v_y} \right) = 0. \qquad \text{(A.18.48)}$$

A.19   THE DIVERGENCE THEOREM [3], [4], [7]

Consider a volume V enclosed by a surface boundary A. If a vector $\mathbf{P}(y_1, y_2, y_3)$ and its derivatives with respect to y_1, y_2, and y_3 are continuous at all points in V, then

$$\iiint \nabla \cdot \mathbf{P} \, dV = \iint \mathbf{P} \cdot \mathbf{n} \, dA, \qquad \text{(A.19.1)}$$

where in the rectangular Cartesian coordinates the operator ∇ is defined by the relation

$$\nabla = \mathbf{i}_m \frac{\partial}{\partial y_m}, \qquad \text{(A.19.2)}$$

and $\mathbf{n}$ is a unit vector along the direction normal to the surface. This statement is known as the Divergence Theorem. In the literature it is sometimes referred to as Green's Theorem or Gauss' Theorem. It can also be written in scalar form as

$$\iiint \frac{\partial p_m}{\partial y_m} \, dV = \iint p_m n_m \, dA. \qquad \text{(A.19.3)}$$

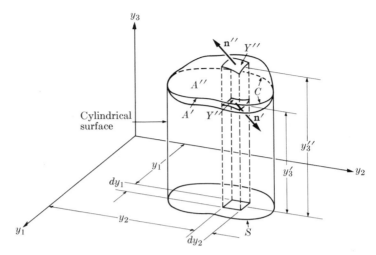

FIG. A.16   A surface represented by A' and A'' and its projection on the y_1y_2-plane.

Here the vectors $\mathbf{P}$ and $\mathbf{n}$ are written in terms of their components,

$$\mathbf{P} = p_m \mathbf{i}_m, \tag{A.19.4}$$

$$\mathbf{n} = n_m \mathbf{i}_m. \tag{A.19.5}$$

To prove the theorem let us first prove that

$$\iiint \frac{\partial p_3}{\partial y_3} \, dV = \iint p_3 n_3 \, dA \tag{A.19.6}$$

for a simple case where the boundary surface A is pierced by a line parallel to the y_3-axis in, at most, two points. As illustrated in Fig. A.16, the entire surface A can be divided into two parts, A' and A'', by a closed curve C which is also on a cylindrical surface with generators parallel to the y_3-axis. The projection of this cylinder on the y_1y_2-plane encloses the area S. We introduce an element of volume which forms a column parallel to the y_3-axis, and has a projection $dy_1 \, dy_2$ on the y_1y_2-plane. The element intersects A' and A'' at $Y'(y_1, y_2, y_3')$ and $Y''(y_1, y_2, y_3'')$, respectively. Thus

$$\iiint \frac{\partial p_3}{\partial y_3} \, dV = \iint_S \left[\int_{y_3'}^{y_3''} \frac{\partial p_3}{\partial y_3} \, dy_3 \right] dy_1 \, dy_2$$

$$= \iint_S [p_3(y_1, y_2, y_3'') - p_3(y_1, y_2, y_3')] \, dy_1 \, dy_2. \tag{A.19.7}$$

Let dA' and dA'' be, respectively, the areas on the two surfaces cut by this vertical column, and $\mathbf{n}'$ and $\mathbf{n}''$ be the corresponding outward unit normals. Then from Eq.

(6.4.13) we have

$$dy_1 \, dy_2 \; = \; -dA'n_3' \; = \; dA''n_3'', \qquad (A.19.8)$$

where n_3' and n_3'' are the direction cosines which connect the y_3-axis with the surface normals $\mathbf{n}'$ and $\mathbf{n}''$, respectively. The negative sign is used in the second term because the normal $\mathbf{n}'$ is in a direction opposite to the positive y_3-axis. Thus Eq. (A.19.7) becomes

$$\iiint \frac{\partial p_3}{\partial y_3} \, dV \; = \; \iint_{A'} p_3(y_1, \, y_2, \, y_3')n_3' \, dA \; + \; \iint_{A''} p_3(y_1, \, y_2, \, y_3'')n_3'' \, dA, \qquad (A.19.9)$$

which can be written in the form of Eq. (A.19.6). In the case where A is pierced by a vertical line in more than two points, the total volume V can be subdivided into a number of regions $V_1, V_2, \ldots$ by a series of surface areas $T_1, T_2, \ldots$ such that the boundary of each of the regions will be intersected by a vertical line in at most two points. Equation (A.19.6) then can be applied to each region. When the individual equations are added, the surface integrals over $T_1, T_2, \ldots$ will cancel; hence Eq. (A.19.6) is also applicable to the total volume.

In a similar manner we can prove that

$$\iiint \frac{\partial p_1}{\partial y_1} \, dV \; = \; \iint p_1 n_1 \, dA \qquad (A.19.10)$$

and

$$\iiint \frac{\partial p_2}{\partial y_2} \, dV \; = \; \iint p_2 n_2 \, dA. \qquad (A.19.11)$$

Equations (A.19.6), (A.19.10), and (A.19.11) can then be combined to yield

$$\iiint \frac{\partial p_m}{\partial y_m} \, dV \; = \; \iint p_m n_m \, dA, \qquad (A.19.12)$$

which is the Divergence Theorem.

A.20 MATRIX ALGEBRA [6], [8], [9]

In Section A.2 the summation and indicial notation for linear homogeneous functions was introduced. There is an alternative way, called the *matrix notation*, to represent such functions. This matrix notation possesses certain pictorial qualities which are helpful in visualizing the structure of systems of simultaneous equations. In addition, the numerical solution of equations is aided by the use of matrices.

For example, let us consider a system of simultaneous linear algebraic equations

$$\begin{aligned}
K_{11}q_1 + K_{12}q_2 + \cdots + K_{1n}q_n &= Q_1, \\
K_{21}q_1 + \cdots \quad \cdots + K_{2n}q_n &= Q_2, \\
\vdots \qquad\qquad\qquad\quad \vdots \\
K_{n1}q_1 + \cdots \quad \cdots + K_{nn}q_n &= Q_n,
\end{aligned} \qquad (A.20.1)$$

which in summation form is

$$\sum_{i=1}^{n} K_{ij}q_j = Q_i, \qquad i = 1, 2, \ldots, n. \qquad (A.20.2)$$

In matrix notation, this is displayed in the form

$$\begin{bmatrix} K_{11} & K_{12} & \cdots & K_{1n} \\ K_{21} & \cdots & \cdots & K_{2n} \\ \vdots & & & \vdots \\ K_{n1} & \cdots & \cdots & K_{nn} \end{bmatrix} \begin{bmatrix} q_1 \\ q_2 \\ \vdots \\ q_n \end{bmatrix} = \begin{bmatrix} Q_1 \\ Q_2 \\ \vdots \\ Q_n \end{bmatrix}, \qquad (A.20.3)$$

or more compactly as

$$[K_{ij}]\{q_j\} = \{Q_i\}, \qquad (A.20.4)$$

or as

$$[K]\{q\} = \{Q\}. \qquad (A.20.5)$$

In general, a matrix $[A]$ or $[A_{ij}]$ represents an array of numbers arranged in m rows and n columns, such as

$$[A]_{m \times n} = \begin{bmatrix} A_{11} & A_{12} & \cdots & A_{1n} \\ A_{21} & A_{22} & \cdots & A_{2n} \\ \vdots & & & \vdots \\ A_{m1} & A_{m2} & \cdots & A_{mn} \end{bmatrix}. \qquad (A.20.6)$$

Thus A_{ij} is the typical element of the matrix $[A]$. Note that the first subscript locates the row, and the second subscript the column of the element. A matrix having m rows and n columns is said to have an order m by n. A matrix with equal numbers of rows and columns is called a *square matrix*, and is denoted by

$$\begin{bmatrix} A_{11} & A_{12} & \cdots & A_{1n} \\ A_{21} & \cdots & \cdots & A_{2n} \\ \vdots & & & \vdots \\ A_{n1} & \cdots & \cdots & A_{nn} \end{bmatrix} = [A]. \qquad (A.20.7)$$

A matrix which has m elements arranged in a single column is called a *column matrix*, and is usually denoted by

$$\begin{bmatrix} A_1 \\ A_2 \\ \vdots \\ A_m \end{bmatrix} = \{A\}. \qquad (A.20.8)$$

A matrix which has n elements arranged in a single row is called a *row matrix* and is usually denoted by

$$[A_1 A_2 \ldots A_n] = \lfloor A \rfloor. \tag{A.20.9}$$

Important elementary operations of matrices are given as follows:

A.21   EQUALITY

Two matrices $[A]$ and $[B]$ are equal, for example,

$$[A]_{m \times n} = [B]_{m \times n}, \tag{A.21.1}$$

only if

$$A_{ij} = B_{ij}, \tag{A.21.2}$$

that is, each element of A is equal to the similarly located element of B.

A.22   ADDITION AND SUBTRACTION

The operations of addition and subtraction are defined only for matrices of the same order. The definitions are for addition:

$$[A]_{m \times n} + [B]_{m \times n} = [C]_{m \times n}, \tag{A.22.1}$$

$$A_{ij} + B_{ij} = C_{ij}, \tag{A.22.2}$$

and for subtraction:

$$[A]_{m \times n} - [B]_{m \times n} = [D]_{m \times n}, \tag{A.22.3}$$

$$A_{ij} - B_{ij} = D_{ij}. \tag{A.22.4}$$

Thus it is observed that corresponding elements are either added or subtracted in the operations of matrix addition and subtraction.

A.23   SCALAR MULTIPLICATION

The operation denoted by

$$l[A]_{m \times n} = [B]_{m \times n}, \tag{A.23.1}$$

where l is a constant is defined by

$$l A_{ij} = B_{ij}, \tag{A.23.2}$$

that is, every element in the matrix $[A]$ is multiplied by the scalar quantity l.

A.24   MATRIX MULTIPLICATION

At first glance the operation of matrix multiplication will appear complicated; a little bit of practice is necessary to gain proficiency.

The multiplication of two matrices $[A]$ and $[B]$ to yield a matrix $[C]$ must be performed in a specified order, that is,

$$[A]_{m \times n}[B]_{n \times p} = [C]_{m \times p}. \tag{A.24.1}$$

The number of columns in $[A]$ must equal the number of rows in $[B]$. To further define the process of multiplication, let us suppose that $[A]$ and $[B]$ are matrices of the orders denoted by

$$[A]_{2\times3} = \begin{bmatrix} A_{11} & A_{12} & A_{13} \\ A_{21} & A_{22} & A_{23} \end{bmatrix},$$

(A.24.2)

$$[B]_{3\times3} = \begin{bmatrix} B_{11} & B_{12} & B_{13} \\ B_{21} & B_{22} & B_{23} \\ B_{31} & B_{32} & B_{33} \end{bmatrix}.$$

Then, for example, two of the elements of $[C]$ are given by

$$C_{11} = A_{11}B_{11} + A_{12}B_{21} + A_{13}B_{31},$$
$$C_{21} = A_{21}B_{11} + A_{22}B_{21} + A_{23}B_{31}.$$

(A.24.3)

The element C_{ik} is defined by the row-by-column rule, which can be stated as

$$C_{ik} = \sum_{j=1}^{n} A_{ij}B_{jk}.$$

(A.24.4)

Thus, if the order of the matrix $[A]$ is m by n, and the order of the matrix $[B]$, n by p, then the order of the product $[C]$ is m by p.

Matrix multiplication is not commutative, that is,

$$[A][B] \neq [B][A].$$

(A.24.5)

Thus, to be specific, the operation $[A][B]$ should be stated as "the premultiplication of $[B]$ by $[A]$," or "the postmultiplication of $[A]$ by $[B]$."

A.25   UNIT MATRIX

A unit matrix $[I]$ is of the form

$$[I] = \begin{bmatrix} 1 & 0 & 0 & \cdots & 0 \\ 0 & 1 & 0 & \cdots & 0 \\ 0 & 0 & 1 & \cdots & 0 \\ \vdots & & & & \vdots \\ 0 & 0 & 0 & \cdots & 1 \end{bmatrix}.$$

(A.25.1)

It is a square matrix with all the diagonal terms equal to unity while all the off-diagonal terms are zero. Thus, premultiplication or postmultiplication by a unit matrix does not alter the original matrix.

A.26   INVERSION OF MATRICES

Unlike the other elementary algebraic operations, the process of division in matrix algebra is not similar to the corresponding process with numbers. Division is accomplished by inverting matrices. The inverse of a matrix $[A]$ is denoted by $[A]^{-1}$

and is defined by both conditions:

$$[A][A]^{-1} = [I] \tag{A.26.1}$$

and

$$[A]^{-1}[A] = [I], \tag{A.26.2}$$

and thus in order to have an inverse, $[A]$ must by necessity be a square matrix.

When the equation

$$[A]\{B\} = \{C\} \tag{A.26.3}$$

is premultiplied by the inverse of $[A]$, we obtain

$$[I]\{B\} = [A]^{-1}\{C\}, \tag{A.26.4}$$

or simply

$$\{B\} = [A]^{-1}\{C\}. \tag{A.26.5}$$

Let $\{C\}$ be a column matrix with the ith element equal to unity while all other elements are equal to zero. Then $\{B\}$ is identical to the ith column of the $[A]^{-1}$ matrix. This shows that the elements of an inverse matrix of order n by n can be obtained by solving n sets of simultaneous equations in the form of Eq. (A.26.5), with the value of unity placed at the appropriate location in the $\{C\}$ matrix.

REFERENCES FOR APPENDIX

(1) A. J. McConnell, *Applications of Tensor Analysis*, Dover Publications, New York, 1957.
(2) I. S. Sokolnikoff, *Tensor Analysis*, John Wiley and Sons, New York, 1951.
(3) L. Brand, *Vector and Tensor Analysis*, John Wiley and Sons, New York, 1947.
(4) I. S. Sokolnikoff and R. M. Redheffer, *Mathematics of Physics and Modern Engineering*, McGraw-Hill, New York, 1958.
(5) G. B. Thomas, *Calculus and Analytic Geometry*, Addison-Wesley, Reading, Mass., 2nd Ed., 1960.
(6) F. B. Hildebrand, *Methods of Applied Mathematics*, Prentice-Hall, New York, 1952.
(7) F. B. Hildebrand, *Advanced Calculus for Engineers*, Prentice-Hall, New York, 1948.
(8) Sam Perlis, *Theory of Matrices*, Addison-Wesley, Reading, Mass., 1952.
(9) R. A. Frazier, W. J. Duncan, A. R. Collar, *Elementary Matrices*, MacMillan, New York, 1947.

Bibliography

CHAPTER 1

1.1 F. Cajori, *Sir Isaac Newton's Mathematical Principles*, Univ. of Calif. Press, Berkeley, Calif., 1960. This is a revision of the original English translation of Newton's *Principia* [1.2]* made by Andrew Motte in 1729. Of particular interest are a series of prefaces which describe the philosophy and motivation for the work, and an Appendix which provides historical notes of the controversies surrounding some of Newton's discoveries and ideas.

1.2 I. Newton, *Philosophiae Naturalis Principia Mathematica*, Jussn Societatis ac Typis Josephi Streater Anno MDCLXXXVII. This is the original treatise in Latin.

1.3 E. Mach, *The Science of Mechanics*, 6th Ed., Open Court Publishing, La Salle, Ill., 1960. This is an English translation of Mach's book which bears the subtitle "A Critical and Historical Account of Its Development." The introduction to this, the Sixth American Edition, provides some interesting and challenging views on the study of mechanics.

1.4 J. L. Synge and B. A. Griffith, *Principles of Mechanics*, 3rd Ed., McGraw-Hill, New York, 1959. Section 1.1 has provided the ideas for Chapter 1 of this book.

CHAPTER 2

2.1 F. Cajori, *Sir Isaac Newton's Mathematical Principles* [1.1]. It is interesting and informative to read Newton's original statements and explanations of the laws of motion. He expresses these in terms of three laws and six corollaries on pages 13 to 28.

2.2 E. Mach, *The Science of Mechanics* [1.3]. Chapter I which is entitled, "The Development of the Principles of Statics," is an excellent presentation not only of the historical background but of the content of statics. The writing is clear and detailed with a minimum of equations. Of especial interest are pages 44–59 of Chapter I which bears the subtitle, "The Principle of the Composition of Forces." Also, the reader will gain additional insight by reading pages 226–247, "The Achievements of Newton."

---

* These bracketed numbers refer to references in this bibliography.

2.3   J. L. Synge and B. A. Griffith, *Principles of Mechanics* [1.4]. Chapters 1, 2, 3, and 10 may be helpful in that the contents of Chapter 2 of this book are presented in more expanded form.

2.4   S. H. Crandall and N. C. Dahl, *An Introduction to the Mechanics of Solids*, McGraw-Hill, New York, 1959. This is one of the best of the recent books on solid mechanics. Chapter 1 of Crandall and Dahl parallels Chapter 2 of the *Statics of Deformable Bodies*. There is a wealth of imaginative problems.

2.5   Sir Horace Lamb, *Statics*, 3rd Ed., Cambridge Univ. Press, New York, 1928. The first edition of this book was published in 1912. It emphasizes geometrical methods as applied to statics. Vectors are used, but it is not until Chapter VI that the scalar product is introduced.

2.6   L. Brand, *Vectorial Mechanics*, John Wiley and Sons, New York, 1930. This is one of the earliest books in English which makes extensive use of vector analysis for statics. Chapters II, III, IV, and V are pertinent to the material covered in our book.

CHAPTER 3

3.1   C. H. Norris and J. B. Wilbur, *Elementary Structural Analysis*, 2nd Ed., McGraw-Hill, New York, 1960. The material contained in pages 60–153 is a very lucid and systematic presentation of the statics of beams and trusses. There are many illustrative examples, and accompanying these are discussions of the fine points of the solutions.

3.2   A. S. Niles and J. S. Newell, *Airplane Structures*, 4th Ed., John Wiley and Sons, New York, 1954. This book, which first appeared in 1929, was one of the earliest texts to be directed toward the structural problems of flying vehicles. Chapter II which deals with beams and Chapter VIII which deals with trusses present slightly different approaches to these two topics. For example, the statics of beams is treated by a series of propositions.

3.3   S. H. Crandall and N. C. Dahl, *An Introduction to the Mechanics of Solids*. Read comments in [2.4]. Chapters 2 and 3 of this book parallel Chapters 3 and 4 of our book.

3.4   L. Brand, *Vectorial Mechanics*. Read comments in [2.6].

CHAPTER 4

4.1   C. H. Norris and J. B. Wilbur, *Elementary Structural Analysis* [3.1]. Pages 400 through 408 provide an excellent presentation of a method of approach to statically indeterminate problems. The examples which come after page 408 require more knowledge than the reader would have at this time.

4.2   S. H. Crandall and N. C. Dahl, *An Introduction to the Mechanics of Solids*. Read comments in [3.3].

4.3   F. R. Shanley, *Strength of Materials*, McGraw-Hill, New York, 1957. The author approaches structural analysis from the standpoint of force transmission. His ideas on force transmission are presented in Sections 1.12, 13.1, 13.2, 14.2, 15.1, and 17.1. This book stresses what might be termed a "physical-intuitive" approach to the mechanics of deformable bodies.

4.4   W. M. FIFE and J. B. WILBUR, *Theory of Statically Indeterminate Structures*, McGraw-Hill, New York, 1937. This is one of the earliest books in this country to treat indeterminate structures in a systematic and coherent manner.

4.5   C. L. M. H. NAVIER, *Resumé des leçons données à l'école des ponts and chaussées sur l'application de la méchanique a l'éstablissement des construction et des machines*, Paris, 1833. This book was first published in 1826 and extensively revised by Navier in 1833 for the second edition. Under the editorship of St. Venant it was further revised in 1863 (Navier died in 1836). Navier was the first to recognize that the elasticity of the structure will supply the additional equations for the solution of problems for which the elementary equations of statics do not supply enough equations, i.e., he was the first to develop a general method of solving statically indeterminate problems.

CHAPTER 5

5.1   A. E. H. LOVE, *A Treatise on the Mathematical Theory of Elasticity*, 4th Ed., 1927, 1st Amer. Printing, 1944, Dover Publications, New York. The first edition of this book was published in 1892 by the Cambridge University Press. Everyone interested in elasticity should have a copy in his bookcase, even though it is difficult to read because the notation and phraseology do not conform to current usage. Chapter I is concerned with the analysis of strain.

5.2   F. D. MURNAGHAN, "Finite Deformations of An Elastic Solid," *American Journal of Mathematics* **59**, 235–260 (1937). This is one of the earliest tensor treatments of strain.

5.3   S. TIMOSHENKO and J. N. GOODIER, *Theory of Elasticity*, 2nd Ed., McGraw-Hill, New York, 1951. The first edition of this book appeared in 1934, and for more than two decades has been the standard reference on elasticity in the United States. It progresses from the simple to the more complicated problems, so that not until page 221 is the analysis of strain in three dimensions discussed. The marvelous physical intuition which blessed the early elasticians is evident in this book. A deficiency of the book from a modern pedagogic point of view is that vectors and tensors are not used. Nevertheless, the *Theory of Elasticity* remains a valuable source-book and belongs on every structural engineer's bookshelf. Strain is discussed in Sections 5, 8, 72, 73, 74, 75, 77, and 78.

5.4   A. E. GREEN and W. ZERNA, *Theoretical Elasticity*, Oxford Univ. Press, New York, 1954. This book has had a tremendous influence in shaping the modern approach to elasticity. It has shown the way to the tensor formulation of the equations of elasticity and has demonstrated the power of these methods to handle complicated geometrical problems. In fact, geometric nonlinearities in elasticity, as well as non-orthogonal curvilinear coordinates, can be easily included in the equations (however, the solution still presents difficulties). *Theoretical Elasticity* is written almost entirely in terms of general tensors (not the Cartesian ones used in *Statics of Deformable Bodies*. Consequently, a great deal of study by the reader is required if any benefit is to be gained. This is not a book for beginners; even the expert unfamiliar with tensors will find it difficult. However, both beginner and expert should be cognizant of this work. Sections 2.1, 2.2, and 2.3 present a general treatment parallel to Chapter 5 of *Statics of Deformable Bodies*.

5.5   V. V. NOVOZHILOV, *Foundations of the Nonlinear Theory of Elasticity*, Graylock Press, New York, 1953. Chapter I of this book, comprising some 60 pages, is a very lucid account of the geometry of strain. The treatment, which uses vectors sparingly and tensors not at all, is in terms of rectangular Cartesian coordinates. Novozhilov's discussion of the transition from large strains to small to linear is the best to be found in the literature. The author is one of the well-known Russian elasticians. The book, originally published in Russian in 1948, has been beautifully translated into English.

5.6   I. S. SOKOLNIKOFF, *Mathematical Theory of Elasticity*, 2nd Ed., McGraw-Hill, New York, 1956. This is one of the earliest books (the first edition appeared in 1946) written in English to approach the theory of elasticity by first developing the three-dimensional equations and then specializing to simpler problems. Chapters I, II, and III parallel Chapters 4, 5, and 6 of the *Statics of Deformable Bodies*.

5.7   B. DE SAINT-VENANT, "Mémoire sur l'équilibre des corps solides, dans les limites de leur élasticité, et les conditions de leur résistance, quand les déplacements éprouvés par leurs pointes ne sont pas trés petits," *Comptes Rendus de l'Académie des Science*, Vol. XXIV, pp. 260–263 (1847). (Memoir on the "Equilibrium of Solid Bodies within the Elastic Limit and on the Conditions of Resistance When the Displacements Experienced by Points in the Body Are Not Very Small.") St. Venant was the first to notice that the relative elongations can be small even though the angles of rotation are numerically large. He recognized the geometrical meanings of the components of the strain tensor.

CHAPTER 6

6.1   A. E. H. LOVE, *A Treatise on the Mathematical Theory of Elasticity*. Read comments for [5.1]. Chapter 2 presents the analysis of stress.

6.2   S. TIMOSHENKO and J. N. GOODIER, *Theory of Elasticity*. Read comments for [5.3]. Stress in this book is discussed in Sections 2, 3, 4, 11, 13, 67, 68, 69, 70, 71, 76, and 79.

6.3   A. E. GREEN and W. ZERNA, *Theoretical Elasticity*. Read comments for [5.4]. Stress is discussed in Sections 2.4, 2.5, and 5.2.

6.4   V. V. NOVOZHILOV, *Foundations of the Nonlinear Theory of Elasticity*. Read comments for [5.5]. Stress is discussed in Chapter 2.

6.5   I. S. SOKOLNIKOFF, *Mathematical Theory of Elasticity*. Read comments for [5.6]. Stress is discussed in Chapter 2.

6.6   A. L. CAUCHY, "Recherches sur l'équilibre et le mouvement intérieur des corps solides ou fluides, élastiques ou non élastiques," *Bulletin des Sciences à la Societé Philomathique*, 1823. Cauchy was the first to show that stress at a point can be expressed in terms of six components. He showed the significance of the principal planes of stress. Also, he was the first to formulate the stress-strain relations in the form which is used in modern times.

CHAPTER 7

7.1   A. E. H. LOVE, *A Treatise on the Mathematical Theory of Elasticity*. Read comments for [5.1]. Sections 6.4 and 6.6 discuss the generalized Hooke's law. Additionally, the first 37 pages of Love's book give an excellent historical summary of elasticity.

7.2   S. Timoshenko and J. N. Goodier, *Theory of Elasticity*. Read comments for [5.3]. Section 6 presents the stress-strain relations for isotropic materials. Note that Timoshenko's results differ from ours by a factor of $\frac{1}{2}$ in three of the relations.

7.3.   A. E. Green and W. Zerna, *Theoretical Elasticity*. Read comments for [5.4]. A general discussion of stress-strain relations for homogeneous isotropic bodies is presented in Section 2.8. Anisotropic materials for linear strain (Green and Zerna use "infinitesimal" for "linear") are discussed in Section 5.3.

7.4   V. V. Novozhilov, *Foundations of the Nonlinear Theory of Elasticity*. Read comments for [5.5]. The stress-strain relations are discussed in Chapter 3.

7.5   I. S. Sokolnikoff, *Mathematical Theory of Elasticity*. Read comments for [5.6]. Sections 20, 21, 22, and 23 are on the subject of the stress-strain relations.

7.6   H. B. Huntington, "The Elastic Constants of Crystals," *Solid State Physics— Advances in Research and Application*, Vol. 7, pp. 213–351. Academic Press, New York, 1958. This is a comprehensive article which approaches the stress-strain relations from the viewpoint of physics of the solid state.

7.7   R. F. S. Hearmon, *An Introduction to Applied Anisotropic Elasticity*, Oxford Univ. Press, New York, 1961. The first 44 pages of this little book discuss the stress-strain relations for anisotropic elasticity.

7.8   I. Todhunter and K. Pearson, *A History of the Theory of Elasticity and of the Strength of Materials*, Volumes I, II, Dover Publications, New York, 1960. The first volume of this set was published by Cambridge University Press in 1886. These volumes will be of interest to those who are interested in a critical review of the development of elasticity. There are more than 2200 pages in this history.

7.9   S. Timoshenko, *History of the Theory of Elasticity*, McGraw-Hill, New York, 1953. This is a very readable book on the history of elasticity.

7.10   C. Truesdell and R. A. Toupin, "The Classical Field Theories," *Encyclopedia of Physics*, Vol. III/1, pp. 226–793, Springer, New York, 1960. This is an exhaustive treatise on the exact and general theory of the continuous field. Included as a special case is the subject which we have called the statics of deformable bodies. This article is not for the beginner in the field. As a matter of fact, even the expert is first advised to read a portion of its appendix on mathematics before tackling the article.

CHAPTER 8

8.1   W. Prager and P. G. Hodge, Jr., *Theory of Perfectly Plastic Solids*, John Wiley and Sons, New York, 1951. Read Chapter 1 on "Basic Concepts." Note again that the conventional definition of shear strain is adopted in Prager and Hodge, hence three of the stress-strain relations differ from ours by a factor of $\frac{1}{2}$.

8.2   O. Hoffman and G. Sachs, *Introduction to the Theory of Plasticity for Engineers*, McGraw-Hill, New York, 1953. Read Chapter 5, "Plastic Stress-strain Relations," and Chapter 6, "Experimental Data."

8.3   A. Nadai, *Theory of Flow and Fracture of Solids*, Vol. I, 2nd Ed., McGraw-Hill, New York, 1950. This book contains detailed discussions of both the mathematical treatment and experimental evidences of plastic deformation of solids. Read Part II of the text.

8.4   F. A. McClintock and A. S. Argon, *An Introduction to the Mechanical Behavior of Materials*, Addison-Wesley, Reading, Mass., in press. Chapters 5, 6, and 7 contain detailed discussions of plasticity in single crystals and polycrystals and of elastic stress-strain relations.

8.5   R. Hill, *Mathematical Theory of Elasticity*, Oxford Univ. Press, New York, 1950. The first chapter contains a brief summary of historical background, and the second presents the foundations of the theory of plasticity.

8.6   H. W. Hayden, W. G. Moffatt and J. Wulff, *Mechanical Behavior of Materials* (Vol. III of a series on "Structure and Properties of Materials"), John Wiley and Sons, New York, 1965. For readers who are interested in the properties of solids from the microscopic point of view, this text book is a good reference.

8.7   A. G. Guy, *Elements of Physical Metallurgy*, 2nd Ed., Chapter 9, "Plasticity of Metals," Addison-Wesley, Reading, Mass., 1959. This chapter presents a discussion of the plastic properties of solids from the microscopic point of view.

CHAPTER 9

9.1   R. L. Bisplinghoff, H. Ashley, and R. L. Halfman, *Aeroelasticity*, Addison-Wesley, Reading, Mass., 1955. Chapter 2 contains a detailed treatment on the determination by energy methods of the stiffness and flexibility influence coefficients of airplane wing structures.

9.2   C. H. Norris, and J. B. Wilbur [3.1]. Chapter 12 presents a different development of the Principle of Virtual Work and includes numerous illustrative examples on the deflections of trusses, beams, and frames. Sections 13.7 and 13.8 contain a discussion of the solution of statically indeterminate structures by the Theorem of Least Work.

9.3   S. Timoshenko and J. N. Goodier [5.3]. Chapter 6 of this text presents strain-energy methods for continuous elastic bodies. The principles referred to are the Principle of Virtual Work, Castigliano's Second Theorem, and the Theorem of Least Work. Plane stress problems are used in the derivation of these principles and in illustrative examples.

9.4   I. S. Sokolnikoff [5.6]. Pages 377–401 present an introduction to the calculus of variation and derivations of the Theorems of Minimum Potential and Complementary Energies, and other related energy principles.

9.5   H. L. Langhaar, *Energy Methods in Applied Mechanics*, John Wiley and Sons, New York, 1962. This book contains energy methods for statics and dynamics of deformable bodies. Chapter 3 presents elements of the calculus of variations, and Chapter 4 presents energy methods for deflections of structures and the solution of statically indeterminate structures.

9.6   N. J. Hoff, *The Analysis of Structures*, John Wiley and Sons, New York, 1956. The complete text contains the treatment of energy principles for static analysis of structures. It also presents many methods derived from the principles of virtual work, potential energy, and complementary energy.

Nomenclature,
Symbolism, and Assorted Marks

A	area
$\mathbf{a}$	acceleration vector
$\mathbf{C}$	couple
C_{mn}	flexibility influence coefficient
dS	differential element of length in deformed body
ds	differential element of length in undeformed body
E	Young's modulus
E_{mnpr}	elasticity tensor
e_{rst}	permutation symbol
F	axial force in a slender beam
$\mathbf{F}$	force vector, body force vector
F_n	component of $\mathbf{F}$ with respect to $\mathbf{i}_n$
G	shear modulus
G_{mn}	metric tensor in deformed body
g_{mn}	metric tensor in undeformed body
I	section moment of inertia of a slender beam
I_1, I_2, I_3	stress invariants
$\mathbf{i}_1, \mathbf{i}_2, \mathbf{i}_3$	unit vectors along y_1, y_2, y_3, respectively
J_1, J_2, J_3	strain invariants
$\mathbf{j}_1, \mathbf{j}_2, \mathbf{j}_3$	unit vectors along $\tilde{y}_1, \tilde{y}_2, \tilde{y}_3$, respectively
K	bulk modulus
K_{mn}	stiffness influence coefficient
k	spring constant
L	length of bar
$l_{m\tilde{r}}$	direction cosine of the angle between y_m- and $\tilde{y}_r$-axes
M	bending moment in a slender beam
$\mathbf{M}$	moment vector
M_1, M_2, M_3	components of moment vector $\mathbf{M}$ with respect to $\mathbf{i}_1, \mathbf{i}_2, \mathbf{i}_3$
m	mass
$\mathbf{n}$	unit normal vector

$\mathbf{P}$	force vector
p	distributed load in a slender beam
P_n	components of force vector $\mathbf{P}$ with respect to $\mathbf{i}_n$
Q	generalized force
q	generalized displacement
$\mathbf{R}$	position vector to point P in deformed body
$\mathbf{r}$	position vector to point p in undeformed body
R_n	components of position vector $\mathbf{R}$, with respect to $\mathbf{i}_n$
S	shear force in a slender beam
S_{mnpr}	compliance tensor
T	torsional moment on a slender beam; thrust; tension force
U	strain energy
U^*	strain energy density
$\hat{U}^*$	distortion energy density (deviator strain energy)
$\hat{\hat{U}}^*$	dilatation energy density (spherical strain energy)
U_c	complementary strain energy
$\mathbf{u}$	displacement vector connecting point p in undeformed body to P in deformed body
u_n	components of displacement vector $\mathbf{u}$ with respect to $\mathbf{i}_n$
V	volume
w	deflection of a slender beam
$\mathbf{X}$	redundant force
y_n	rectangular Cartesian axes. Also components of position vector $\mathbf{r}$, with respect to $\mathbf{i}_n$
α	coefficient of thermal expansion
γ	shear strain
γ_{mn}	strain tensor
$\hat{\gamma}_{mn}$	components of deviator strain tensor
$\hat{\hat{\gamma}}_{mn}$	components of spherical strain tensor
ΔT	change in temperature
δ	deflection
δ_{mn}	Kronecker delta
ϵ_{mn}	linear strain tensor
$\bar{\epsilon}$	equivalent strain
λ	one of the two Lamé constants
$\lambda_1, \lambda_2, \lambda_3$	direction cosines
μ	shear modulus, also one of the two Lamé constants $(=G)$
ν	Poisson's ratio
π_c	total complementary energy
π_p	total potential energy
σ	normal stress
$\bar{\sigma}$	equivalent stress
$\boldsymbol{\sigma}$	stress vector (force per unit area)
$\boldsymbol{\sigma}^*$	prescribed surface stress

$\boldsymbol{\sigma}_m$	stress vector acting on element of area for which y_m is a constant
σ_o	yield stress in simple tension
σ_{mn}	stress tensor in rectangular, Cartesian coordinates (force per unit area)
$\hat{\sigma}_{mn}$	components of deviator stress tensor
$\hat{\hat{\sigma}}_{mn}$	components of spherical stress tensor
τ	shear stress
ϕ	Airy Stress Function
$(\ )^e$	indicates elastic strain components
$(\ )^p$	indicates plastic strain components
$(\ )_n(\ )_n$	repeated subscripts are to be summed
$(\ )_n$	subscript indicating values $1, 2, 3, \ldots$
$(\sim)$	pronounced "til'de." Usually indicates another coordinate system
$(\frown)$	deviatoric components
$(\widehat{\frown})$	spherical components
$(\ )^{(\mathrm{I})}, (\ )_{\mathrm{II}}$	Roman numeral subscripts or superscripts indicate quantity is a principal one
$(\ )\cdot(\ )$	indicates scalar product
$(\ )\times(\ )$	indicates cross product

Index

Index

LE CORBUSIER: IDEAS AND FORMS

LE CORBUSIER:
IDEAS AND FORMS

William J R Curtis

Library of Congress Cataloging-in-Publication Data:

Curtis, William J.R.
   Le Corbusier: Ideas and Forms
   Bibliography: p.
   Includes index
   1. Le Corbusier, 1887–1965 — Criticism and
interpretation. I. Title.
   NA1053.J4C8   1986   720′.92′4   86-6499
ISBN 0-8478-0726-6

Designed by Brian Lock

Printed and bound in Great Britain

Frontispiece: Villa Savoye, Poissy, 1928–9.

ACKNOWLEDGEMENTS

The author and publishers wish to thank the Fondation Le
Corbusier/SPADEM for permission to reproduce paintings,
drawings, sketches and plans by Le Corbusier that are still in
copyright.
The location or published source of such works is given in
the captions, with the exception of the following, which are
reproduced from the relevant volumes of the *Oeuvre complète*: Pls.3, 22, 38, 39, 50, 51, 57, 58, 59, 74, 85, 87, 88, 91,
96, 102, 107, 118, 119, 125, 126, 128, 129, 130, 164, 165, 168,
169, 170, 176, 181, 188, 192, 201, 203, 218, 231, 233. Grateful
acknowledgement is made to the following photographers and
owners of photographs: Bauhaus Archive, Pls.36, 86; Tim
Benton, Pl.25; Bibliothèque de la Ville, La Chaux-de-Fonds,
Pls.7, 8, 20, 28, 32, 40, 43, 64, 132, 177; Catherine J. Dean,
Pl.142; Balkrishna Doshi, Pl.212; Lucien Hervé/SPADEM,
Pls.52, 53, 54, 55, 60, 71, 73, 77, 79, 83, 93, 100, 106, 110,
112, 116, 117, 121, 166, 171, 183, 241; Ludwig Mies van der
Rohe Archive, Museum of Modern Art, New York, Pl.99;
Novosti Press Agency, Pl.103; Open University, Pl.94.
F.R. Yerbury, Pls.62, 69, 70, 81, 82, 84; Jean-Louis Véret,
Pl.163. Pls.80, 199, 213, 214 and 223 were redrawn by Brian
Sechrist.
All the black and white and colour photographs not
acknowledged above or separately in the captions are by the
author.

CONTENTS

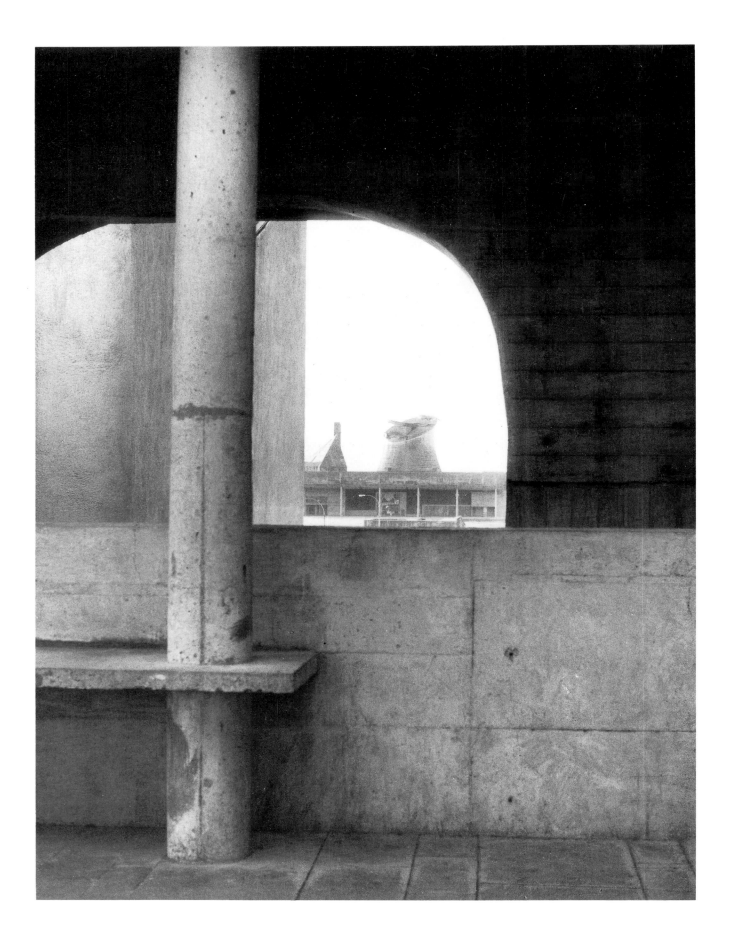

PREFACE

It is impossible to understand architecture in the twentieth century without first coming to terms with Le Corbusier. His buildings can be found from Paris to La Plata to the Punjab, and his influence has extended over four generations world-wide. His projects for the city have become enmeshed with the hopes, disappointments and crises of industrialization. Individual masterpieces such as the Villa Savoye at Poissy, the Chapel of Notre Dame du Haut at Ronchamp, or the Parliament Building at Chandigarh, will bear comparison with the works of any age. As well as an architect, Le Corbusier was also a painter, sculptor, urbanist and author; even a philosopher who ruminated on the human condition in the modern age. Like Freud, Joyce or Picasso he helped to give shape to the thought and sensibility of an epoch by investing his insights and findings with a universal tone. Whether we like it or not, these discoveries have now become part of our tradition.

Twenty years ago, when Le Corbusier died, there was a nebulous consensus that he should be regarded as the leader of world architecture. Since then his name has attracted both reverence and denigration. The faithful have put him on a pedestal, treating his buildings as edicts of wisdom. The sceptics have set out to smash the idols, concentrating less on individual works than on determinist and dictatorial aspects of Le Corbusier's urban planning. The 'good' and 'bad' of Le Corbusier's influence on others is a complex question that depends on prejudices and points of view, but judgements of any kind are best based on accurate information rather than the vagaries of contemporary criticism. This is a figure of unusual historical dimensions who needs to be seen in a long perspective: one of those rare individuals who have altered the assumptions of their art in basic ways.

The moment is right for a new synthesis, as the few general books of value on Le Corbusier have been eroded by the flood of new findings issuing from the archives of the Fondation Le Corbusier. In the past decade scholars have worked closely with the evidence afforded by drawings, letters and sketchbooks, and have been able to penetrate individual themes with greater depth and accuracy. Many fine fragments of scholarship are lying about, waiting to be integrated into a new general structure because the old one will no longer do. Le Corbusier needed this shake-up, for there was a tendency in an earlier generation to treat him as an unexamined fact of life. From the present perspective it is just possible to look at him as a fact of history — as a figure who continues to influence the present, to be sure, but also as a major creator in the history of art, like Palladio, Sinan or Ictinus.

Many different books could be written around someone as complex and wide-ranging as Le Corbusier. This one is called *Le Corbusier: Ideas and Forms* because it is concerned above all with the ways in which the architect compressed many levels of meaning into his individual buildings, treating them as symbolic emblems or microcosms of a larger world view. They crystallized general themes and employed typical elements which the architect extended and transformed on each new occasion. Their vocabulary cannot be understood apart from Le Corbusier's activities as a painter, sculptor, urbanist and writer; nor apart from his attitudes to society, nature and tradition. He drew history, *objets trouvés*, ideas, through a filter which gave them a new status within the structure of his own myths. His buildings need to be understood as imaginative metamorphoses of the world.

They must also be seen, of course, as solutions to a host of social, practical, technical, expressive and symbolic problems. To grasp them properly we need to reconstruct the conditions and limitations under which Le Corbusier worked. Drawings, sketches and letters enable one to reconstruct the process of design, the creative transactions between client and architect, architect and co-workers. They bring one closer to the mind of the artist, to intentions behind the individual work, and to the tensions between the ideal vision and the constraining reality. They allow one to avoid the limitations of either a simplistic social determinism or a simplistic formal determinism.

Le Corbusier's forms in all media derived part

1 (*opposite*) Chandigarh, India, 1951–65, view from the High Court towards Parliament.

of their authenticity from ethical and political commitments, from a driving social vision, from an idea of the way things ought to be. Although he never constructed his ideal city *in toto*, he did treat individual buildings as demonstrations of urbanistic ideas. He also considered it part of the architect's job to penetrate to the deeper human meaning of building programmes and to idealize institutions. If he had not succeeded in translating his social theories into buildings of haunting power we probably would not bother to deal with his utterances on society. However, it is unlikely that his architecture could have achieved its . strength without the transcending social content. Le Corbusier was neither just an ideologist nor just an aesthete: ideas prompted forms, forms, ideas. To understand this internal chemistry we have to steer towards the difficult area between the two.

Throughout his career Le Corbusier tried incessantly to anchor symbols appropriate to his age and its techniques, in the kind of 'fundamental' order that he had sensed in nature and in the great works of tradition. We do well to take him seriously when he declares that history was his 'only real master'. He looked for common themes underlying past buildings of different styles, and blended these together, transforming them to his own purposes. He sketched heroic and humble buildings in order to extract some essential or remarkable feature, then let impressions soak in his memory, from which ideas might emerge years later having undergone a 'sea change'. He tried to abstract principles from tradition, and to distil these into a formal system with its own rules of appropriateness.

Before entering a world of such imaginative richness, we do well to leave aside simplistic theories concerning the genesis of forms. Part of the tension of Le Corbusier's art stems from its fusion of paradoxes and polarities. A utopian with one eye on the future, he turned to the past for inspiration; a rationalist and lover of systems of classification, he experienced the world mythopoeically in all its uniqueness; an individualist, he tried to contain the anarchic forces of modern technology in what he piously hoped were 'unchanging' and natural laws; an internationalist, he remained sensitive to regional differences. Polarities of theme were sometimes reflected in contrasts of a form, which brought a rich ambiguity to even the most apparently simple designs. He was the supreme formal dialectician, placing rectangular against curved, open against closed, centric against linear, plane against volume, mass against transparency, grid against object, object against setting. His forms were a blend of sensual and abstract, material and spiritual, enthusiastic and ironical. In all this he learned from Cubism, not only for its plastic language, but also for the topsy-turvy order it gave to the world.

Like many other artists born in the late nineteenth century, Le Corbusier regarded himself as something of a prophet, revealing the 'essence of the times' to his fellows. Historicist, progressive and idealistic patterns of thought were embedded in his outlook; they were intrinsic to the very idea of 'modern' architecture. Le Corbusier rejected facile revivalism *and* materialist functionalism. He saw architecture in lofty, even spiritual terms. He grappled with age-old human and artistic questions, invoking what Wright called 'that law and order inherent in all great architecture'. He realized that the best in the new must touch the best in the old. He was a traditionalist as well as a modernist, who felt that a purification of architecture in terms of his own time might also take it back to its roots.

The role of 'modern master' cast for Le Corbusier by early historians of modern architecture never did justice to the formal and metaphorical complexity of his work. It excluded vast areas of his historical imagination, his regionalist and classicizing formative works, the primitivism of his middle years, and the ideological contradictions of his urbanism. Even the 'white architecture' of the 1920s (much of it actually polychrome!) suffered from being lumped together under that questionable heading 'International Style'. To present the myth of a unified style of the times it was necessary to confound Le Corbusier's lyrical villas with many lesser creations that obediently wore the period uniform of boxes on stilts and strip windows. The demonologies of current post-modernist folklore also revert to stereotypes: modern architecture sinned (we learn) by rejecting the past, meaning, culture, for an arid world of rootless functionalism. The works of the modern masters are lumped together with any old glass box without discrimination. Happily scholarship does not have to follow architectural fashion. The cramped categories of modernist *and* post-modernist rhetoric fail to touch what is really interesting about architects like Frank Lloyd Wright, Mies van der Rohe, Alvar Aalto, Louis Kahn and, of course, Le Corbusier.

Not that one is recommending a Corbusian academy. Enough of these have existed already, with their trite tricks and cultish practices. If Le Corbusier has lessons for the future they are probably not in the imitation of externals of his style, but rather in emulation of his principles and processes of transformation. Even if one decides that Le Corbusier's analyses of the modern condition are no longer relevant (and this is debatable), his work begins to settle into history as a major contribution. Architecture of any profundity outlives the culture, conflicts and conventions that brought it into being. Surely there is a quality in any artist of stature which transcends merely period concerns to link up with fundamentals of the medium. It is what Le Corbusier was himself talking about when he wrote in *Vers une architecture*: 'Architecture has nothing to do with the various styles'.

The historian who sets out to touch on these timeless levels in Le Corbusier draws on the collected insights of the past decades, and especially (I think) on the interpretations of Stanislaus Von Moos, Peter Serenyi, Reyner Banham, Colin Rowe and Alan Colquhoun. I have included specifically scholarly acknowledgements in text, notes and bibliography, but I also wish to single out Eduard Sekler and Denys Lasdun, the former for showing me (a decade and a half ago) that Le Corbusier was an architect deserving the most careful art-historical scrutiny, the latter for sharing over many years his understanding of a master who played a major part in his own formation. I have also gained from conversations with Timothy Benton, Pat Sekler, Jerzy Soltan, Paul Turner, Roggio Andréini, Charles Correa and P.L. Varma. Finally I would like to thank Madame Frey of the Bibliothèque de la Ville, La Chaux-de-Fonds, and the Fondation Le Corbusier for their co-operation, and Phaidon Press (especially Bernard Dod) for doing the usual fine job.

Le Corbusier entered my imagination long before I had ever heard of something called 'art history'. I came across the *Oeuvre complète* in the school library at the age of fifteen and was immediately captivated by this curious world of white villas and huge black cars, of concrete scoops and wiry pen and ink doodles. I hitch-hiked to see the real thing for myself. Le Corbusier's buildings seemed then (and still seem now)

haunting yet secretive. They elude glib categories and have a silent life of their own. I shall be quite content if I have succeeded in this book in presenting what is so far known in a clear form, and adding a few fresh insights. You cannot be 'definitive' about architects like this.

This book was thought out in a rugged spot on the northern fringes of the Midi, with cypresses and vines visible through the window. It is the kind of landscape that the artist loved and often sketched, and I found this a good place to reflect on Le Corbusier's debts to the ancient Mediterranean world. Nearly two-thirds of his buildings were within a few hours' drive and I visited them often. The task of putting ideas straight was made more pleasant by the endless hospitality of Monsieur and Madame Raymond de Bournet, and through the constant encouragement of my wife, Catherine. She has accompanied my Corbusian quest through Indian dust, monks' cells and Roman ruins: I dedicate this book to her.

William J.R. Curtis
Bournet, Ardèche, October 1985

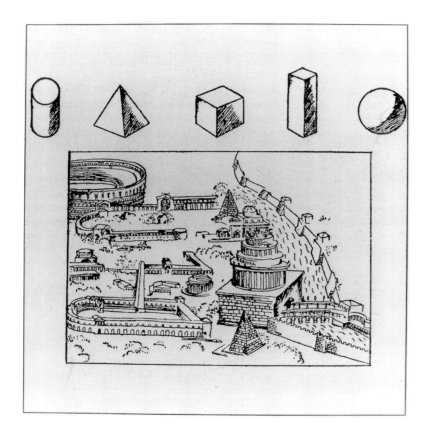

2 Sketch from *Vers une architecture* of primary solids and Ancient Rome: the abstraction of principles from tradition.

la passerelle d'ascenion PP/ p₂ p₃ a 1,2 3 Je loge
et s'accroche où elle peut : sur l₁ poteau M portant
tortue et a passage de l₁ Selly, offices etc

la tortue T de l'Assembly .

Bombay
19 ... 53

les évaporateurs indiens
d'Ahmedabad
survolant d'une ville
avant d'atterrir

INTRODUCTION
Notes on Invention

'The first condition of design is to know what we have to do; to know what we have to do is to have had an idea; and to express this idea we must have principles and a form, that is, grammar and a language.'

Eugène Viollet-le-Duc

When Le Corbusier died twenty years ago, he left behind him his *oeuvre*, his writings, a sizeable legend and a legacy of notebooks, drawings and letters that he must have known would eventually disturb the over-tidy picture. Much of this evidence was stored in the Fondation Le Corbusier in Paris which opened to scholars in the early 1970s. A number of fine monographs and articles came out a few years later; publications on the 32,000 (or so) drawings and on the tightly guarded sketchbooks have emerged only recently. The effect of this flood of information and interpretation has been to raise many new general questions about the architect. The few serious historical accounts of Le Corbusier written before all this material became available had to rely on the buildings themselves, on the depleting number of people who had known the architect firsthand, on the stray published sketch or drawing, and on the version of Le Corbusier created by Le Corbusier himself in his numerous publications. Little wonder that the architect began to resemble a monumental cliché hedged in by set-piece interpretations.

The challenge of the new fund of information on Le Corbusier is knowing what questions to ask. Without fresh insights, history degenerates into an arid scholasticism or, still worse, into a shadow of passing fads. This book takes as its main focus the genesis of Le Corbusier's buildings in their physical and cultural context, concentrates on the realm of form and meaning, and delves into various of Le Corbusier's design processes to show his style in action. It examines his creative method, his manner of thought and his techniques of invention.

The cult of unrestrained genius does an artist like Le Corbusier an injustice. His work becomes so much more interesting if one understands how he gave order to the diverse demands of clients, sites and programmes; if one is able to reconstruct his intentions and the alternatives that were considered; if one can see how he worked with others and how he translated ideas into materials and structural means. The recently published drawings are a valuable aid in this task. Not only do they chart individual design processes in detail; they also show how generic themes and type-solutions recurred in different contexts. Le Corbusier worked from general to particular and from particular to general when solving problems. His mind was well stocked with ideas, devices, configurations and images gleaned from tradition, from painting, from observation, and, of course, from his own earlier works including ideal projects. To penetrate the anatomy of his style is to understand the internal rules of appropriateness governing the relationship between forms and forms, forms and functions, forms and ideas; it is also to see why one configuration rather than another was used.

When presented with a new job Le Corbusier was in the habit of letting the matter rest in his subconscious for a period of incubation. One can only guess about the 'life of forms in the mind'. Probably the new problem was made amenable to schemata that were well embedded. Old elements and new would combine as an amalgam around dimly felt intentions. Le Corbusier's inventions were sometimes triggered by analogical leaps of thought between disparate phenomena, as when he sensed the relevance of cooling towers to the Assembly space in Chandigarh (Pl.3), or the pertinence of a crab shell to the roof of Ronchamp. At the right moment, images would float to the surface where they could be caught, condensed and exteriorized as sketches. Le Corbusier's vocabulary was composed of elements like the *piloti*, the ramp, the *brise-soleil*, etc. which recurred time and again. In turn these were governed in their overall disposition by systematic 'grammatical' arrangements like the 'Five Points of a New Architecture'. At another level there were preferred formal patterns — ways of putting together curves, rectangles and grids, for example — which would help to channel a solution towards its destination. The interiorized style of an artist is the very means that allows him to select while analysing a problem: at the same time it puts limitations on what is possible in coming up with a new idea. To penetrate the design process with the help of drawings is to sense how old forms could be agitated into new combinations and to see how

3 Sketches for the Parliament Building, Chandigarh, comparing the Assembly Chamber to cooling towers, 1953 (Fondation Le Corbusier).

4   Early sketches for the Villa Savoye, Poissy, Autumn 1928 (Fondation Le Corbusier).
'These rapidly changing, impatient metamorphoses, coupled with the earnest attention given them by the artist, develop a work of art under our very eyes — with what do they provide us? Points of reference in time? A psychological perspective? A jumbled topography of successive states of consciousness? Far more than these: what we have here is the very technique of the life of forms itself, its own biological development.' (Henri Focillon, *The Life of Forms in Art*.)

and why breakthroughs in vocabulary were made; it is also to sense how many levels of meaning were compressed together through a prodigious abstraction. As one grasps the patterns prevailing in a number of works, one is able to generalize about the ways the architect embodied his world view in symbolic forms. The path from ideology through poetic myth to form was not straightforward.

Le Corbusier's drawings are highly condensed abstractions in two dimensions of spatial experiences which he was anticipating in four. Movement around, into and through the building was central to his thinking. 'Form' for Le Corbusier was an active, volatile, living force which animated the systems of a structure, lending tension and complexity to all the parts, which were none the less held together in a tight unity by a dominant *Gestalt*. In *Vers une architecture* he suggested that 'to fix a plan is to have had ideas', and that a good plan is an abstraction, a crystalline thought form, an emblem dense in meanings. But fixing a plan was also a matter of compressing together many formal layers and orchestrating their hierarchy in a manner appropriate to intentions. It is for this reason that one feels Le Corbusier's buildings bursting with an inner life, a tension which radiates through details as well as overall configurations. As in a piece of music, themes rise, fall, repeat, reinforce, and are felt in ever-changing juxtaposition. To move through a Corbusier building is to sense how various schemes of order may give way to each other while still contributing to the dominant image within.

If the design process offers clues concerning the genesis of forms, it is also the arena of transactions between the architect and the client. The matter of social content in Le Corbusier's architecture can scarcely be considered apart from his

clients' aims and ideological assumptions. The ethos encoded in a building relies upon a translation of programmatic aims (many of them unstated) into the terminology of the artist's social vision; on occasion the values of architect and patron may even clash. Le Corbusier's clients were an extraordinarily varied group, from the provincial bohemians of La Chaux-de-Fonds to the chic upper middle classes of Paris; from the Soviet Government to the Catholic Church; from the Salvation Army to Harvard University. It is important to understand what these people saw in Le Corbusier, and what he saw in them. As well as being responses to human needs in a utilitarian sense Le Corbusier's solutions were idealizations of institutions. In fact they were fragments of his own utopian dream, his aspiration towards a new harmony between men, machine and nature.

Le Corbusier's quest for an ideal involved him in both futurism and nostalgia. His social outlook does not fit comfortably into any ideological pigeonhole. It was a blend of idealistic and realistic, of authoritarian and egalitarian, of poetic and pragmatic. It comprised a Rousseau-esque conception of the inherent moral good of man with a tragic sense of the transience of life. It embraced a historicist idea of social progress through a sequence of epochs, and an obsession with the archetypes behind institutions. It implied a naïve environmental determinism, as if the right architecture could on its own generate human betterment. In this vision the artist was to play a lofty role. Like Plato's 'philosopher king' he was supposed to paint a picture of the ideal state in the form of a perfect city.

It is perhaps necessary to distinguish between Le Corbusier's 'visionary politics' — the utopian content of his architecture — and his political affiliations and activities, because there were some contradictions between the two. The brief admiration for capitalism in the mid-1920s was followed by a flirtation with the international Left, a conversion to Syndicalism and an uncomfortable proximity to the extreme Right in the early 1940s. In the post-war years Le Corbusier was happy to help define India's new democratic institutions at Chandigarh, and to grapple with the roots of Christian belief in Ronchamp and La Tourette. Some of the dancing about was probably opportunism, but at the heart of Le Corbusier's *Weltanschauung* was the conviction that the *plan*, his plan, was an automatic blueprint for a better civilization, and that its inherent qualities would outweigh any political compromises necessary for realization. He put the end above the means.

To piece together the strands of Le Corbusier's vision, and to show how it was given form, requires that one start with his early biography and with the time at which he acquired his basic prejudices and entered a particular niche in architectural tradition. It is a story that begins in provincial Switzerland at the end of the nineteenth century, and which gradually extends in space and time as the young Charles Edouard Jeanneret (his real name) began to grasp the true dimensions of his historical mission through travel to ancient sites in Turkey, Greece and Italy, and through contact with various urban centres of modern art such as Paris, Berlin and Vienna. The moment of his entry was critical. The turn of the century: industrialism was rapidly transforming the landscape and the city, but distinct regional cultures still existed, at least in southern Europe. La Chaux-de-Fonds offered a marginal starting point from which Jeanneret sensed vacillating allegiances between French, Mediterranean and German cultural traditions. It also exposed him to various strands of nineteenth-century thought (Idealism in particular) and to a succession of artistic movements including Jura Regionalism and Art Nouveau. From his travels to major capitals he in turn grasped Rationalist ideas, and felt the consolidation towards an abstracted Classicism in rejection of both nineteenth-century revivalism and the more florid aspects of Art Nouveau.

Le Corbusier's formative period comes to an end soon after the First World War, when we find him in the post-Cubist avant-garde of Paris and when we see his beliefs and years of self-education coming to fruition in the synthesis of Purism, in the book *Vers une architecture* and in the formation of a new architecture. Painting, an Idealist view of the world and the cult of the machine coalesce in an outlook that none the less tries to transform fundamental, 'universal' laws from the past. The years 1920–2 are pivotal: Le Corbusier lays down the basis of his domestic vocabulary in the Citrohan House, and his ideal diagram for the modern city in the Ville Contemporaine. The second part of this book examines the whole range of Le Corbusier's activities in the interwar period, from painting to grand urban schemes, from houses for the art-loving rich, to projects for the down-and-outs of Paris. The classic villas of the 1920s are examined in detail,

as compromises between ideal intentions and practical limitations. The architect's position in the modern movement is assessed. One sees the emergence of basic themes and type-forms that would continue to guide Le Corbusier, and undergo transformation in later years. The architect's vocabulary was stretched as he grappled with problems of state representation (for example, League of Nations and Palace of Soviets projects) or programmes of a communal and collective nature (the Pavillon Suisse, the Cité de Refuge, the projects for the Ville Radieuse and Algiers).

Le Corbusier's style can be mapped out in a number of ways. It is possible to chart vertical strands through his production by following a single idea or motif and watching it recur and transform. Or one can adopt the more traditional method of artistic biography which is to move along chronologically project by project. This book tries to combine both methods, occasionally focusing on single buildings to do this, or else standing back and examining broad urbanistic or ideological themes. It is impossible to understand Le Corbusier's inventions properly apart from the unending battle between intentions and constraints. Changes in his forms were stimulated by internal shifts in sensibility and belief, by external stimuli and inspirations and, of course, by the altering demands of society's programmes.

These remarks apply particularly well to the architect's years of reassessment between 1930 and 1945, in which he invented the *brise-soleil* or 'sun breaker' to deal with hot climates, and explored the expressive possibilities of both regionalism and primitivism. These tendencies were consolidated after the Second World War in the rugged concrete forms of Marseilles Unité, the monuments at Chandigarh in India, the Monastery of La Tourette and the Chapel at Ronchamp. The taut machine-age precision of the 1920s was left far behind in the pursuit of a heroic sense of mass and an archaic mood. Yet when one penetrates beyond the obvious differences in style, earlier schemata are found to persist beneath the surface. One of the values of considering Le Corbusier's vocabulary as a fusion of different formal 'levels' is that it allows one to dissect the internal anatomy, to trace sources, and thus to appreciate better his powers of synthesis. Le Corbusier's late works are historical collages of extraordinary depth and richness. The Indian buildings drew lessons from both Eastern and Western monumental traditions and explored common ground between the two.

To have any chance of succeeding, history has to describe the inside and the outside of events simultaneously, to identify with the actors while maintaining an objective stance. I have done my best to make the line between the factual and the interpretative clear, and to offer critical judgements in a straightforward way. Le Corbusier is now a major part of our history who stands immutably between us and the more distant past. It seems to be a good idea to try to understand the principles behind his work before canonizing him, decrying him or just leaving him alone.

PART I
THE FORMATIVE YEARS OF CHARLES EDOUARD JEANNERET 1887 – 1922

Chapter I

The Home Base

'Artists do not stem from their childhood but from their conflicts with the achievements of their predecessors; not from their own formless world, but from the struggle with the forms that others have imposed on life ...'

André Malraux

The time and place at which an artist makes his entrance, learns his trade and encounters a certain perspective on tradition, are bound to influence the range of his early choices. Le Corbusier was born in 1887 in La Chaux-de-Fonds, Switzerland, a provincial town in the Jura, a region that today straddles the frontier with France, but which in the nineteenth century had been partly under Prussian control. La Chaux-de-Fonds lies at an altitude of about 1,000 metres in a shallow valley flanked by low mountains, wooded slopes and deep-cut valleys of a distinctive geological character; it stands on the crossroads between Le Locle and Biel, Neuchâtel and Belfort. In 1794 the old centre burned down leaving few visual reminders of great age or quality. During the nineteenth century the town developed rapidly, following the outlines of a new grid plan which had little respect for the topography. The pre-existing rural culture left its mark on the surrounding landscape in the form of farmhouses and barns which constituted a distinct regional vernacular. The rapid transition from a rationally planned urbanism to a ravishing nature was basic to the geography of Le Corbusier's childhood.

Throughout the nineteenth century the peasantry was gradually absorbed into the city, so that by the year of Le Corbusier's birth the population stood at close to 27,000. They left behind the land for a milieu of small workshops where they involved themselves in the design, fabrication and decoration of watches. The watches of La Chaux-de-Fonds had achieved international recognition, so despite the marginal position of the town in Swiss affairs, and despite its relatively small size, it had many economic and cultural ties abroad. Craftsmanship was highly valued and a cosmopolitan artistic culture of some sophistication was able to flourish. The local bourgeoisie took a direct interest in design education as a means of keeping up with foreign competition in the watch trade. At an early age Le Corbusier was exposed to a variety of *fin de siècle* tendencies in design — from the Arts and Crafts to Art Nouveau — as well as to contacts with London, Paris, Turin and Vienna. His

formative years coincided with major shifts in sensibility that would culminate in abstract painting and sculpture, and there were even hints of this reaction against academic and realist tendencies in his own education, which stressed the idea of 'basic' formal languages of expression. His first architectural experiments, undertaken in his late teens and early twenties, combined this quest for fundamental shapes with a regionalism steeped in the 'folklore of the fir-tree'. It was a cultivated nostalgia for rapidly disappearing peasant values, in a town that was largely nineteenth-century in construction. Le Corbusier was born late enough to look back on local 'montagnard' roots through a haze of romanticism.

Another aspect of local mythology was the pride taken in a stance of political rebellion and religious independence. Throughout the period of Albigensian heresy in the twelfth and thirteenth centuries, persecuted refugees had flocked to the Jura valleys from south-western France. A similar thing happened during the Wars of Religion when Protestants left France after the Revocation of the Edict of Nantes in 1685. A secular echo was still sensed in the nineteenth century, and Le Corbusier liked to think of himself in terms of a free-thinking tradition. He was specially proud of the role that his family had played in the struggle against the Prussians, and of the action that his grandfather had taken in the Revolution of 1848, storming the castle of Neuchâtel virtually single-handed 'without shedding a drop of blood'. There was also a family legend linking ancestors to the mystical heresy of 'Catharism' in the Languedoc. Le Corbusier grew very attached to this supposed connection and in later life read all he could about the sect. The importance of this lies in the pedigree that Le Corbusier decided to construct for himself given the available fragments and reminiscences, for this gives us an idea how he saw himself. Perhaps he identified with a persecuted minority holding tenaciously to its ideals of spiritual revelation against the onslaughts of official religion; certainly it was crucial to him to feel that he had roots in the Mediterranean world.

The lack of a distinctive visual heritage in La

5 (*previous page*) Maison Favre-Jacot, La Chaux-de-Fonds, 1912, detail of south façade.

Chaux-de-Fonds encouraged its artistic élite to seek out traditions elsewhere and even to invent fictive local histories. The regionalism which surrounded Edouard's formation was a traditionalism concocted in the face of broken regional traditions. His search for a cultural identity would take him out and back between Berlin, Vienna, Paris, the Mediterranean and the little hub of La Chaux-de-Fonds over a number of years. He did not take the name 'Le Corbusier' until he was thirty-three, installed in Paris, and confident of his path (he co-opted it from ancestors on his mother's side called 'Lecorbesier'). It was as if his faltering first efforts — many of them actually creditable — had to be repressed and replaced by the activities of a new persona. In the same vein, Le Corbusier published almost none of his earliest buildings, unless they fitted in with the version of himself that he liked to believe in. It is only in the past few years that his early debts to others, and the nature of his first experiments, have been submitted to scholarly scrutiny. Probably Le Corbusier liked to encourage the myth that his genius flowered suddenly into full maturity; but I suspect that this silence about years of confusion also says something about the artist's need to exclude a precarious side of his nature.

His real name was Charles Edouard Jeanneret — although he was usually known as 'Edouard' — and he was born on 6 October 1887 in the family home at 30 rue de la Serre in La Chaux-de-Fonds, the town where he was to spend the better part of his first thirty years. His father Georges Edouard Jeanneret-Gris was employed in the watch business as an enameller, as had been *his* father. His mother Marie Charlotte Amélie (née Perret) was a pianist and music teacher whose activities contributed to the family budget. Albert, Edouard's brother, was nineteen months his elder, and destined to become a musician. The Jeannerets had relatively modest means but they valued cultural accomplishments. Monsieur Jeanneret exemplified the fastidious concern for precision and manual excellence of the urban craftsman, while Madame, who was higher born, encouraged a musician's dexterity as well as more abstract pursuits. The young boy grew up somewhere in the middle of the middle class. He eventually found a way out of this somewhat restricted atmosphere via a bohemian stance and through contact with the wider possibilities offered by the well-to-do. The eventual growth away from Papa Jeanneret's craftsman's culture probably generated considerable tension.

It was a family in which technical, intellectual and aesthetic competence were all prized. A childhood photograph of Edouard and his brother shows them sitting or standing around a table with their cousins, all dressed in their Sunday best. Albert has a violin casually under his arm and is self-consciously pondering a book that his female cousin is holding open. Young Edouard is seated at the other end of the table and has a pen in his hand; he would be drawing except that his impish expression is focused beyond the camera. In a family where the eldest son had taken up the

mother's art, and in which competence in an art or craft was central, one can guess how important it may have been for him to display *his* competence, *his* interest. As a child he never stopped drawing from the moment he came back from school. He even requisitioned his mother's clothes line for drying watercolours. As Le Corbusier put it years later:

'It was a matter of occupying a particular square on the chessboard: a family of musicians (music heard all through my youth), a passion for drawing, a passion for the plastic arts ... a character that wanted to get to the heart of things ...'

Madame Jeanneret emerges as a major inspiration for her children. Devoted, strict and Protestant, she seems to have conveyed to them values of discipline, adherence to principle and

6 The Jura landscape.

7 La Chaux-de-Fonds at the turn of the century.

sea of mist stretched away to infinity it was just like the real ocean — which I had never seen. It was the most magnificent sight.'

Up to the age of fourteen and a half, Edouard's education was conventional. But in 1902 he was enrolled in the 'Ecole d'Art' at La Chaux-de-Fonds as the first step towards an eventual apprenticeship in watch engraving. The school had been founded in 1873 precisely to train youngsters in the applied arts. A report written in 1887 spoke of the need to develop 'the spirit of invention, purity of taste, knowledge of ornamentation' in future watch decorators, and of the desire to reconcile 'artistic perfection' with 'good value'. By the time Jeanneret entered the school there were 365 pupils and an elaborate curriculum that attempted to combine the practical and the aesthetic in a balanced way, including drawing, painting, sculpture, geometrical studies, life drawing, sketching from nature, study trips and lectures in art history, as well as technical and pre-professional studies in metalwork and engraving.

Edouard's mentor in this period (and for a few years to come) was a certain Charles L'Eplattenier. His courses had a distinctive character and message. L'Eplattenier believed that the most vital aesthetic principles were rooted in an understanding of nature, not at the level of superficial imitation, but at the level of underlying structure. He encouraged his students to abstract the essential geometrical features of everything they drew and to translate the resulting forms into emblematic patterns following simple laws of combination. L'Eplattenier had been trained in Budapest, and in Paris at the Ecole des Beaux-Arts and Ecole des Arts Décoratifs. He had a broad grasp of recent aesthetic doctrines and tendencies towards abstraction. Perhaps it was his intention to imitate Victor Prouvé's applied arts school at Nancy, which he seems to have admired. Via an English friend, Heaton, he had imbibed Arts and Crafts ideals from William Morris, and was a passionate admirer of the ideas of John Ruskin. L'Eplattenier endowed the limited aims of a provincial art school with an apocalyptic tone in which the student was invited to improve the moral tenor of society through the translation of principles learned from God's creation — nature — into artefacts of high formal quality. This was heady stuff and it appealed to young Jeanneret, who seems to have needed an artistic father-figure at this stage in his development.

L'Eplattenier was also influenced by Owen Jones's *Grammar of Ornament*, a book that Le Corbusier remembered studying intensely in the library at the Ecole d'Art. Jones had argued that the true basis of architectural forms and decorative motifs lay in the transformation of local, natural features. Egyptian columns, for example, were imitations of Nile valley plants like the lotus and the papyrus. L'Eplattenier argued that the right forms for the Jura region would be ones abstracted from rock strata and conifer trees. His passion for studying local geology

8 Edouard, his brother and cousins; Edouard is sitting to the extreme right, Albert is standing on the left and has the violin.

pride in a job well done. In later life Le Corbusier liked to quote her: 'Whatever you set out to do, be sure that you actually do it'. While he did not follow any particular religious faith, he seems to have derived something of his sense of a high moral mission from her example. For some of his childhood his Aunt Pauline lived with the family too; she was also devout as well as being interested in the family legends.

Monsieur Jeanneret emerges as a more shadowy presence in Edouard's early years; there are far fewer references to father than to mother in later life. Georges probably took it for granted that his boy's graphic aptitude would lead him naturally into the family trade. For relief from the long hours concentrating at the workbench, Georges devoted much of his free time in the spring and summer to trekking and mountain climbing, and was president of the local Alpine Club. Edouard was sometimes taken along on these trips and was encouraged from his earliest days to look hard at nature. Close inspection of the structure of machines in the watch industry accorded well with the cultivated arts of plant and rock inspection that were part of Monsieur Jeanneret's leisure. By his late teens, Edouard also knew the geology and flora of the region intimately; indeed these were to play a major role in his early designs. The forests and mountain tops were haunting, awesome places which provided young Jeanneret with moments of inner liberation before the grandiose and epic forces of nature. He recalled many years later:

'We were constantly on the summits; the immense horizon was quite usual for us. When the apparently knew no limits: he would clamber into the bed of the Doubs river in mid-winter to sketch rock fissures and ledges. His interest in fir and pine trees, their overall forms, their hierarchy of structure, their branches, leaves and cones was equally fanatical. Patricia Sekler has suggested that he and his students were guided by the detailed observations on drawing trees in Ruskin's *Elements of Drawing*. L'Eplattenier and his circle developed an entire 'folklore du sapin' ('folklore of the fir-tree'), invoking the moral overtones of its upright stance and the rectitude of its sharp, triangular silhouette.

Artists do not draw upon nature for inspiration in a passive way. There may be direct intuitive apprehension, a magical attraction to certain objects, but perception is also guided by categories and ideas. From Ruskin Edouard learned to look at nature minutely; from L'Eplattenier to try and abstract the structures that he saw; and from both to think that natural creation revealed a spiritual order that one should try to emulate in design. Many of Edouard's drawings of this period were studies of trees, rocks and landscapes in which spaces between forms were as positive as the forms themselves. In some sequences of doodles he gradually transformed and simplified what he had initially rendered into emblematic, abstract patterns. A watch-case that he designed around the age of fifteen was ornamented with block-like geological striations and swirling, vegetal curves. Private worlds of childhood were thus, in adolescence, channelled into a regionalist imagery and a period style with links to simplified Art Nouveau — perhaps Mackintosh or the Viennese Sezession. Like any design student Jeanneret was not above glimpsing at the international magazines.

By 1905 it had become clear that watch-engraving was too taxing for Edouard's fragile eyesight. Anyway, L'Eplattenier had already made up his mind that his most gifted pupil had the makings of an architect. Family and school went along with the idea as, eventually, did Edouard, who had tended to think of himself as a painter. He continued to study with the same instructors, drafting being substituted for engraving. But the Ecole d'Art of La Chaux-de-Fonds was not able to offer training in structures, building materials and engineering. L'Eplattenier believed in learning by doing and so attempted to secure commissions for his pupils. Between 1905 and 1907, he and a group of students, were involved with a project for the Union Chrétienne de Jeunes Gens in La Chaux-de-Fonds, known as Beau Site (which came to nothing); with the design for a music room for L'Eplattenier's neighbour Matthey-Doret; with a commission to redecorate the interior of the chapel at nearby Fontainemelon; and with the design and decoration of a house for Louis Fallet *fils*, a member of the overseeing Commission of the Ecole d'Art, and a small-scale watch manufacturer.

The Fallet commission was reserved for Jeanneret, although the others helped in the creation of ornaments and decorations, and a local architect by the name of René Chapallaz

9 Watch case, *c.*1903.

(who worked competently in a style based on local vernacular precedents) was called in to help the precocious teenager translate his ideas into practice. The chosen site was north of La Chaux-de-Fonds, only a few hundred metres beyond the grid, at a place where the hills sloped upwards to the forest of Pouillerel, offering long views back over the town and the valley. The character of the place was rustic; even now is only semi-suburban. L'Eplattenier lived close by in a house designed by Chapallaz and it is possible that he was thinking of the area as an artists' colony. Given Fallet's supportive stance towards the Ecole and towards L'Eplattenier in particular, this was obviously an opportunity to attempt an essay in Jura regionalism (Pl.131).

The Fallet House employs common-sense devices derived from the local vernacular such as steep, overhanging roofs to protect from the snow, a stone base jutting from the terrain, and deep eaves adjusted to exclude summer heat and include winter sunlight. The rustic imagery is fused with up-to-date and cosmopolitan notions such as the double-height stair well (marked 'hall' on the plans, thus betraying the likely influence of Hermann Muthesius's *Das Englische Haus*), and the cubic stone brackets which look as if they may have come from a Viennese Sezessionist source. But the real significance of the design lies in its translation of Jurassic emblems into overall form, silhouette, details and ornaments. The diagonals of the roof echo the profiles of pines and firs; jagged ends of rafters mimic the shagginess of foliage; window bars recall branches and twigs; sculpted stone details echo the geological stratification of Edouard's watch-case design. The earth colours and contrasting textures of natural materials harmonize with the setting. But the Fallet House avoids being just a picturesque pastiche of a chalet. Its forms are brought into

10 (*above*) Sketches of pine cones, *c*.1904 (Fondation Le Corbusier).

11 (*above right*) Plate from Owen Jones, *The Grammar of Ornament*: Egyptian motifs based on natural forms.

12 Charles Edouard Jeanneret, René Chapallaz and colleagues. Maison Fallet, La Chaux-de-Fonds, 1905–6, detail.

taut life through abstract discipline and ideological conviction. The Rousseauesque hut is steeped in Ruskinian morality, Arts and Crafts ideals and regionalist symbolism. If one compares it to Chappallaz's buildings of the same time one is bound to conclude that young Jeanneret's sculptural sense made this a superior work.

There are a few design-process sketches by Edouard. In an early scheme he experimented with a diagonal entry into a steeply pyramidical composition of roofs. Later he struggled with the problem of blending details and ornaments with the building's guiding triangular, arboreal and geological themes. In the sgraffito ornaments of the south façade jagged triangles were spliced together with pine-cone outlines and stepped motifs. Figure and ground were interwoven in a lively pattern recalling textile designs and demonstrating how a single shape might evoke simultaneously a tree, clouds, a cone, rays and a sense of bursting growth.

These patterns recall some of the plates from Jones's *Grammar of Ornament*, but probably also reflect the impact of Eugène Grasset's *Méthode de composition ornementale* (Paris 1905). This addressed the idea of an entire system of ornament grounded in geometry and simplifications of natural forms. It illustrated how points, lines, planes, squares, triangles, lozenges, circles, ellipses and polygons could be combined and recombined according to certain rules of repetition, diminution and transformation. One guesses that this must have appealed to Jeanneret's mathematical and musical sensibilities, and it is tempting to see the Fallet House as a miniature *symphonie pastorale*. Grasset rejected facile eclecticism and proclaimed that this geometrical spirit would produce an

order 'parallel to that of nature and following the same laws'.

In its modest way the Fallet House resembled some of Louis Sullivan's and Frank Lloyd Wright's nearly contemporary attempts at forming an architectural grammar based on the abstraction of natural forms like seeds, leaves, branches and trees. It also conformed to the *fin de siècle* ideal of a 'total work of art' in which architecture, craft and furnishings were united by common themes, betokening the harmony of an integrated society. The youthful band of craftsmen working on the Pouillerel slope were actually guided by ideas concerning moral honesty with a strongly Ruskinian pedigree; even by the ideal of the 'true' expression of materials. A year after the construction of the house was complete (it took from 1905 to 1907), Jeanneret wrote to L'Eplattenier from abroad, summarizing what he felt to be the philosophy behind the design:

'You have set in motion an art movement in La Chaux-de-Fonds ... essentially based on *nature* on the one hand, and on probity in the use of materials on the other. A fundamental logic rules it, the logic of life which develops from an embryo by roots, to the stalk and the leaves to arrive at the flower. The corollary of this logic rules the execution of ideas. The stone's appearance being the expression of its actual construction, the wood being an expression of its assemblage, the roofs serving to protect from wind and rain.'

While the later Le Corbusier was never a consistent architectural theorist, he had a passionate attachment to ideas. Reading played a major role in his formation, as it did in his family's culture, especially through the long

winters when La Chaux-de-Fonds was under
snow for six months. John Ruskin, Eugène
Grasset and Owen Jones were part of the school
diet; so probably was Charles Blanc, whose
Grammaire des arts du dessin described architecture as the mother of the arts, and presented
history not as a series of recipes for facile revival,
but as a fund of ideas for transformation into a
new architecture. Jeanneret also began to form
his own library at a young age. He read intensely,
often marking passages with comments. As Paul
Turner has suggested, a highly idealistic view of
art and artists was reinforced by such virtually
unknown curiosities as Henri Provensal's *L'Art
de demain* (Paris 1904), a book which bore the
subtitle 'Vers l'harmonie intégrale' — the sort of
phraseology that Jeanneret would later himself
employ. In one place Provensal spoke of architecture as '... the cubic, harmonious expression
of thought', a close prefiguration of some of the
ideas expressed in *Vers une architecture* nearly
twenty years later. Seen in a long perspective of
the history of ideas, Provensal is a tiny footnote
to the German Idealist tradition; but from Jeanneret's point of view these were strong confir-
mations of intuitions he felt deep within himself.
Another book that probably functioned in the
same way was Edouard Schuré's *Les Grands
Initiés*, given to Jeanneret by L'Eplattenier in
1907. The basic theme was the role of great
spiritual leaders in the regeneration of civilization
(Rama, Moses, Pythagoras, Plato and Jesus are
all mentioned). Schuré clearly felt that modern
civilization was in a decline because of materialism and the impact of philosophical positivism.
He had much to say about the need for new
leaders — initiates into spiritual knowledge —
who would lead a revival and reintegration.
Jeanneret seems to have been especially curious
about the chapter on Pythagoras and divine
numerology.

In September 1907, with the Villa Fallet fees in
his pocket, Jeanneret set off for Italy, taking with
him Hippolyte Taine's *Voyage en Italie* and John
Ruskin's *Matins à Florence*. In later life he liked
to present this, his first truly independent
journey, as a solitary voyage of the spirit.
Actually he travelled with Léon Perrin, a chum
from the Art School. His letters home and to
L'Eplattenier were full of amusing incidents as
well as some acute observations on art. After
seeing Mantegna's works in Padua he wrote: 'trop
de dessin pour trop peu d'idée' ('too much
drawing for too little idea'). In all they visited
sixteen major cities in northern Italy including
Siena, Florence, Venice, Ravenna, Padua and
Pisa, but they did not go down as far as Rome.
Along the way, Jeanneret spent hours doing
watercolours and sketches of paintings, mosaics
and sculptures. He was enthralled by Giotto's
Arena Chapel and by Donatello's *Gattamelata* in
Padua, as well as by the decorations in Ravenna.
His sketches of buildings were usually close-ups
of ornament and details: microscopic renderings
in the style of Ruskin which were sometimes
accompanied by detailed analytical notes. The
Cathedral at Pisa, which Jeanneret was to sketch

in terms of abstract volumes four years later
(towards the end of the 'Voyage d'orient'), was
analysed for certain details of the arcading
system. In one of his letters he complained that
he found the Signoria in Florence too vast and
abstract to comprehend in its totality. It was to
take him some years to evolve a graphic short-
hand that could capture the overall organization
of buildings. Travel was actually an essential part
of Jeanneret's education bringing him face to face
with the objects of history. Sketches and watercolours allowed him to capture the past and to
translate it into his own terminology. In later life
the transaction between observation and invention, description and prescription, would
continue — drawings being essential tools for
transformation. Written descriptions also played
a role in anchoring impressions; during the Italian
trip, Jeanneret wrote long letters to L'Eplattenier
— gushing prose-poems evoking the mood of
buildings and places.

Another striking feature of Jeanneret's journey
was his apparent lack of interest in Classical or
Renaissance architecture. When he and Perrin
passed through Vicenza, they did not even get off
the train to look at Palladio, an extraordinary
omission given the architect's later passion for
the mathematical abstraction and ordering
devices of Classicism. Jeanneret saw Venice
through Ruskin's eyes in terms of gorgeous
polychrome ornament; light, shade and texture
on cracked stones; fragments oozing with nostalgia. Among the most careful of his studies was
one of the arcading on the Doge's Palace. This
realistic detail was accompanied by a more
abstract study which attempted to convey the
underlying joints of the masonry as in his earlier
sketches of twigs and branches. Travel opened his
eyes to new things, but the prejudices of his
training forced him to focus on some more than
others. If he had swivelled around, Jeanneret
would have had a breathtaking view of Palladio's
San Giorgio Maggiore across the water. This was
on Ruskin's 'forbidden' list, as was most of the
Renaissance.

One building did make a huge impact on
Jeanneret for its overall order and character. This
was the Carthusian monastery near Galluzzo in
the Ema valley close to Florence. In September
1907, he wrote to his parents:

'Yesterday I went to see the Chartreuse ... there I
found a unique solution to workers' housing. But
it will be difficult to duplicate the landscape. Oh
those monks, what lucky fellows.'

Le Corbusier would return time and again to the
prototype of Ema when designing schemes which
combined private with communal. The memory
of a vignette of Tuscan greenery seen from a
double-height cell over a private garden would
continue to haunt him. For an artist who would
think of his own quest for truth in almost religious terms, the appeal of monastic purity and
submission to a rule was overwhelming. Ema
embedded itself in Jeanneret's subconscious as a
personal archetype.

In November Jeanneret and Perrin left Italy for

Vienna, passing via Budapest on the way. L'Eplattenier had led them to believe that the capital of the Austro-Hungarian empire was also the hub of modern architecture, an impression that may have been supported by magazines bearing photographs of designs by the likes of Otto Wagner, Josef Hoffmann or Josef Maria Olbrich. In 1895 Wagner had published *Moderne Architektur*, a book which criticized superficial revivalism and spelt out the need for a new architecture expressing 'modern life' and using modern means of construction. He had envisaged a style based on bold and simple forms, and with the Post Office Savings Bank of 1904–5 had showed what he meant. Olbrich and Hoffmann concentrated on the reform of the decorative arts, the former in the artists' colony of Grand Duke Ernst Ludwig at Darmstadt, the latter in the 'Wiener Werkstätte' which opened in 1903. Adolf Loos was also in Vienna, but it does not seem that Jeanneret knew of his famous article of 1908 attacking ornament ('Ornament and Crime') until years later; if he knew any of Loos's designs he remained silent on the subject.

It would make a neat theorem to suggest that the future Le Corbusier, eventual leader of the Modern Movement of the 1920s, found a major springboard for his own aspirations in the Vienna of 1907 to 1908. But it simply was not so. Jeanneret had trouble finding examples he had been told were important, and when he did find them he was often downright negative. In his letters to L'Eplattenier he complained about the lack of feeling for nature, dishonesty in construction, cosmeticism in detail (he did not like Hoffmann's veneers), and a brutal, sanitary coldness in the use of materials which reminded him of bathrooms.

Jeanneret's criteria in making these sweeping criticisms — some of which he would later reverse — were derived equally from L'Eplattenier's regionalist training and from his recent impressions of artistic excellence in Italy. Perhaps the provincial boy was put on the defensive by the sophisticated tastes of a grand metropolis. His over-reactions also stemmed from confusion about how best to continue his education. Clearly he sensed his lack of technical know-how and wondered if formal schooling might not be the answer. But his German was poor and his grasp of mathematics was merely elementary. In the upshot he spent four and a half months in Vienna, living in various furnished rooms and designing two more houses for La Chaux-de-Fonds through the mail; Villas Jaquemet and Stotzer. He was so busy with these that he lived in a state of relative insulation from the Viennese culture around him, although he did find time to enjoy the occasional opera and concert.

Quite when these two domestic commissions crystallized is uncertain. L'Eplattenier probably did the spade-work. Ulysse Jules Jaquemet was Louis Fallet's brother-in-law, Albert Stotzer was also married to a Fallet, and both belonged to the progressive bourgeoisie of the watch trade. The former was a 'polisseur des boîtes', the latter a teacher of mechanics at the Ecole d'Horlogerie in

14 Sketches of arcading, Doge's Palace, Venice, 1907 (Fondation Le Corbusier).

La Chaux-de-Fonds. Even the sites were similar to that of the Fallet House: a stone's throw away on the south-facing slope of the Pouillerel. But the programmes were different; both houses were to contain two apartments apiece yet give the impression that they were single-family homes.

Jeanneret organized the interiors of both buildings in analogous ways with entrances on the north side off the highest point of each site and stairs tightly packed into a narrow, central slot on axis. Kitchens, bathrooms and studies were tucked into east and west extremities where they were lit by bow windows to maximize light and view. Hooded roofs above these windows hinted at a cross-axis and gave each house a more varied silhouette. Sitting/dining rooms (combined) and master bedrooms were placed in the southern area of each floor of each building, to make the most of sunlight, views and nature. At Stotzer an upper balcony was even installed, while in both buildings — as at Fallet — the ground floor

15 Aerial view of the Carthusian monastery at Galuzzo, valley of Ema, Tuscany.

16 Studies for Maison
Jaquemet, La Chaux-de-
Fonds, 1907 (Bibliothèque
de la Ville, La Chaux-de-
Fonds).

extended on to a terrace supported by the rusticated base. In the Villa Stotzer, the terrace was
further dramatized by lateral stairs over an arch,
a detail that Jeanneret could have seen in old
Jura farmhouses (Pl.2).

The Jaquemet and Stotzer Houses recall the
regionalism of Villa Fallet, but they are plainer;
mass and structure are more boldly expressed,
and there is a loss of intensity. The buildings are
held up by massive parallel walls supporting cross
floors of concrete; buttresses and overhangs are
emphasised by mouldings; rusticated brackets
recall details that Jeanneret had sketched in
Florentine medieval buildings. The early scheme
for the Villa Stotzer had an evocative curved
profile to its roof suggesting possible knowledge
of domestic designs by Olbrich at Darmstadt; but
the form could also have been suggested by leaf
and pine-cone studies done a few years earlier,
like those in the sgraffito ornaments of the Fallet
façade. The curved roof had to be simplified into
a form with two straight edges on each side
because Jeanneret's original idea was hard to
construct. L'Eplattenier and Chapallaz received
drawings and models through the mail, conveyed
them to contractors, then relayed criticisms and
suggestions back to Vienna.

These two houses were the end of the folklore
line for young Jeanneret, who was already doubt-
ing some of L'Eplattenier's teachings. He was
in search of philosophical grounds of his own,
and oscillated between elation and depression,
enthusiasm and scorn, as he looked for appropriate examples and mentors. Throughout the
winter months of early 1908 he wrote to L'Eplattenier with his complaints, doubts and hesitations. Should he enrol in a school in Austria
or Germany? Should he try to work with an
architect? Despite his earlier misgivings, he
presented himself in early March to Josef Hoffmann, who thought well of his drawings and
offered him a job. He seems to have declined
because in two weeks, despite L'Eplattenier's
suggestion that he study in Dresden, he was off
on his travels again, accompanied by Perrin. They
passed through Munich, where Jeanneret con-
ferred briefly with Chapallaz over plans of

17 (*opposite*) Maison
Jaquemet, La Chaux-de-
Fonds, 1907–8.

execution for the Jaquemet and Stotzer Houses;
then moved on to Nuremberg where he was
entranced by the medieval fortifications and the
Gothic furniture in the museum. A few months
later Jeanneret sent some photographs of the city
with an attached note 'taken at Nuremberg
during our escape from the prison of Vienna'. By
the time he wrote these words he was installed in
the city he had decided would supply him with
the next stage of his self-education, and which
was destined to become his spiritual home: Paris.

Although Jeanneret was now in reaction
against La Chaux-de-Fonds and L'Eplattenier, he
was deeply indebted to both. The future Le
Corbusier had been given a strong foundation.
Some of the terms of his later polarities were
already in place: the manual craftsmanship of his
father, the musical abstraction of his mother; the
dreariness of an industrial grid, the ravishing
beauty of neighbouring nature; regionalist myth-
ologies and the forces of internationalism. More
than that, L'Eplattenier had introduced him to
the philosophical importance of the nineteenth
century, to a spiritual idea of design and to the
notion of drawings as instruments to penetrate
beneath the surface of reality.

'My master used to say, 'Only Nature is inspiring
and true; only Nature can be the support for
human works. But do not render Nature as the
landscapists do, showing only the outward aspect.
Penetrate the cause of it, its form and vital
development; make a synthesis from it by
creating *ornaments*.' He had an elevated
conception of ornament which he wished would
be a sort of microcosm.'

If ornaments could be 'microcosms', so in later
life could paintings, buildings and city plans.
Edouard had learned to sense the typical behind
the incidental and to translate moral concerns
into emblematic geometry. The 'folklore du
sapin' might fade into insignificance — a minor
provincial episode of Art Nouveau — but the
method for transforming the underlying structures of nature into symbolic forms would live on
in the mind of the mature Le Corbusier until the
end.

Chapter 2

In Search of Personal Principles

'As for me, I do not contribute to the idea that you have to have a position in life by the age of 25 ...
    I feel drawn to a much less tied-down idea of life ... more like a symphony than the ticking of a clock.'
                    Charles Edouard Jeanneret, 1911

In retrospect Jeanneret's choice of Paris as the next stage in his self-education may seem obvious given what one knows of avant-garde vitality in the city in the first decade of the twentieth century. But the young Swiss provincial knew very little about the place when he arrived, and had no contact with emergent modern tendencies like Fauvism, Cubism or Futurism during his fourteen-month stay. From his vantage point in 1908, Paris could even have seemed a bastion of Academic culture. In later life he claimed rather flimsily that it had been a performance of the opera *La Bohème* (seen in Vienna) which persuaded him to pack his bags and make for the gay life of artists' garrets and café tables.

Vienna had been a flop but he still sought the stimulus of a major artistic centre, and he could not think of returning to La Chaux-de-Fonds without something to show for his flagrant departure from the route L'Eplattenier had mapped out for him. Besides, Paris allowed Jeanneret to speak his native tongue and therefore to continue broadening his intellectual horizons. Conceivably he was attracted by Art Nouveau, which combined an attention to modern materials with the abstraction of natural forms. If so, there was nothing urgent about his pursuit of an appropriate apprenticeship. Many weeks after his arrival he approached Franz Jourdain, architect of La Samaritaine department store, a building which made adventurous use of iron and glass. Jourdain admired his travel sketches but had no job to offer. So Edouard went to Charles Plumet, and then on to Henri Sauvage (designer of the later stepped apartments on rue des Amiraux), who had a decorating position that Jeanneret did not take. Edouard was after something without knowing quite what. The breakthrough came when he tracked down Eugène Grasset, the theorist on ornament who had been so revered in the Ecole d'Art in La Chaux-de-Fonds. Grasset delivered Edouard a long sermon on the decadence of recent work, the lack of concern for essentials, and then told him that good things were being done by a certain Auguste Perret who was experimenting with reinforced concrete.

The office of Perret Frères was on the ground floor of an apartment building at 25bis rue Franklin in the 16th arrondissement, a building Perret had himself designed on the armature of a concrete frame in 1902. Fifteen years Jeanneret's senior, he took to the youngster immediately, admired his travel sketches, and told Edouard that he would become his 'right hand'. Jeanneret was set to work for five hours a day, an arrangement which allowed him time to study. The atelier introduced him to a modern practice founded on a well-worked-out philosophy of building. Perret took an interest in his new assistant's education, suggested things for him to see, and insisted that he study mathematics and structures: of both Edouard was virtually ignorant. Perret also steered him towards the Rationalist writings of Eugène Viollet-le-Duc (his own bible). By degrees Perret took over from L'Eplattenier as Jeanneret's chief mentor.

Rationalism stressed the primacy of structure in the generation of architectural form. Viollet-le-Duc had rejected the facile revivalism of the mid-nineteenth century, claiming that a new style must be formulated on the basis of 'truth' to structure and programme. The past was not to be imitated directly, but transformed at the level of underlying principles. Viollet's own preferences were for medieval buildings, but Perret had studied at the Ecole des Beaux-Arts under Julien Guadet, who had advocated Classical examples and had implied that the age-old lessons of this tradition could be translated at an organizational level to modern means. Perret's aim was now to blend the structural potentials of concrete with the logic of contemporary plans and the proportions and procedures of Classical design.

The building in which Edouard went to work every day — 25bis rue Franklin — was an experiment in this direction. Weight was concentrated on a few slender supports instead of thick masonry walls. The concrete frame allowed open plans, and wide apertures in the façades, as well as a flat roof that was used as a garden. Aesthetic effects arose from sober proportions and an emphasis on structural lines of force through judiciously placed but restrained orna-

18 Auguste Perret, apartment building, 25bis rue
Franklin, Paris, 1902.

ment. At the top, where it broke free of the usual system which employed infill panels the skeleton was expressed. Drip mouldings, grooves and brackets were simplified versions of seventeenth-century precedents. Structure was translated into art through an intuitive grasp of Classical principles of organization.

From Perret, Jeanneret learned to think of concrete primarily in terms of rectangular frames as if it were timber. Actually concrete is a flexible material which depends on the form of the mould into which it is poured. Edouard surely knew of Anatole de Baudot's reinforced cement church of St-Jean-de-Montmartre (1897), which used medievalizing arches and vaults to fit prejudices and precedents quite different from Perret's. But Jeanneret was not worried about style alone: he was looking for guiding principles that might crystallize as forms later. Rationalism gave him a new perspective on tradition, less concerned with ornamental details than with the anatomy underlying past forms. With his first paycheque (August 1908) he bought Viollet-le-Duc's *Dictionnaire raisonné de l'architecture française*, and next to an illustration of the Gothic flying buttress wrote: '*art lives by its skeleton. As Aug. Perret was telling me, grasp the skeleton* and you can grasp the art ...'

Jeanneret enrolled in art history courses at the Ecole des Beaux-Arts and immersed himself in Edouard Courroyer's *L'Architecture romane*

19 Plate of Hagia Sophia, Istanbul, from Auguste Choisy, *Histoire de l'architecture*.

(Paris, 1888). This presented Romanesque for its grammar of walls, columns, arches and domes, and showed how these simple structural elements had been combined and re-combined to make different types of building, thus corroborating Perret's notion of architecture as a poetry based on the language of construction. Later Jeanneret studied Auguste Choisy's *Histoire de l'architecture* which treated other great styles of the past as expressions of basic systems of support. The argument was illustrated with stunningly simple and clear diagrams. Some buildings were shown from below with volumes, spaces, walls, columns, arches, pendentives, domes projecting above — truly the plan as the generator. The spirit of these precise prints was a long way from Ruskin's microscopic watercolours of light, shade and ornament, being closer to that of a geometry textbook or a biological chart of classifications. Jeanneret was being exposed to graphic means for 'grasping the skeleton' and for conceiving buildings as three-dimensional totalities. Period styles were shown as variations on structural elements and plan types, not just as rearrangements of façade decorations.

Jeanneret's small rented room was at 3 quai St-Michel, conveniently close to both the Latin Quarter and the Ile de la Cité. Far from abandoning his fascination with medieval architecture, he spent many long hours clambering over the roofs of Notre Dame sketching gargoyles and buttresses. No doubt Perret encouraged him to examine key works of the Classical tradition as well: Gabriel's Petit Trianon at Versailles (later selected by Le Corbusier for illustration in *Vers une architecture*) was, after all, only a short train ride away. As he absorbed techniques of modern practice among the concrete posts of the Perret studio by day, or studied among the slender iron columns of Labrouste's Bibliothèque Ste-Geneviève by night, he also grappled with the question of industrialization and architecture. His wanderings around Paris surely took him to the Eiffel Tower, the train sheds of the Grandes Gares, the concrete ramps and metal windows of garages and factories in the outer faubourgs. He recalled a tiny fragment of 'the poetry of modern life' when an aeroplane circled the Eiffel Tower. Paris, 'capital of the nineteenth century', intellectual bazaar at the heart of a world empire, was stashed with loot to feed the mind. He sketched in the Louvre, wandered through the ethnographic museums, picked among the literary bric-à-brac on the bookstalls of the Seine.

This was Jeanneret's first extended stay in a city of this size and complexity, and it surely forced him to think about the positive and negative features of life in a modern metropolis. His viewpoint was marginal and bohemian. He knew the poky attic room, the café table as ringside seat from which to watch the life of the street. One can imagine Edouard as the perpetual *flâneur*, his reveries mingling with the clank of trolley cars, the reflecting glass of arcades, the fragmentary incidents and printed advertisements glimpsed from the moving métro. In moments he could wander from the Paris of bourgeois con-

sumption to the less-known Paris of 1908, with its
putrid drains, slimy passageways and disease.
Paris revealed to him how a city could be a
concentration of abilities, a scenario of the rich
and the poor, a repository of collective memories,
a spiritual manifestation of order and national
glory. The city gave him so many of the elements
of his later urbanism — classical vistas, parks with
curving paths, transportation lines on different
levels. It formed his very idea of urbanity.

The few photographs of Jeanneret during his
Paris stay show him as a jolly aesthete sporting a
floppy hat and artist's smock. Actually this was a
time of turmoil in which he wavered between
certainty of his Olympian role and deep self-
doubts. He retreated to his garret to read
Nietzsche's *Thus Spake Zarathustra* and Renan's
Life of Christ, and began to think of his own
future in terms of a prophetic mission of salvation. Supported by his new architectural faith
of Rationalism Jeanneret wrote to L'Eplattenier
in the late part of 1908 blaming his earlier teacher
for the impracticality of his early education. In
hackneyed phrases derived from Perret and
Viollet-le-Duc he preached that the great architectures of the past had been direct expressions
of the social state, technologies and building
materials of their times. This reiteration of nineteenth-century determinisms was accompanied by
wildly individualistic claims for the 'higher truths'
perceived by artist prophets. Jeanneret's letter
was laced with references to the artist's 'divine
self', 'profound matters of being' and the need for
suffering in the creation of great art.

Jeanneret was evidently grappling with inner
demons, and beginning to realize that he must
pursue a singular destiny. A huge inner ambition
did not allow him to sink back into the comfort of
other people's definitions of life or architecture.
At the same time, he was woefully unprepared
for his mission as one of Nietzsche's 'historical
world individuals'. It was part of the psychological pattern that he should latch on to mentors
in a desperate demand for certainty, absorb all he
could, and then turn away in disgust at the incom-
pleteness of the lesson. This was already happen-
ing with L'Eplattenier and would later happen
with both Perret and Amédée Ozenfant. As he
could not find living mentors of appropriate range
and ability, Jeanneret would seek them out in
history. For individuals of this artistic calibre, the
classic works of tradition act like sounding
boards, helping them to find their own level.

But Jeanneret had not rejected his earlier La
Chaux-de-Fonds self completely, nor the aesthetic and philosophical formulations that went
with it. In November 1909 he left Paris and
returned to the Jura, having announced in
advance that he intended to spend the winter in
a rural retreat, an old farmhouse at La Cornu,
some way out of La Chaux-de-Fonds. The winters
were fierce and these old Jura farms had a funnel-
shaped room around the fireplace into which
everyone could climb to warm themselves.
Throughout his life Le Corbusier remained
fascinated by the architectural idea of objects
within objects, and in the funnel form of the

20 Charles Edouard
Jeanneret as the Parisian
bohemian in his garret, 1909.

21 Jura farmhouse with
stack.

22 Project for Ateliers
d'Artistes. 1910.

Assembly Building at Chandigarh (designed
1951–7) it is possible that one finds a recall of
youthful memories.

Edouard was soon involved again at the Ecole
d'Art, especially with a group of his old associates
who called themselves 'Ateliers d'art réunis'.
L'Eplattenier set them up with commissions: the
decoration of the hall of the new Post Office, the
crematorium, the entrance hall of the Hirsch
Pavilion in the Observatory at Neuchâtel. Jeanneret designed a scheme to house the Ateliers in
the rue des Vieux Pompiers in La Chaux-de-
Fonds. The individual studios were grouped
around the perimeter next to individual gardens
(a cross between the cells at Ema and watch-
makers cabins), and in the centre was the 'salle
du cours' under a pyramid. With its square plan
and corner minarets, the project had a vaguely
sacral character, a bit like a mosque, no doubt
appropriate to the lofty cultural aims of the
institution. Loose resemblances to late eighteenth-century 'Revolutionary Classicism' (Boullée, Ledoux, etc.) are probably coincidental.

While perched in his rural retreat, Edouard
began to write his first book, *La Construction
des villes*. This occupied much of his time in
the coming year, and later underwent several
revisions as his ideas changed, but it never saw
the light of day as a publication. In part it was a
critique of his dreary home town: the grid and
bleak rows of apartment houses scarcely afforded
urban variety and richness. But the book also
encapsulated Jeanneret's ambition of going
beyond the scale of the individual building, to the

spaces and streets, even to the city as a whole.
Many of the ideas were derived from Camillo
Sitte's *Der Stadtbau* of 1889, which had stressed
the need for intimate complexity in the placement
of buildings, squares and streets, and which had
been heavily illustrated with examples from
medieval Italy. Given the mature Le Corbusier's
later love of grand Baroque vistas, axes and
enormous open spaces, it is quite curious to find
him on the opposite tack in his first attempt at
formulating urbanistic principles. Not that his
own proposals were merely picturesque: they
were guided by piecemeal Classical aspirations
too. One can see this in the projects that Jeanneret sketched for the north-east end of avenue
Léopold Robert and for the place de la Gare in
La Chaux-de-Fonds in 1910. The latter was an
ingenious solution for turning the axis of the main
boulevard, accommodating a cross-axis from the
grid of the town, and providing a formal *cour
d'honneur* for the station. The figure/ground
subtleties of Jeanneret's ornamental designs here
emerged at an urban scale.

In the spring of 1910 Jeanneret left Switzerland
for Germany. With unfailing loyalty L'Eplattenier had acquired a grant for him to write a
study on the decorative arts in Germany. This
gave the 22-year-old quasi-official status which he
used to the full to visit schools, factories and
workshops, and to make the acquaintance of the
German architectural élite. In June 1910 he
attended the Deutscher Werkbund Congress in
Berlin, and by November (after a trip to La
Chaux-de-Fonds for the dedication of L'Eplat-

tenier's Monument de la République) he was
installed in the office of Peter Behrens. Jeanneret
seems to have had an uncanny knack for lodging
himself with people destined to make a major
historical impact.

The Berlin experience gave Jeanneret quite a
new perspective on design. Behrens was trying to
fuse engineering Rationalism and abstracted
Classicism in his industrial buildings for the AEG
(Allgemeine Electricitätsgesellschaft) and this
was related to the broader ambition of defining
a new cultural harmony for the German state.
The position was well represented by the AEG
Turbinen-Fabrik in Berlin of 1908, a building
whose form combined a judicious attention to the
structural gantry function of a major assembly
factory with the dignity and poise of an abstracted
Classical temple. Behrens's office designed a wide
range of industrial products — including lamps,
logos and simple functional objects — and this
impressed Jeanneret deeply, though most of his
time was spent working on some grand crypto-
Classical houses for well-to-do Berlin clients. The
young Jura Swiss was not at home in this Teutonic setting. He found Behrens gruff and the
other staff correct and distant. While he admired
the high level of technical organization in the
office and called Behrens's architecture 'une
création intégrale de notre époque', he also found
it cold and impersonal. In his report on the
applied arts he generalized in terms of national
characteristics: 'If Paris is the home of Art,
Germany remains the big production site.'

Despite these criticisms and hesitations about
German culture (which tended to confirm his
French allegiances), a good deal rubbed off on
Jeanneret. He made contact with the Deutscher
Werkbund, the national organization devoted to
quality in all areas of design, and especially with
the 'classical wing' of the group, which stood out
against materialistic functionalism on the one
hand, and against the wilful excesses of Expres-
sionism on the other. The aim was the creation of
types amenable to modern uses and productive
processes, yet approximating to Platonic ideas.
Mathematical proportions and modular systems
were to generate order in design. It was a lofty
view of architecture, in which Schinkel was the
hero and Hegel the philosophical grandfather.
One of the chief theorists of the Werkbund,
Hermann Muthesius, wrote: 'Far higher than the
material is the spiritual; far higher than function,
material and technique, stands Form. These three
material aspects might be impeccably handled
but — if Form were not — we would still be
living in a merely brutish world.' From the
Werkbund Jeanneret absorbed the idea that
architecture must have a major cultural mission
in industrial society through the spiritualization
of types for mass-production. The idea would be
central to Purism a decade later.

Both Ludwig Mies van der Rohe and Walter
Gropius were also associated with the Behrens
office in this period, but there is no evidence of
exchange between them and Jeanneret. It so
happens that Frank Lloyd Wright was also in
Berlin overseeing publication of his collected

works at the Wasmuth publishing house: *Ausge-
führte Bauten und Entwürfe von Frank Lloyd
Wright*. The drawings and plates would make a
major impact on the development of modern
architecture in Europe, above all in Holland
where Berlage eulogized Wright as the leading
contemporary master. Especially seen in black-
and-white photographs, Wright's Prairie Houses
announced a new language of abstract, rectangular masses, hovering planes and fluid spaces,
that could not fail to impress any architect grop-
ing beyond the florid excesses of Art Nouveau.
It is not yet certain when Wright's work first
entered Jeanneret's consciousness, but he probably knew about him by 1914 or 1915: both the
Dom-ino House projects and Maison Schwob
may have been influenced by his example.

One of the dangers of writing architectural
history in terms of 'movements' is that it posits
independent forces running through time, and so
oversimplifies the relationship between the
individual talent and period style. With a major
figure like Le Corbusier, entering tradition in a
period without a strong consensus, the process of
grappling with predecessors, searching for models
to fit nascent aspirations, and defining the kernel
of a personal style involved hesitations, commitments and retractions. Ideas that were to be
really important sometimes took a long time to
embed themselves in his mind, to re-emerge later
in creative action. In his first few months in
Berlin, as the winter dragged on, Jeanneret was
not particularly conscious of the need for a new
machine-age architecture. In fact he was obsessed
with a regional style for his homeland, the Jura,
but based on Mediterranean sources. This
unlikely marriage of disparate places was
suggested by a book he ordered specially from a
Geneva bookshop through the mail, and read in
November 1910: *Entretiens de la villa du Rouet*
by Alexandre Cingria Vaneyre.

The book was a series of dialogues between
aesthetes who somehow had the time to hang
around a Florentine villa formulating an artistic
identity for the 'Suisse Romande' — that French-

23 Study for the improve-
ment of the Place de la
Gare, La Chaux-de-Fonds,
1910 (Fondation Le
Corbusier).

speaking part of Switzerland around Neuchâtel and Geneva including, at one extremity, La Chaux-de-Fonds. The author inveighs against German 'cultural domination', argues that the true spirit of the region is *Mediterranean*, and implies that a Renaissance will occur once this Classical soul is laid bare. The landscape is compared to that of Greece, and to that close to Istanbul — a parallel which makes some sense for the vineyard slopes facing south over Lac Léman

24   Peter Behrens, lamp designs for A.E.G., 1906.

or Lac Neuchâtel, but which is scarcely tenable for La Chaux-de-Fonds. Such details did not deter Charles Edouard Jeanneret, who was ripe for a myth of this kind, the more so as it affirmed private fantasies about his own family's supposed 'Mediterranean origins'.

Cingria Vaneyre did not hesitate to prescribe the architecture appropriate to the regional resurgence. This would have nothing to do with chalets or fir trees, but would be based on a 'Greco-Latin formula': buildings of calm, regular volume standing out against the slopes — ivory, olive, ochre or cream in colour — with graceful curves to offset the rigidity of the dominant rectangles. It might be thought that Jeanneret — L'Eplattenier's star pupil, soaked in Ruskin, medievalism and the 'folklore du sapin' — was appalled. It is a testimony to the impact on him of a new wave of Classical values in European architecture that he was delighted. He scrawled with excitement that these ideas were 'absolutely right for the Haute Jura'. At the end of the book he even wrote a profession of faith which he dated 23 November 1910:

'... this book comes along at the right moment to help me with my direction. It provokes an examination, normal, clear, luminous deductions; it unlocks the German grip from me. In one year's time, in Rome, I shall read it again, and, through sketches, I shall found my Jurassic, Neuchâtelois discipline.'

Jeanneret was to fulfil the ambition of being in Rome a year later almost to the day. In the spring

25   Peter Behrens, A.E.G. turbine factory, Berlin, 1908.

of 1911 he left Behrens, finished his study on the German applied arts (*Etude sur le mouvement d'art décoratif en Allemagne*, La Chaux-de-Fonds, 1912) and set off with Auguste Klipstein, a friend who was writing a thesis on El Greco and needed to visit Bucharest and Budapest. Eventually he was persuaded to accompany Jeanneret on a journey that would last six months and take them through the Balkans, along the fringes of the Ottoman Empire, to Turkey and Greece, and then to Italy; Edouard was probably dreaming of an even longer trip to the Levant and Egypt. To help finance the venture he arranged to write a series of articles for *Les Feuilles d'Avis*, a newspaper in La Chaux-de-Fonds. Along with his sketches, photographs, postcards and later recollections, these provide a graphic record of his adventures. Published posthumously as *Le Voyage d'orient*, the articles show that the written word was an important tool for anchoring poetic reactions to people, places and buildings.

The Voyage d'orient was in the grand Romantic tradition of the northern European who goes south to the shores of the Mediterranean to find the roots of Western civilization and to achieve an inner liberty. The time had come for Edouard to experience the seminal works of Classicism first-hand, and not just through books. All this was quite beyond his father, who grumbled about his sons' never settling down (Albert had also been travelling), and who never really forgot that Edouard had turned away from the family trade. He would later jab sarcastically at his son, saying that his reports said rather little about buildings for someone who intended to be an architect. Madame Jeanneret, on the other hand, wished Edouard well. So did Albert: 'He is doing what other people only dream of doing all their lives, and at the only time possible: youth. He has the guts and the will to live, far more than most; one has to give him warm encouragement.'

The first leg was through Romania and the Balkans, where Jeanneret was enthralled by living folk traditions in music, fabrics, dance and vernacular architecture. To him this was a magic world far away from the dreariness of industrial northern Europe. He romanticized the peasant for his life following the rhythms of nature and wrote that 'popular art overwhelms that of the higher civilizations'. Later he reflected that his travels revealed 'in the diversity of the races the fundamental unity of human nature'.

By late July they had got to Istanbul where they lived for two months in a room with white-washed walls (a detail which clearly delighted him). He sketched wooden-framed houses on the Bosphorus and mosques. Up to now he had had little exposure to Islamic architecture, but he took many photographs of buildings and tombs. He did a watercolour of the haunting silhouette of the city seen across the water, and an aerial view sketch of the Suleiman Mosque by Sinan, showing the platform, the jostling play of volumes above the plan, and the hierarchical expression of the idea in the geometry of the domes. Choisy's lessons on the crystalline totalities of architectural arrangement had not been

lost on him. Compared with his travel sketches of winter 1907, his 1911 drawings were firm and assured. He was now 'seeing' history for its primary lessons. In one note he wrote: 'The white sanctuary pushes its domes on large masonry cubes in the city of stone. An elementary geometry disciplines the masses: the square, the cube, the sphere.' Drawing here became the tool to penetrate the intentions behind past architecture and to store up schemata in the memory where they might mature and transform into the stuff of the artist's own imagination. L'Eplattenier had told him to 'penetrate the cause'

behind nature, and he now did the same for the objects of history.

By late summer they were moving westwards again through Thrace to Mount Athos where they spent three weeks in the monasteries. Jeanneret's earlier enthusiasm for the spiritual value of retreat and monastic rule had not deserted him. Some of the Athos monasteries were perched above the rocks with flat tops, irregular lower levels, and jetties of balconies projecting over the landscape; it was an arrangement that he would not forget when he had to design a monastery himself over forty years later. But the most profound architectural experience of the entire journey was on the Acropolis at Athens.

Jeanneret visited the Parthenon every day for three weeks, drawing it in changing lights and from many points of view. He tried to pin down the animated sculptural presence of the building, its tense action across space, the subtle curved entasis of the columns, the slight bending of the stylobates, the compression of close-up profiles with long, distant vignettes of mountains and sea. Here was a revered work of architectural history which transcended all the encrusting clichés about 'Classicism', which touched deep chords in Jeanneret, and spoke of universality. With him he was carrying a pamphlet by Renan called *Prière sur l'acropole*, and this referred to the Parthenon in lofty terms as 'l'idéal crystallisé en marbre pentélique'. Ravished by the proportions, Edouard

26 Sketch of the Suleiman Mosque, Istanbul, 1911 (from *Vers une architecture*).

27 Sketch of the Acropolis, Athens, 1911 (from Petit, *Le Corbusier: Lui-Même*.)

noted that it was an example of 'supreme mathematics', and compared its rigorous discipline to that of a machine. He did not try to trap the building in dry Rationalist categories of structural logic, but concentrated on the precise expression of ideas in a vital sculptural form. The Parthenon embodied an elusive absolute that would continue to haunt him for the rest of his life. A decade later in *Vers une architecture* he spoke of the building in terms of 'Architecture pure création de l'esprit':

'The Greeks on the Acropolis set up temples which are animated by a single thought, drawing around them the desolate landscape and gathering it into the composition. Thus on every point of the horizon, the thought is single. It is on this account that there are no other architectural works on this scale of grandeur. We shall be able to talk 'Doric' when man, in nobility of aim and complete sacrifice of all that is accidental in Art, has reached the higher levels of the mind: austerity.'

In early October 1911 the two travellers crossed the Adriatic to reach Italy at Brindisi, having stopped off at Delphi on the way to the Greek port of exit. Edouard was not happy in being back in what he probably thought of as 'Occidental' Europe. He missed the tough, rocky landscape, the light, the mystery of the archaic: 'For my part I hate being here. Suddenly all that was left behind.' But his spirits were restored by Pompeii and Ancient Rome which he was now seeing for the first time, with that special perspective which comes from having seen ancient Greek architecture first. At Pompeii he sketched the Forum, the House of the Tragic Poet, and the House of the Silver Wedding (which he called the 'Casa del Noce'). A notable historian of Renais-

28 Edouard next to the Parthenon.

sance architecture has suggested that 'every artist finds his own antiquity': in the houses at Pompeii, Charles Edouard Jeanneret, a future leader of the modern movement, found domestic archetypes that would influence his own ideas on houses profoundly. In his sketches he focused on the gradations of axes, the subtle shifts of view, the integration of light, structure and procession. Again the word 'Classical' was given a new shot of vitality, far away from the preciosity with which he (oversimply) associated the Ecole des Beaux-Arts: In *Vers une architecture* he would write:

'CASA DEL NOCE, at Pompeii.
Again the little vestibule that frees the mind from the street. And then you are in the atrium; four columns in the middle (four *cylinders*) shoot up towards the shade of the roof, giving a feeling of force and a witness of potent methods; but at the far end is the brilliance of the garden seen through the peristyle which spreads out this light with a large gesture ... making a great space. Between the two is the Tablinum, contracting this vision like the lens of a camera ... Magistral grandeur, order, a splendid amplitude: you are in the house of a *Roman* ... After twenty centuries, without any historical reference, you are conscious of Architecture ...'

Jeanneret also visited Hadrian's Villa at Tivoli, where he was moved by the play of light and shade on simple wall surfaces, and by the compression of views of nature through screens and rectangular openings. In the Serapeum he drew the dramatic top lighting system of the grotto — which had also intrigued Piranesi. Forty years later he would transform this into the light towers of the Chapel at Ronchamp. The decapitated archaeological remains with low walls curving around grids of columns revealed the carcase of an ancient system in which rhythm and plastic variation were created on the basis of standardization. Jeanneret did not want or need the full regalia of Classical ornament in his search for essentials. The Colosseum, the Pantheon, the stark brick masses of the *thermae* heaving in light and shadow, these appealed to his predilection for geometry, *gravitas* and proportion. Alongside such primal statements, much later Classicism could only seem trivial, as did Jeanneret's earlier Italian fascination with medieval ornament. What Wittkower wrote of Palladio could apply to the later Le Corbusier too: 'The remains of Antiquity were his constant measure of permanent values.'

Prime objects of Antiquity were also the means by which Jeanneret judged later transformations of Classicism and found them sorely lacking. He seems to have had a blind spot for much of the Renaissance and Baroque. But he was astonished by Michelangelo, an artist who transcended the limitations of mere reuses of Classical language with sculptural statements of incredible force. Above all Jeanneret was impressed by that 'gigantic geometry of harmonious relationships', the apses of Saint Peter's. These embodied a sublime 'terribilità' that could be ranked with the Parthenon. He thought that the sculptor Phidias

was chiefly responsible for the excellence of that temple, and here, two thousand years later, was Michelangelo, another great sculptor, infusing stones with a turbulent drama of unimpeachable quality. One has the sneaking suspicion that these two artists, far in the past, became the mentors of Edouard's imagination, the guardians of his aesthetic conscience.

The direct apprehension of what Jeanneret intuited as perennial values unleashed an extraordinary rush of images in his mind, related to

29 Sketch of the House of the Silver Wedding, Pompeii, 1911 (from *Vers une architecture*).

the task of rethinking the old in the new:

'Italy is a graveyard where the dogma of my religion now lies rotting. All the bric-à-brac that was my delight now fills me with horror. I gabble elementary geometry; I am possessed of the colour white, the cube, the sphere, the cylinder and the pyramid. Prisms rise and balance each other setting up rhythms ... in the midday sun the cubes open out into a surface, at nightfall a rainbow seems to rise from the forms. In the morning they are real, casting light and shadow and sharply outlined as a drawing …'

This vision of ideal geometries and basic mental forms was followed by an extraordinary prophetic glimpse of Le Corbusier's later urbanistic utopia. There were references to 'straight roads', 'roads on rooftops amidst trees and flowers', 'no ornament' and 'wide open spaces where one can breathe'. A basic premise of *Vers une architecture* and of the architect's later production was spelt out clearly at the age of 24: the greatness of past inventions should be repeated not through imitation, but through a reiteration of constants, and a search for equivalent magnificence in modern terms.

'We should no longer be *artists* but rather penetrate the age, fuse with it until we are indistinguishable. Then we should leave behind us Colossea and Baths, an Acropolis and mosques, and our Jura mountains would provide as beautiful a setting for these as the sea. We too are distinguished, great and worthy of past ages. We shall even do better still, *that* is my belief …'

It is slightly droll to realize that Jeanneret imagined this resurgence of Mediterranean culture could happen in a tiny province of Switzerland: he would need a world stage for ambitions of this size. But he was now on the homeward leg of his journey, and for the moment was still aiming at a Classicism for the Jura. L'Eplattenier wrote to say that there might be a job at the Ecole d'Art, and his mother sent word that she was longing to see him, but warning him that he might find life in La Chaux-de-Fonds dreadfully narrow after his amazing adventures. Edouard fortified himself for the shock with visits to two of his favourite Italian ensembles — the monastery at Ema and the Campo at Pisa — then, in November 1911, returned to La Chaux-de-Fonds in time for the long, cold Jura winter.

Jeanneret could look back over the previous four years as his idiosyncratic equivalent to a university education, in which he had gathered together techniques, insights, principles and first-hand impressions that would help him define his own path. The portrait of this particular artist as a young man includes the flashes of insight that it would take him years, even decades, to realize in the forms of architecture and urbanism. At the heart of it all was the gradual intuition of a major historical mission, dimly sensed as having to do with discovering an architecture right for the modern era, but rooted in the lasting values of Antiquity. The Voyage d'orient gave Jeanneret new touchstones of excellence to emulate rather than imitate.

30   Sketch section of a typical cell of the monastery at Ema, 1911 (from Petit, *Le Corbusier: Lui-Même*).

Chapter 3

A Classicism for the Jura

'The vocation of putting my country in harmony with itself had thus grasped me. I had refrained from anything that could pull me away from the south, from Rome and from the Mediterranean: it was the salvation for Classical culture.'
Alexandre Cingria Vaneyre, 1906

Madame Jeanneret had been right: it was a cold shock for her son to come back to the cramped world of La Chaux-de-Fonds. Edouard characterized his homeland as a 'harsh country', 'incredibly dark', 'the firs about as friendly as a saw ready to cut you in two ... the horizon right up under your nose.' But it had been his own decision to return and he would remain based there for nearly five more years. While in Istanbul, he had run across Auguste Perret, who had offered him a job working on the Théâtre des Champs-Elysées, but he had not taken this chance of returning to Paris. Perhaps Jeanneret wanted to set up his own practice and felt that this would be safest in familiar surroundings; perhaps he really did think it was possible to stimulate a new 'Jurassic discipline' of Classicism for the Suisse Romande.

As faithful as ever, L'Eplattenier had reserved a place for him as a teacher at the Ecole d'Art in the 'Nouvelle Section'. A continuation of the previous 'Cours Supérieur', this was still devoted to the broad aim of establishing an ornamental alphabet derived from local natural phenomena as the basis of a supposed cultural regeneration. A page from the prospectus of 1912 shows the familiar motifs: pine-cones, trees and animals, abstracted into geometrical hieroglyphs. Léon Perrin and Georges Aubert were also invited to teach, so Jeanneret would be among old friends. How provincial it must have seemed after his experiences in the great capitals of Europe and after his epic journey. During the year or two after his return he would try to fuse together ancient planning principles with various cosmopolitan sources including (ironically enough) Viennese and German ones, in his search for a viable Classical regionalism.

In early 1912 Edouard was lucky enough to receive two commissions to design houses which allowed him to give his new conceptions scope. The first was a new home for his parents, who had acquired land near the Pouillerel on the rue Montagne, a little further up the slope from Maisons Fallet, Stotzer and Jaquemet. To amble up the hillside from the auburn tones and rusticity of these works to the chaste white forms, regular geometry and urbanity of the Maison Jeanneret is to become aware of a major transition in the artist's outlook. The Jeanneret House is formal, even grand, with its relatively simple cubical, pyramidical and curved volumes, its strong axial emphases, its supporting plinth surmounted by a garden colonnade, its beaded mouldings emphasizing corners and rims and its simplified pediments. The upper windows are laid out as a strip under the lid of steep roof and are articulated by piers ornamented with local flora. There are echoes of Tessenow, Behrens, perhaps even Hoffmann. But the plan also has a vaguely ecclesiastical character on account of its axes, apsidal volume at the end of the dining room, and symmetrical structure. One enters by a circuitous route from the garden gate, up over the platform and around to the back: a family version of the procession around the Parthenon. The programme was relatively modest — a medium sized home with atelier for Monsieur and music studio for Madame — but Edouard was determined to infuse his first major commission with a noble Classical sense. Once inside there are a foyer, the main living and dining rooms, and a cross-axis giving on to the southerly view. An early project had a flat roof and resembled some of the Turkish houses he had sketched during his trip. He seems to have accepted Cingria Vaneyre's suggestion of links between the Jura and the Mediterranean world (Pl.133).

Jeanneret's other major commission of early 1912 came from the top end of the social spectrum: the watch magnate, Georges Favre-Jacot. Favre-Jacot had been a large-scale success story who by 1901 had 600 employees turning out over 100,000 watches a year under the brand name 'Zenith'. His operation was based in Le Locle, the town between La Chaux-de-Fonds and the French frontier. A certain seigneurial pretension was intrinsic to the programme. Favre-Jacot needed a villa with all the latest amenities that would stand up to the best being done in Berlin, Vienna or Paris, but that would harmonize with the Jura landscape too. It is testimony to his adventurousness and his good judgement that he should have taken on someone as young as Jeanneret as his architect.

The site was perched on a sliver of terraces on a south-facing slope overlooking his mini-empire of factories and warehouses and was approached up a long lane on a diagonal, past a stable building that had to be preserved. Jeanneret decided on a variant of a Palladian scheme: an oblong with extending curved wings embracing a *cour d'honneur*. He adjusted the forecourt to the turning circle of Favre-Jacot's car. The main massing had to be juggled to generate a pseudo-symmetry, and the curved wing had to be distorted to fit the kitchen on one side, and a small, lower lane for the garages on the other. The problem of resolving a diagonal line of approach, the circular drive and the turn on to the building's own axis was addressed cleverly with a circular portico which acted as a hinge. This was surely modelled on an analogous device used by Behrens in the Cuno residence of 1909, or even on the peristyle portico of the seventeenth-century Hôtel de Beauvais in Paris (Pl.134).

This portico hinted at later variations on a circular geometry. The guest arriving at the Favre-Jacot residence would pass through a low entry zone into a double-height cylinder containing the vestibule, the stairs tightly fitted around it: the view to the garden would draw him into the salon giving on to a terrace: and in the original design the same axis would have continued into the garden to bisect an oval pond. Lateral movements were handled no less ingeniously. To the left, on the south side, was a library and den for Monsieur Favre-Jacot with a loggia looking down over his empire. Further on, to the right, the route was guided over to the north-west corner where the dining room was contained in a pavilion protruding slightly into the garden, its axis parallel to the main one. This was surmounted by a studio looking out over a terrace into the formal garden at the rear, and emphasized by a simplified pediment.

The most obvious debts of the Favre-Jacot House were again to Behrens and Hoffmann. The pale earth and pink colours and simple, dignified volumes fitted Cingria Vaneyre's prescriptions for a Suisse Romande Classicism, as did the formal garden with its walkways and terraces. Jeanneret designed a highly simplified and linear Classical ornament of pediments, grooves, panels, pilasters and mouldings, the capitals blending pine-cones and other vegetal motifs. The clever use of curves to accommodate site distortions suggests the suave playfulness of a Rococo *hôtel particulier*, while the orchestration of axes and views may owe a debt to the houses in Pompeii. In the Favre-Jacot House he treated the car approach, the movement through the house, the driveway, paths and terraces as part of a single idea. The oblong, main masses were set off against sinuous landscape contours, and curves were used to channel both exterior and interior movement. Many of these devices would recur in Le Corbusier's villas of the 1920s where they would be recast in the Purist language of guitar shapes and free-plan partitions. In 1913 Jeanneret made a proposal for another Favre-Jacot property — an old Jura farm called La Maison du Diable — which included a roof terrace of greenery. This idea too would be central to his later vocabulary.

In February 1912 Edouard opened his own office at 54 rue Numa Droz in La Chaux-de-Fonds. He put together a circular letter to attract clients. This shows what Jeanneret admired in his own background, and what he thought it necessary to emphasize for the local market. He stressed his 'understanding of present needs' and (with some exaggeration) his 'six years of practice ... alongside architects of the highest reputation':

'I can deal with the creation of plans and the construction of villas, country houses and all industrial buildings (with a speciality in reinforced concrete), rental accommodations, shop installations, repairs and transformations, as well as interior design and the architecture of gardens.

Among other things, an apprenticeship of two years, as the primary designer, at Messrs. Perret Bros. Public and private works in Paris (with a speciality in reinforced concrete), and another apprenticeship with Professor Peter Behrens of Berlin, the artistic and architectural counsellor of AEG, have introduced me to the most modern procedures.'

Both François Hennebique and François Maillart had established the relevance of reinforced concrete to Switzerland by this time, the former in industrial structures, the latter in a series of superb bridges. René Chapallaz had constructed factories for the watch industry in La Chaux-de-Fonds as early as 1907, and it was probably towards this sector that Jeanneret aimed his expertise: concrete provided flexibility, fireproofing and wide spaces. But he was not to have much luck in this direction. His proposals in concrete remained theoretical or unbuilt. The major exception would be the Maison Schwob, but this was still four years away.

Jeanneret was off to a reasonably good start, but with the building slump of 1913 his attitude quickly soured. He began to dream of getting out, of going to Paris, of joining the 'rising edifice of modern art'. His teaching in the Art School was increasingly at odds with the 'folklore du sapin'. He had his students doing work based on primary geometries and on simple proportional systems. Schemes emerged which had an up-to-the-minute, somewhat Viennese or German character. But when the Nouvelle Section came under attack Jeanneret preserved a unified front with L'Eplattenier and with his colleagues. Entrenched craftsmen in the town claimed that it threatened their existence: socialists argued that it turned out people who were no use to industry; other faculty staff tried to undermine it because they were jealous of its verve. Despite his own doubts, Jeanneret drummed up international support from Eugène Grasset, Peter Behrens, Hector Guimard and a roll-call of other notables. But the Nouvelle Section collapsed and in 1913 L'Eplattenier resigned. Jeanneret withdrew into himself, renting another farmhouse outside the town where he could concentrate on his tenuous Olympian mission. He was leaving his old teacher behind and so were events. With moves towards automation in the watch industry, L'Eplattenier's ideas seemed anachronistic. Jeanneret's office advertisement was a much more frank assessment of new realities in which concrete factories could be expected to replace small craftsmen's ateliers.

Throughout this period, Jeanneret relied on his connections through the Ateliers d'Art for income. He designed furniture in a stripped Classical style and was hired as an interior decorating consultant, sometimes acquiring antiques

33 Sketch for a house (probably for Auguste Klipstein, 1912): note Mediterranean vegetation (Bibliothèque de la Ville, La Chaux-de-Fonds).

31 (*opposite*) Charles Edouard Jeanneret, house for his parents, La Chaux-de-Fonds, 1912.

32 (*opposite below*) Jeanneret parents' house, view from pergola to rear entrance, parents in foreground, boys in background.

34 Maison Favre-Jacot, La
Chaux-de-Fonds, 1912, view
of the south façade.

35 Cutaway plan and site
plan of Maison Favre-Jacot
(Bibliothèque de la Ville, La
Chaux-de-Fonds).

for his clients on commission. This was a long
way short of his ambition of founding a new
artistic movement, but he continued to revise his
book, *La Construction des villes*, occasionally
visiting Paris to do research in libraries. He
designed a house for Klipstein (his friend from
the Voyage d'orient) with various Mediterranean
references, but this came to nothing. He also
received encouragement from William Ritter, a
friend twenty years older than himself, who
combined the talents of musician, art critic,
novelist, watercolourist, cosmopolitan aesthete
and socialite. Ritter introduced him to members
of the local intellectual élite including Cingria
Vaneyre himself, and they met for cultivated
dinners called (with Classical pretension) *agapes*.
Oddly enough there are no references to girl-
friends at this point in Jeanneret's life. His affairs
were either secret, casual or non-existent.

If Ritter opened the doors to highbrow society,
Max Dubois helped Jeanneret with business, and
especially with the commercial possibilities of
reinforced concrete. Dubois was a graduate in
engineering of the Zurich Polytechnic and had
translated Morsch's book *Eisenbeton* into French.
In 1912 he and Jeanneret considered working
together on an electricity plant for the Doubs
river. It was another dead-end but the experience
of synthesizing form and engineering proved
useful. In 1913 Edouard did a proposal for the
Dittisheim Store and Warehouse to stand in the
heart of La Chaux-de-Fonds: a reinforced concrete reinterpretation of a *palazzo* type, with tall
arches for the shop windows and a *piano nobile*
stretched to accommodate recessed floors for
storage above. The composition was framed by
rounded corner piers and crowned by a simplified
cornice. Ideas from Perret, Behrens, possibly

even Louis Sullivan or the Chicago School were combined. Art Nouveau and the Arts and Crafts seemed a long way in Jeanneret's past. In its own modest way the Dittisheim design (unfortunately not built) took its place alongside similar experiments in 'scraped Classicism' being undertaken in the United States and Europe in the years leading up to the First World War.

Among these was the Deutscher Werkbund Pavilion at the Cologne exhibition which Jeanneret visited in the summer of 1914. This was a sophisticated evocation of Werkbund doctrines in concrete, glass, brick and steel laid out over a Classically inspired plan. The spiral glass stairs and Deutzen Motoren Pavilion (with a diesel engine displayed like a cult symbol inside it) were *tours de force* of transparency and mechanized imagery. There were echoes of Wright in the horizontal proportions and hovering overhangs of the main façade. At the same exhibition Bruno Taut's Glass Pavilion used glass bricks, steel and coloured glazing to create a crystalline expressionist fantasy vaguely like a shrine.

It is clear from Jeanneret's notes and correspondence that his earlier misgivings about German technocracy were giving way to a positive acceptance of the idea of unifying form, industrial technique and societal symbol in a way related to the historicist and progressive idea of a machine age. He acquired the Werkbund *Jahrbuch* of 1913 with its evocative photographs of grain silos, factories and battleships, and with its article by Walter Gropius discussing aesthetic form in engineering. This compared the Canadian and American grain silos to monuments of ancient Egypt, rejected 'fits of historical nostalgia' and called for a new style based on bold masses, clear proportions and simple shapes. 'The new times demand their own expression. Exactly stamped form devoid of all accident, clear contrasts, the ordering of members, the arrangement of like parts in series, unity of form and colour ...' The emphasis on primary geometries was entirely in accord with Jeanneret's prejudices, and even with his intuition of substructures in the Classical tradition. But here simple forms were given a specifically 'modern' connotation as one of the keys to a style in harmony with the spirit of the times.

In the summer of 1914 Jeanneret was also in Lyons where he seems to have visited Tony Garnier, the architect, town planner and author of the book *La Cité industrielle* which came out in 1917. In 1914 he was translating part of his ideal city into reality under the patronage of the socialist mayor of Lyons, Edouard Herriot. Garnier had been formulating his urbanistic principles since 1901, and in *La Cité industrielle* he tried to lay out all the problems and solutions of the 'most general case' of the Industrial City. A rationalized system of zoning was used to separate industry from habitation, and he thought of the city as a big park, articulated by axes and regular geometry. There was a civic area towards the centre and small family villas were laid out alongside streets lined with trees. There were also flat-topped apartment buildings with terrace

roofs. Reinforced concrete was used extensively. Garden City principles concerning the sanitary role of nature were rethought in ways which faced up to the techniques, potentials and values of an industrial society, but the whole was pervaded by a latent Classical sense, and the suburbs evoked a dream of Grecian villas. Tafuri has referred to Garnier's Cité Industrielle as 'a New Hellas': 'For him the future was anchored in a past fondly pictured as a Golden Age, as an ideal equilibrium to be won again.'

By 1914 Jeanneret's Sittesque version of the manuscript for *La Construction des villes* seemed hopelessly dated. But he did not abandon the general idea of formulating doctrines for town planning. Soon after his return from Germany and Lyons, he wrote to Dubois: 'I have prepared a tract on ultra modern architecture: concrete, iron, American houses, the Perrets, Tony Garnier, Lyons, reinforced concrete bridges, New York, tramways, etc. I feel I have it in me to be someone one day. I am obsessed with building on a large scale, useful and noble, for that is what architecture is all about.' The tone was almost Futurist, but it is not certain when Jeanneret first heard of Futurist ideas with their romantic celebration of the big city, mechanization, speed and dynamism. The first Futurist manifesto by Tommaso Marinetti had been published in Paris in *Le Figaro littéraire* in February 1909, when Jeanneret had been at Perret's. Later manifestos on painting and sculpture had appeared in French in 1912 and 1913, and in 1914 Antonio Sant'Elias's sketches of a 'Citta Nuova' were exhibited in Milan, accompanied by the 'Messaggio', a plea for a new architecture built of steel, concrete and glass, leaving behind all past traditions, and expressing the spirit of a new mechanized age. The 'Messaggio' visualized a new kind of city, illustrated in some of Sant'Elias's drawings:

'We must invent and rebuild *ex novo* our Modern City like an immense and tumultuous shipyard, active, mobile and everywhere dynamic, and the modern building like a gigantic machine ... lifts must swarm up the façades like serpents of glass and iron. The house of cement, iron and glass, without carved or painted ornament, rich only in the inherent beauty of its lines and modelling, extraordinarily brutish in its mechanical simplicity ... must rise from the brink of a tumultuous abyss; the street itself will no longer lie like a doormat at the level of the thresholds, but plunge storeys deep into the earth, gathering up the traffic of the metropolis ... we must resolve the problem of modern architecture without cribbing photographs of China, Persia, or Japan, not stultifying ourselves with Vitruvian rules, but with strokes of genius, equipped only with a scientific and technological culture ...'

It is unlikely that Jeanneret knew of these ideas as early as 1914. The legacy of Futurism would affect his work after his move to Paris in 1917. Then the intellectual problem, addressed by Purism, would be to combine admiration for 'a scientific and technological culture', with the

36 (*above*) Walter Gropius, Deutscher Werkbund Pavilion, Cologne, 1914.

37 (*above right*) Tony Garnier, villas from *La Cité Industrielle*.

high-mindedness of Werkbund theory, and the intuition of lasting values from the Classical tradition. Meanwhile Jeanneret continued to have flashes of inspiration that were premonitions of later, developed ideas: in one of his sketchbooks, in 1915, he drew a city of skyscrapers surrounded by trees with traffic running between — it was the embryo of his 'Ville Contemporaine' of 1922.

The First World War began in autumn 1914. Edouard was quick to grasp that it might mean the end of an old order and the creation of a world in which modern architecture could be central. He watched from the neutral Swiss sidelines as mechanization — the supposed force for emancipation — was employed for wholesale slaughter in the trenches. He had dreamed of an entente between French cultivation and German efficiency, and instead saw the 'Schlieffen Plan' drive Teutonic industrial might deep into Flanders and the Marne. He naîvely imagined that the war would be finished in a few months and that the reconstruction of the devastated areas could then begin. For this purpose he proposed a rapid construction housing system based on a cheap and standardized concrete skeleton, using rubble for infill walls, and mass-produced windows, doors and fixtures. The houses would be laid out end to end in formal patterns, some of them indented around grassy communal areas. Aesthetic effects would arise from proportions of rectangular volumes, plain mouldings, linear cornices and simple apertures. He called the system Dom-ino, a name that invoked *domus* (Latin for house) and the game of dominoes: in plan the six-point supports set in an oblong did resemble a rectangular domino chip.

Jeanneret excited some interest in his scheme among Flemish Members of Parliament, but the war dragged on. None the less the Dom-ino experiment was seminal in his own evolution as a planner and an architect. His image of the garden

suburb was formal, not unlike Garnier's, but less Hellenic. In style the houses recalled Turkish wooden frame buildings with flat roofs, open terraces and tumbling foliage. There were echoes of his recent experiments in Reductivist Classicism, of Gropius's Werkbund Pavilion and perhaps even of Wright's projects for simple concrete houses. At the time Jeanneret was also studying Benoît Levy's theories on Garden Cities, and these insisted that urban forms should be seen as expressions of their times. In the Dom-ino designs he continued to use a simplified, contemporary style based on the potentials of reinforced concrete.

For Jeanneret's later development, the structural skeleton of the Dom-ino was even more important than the houses. It was formed from three rectangular horizontal slabs supported on six slender stanchions, each square in plan. The bottom slab was on blocks; stairs linked the levels. There were no capitals or beams: the slabs were smooth above and below. The slabs were to be made of pot-tile with steel reinforcing, and to be constructed with the aid of movable shuttering supported on steel 'T' beams. Jeanneret was floundering on the technical aspects of the system until he received help from Dubois, and even a few tips from Perret. The Dom-ino was a different idea from Perret's timber-like frames with their infill panels, because now the slabs cantilevered beyond the edge of the building on their own, leaving the verticals inside to do the structural work. Jeanneret made much of this 'separation of powers'. Liberated from structural constraints the envelope of the building could now be organized to suit aesthetic or climatic demands, or else to fit with criteria of composition or view. Partitions on interiors could be organized independently of the grid, and external walls could even be done away with altogether leaving a building formed from sandwiches of horizontal

38 Dom-ino skeleton 1914–15.

39 Dom-ino house, 1915.

spaces. Admittedly the Dom-ino houses exploited these potentials only slightly (in one or two cases windows were shown daringly placed in corners), but they were to be quite central to Le Corbusier's 'Five Points of New Architecture' in the 1920s (the *piloti*, the free plan, the free façade, the strip window and the roof terrace), and were also to be basic to his urbanistic proposals. 'Grasp the skeleton', Perret had suggested, 'and you grasp the art': now Jeanneret was doing just that, and discovering the nucleus of his later architectural language.

Fourteen years later, in the *Oeuvre complète*, volume I, Le Corbusier published the Dom-ino skeleton on its own. By this time it had taken on the status of an icon of modern architecture. The formal characteristics of what was later called the 'International Style' — hovering horizontal volumes, taut skins, regular lines of supports —

were based on analogous systems in concrete or steel. It may be, as Turner has suggested, that the Dom-ino was a synthesis of two disparate traditions of thought with which Jeanneret had been grappling, the Rationalist and the Idealist. As a generative structural instrument it recalled Perret, Choisy and Viollet-le-Duc; as a crystalline diagram of pure idea and form it embodied L'Eplattenier's search for essentials and the Werkbund conception of an ideal type. The Dom-ino was trabeation in an elemental form — pure column and pure slab — an industrialized equivalent to Laugier's Primitive Hut. One is not surprised by the legend which states that the ageing Le Corbusier kept a picture of the Dom-ino on his wall next to a photograph of the Parthenon: both were central to his lifelong production, and both embodied notions he regarded as fundamental.

40 Charles Edouard Jean-
neret and René Chapallaz,
La Scala Cinema, La Chaux-
de-Fonds, 1916.

But this is to move ahead into lucid territories that were still a long way off in 1915. While the war raged on to the north and Jeanneret confided grandiose ideas to his sketchbooks, he continued to stumble in his practice. In 1915, he and Dubois entered a competition for the Pont Butin over the Rhône near Geneva with a scheme modelled on a Roman viaduct. The following year, Jeanneret designed the exterior of the Scala Cinema in La Chaux-de-Fonds, having taken over the project from Chapallaz in questionable circumstances. His façade solution was a sophisticated overlay of ideas derived from Behrens, Ledoux, Sullivan's Owattana Bank, even (as H. Allen Brooks has suggested) from della Porta's Villa Aldobrandini at Frascati: one can also mention Palladio's church façades in Venice. Whatever the range of sources, they were suavely combined in a composition with pediments, a blank central panel, and a tripartite façade. While this arrangement went well with the layout of a cinema (access gangways at the sides, screen and seats in the middle), it seems to have had a more general appeal to Jeanneret. He used the leitmotiv of a blank central panel in later works, and a variation on the theme recurred in the Maison Schwob of 1916–17.

The Schwobs constituted a virtual dynasty in the watch-making industry in La Chaux-de-Fonds, producing both 'Tavannes Watch' and 'Cyma' brands. They were Jewish (of Alsatian and Russian origin), supported the local synagogue and took an active interest in the arts. A member of the family had been impressed by Jeanneret's parents' house. According to one version, Anatole Schwob spotted a Perret design in Edouard's portfolio and asked for something similar. The building needed to give dignified expression to the local status of the family. The site was on the rue de Doubs at the western end of the grid, close enough to other grand residences to merit a degree of urban formality, yet enough on the outskirts to suggest a suburban

aspect. A diagonal street sliced off one corner of the lot, which sloped from north to south. The site was high enough on the hillside to afford views over the valley. There was an inherent duality between the cold north side facing the street, and the warm south side facing the garden, the long views and the sun.

Jeanneret's first idea was for a symmetrical building with a double-height living room in the centre, flanked by equal-sized apses and preceded by a vestibule: a tidied-up version of his parents' house, but with the flat roof that he had originally intended. To the north the building presented a blank façade to the rue de Doubs, but on the garden side it was opened up by a two-storey window. From the outset he thought of the building in terms of a reinforced concrete frame with a brick infill. Four main piers flanking the grand space were to support most of the weight. A secondary lattice was to carry the double membranes of either brick or glass between which warm air was to be pushed by mechanical means in the winter. The flat roof was sloped slightly inwards to drain melting snow. Pipes were to run down inside the building to avoid freezing. The traditional Jura solution of a steep pitched roof was rejected in favour of a modern device which afforded a purer volume and a usable roof terrace.

As the design developed it became more complicated. The client insisted that the kitchen be brought up out of the basement, so Jeanneret put it in a side wing. Fortunately the resulting asymmetry was useful in dealing with the diagonal street cutting off and approaching the site. Besides, such appendages could be disguised behind a long garden wall. But other complications stemmed from the architect's ambitious intentions. At last he had a commission and he was determined to make the most of it. Maison Schwob is a lexicon of Jeanneret's recent obsessions from concrete to Classicism, from Perret to Palladio. It is both suburban villa and modern *machine à habiter*. Yet despite the surfeit of ideas condensed in it, despite its complex eclecticism, it manages to hold together as a convincing plastic unity and as a fresh (though clumsy) breakthrough towards a personal style.

The main façade is full of teasing contradictions. Seen head-on the central box seems to sit on the slender supports of the canopy, which look too thin for the load above and are also detailed so that a shadow separates capital from slab. There are bizarre leaps in scale between the *oeils de boeuf* windows and the blank central panel. The building has a mysterious air, like the lodge of a secret society, and it is not at all clear which of the two doors one should take as both are apparently the same, although one actually leads to the kitchen and the other to the hall. The façade plane reads as an extension of the garden wall, but also as the preface to the box with turbulent curved volumes pulling back to each side.

To enter one is forced off the main axis, the first of a number of lateral emphases in the design. Once inside, the axis is rediscovered in

41 Villa Schwob, La Chaux-de-Fonds, 1916, view from the north-west.

42 (*left*) Study sketches for Villa Schwob (Bibliothèque de la Ville, La Chaux-de-Fonds).

43 (*below left*) Villa Schwob, south façade, shortly after construction.

44 (*below*) Villa Schwob, ground-floor plan.

the hall. The transition into the double-height living room is handled through a small central door. The space explodes upwards towards the balconies and outwards towards the double-height window, the garden, the sun and the view. A few feet further and one is aware of the cross-axis linking the interior of the apses, one containing the dining room, the other the *salle de jeux*. The lateral emphasis is repeated in a lower key just inside the glass at the back, a library to one side, a nook by the fireplace to the other. In one scheme Jeanneret envisaged ramps descending into the garden each side of the axis, and pavilions in the corners of the site: both Renaissance touches. From the rear the building presents a large rectangle of glass between the wall panels and the apses: a curious collision of mechanical and antique. It is much more than a house: it is a monument.

Many different sources and periods are fused together in Maison Schwob. The debts to Perret and the Werkbund are fairly obvious, and a case can also be made for the impact of Wright on the plan, and of Hoffmann's Villa Ast on the cornice. In Jeanneret's own oeuvre this is a combination of the Dom-ino studies and the various essays in simplified Classicism from 1912 onwards. Even his earliest chalet-like houses had used cross-axes, lateral protrusions and open southern exposures to make the most of winter sun. At Schwob those regionalist responses have been cross-bred with Renaissance domestic typologies. The formal street façade is a twentieth-century version of a palace, and has been related by Rowe to Palladio's small Casa Cogolo in Vicenza. The double-height central space, noble proportions, extending wings and (in project form at least) corner pavilions with symmetrical garden terraces and ramps, invoke a variety of villa examples. 'Une maison, un palais' ('A house, a palace') was to be a catch-phrase of Le Corbusier's in the 1920s, implying the ennoblement of the dwelling through mathematical control and monumental intensity. At Schwob the theme is already evident, but in the service of 'a Classicism for the Jura' (Pls.135, 136).

Various non-Classical sources can also be related to the house with feasibility. The theme of the central blank panel with small side entrances occurs in a fountain that Jeanneret took the time to photograph in Istanbul during his travels. The slender tapering columns under the canopy crop up in his sketchbooks, transcribed directly from *L'Art antique de la Perse* by Dieulafoy. The curious bisected window low down in the main façade is close to windows he had sketched in Nuremberg in 1907. And the plan with a central rectangle and extending apses recalls numerous Byzantine or Venetian ecclesiastical exemplars. Linear mouldings and canted cornices like those on Maison Schwob had been sketched on the Voyage d'orient, and it is clear that Jeanneret wanted the house to be covered in greenery like ones he had noted in the Balkans and in Turkey. Among his travel photographs there was one showing a garden wall flush with a façade, vines poking invitingly over the garden wall to one side — an effect repeated in the rue de Doubs elevation where the pergolas peek over the rim.

Jeanneret had the sort of mind that could compress observations and transform them into new terms, and by 1916 certain key schemata picked up from tradition were already becoming distinctly his own. A longitudinal section through Maison Schwob echoes his sectional sketches of the Monastery of Ema, with double-height cells preceded by a covered walkway, and an upper gallery looking down over nature. This arrangement took on the status of an emblem of the ideal life. Variations on it would recur in the Maison Citrohan and 'immeubles villas' of 1922, and in the unités d'habitation of the 1950s. The conception of a house as a closed urban façade, a tight vestibule, then an expansion of spaces experienced as a sequence and culminating in a garden at the rear, may have been a re-interpretation of what Jeanneret had seen at Pompeii. Buildings like the House of the Tragic Poet (which he had sketched carefully) seem to have corresponded to Mediterranean archetypes of the dwelling in his imagination. Variations on the Schwob scheme, accentuating the contrast between formal entrance façade and more open garden façade would be made in many villas of the 1920s and even as late as the Millowners' Building in Ahmedabad of the 1950s. Jeanneret was here revealing his capacity to penetrate to substructures in tradition, then to manipulate, compress and fuse the resultant types into new syntheses — a procedure that would remain quite basic to his creative method. It would have resulted in facile collages of quotations if he had not been able to transform sources into new symbolic forms deeply embedded in his own myths, ideology and philosophy of life.

Maison Schwob might well have established Jeanneret's professional reputation in the Jura; as it was, it nearly undermined it. His budgeting calculations were slovenly, and construction costs escalated drastically. Smears were made against him, squabbles occurred over fees, and it all degenerated into a legal case. This was the last straw and Jeanneret made his exit to Paris. Maison Schwob entered the folklore of La Chaux-de-Fonds as 'la Villa Turque'.

Despite these calamities, the mature Le Corbusier would look back on the building with pride. Of all his juvenile experiments it was the one he was happy to associate with his later production. He published it in *Vers une architecture* (1923) in the chapter on 'Regulating Lines', showing how its proportions were established by harmonious geometries; he also included it in volume I of the *Oeuvre complète* (1929). A synthesis of the themes and obsessions which had dominated his years of youthful adventure and discovery, Maison Schwob was also a breakthrough in his quest for an authentic modern architecture rooted in age-old principles. As Julien Caron would write in the early 1920s in the magazine *L'Esprit Nouveau*: '... it constitutes a beacon for the architectural aesthetic of our time ... The villa of Le Corbusier is more than a house. It is an architecture.'

45 (*opposite*) Villa Schwob, detail of apse.

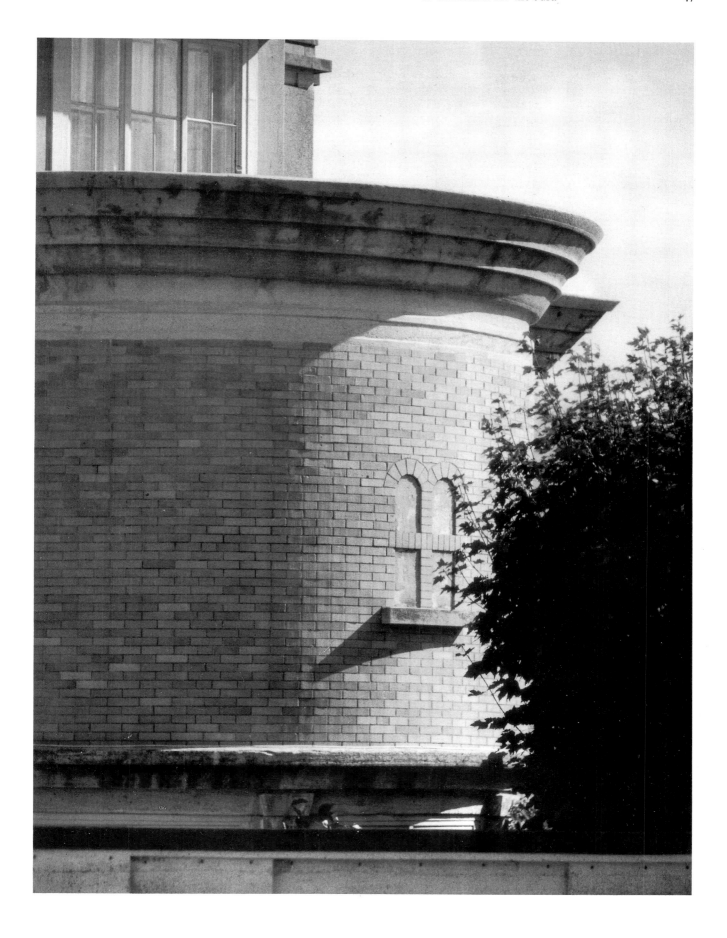

Chapter 4

Paris, Purism and 'L'Esprit Nouveau'

'For deep in every revolution, discreetly hidden, resides a Classicism, which is a form of constant.'
Amédée Ozenfant

Individual artists create movements but movements also reveal new possibilities to individuals, and by 1916 Charles Edouard Jeanneret was thirsty for contact with the ideas of the French avant-garde. The ensuing six years were ones of crystallization, in which he laid down many of the themes in painting, architecture, urbanism and theory that would guide his life's work. A clear direction was helped by his contact with Cubism and his exchange of ideas with Ozenfant. But Jeanneret lived a double life. On the outside he was the struggling bohemian supporting himself with a range of jobs and rickety commercial ventures; inside, he was teeming with grandiose visions of a new social order contained in utopian urban plans and pristine architectural forms. Without commissions of significance he was forced to channel his dreams into drawings, paintings and theories.

Edouard's move to Paris in the winter of 1916–17 was certainly not discouraged by the mess over the Maison Schwob. Max Dubois put him in touch with a company which dealt with a wide range of jobs using reinforced concrete, the Société d'Applications du Béton Armé, where he started work in January 1917. During his first year of consultancy he designed a water tower at Podensac and worked on an arsenal, a hydroelectric plant and a project for an industrial slaughterhouse at Challuy. In this, simple functional volumes were laid out along an axis of conveyors dramatized in sloping bridges. Concrete mushroom columns and ramps were used on the interiors. Jeanneret also designed workers' housing for the outskirts of Saintes (translating some of the Dom-ino ideas) and for St-Nicholas-d'Aliermont near Dieppe, where he attempted to transform local vernacular types into a Garden City layout (virtually nothing was constructed). He opened his own studio in rue Belzune but this served principally as a laboratory for private ideas. It was hardly the best moment to set up a practice: with the outcome of the war uncertain, clients were not about to risk investing in new construction. To help pay the bills Jeanneret ran a brick factory, but this was periodically flooded by the Seine and went bust.

As an adolescent Edouard had dreamed of becoming a painter. In 1918 this ambition was rekindled when he met Amédée Ozenfant. Ozenfant was a habitué of the Parisian *haut monde* who ran a fashion shop, was interested in modern painting and photography, and also dabbled in poetry, anthropology and philosophy. He was equally at home with Hispano Suiza automobiles or the ideas on 'duration' of Henri Bergson, and introduced the hesitant Swiss *immigré* to the ideas, forms and personalities of the post-Cubist avant-garde, including Guillaume Apollinaire and Fernand Léger. Despite the havoc being wrought by modern weaponry within earshot of Paris, Jeanneret and Ozenfant were united in some vague expectation that a new era was about to dawn in which mechanization would be a force for the good. They were even capable of praising the 'rigour' and 'precision' of captured German artillery on show in the boulevards.

Through Ozenfant, Jeanneret was forced to grapple with the inheritance of Cubism; more than that, he had to confront the entire change of sensibility brought about by Cézanne's penetration to the geometrical substructures of nature and by the Symbolists' idea that the work of art should act directly on the senses without recourse to clumsy representation. L'Eplattenier's training prepared Jeanneret for these points of view but not for the complex plastic syntax of Cubism, nor for the mechanistic romanticism of Futurism. In the years since the Futurist manifestos and exhibitions before the war the Parisian avant-garde had attempted to fuse lessons from Braque and Picasso with a rhythmic and abstract, rather than merely realistic, evocation of the poetry of modern life. Among the key figures in this transition were the Delaunays, Duchamp, Metzinger, Juan Gris and Fernand Léger. Gris absorbed from the 'Section d'Or' ('Golden Section') group an interest in proportional systems and symbolic mathematics. These lofty concerns were combined with fragments of modern reality. Léger conveyed the impact of the machine in bold contrast of forms, primary colours and metallic lighting effects. By 1917 his restless prewar style had been replaced by a static monu-

46 *Still Life with Stacked Plates*, 1920. Oil on canvas, 32 x 34¼ in. (81 x 99.7 cm.). New York, Museum of Modern Art, Van Gogh Purchase Fund.

mentality, a shift well represented by paintings like *The City*, in which flanges of pure colour were spliced together with vignettes of the industrial landscape. Both Gris and Léger showed that it was possible to symbolize Futurist myths in hieratic forms.

The transition from a faltering Jura regionalism to the sensibility of the Parisian avant-garde was a shock for Jeanneret, and he looked to Ozenfant, who seemed so self-assured, for direction. In fact Ozenfant was only slightly older but he took Jeanneret by the hand and encouraged him to paint. In the autumn of 1918, just after the Armistice, they exhibited together at the Galerie Thomas; or, to be precise, two canvases by Jeanneret were hung alongside many more by Ozenfant. They called themselves 'Purists' and the catalogue was a joint effort entitled *Après le Cubisme* (*After Cubism*). It was a manifesto inveighing against the bizarre, decorative aspects of Cubism in favour of logic, clarity, simplicity and calm order. The Classical tradition in painting was drawn in as a pedigree: Seurat, Ingres, Poussin, Piero della Francesca and Platonic aesthetic theories all figured in the Purist Pantheon. 'Classicism' was treated as a repository of higher formal values rather than a direct source of subject-matter. The spirit was conveyed by the reflection that: 'The work of art must not be accidental, exceptional, impressionistic, inorganic, protestatory, picturesque, but, on the contrary, generalized, static, expressive of the invariant.'

The paintings in the exhibition did not do justice to the intellectual programme. Ozenfant's were merely competent extensions of Braque or Gris, and Jeanneret's curious still life *La Cheminée* might have been done by any realist intent on formal simplification. But by 1920 he was able to paint a picture of stunning concentrated power like the *Still Life with Stacked Plates*. In this, the puzzling fragmented world of early Cubism was reintegrated, machined, polished and endowed with static, mathematical precision. Banal, everyday objects were reduced to the most generalized curves and rectangles, then disposed in flat planes parallel to the picture surface. The pictorial conception was not perspectival, but resembled an engineering drawing where the elevation and plan of an object might be included together on the same sheet. The Cubist principle of fusing different views was here regularized: the bottle-top for example was treated as a pure circle. Objects and surfaces were contained in their outlines and were spliced together with purely abstract shapes in flat layers. Colour was also restricted by boundaries, and was painted in after the contour had been fixed in a drawing, whereas in analytical Cubism the method had been integral: take the colour away and nothing is left. The Purist range of colours included electric blues, light greys, pinks, ochres, earth reds, greens, black and white. Light was even, pearly and opalescent (Pl.141).

Jeanneret's painting vocabulary — like his architectural one — pulled together a variety of sources. Despite the anti-Cubist rhetoric, part of the tension between figure and ground in the work derived from his understanding of spatial ambiguities in Cubism. The ambition of finding a static order behind contemporary existence owed as much to Seurat. And like Seurat, Jeanneret and Ozenfant treated painting in quasi-scientific terms, exploring theories of colour and light as well as the idea that certain proportions and geometries might guarantee beauty. The Purists studied the Renaissance too, particularly Piero della Francesca, a master of mathematical forms and lyrical lighting. One wonders if they also knew of Renaissance theories of painting. In Leon Battista Alberti's writings they could have found an emphasis on 'disegno' (design by drawing) which corroborated their own notion that drawn outline should carry the essence of a formal idea.

The Purists thought that neither the human figure nor landscape were relevant to their aims, and were also suspicious of Mondrian's non-objective painting. They wished to portray familiar everyday objects and to raise these to the level of symbols by extracting their most generalized characteristics. Still life — the lowest genre in academies — was elevated to a role in which it would crystallize the heroics of modern life. In their attitudes to form the Purists revealed an idealistic pedigree, for they believed that painting could penetrate to a higher idea beyond the flux of appearances. Their obsession with the 'typical' also recalled Werkbund theories about mass-produced items for a new machine-age civilization, and in this respect there was a deep link between the bottles, pipes and glasses of the pictures, and the elements of Le Corbusier's later architecture, as if *pilotis*, strip windows, skyscrapers, etc. were themselves inevitable crystallizations of the basic realities of industrialism. They wrote:

'… objects tend towards a type that is determined by the evolution of forms between the ideal of maximum utility and the necessities of economical manufacture which conforms inevitably to the laws of nature. This double play of laws results in the creation of a certain number of objects that may be called standardized.'

Purist painting was important for architecture in other ways too; it supplied a visual language which answered to private intuitions and to demands of 'modernity' simultaneously, while also touching 'constants' that Edouard dearly believed to be universal. The rectangles, curves, proportions, spaces and colours of the paintings might infuse the plan, section, façade or interiors of a building. It was not a case of copying from easel to drawing-board, but of treating painting as a laboratory in which forms could be brought to the surface that might inform architecture in a separate but linked process of creation. Rather as the La Chaux-de-Fonds ornaments had been 'microcosms' of regionalism, the Purist paintings were 'microcosms' of Jeanneret's new, Olympian ideals for an age of harmony.

The Purists were not alone in regarding paint-ing as a key to a new architecture. In Holland the de Stijl movement was attempting to extract an entire design vocabulary from the rectilinear, spiritual abstractions of Mondrian and van Doesburg. In Russia the architectural avant-garde drew on Gabo's Constructivist experiments, Malevich's Suprematist abstractions and El Lissitzky's Elementarist paintings in its search for a post-revolutionary symbolism. At the Bauhaus (especially after 1922), the educational programme incorporated painting and sculpture as 'basic design' disciplines. A common theme emerged: the 'essence of the times' was to be revealed in a naked and universal language of geometry infused with the utopian sentiment of salvation via mechanization. Purism occupied a special position in the spectrum of post-war avant-gardes, implying cultural renewal through industrialization, but without the revolutionary politics of Constructivism, and avoiding altogether the post-war cynicism of the Dadaists. It posed as a quasi-spiritual movement above the messy conflicts of class and political ideology, and in some ways was even restorative. As Von Moos suggests: 'It glorified logic, culture and technological progress … the time had come for a new era of post-war reconstruction in all fields based upon reason and idealism.'

Relatively little is known about Jeanneret's struggling years from 1917 up to 1923 when he worked on his first Parisian architectural commissions. He was often short of money and it was not just out of respect for bohemian convention that he lived in a garret high above rue Jacob in the Quartier Latin. In 1918 he lost the sight of one eye, a traumatic event with unknown repercussions for his art. Perhaps monocular vision was partly responsible for curious spatial ambiguities in his painting and architecture. On his friendships with women we continue to draw a blank until 1922 or 1923 when he met Yvonne Gallis, his later wife. His sketchbooks of around 1917 contain gaudy bordello scenes which Ozenfant characterized as 'humorous gouaches, caricatures, somewhat Venetian in tone, and extremely baroque … scenes of brothels, peopled with corpulent bodies of women.' However, these indulgences were well disguised in Jeanneret's carefully arranged persona. Perret described him as a 'drôle type' — an odd fellow — which he certainly seemed with his dark, clerical suits, his gaunt birdlike features, and his wire spectacles. Dubois arranged many introductions for his friend, especially among the Swiss circle in Paris. In this way Jeanneret met Raoul La Roche, a banker with a great interest in art who was to help the Purists in their publishing ventures, buy their paintings, and even employ them to bid at the famous Kahnweiler auctions in which La Roche acquired a stunning collection of Cubist and post-Cubist art. As we shall see La Roche was later to have a house designed by Edouard. Modern architecture was to emerge in the cracks and crevices of the chaotic bourgeois city, and Jeanneret was already making connections with well-placed people who might become clients. Then there was the intangible flavour of the post-war years in the French capital: the relief at victory combined with a gnawing vacuum; the feeling that an old order had been swept away, but the anxiety that something worthy should replace it.

In 1920 Jeanneret and Ozenfant founded the magazine *L'Esprit Nouveau*. In all twenty-eight numbers would appear in the next five years, devoted to themes of 'living aesthetics'. There would be articles by André Salmon, Theo van Doesburg, Louis Aragon, Jean Cocteau and Charles Henry — the last being director of the laboratory of perception at the Ecole des Beaux-Arts. His theories attempted to show that there were direct links between certain lines, proportions, forms and colours and structures within the mind; this appealed to Jeanneret's belief in 'constants' behind appearances. The magazine signalled a 'rappel à l'ordre' ('recall to order'), published various international figures (Adolf Loos's article of 1908 attacking ornament appeared, as did some of the de Stijl manifestos), and also functioned as the mouthpiece of the two Purist artists themselves. They published under pseudonyms. Ozenfant chose his mother's maiden name 'Saugnier', but Jeanneret's equivalent would have been 'Perret', so to avoid confusion they came up with the idea of using an ancestral name from the south-west of France: 'Lecorbesier'. At Ozenfant's suggestion this became the more impressive 'Le Corbusier'. The name echoed the word 'corbeau' — raven — a bird that Edouard certainly resembled, but also recalled a grand heritage of French artists: Le Brun, Le Nôtre, etc. It had an affirmative yet objective tone as if referring to a historical phenomenon rather than just an individual man.

The first edition of the magazine proclaimed that there was 'a new spirit ... a spirit of construction and of synthesis guided by a clear conception'. A number of ensuing articles were on architecture, and these were eventually gathered together and published as the book *Vers une architecture* (*Towards an Architecture*) in 1923. The title is often mistranslated *Towards a New Architecture*, but this gives the false impression that the author was interested in modernity only; in fact he was also concerned with restating lessons from tradition. *Vers une architecture* did not try to argue theses in a straightforward, logical way. It made its points through pithy aphorisms and stunning visual analogies between such disparate things as temples and cars, palaces and factories, car advertisements, scholarly diagrams and free-hand sketches. The book illustrated the touchstones and obsessions of an artist's creative myth; it was like a map of some complex mental landscape of the imagination. It presented Le Corbusier's philosophy of architecture and displayed a few projects (this had the intended effect of attracting clients). It also established the author in the international avant-garde alongside figures like Theo van Doesburg, El Lissitzky and Walter Gropius. The underlying theme of a grandiose synthesis between mechanization and universal formal values touched a general mood.

One of the main ideas is laid out at the beginning: that contemporary architecture is in a state of decay because it is buried under stylistic frivolities and has lost touch with the great primary values of masses in light, proportion, fitness to purpose and the clear expression of plan ideas in moving sequences of spaces. It argues that a new culture is coming about based on the machine, but that this has not yet found its true architectural and urban form. Hints in the direction of a correct modern language are given by 'the first fruits of the new age', silos, factories, liners, aeroplanes and cars; even by objects such as filing cabinets, bowler hats and briar pipes. But for all their sober harmony these objects lack the sublime order of 'architecture pure creation of the mind'. The task, then, is to blend the images embodying the *Zeitgeist* of the machine age with 'constants' abstracted from great works of the past such as the Parthenon or the Pantheon. Unless an appropriate synthesis is made, the result will be urban disarray, social chaos, even revolution. But if the 'Esprit Nouveau' is allowed to pervade painting, furniture, houses, cities — in fact, all the equipment of the new epoch — then harmony will reign between man, machine and nature.

Vers une architecture has been called 'one of the most influential, widely read and least understood of all the architectural writings of the twentieth century'. It was neither just a work of theory nor just a manifesto, but a mixture of the two which also pulled together the various strands of the architect's formation: echoes of Provensal, Perret, Werkbund theory, travel experiences and Purism are found throughout. Nor was it a functionalist tract as some have tried to claim: Le Corbusier makes it clear that a solid understanding of programme and structure are mere prerequisites for the higher ambition of Architecture, 'a thing of the emotions ... outside questions of construction and beyond them'. He defines architecture in lofty terms which recall the Idealist aesthetics of Purism and his earliest readings.

'Architecture is the masterly, correct and magnificent play of volumes brought together in light. Our eyes are made to see forms in light ... cubes, cones, spheres, cylinders or pyramids are the great primary forms that light reveals to advantage ... It is of the very nature of the plastic arts.'

The 'Three Reminders to Messrs. Architects', 'mass', 'surface' and 'plan', are all concerned with the problems of unity and integration, and are liberally illustrated with diverse historical examples. The idea of the plan as generator is reinforced by Choisy drawings of Indian temples, Hagia Sophia, and the Acropolis (among others); while the conception of proportional 'Regulating Lines' is illustrated by the Capitoline Palace in Rome, the Petit Trianon, the façade of Notre Dame, some dubious historical reconstructions of a gate at Piraeus, and the Villa Schwob. Since his Ruskin days, Edouard had shifted ground towards the great primary values of geometry.

L'*Aquitania*. Cunard Line.

A MM. les Architectes : Une villa sur les dunes de Normandie, conçue comme ces navires, serait plus seyante que les grands « toits normands » si vieux, si vieux ! Mais on pourrait prétendre que ceci n'est point du style maritime !

L'*Aquitania*. Cunard Line.

Aux architectes : La valeur d'un long promenoir, volume satisfaisant, intéressant; l'unité de matière, le bel agencement d'éléments constructifs, sainement exposés et assemblés avec unité.

Il y a des formes simples déclancheuses de sensations constantes.

Des modifications interviennent, dérivées, et conduisent la sensation première (de l'ordre majeur au mineur), avec toute la gamme intermédiaire des combinaisons. Exemples :

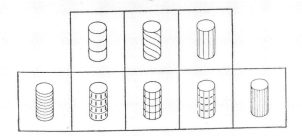

47 (*above*) Liners from *Vers une architecture*.

48 (*above right*) Plate from *L'Esprit Nouveau* showing primary volumes, Ancient Rome and secondary articulation of cylinders.

PAESTUM, de 600 à 550 av. J.-C.

Le Parthénon est un produit de sélection appliquée à un standart établi. Depuis un siècle déjà, le temple grec était organisé dans tous ses éléments.

Lorsqu'un standart est établi, le jeu de la concurrence immédiate et violente s'exerce. C'est le match; pour gagner, il faut

Cliché de *La Vie Automobile*.   HUMBERT, 1907.

Cliché Albert Morancé.   PARTHÉNON, de 447 à 434 av. J.-C.

faire mieux que l'adversaire *dans toutes les parties*, dans la ligne d'ensemble et dans tous les détails. C'est alors l'étude poussée des parties. Progrès.

Le standart est une nécessité d'ordre apporté dans le travail humain.

Le standart s'établit sur des bases certaines, non pas arbi-

DELAGE, Grand-Sport 1921.

49 Temples and cars from *Vers une architecture*: the evolution of 'standards'.

Thus, Egyptian, Greek and Roman examples are praised and the Gothic Cathedral (except for Notre Dame) finds itself relegated to a secondary level. It is also notable that he has next to nothing to say about regionalism, climate or inspiration from nature. He now aspires to a supposedly universal grammar of design, above place and time.

Le Corbusier felt that the Classical Orders were dead, a defunct symbolic system, that needed to be replaced by a new set of conventions for the machine age. But he certainly did not advocate throwing tradition away completely. In fact he even seemed to think that the purification of the machine was on the point of realizing fundamentals of Classicism such as proportion, repose, tightness of idea and form, in a new language. *Vers une architecture* abounds in mechanical metaphors and analogies. 'The machine' becomes an idea, a major instrument of the world process and an icon of the *Zeitgeist*. Le Corbusier was here drawing on a long philosophical tradition for comparing the workings of the universe to a mechanism functioning according to precise laws. Similarly the idea of a house as a 'machine à habiter', a 'machine for living in', did not mean reducing the dwelling to a merely utilitarian object, but sublimating practical concerns to the level of a sort of analogue of universal order.

Rather as Adolf Loos claimed that the engineer was a species of noble savage, creating the unselfconscious yet true folklore of the modern period in bridges and tools, so Le Corbusier looked upon ships, aeroplanes and cars as more genuine expressions of the times than the style-bound creations of official architecture. The captions in *Vers une architecture* associate the pristine forms of ships with moral values like temerity, efficiency, and purity. Aeroplanes are praised as rigorous solutions to new problems, employing modern means, and cars are regarded as examples for the house designer because they are based on type elements or 'standards' that are conceptually clear, functionally appropriate and mass-producible. There are echoes here of pre-war Werkbund ideas and images (actually some of the illustrations in *Vers une architecture* were taken from the *1913 Jahrbuch* and retouched to make them look even simpler). As Behrens had done, Le Corbusier insisted on the importance of fusing the mechanical and the Classical. One of the strongest comparisons in *Vers une architecture* is that between the relatively crude 'Basilica' at Paestum (sixth century BC) and the Parthenon (fifth century BC), with a Humber automobile of 1907 facing a Delage sports car of 1921 underneath. This has the double effect of suggesting that forms based on standards evolve inevitably towards perfection (Le Corbusier's historical thought abounds in Darwinian fictions), and of implying some necessary connection between the kit of parts of a temple (columns, triglyphs, mouldings, etc.) and the kit of parts of a car (wheels, chassis, lamps, etc.). Le Corbusier hopes that the elements of the machine-age house will be defined with similar clarity, and that it too will then evolve towards perfection:

'Let us display then the Parthenon and the motor car so that it may be clear that it is a question of two products of selection in different fields, one of which has reached its climax and the other is evolving. That ennobles the automobile. And what then? Well then, it remains to use the motor car as a challenge to our houses and our great buildings. It is here that we come to a dead stop: 'Rien ne va plus'. Here we have no Parthenons.'

The interweaving of modern and ancient is one of the basic ideas of *Vers une architecture*, and after his sermon on the supposed moral values of the machine, Le Corbusier comes to a section entitled simply 'Architecture' which is broken down into three parts: 'The Lesson of Rome', 'The Illusion of Plans' and 'Architecture Pure Creation of the Mind'. The main theme is the return to basics in tradition and it is supported by sketches of ancient buildings from the Voyage d'orient, and by a series of superb written evocations of the houses at Pompeii, the mosque at Bursa, the Pantheon, the apses at St Peter's, etc. Le Corbusier misses no chance to denigrate the 'Rome of Horrors' which is largely post-Baroque and nineteenth-century, as well as to attack that 'cancer', the French academy in Rome. The Ecole des Beaux-Arts comes in for repeated knocks, although via Perret, Gaudet and Garnier he had absorbed some ideas from this institution. The whole point of 'The Lesson of Rome' is to show that official architecture is out of touch with the true Classical sense which Le Corbusier felt he knew about from his travels. One of the most telling images of this chapter is a free-hand sketch showing Ancient Rome, the Pantheon, the Colosseum, the Pyramid of Cestius, etc., above which are drawn very precisely, the primary Platonic solids of cylinder, pyramid, cube, oblong and sphere. It seems to illustrate young Jeanneret's extraordinary daydream mentioned at the end of Chapter 2, (when he had a vision of prisms in the Roman sunlight), as well as the conviction that the Purist imagination was on the point of rediscovering perennial values. Whether Le Corbusier knew it or not, his little diagram placed him in a grand vista of Classical thought extending back through Boullée and Ledoux to Alberti and Palladio, and well represented by Christopher Wren when he wrote: 'There are two causes of beauty — natural and customary — geometrical figures are naturally more beautiful than irregular ones ...' In the same spirit Le Corbusier's 'Primitive Temple' in *Vers une architecture* was a geometrical abstraction (not a log hut like Laugier's), imitating the mathematical harmony of natural order.

The section called 'The Illusion of Plans' castigates the Beaux-Arts for cranking out graphic tricks with stars and axes, rather than making plans that register the impulse of true intentions. Le Corbusier sees a good plan as a meaningful hierarchy of ideas which, projected into space and mass, generate a 'promenade architecturale' of experiences linked to the building's meaning.

Among the exemplars of this is, of course, the Acropolis with its sequence of views gradually revealing the sculptural life of the building and its radiation to the setting. The climax of *Vers une architecture* is surely 'Architecture Pure Creation of the Mind', which is devoted almost exclusively to the Parthenon, portrayed in a stunning montage of near and far views (some of the photographs are from Collignon, Mansell and Boissonas's book on the Parthenon of 1912). The effect of these images and their captions is almost like a film — an analogue to the dynamic experience of a building from various points of view, and to the flux of thought and feeling as the artist recalls one of his most profound architectural experiences.

Even when he had first seen the Parthenon in 1911, Edouard had compared it to a machine and had spoken in awe of the building's divine mathematics. *Vers une architecture* compares the mouldings to 'polished steel' and praises the 'unity of aim', 'the precise relationships' and 'the sacrifice of all that is accidental'. Le Corbusier rejects merely Rationalist theories which overstress the role of construction, demeans the comparison sometimes made between the columns and trees, and ridicules pompous academies for treating the Parthenon as a canonical work without discussing its distinguishing sculptural virtues. Instead he praises the Parthenon as being a 'pure création de l'esprit', in which every line, moulding, contour and shadow is alive with energy. The guiding idea spreads its way through every part and detail, and even seems to draw the landscape and sea into the composition. The Parthenon is the paragon to which Le Corbusier aspires, and he heads the chapter with a marvellous profession of faith:

'You employ stone, wood and concrete and with these materials you build houses and palaces: that is construction. Ingenuity is at work.

But suddenly you touch my heart, you do me good, I am happy and I say: 'This is beautiful'. That is architecture. Art enters in …

These shapes are such that they are clearly related in light. The relationships between them have not necessarily any reference to what is practical or descriptive. They are a mathematical creation of your mind. They are the language of architecture.

By the use of inert materials and *starting from* conditions more or less utilitarian, you have established certain relationships which have aroused my emotions. That is architecture.'

So far it might almost be thought that Le Corbusier had completely forgotten the Rationalist themes of his formative years. But throughout *Vers une architecture* it is simply taken for granted that one has to define the tasks and technologies appropriate to modern industrial conditions and then find the right forms. Thus the early section on 'plan' includes Garnier's Cité Industrielle and some urban schemes for high-rise buildings of Le Corbusier's own, and implies that it is now necessary to set the 'plan' of a new civilization, while the last part of the book is given over entirely to 'Mass-Production Houses', presented as a means of salvation for a society 'oscillating dangerously out of gear'. The Domino Houses are illustrated at some length, as are more recent experiments such as the vaulted asbestos and concrete Monol Houses of 1919, and the whitewashed cubic Citrohan of 1920–2. The illustrations mostly showed industrial garden suburbs, but Le Corbusier was already thinking in much more grandiose terms, as will be shown in the next chapter.

'Citrohan' was a pun on 'Citroën' — a house like a car. Le Corbusier hoped to mass-produce the pieces of the building by Taylorized methods like those being used in automobile factories. Housing shortages in post-war France were a critical matter, and the architect was directing his ideas at government agencies and industrialists as much as at private clients. The stance — like so much else about *Vers une architecture* — recalled the Werkbund idea of defining a type that would improve the tenor of social life through its appropriateness and restrained beauty. The Citrohan embodied the conception of a 'machine à habiter' — a 'machine for living in' — a functional tool raised to the level of art through judicious proportions, fine spaces and the stripping away of pointless decoration and purposeless habits. It was a utopian challenge to the status quo.

The Maison Citrohan was cubic with a flat roof, a double-height living room and a large area of factory glazing; in the later version the box was raised on stilts to liberate the soil beneath for parking but also to suggest independence from the terrain. The bare interiors responded to the demands made in the 'Manual of the Dwelling' (a subsection of *Vers une architecture*) for healthy, well-lit spaces, contact with nature and a rigorously worked out plan. In line with Purist pretensions to universality, the Citrohan was intended for everyone everywhere: an abstract product of technology above differences of region. In fact, it seemed to be directed at the habits of an artist monk: the Parisian studio type of house (with large north glazing) cross-bred with the cell of the monastery of Ema. There were Mediterranean overtones in the whitewashed cube and nautical ones in the terraces like decks, but the section with a gallery slung along the back of a double-height living room was also inspired by a working men's café in Paris.

The image of the Citrohan haunted Le Corbusier's house designs of the 1920s, and its layout was also the basic unit of the apartment houses of his ideal city of 1922, the Ville Contemporaine. In 1922-3 he at last received commissions that allowed him to put his hypotheses to the test. One of these came from Georges Besnus who had been impressed by a model of the Citrohan at the Salon d'Automne of 1922, and had said that he wanted something similar. But the eventual site was at Vaucresson in the western suburbs of Paris and demanded quite a different solution, especially as it was a whole storey higher on the garden side than on the street. Instead of a Citrohan, Besnus got a 'modern middle-class version of the Petit Trianon at Versailles'. The

50 Maison Monol, 1919.

51 Model of Maison Citrohan, 1921–2.

52 Villa Besnus, Vaucresson, 1922–3.

main block facing the garden was symmetrical, with ledges either side for sculptures, and windows composed with 'Regulating Lines'. Schematically this elevation echoed the proportions of solids to voids in the Trianon in a striking way, but these Classical resonances were made in a vocabulary very different from that of the Maison Schwob six years earlier. Mouldings were almost completely shorn away, leaving smooth plaster surfaces which were painted white. Simple industrial windows were set flush with the façade plane. The roof was flat, and this too reinforced the prismatic character of the building. In an early version of the design the stair was expressed as a curved volume attached at 90° to the main part of the building, and in his notes Le Corbusier made much of his discovery that he could turn the element around and blend it into a single unified oblong. The resulting street façade combines symmetries and asymmetries with advancing and receding planes. The dynamic composition hints at the 'free plan' within.

Le Corbusier's other early commission came from his friend Ozenfant who had a vested interest in helping him to realize his ideals. He needed a combined house and studio, and his plot was on a corner between avenue Reille and a diagonal alleyway in the fourteenth arrondissement in an area already populated by artists' studio houses in various exotic styles. As the Citrohan had been partly derived from the 'atelier-maison' type in the first place, it was here quite fitting. But it still needed adjusting to a tight urban lot which gave only two exposed façades and made an awkward wedge shape towards the rear.

Le Corbusier placed the caretaker's flat and the garage at ground level, the domestic functions on the first floor and the double-height studio on top. The site provided both north and east exposure and this permitted extensive glazing without problems of glare and heat gain. On the other side of the avenue was a reservoir behind an embankment, and the large windows high up the building permitted a full enjoyment of this view. Light, space and greenery would be central concerns of Le Corbusier's urbanism and in his house designs he did all he could to make these rare urban commodities available to the inhabitants. The studio was lit from above through sawtooth factory windows, the light then being filtered into the painter's work space through a smoked glass ceiling. Apertures and wall planes were again detailed to appear taut and weightless. Mullions were varied in thickness and size to activate the surfaces, give hierarchy to the composition of rectangles (again laid out with regulating proportions), and to dramatize the approach of two large glass surfaces at the corner.

The entrance up to the dwelling was announced by the spiralling concrete stair detailed so that it read as a thin, curling plane. Echoing various curves in the context, it graphically described an ascending path before feeding one into the box where a tight vestibule offered a choice between the main apartment or another, interior spiral stair continuing to the studio above. Within this luminous space, delicate tubular steel ladders

continued the tortuous 'promenade architecturale' to mezzanine landings, one of them
resembling a piece off the bridge of a ship. The
fusion of abstract geometry and mechanical
references duplicated the strategy of Purist
painting but with actual objects in three dimensions. Pure curves bathed in light echoed one
another across a liberated interior space. Each
level of the building was laid out independently of
the others, a tentative exploration of the 'free
plan' allowed by concrete floors. Partitions and
stairs were jointed together neatly like gears and
levers in a watch.

The Ozenfant Studio was a small fragment of
Le Corbusier's machine-age dream: a limpid
shrine dedicated to L'Esprit Nouveau. The
glazing had to be made specially by hand to look
mass-produced; tubular railings and metal companion ladders evoked the era of steam power.
Thonet chairs, guitars, a Purist still life stated the
morality of sober 'objets-types'. Through an
intense abstraction, naked industrial facts were
transformed into icons of a new way of life. The
studio was evidence that Le Corbusier was at last
able to translate his vision of a new architecture
into a haunting and tangible reality.

55 Ozenfant's Studio
looking north over avenue
Reille towards the reservoir.

53 (*opposite above*)
Amédée Ozenfant and his
wife, Le Corbusier and
Yvonne Gallis (his future
wife) in the 1920s.

54 (*opposite below*) Maison
Ozenfant, Paris, 1923.

PART II
ARCHITECTURAL IDEALS
AND SOCIAL REALITIES
1922 – 1944

Chapter 5

Defining Types for the New Industrial City

'Architectonic arrangements vary according to the nature and form of the society whose image they are. In every age they express the fundamentals that constitute the social state ...'
Victor Considérant

By 1923 Le Corbusier had succeeded in synthesizing the strands of his formative years into a personal vocabulary which he believed to be rooted in the conditions of industrial society. His whitewashed cubic villas and studios of the early to mid-1920s with their metal window frames, chunky hardware and bold geometries possessed the freshness and slight crudeness of strong innovations. They took their place alongside other exploratory works of the modern movement, such as Gerrit Rietveld's Schroeder House of 1922-4, Mies van der Rohe's Brick Villa proposal of 1923, Walter Gropius's Weimar Bauhaus Office interior of the same year, or Rudolph Schindler's Lovell Beach House of 1922-4. In retrospect one sees these as first steps towards what historians later called — oversimply — the 'International Style'.

While Le Corbusier exchanged ideas with his contemporaries, he gave more than he received. There is only limited value in demonstrating that he shared elements of period style, such as strip windows, hovering volumes and planar surfaces, with them. Each architect has his own pedigree, ideology, social situation and view of tradition, and Le Corbusier's buildings of the 1920s had a unique lyricism and force. It is also misleading to treat his designs merely as clever exercises in proportion and Cubist space (as various formalist critics have done), for this is to ignore the many levels of symbolic content. The seminal works of the modern movement were concerned with the way life should be lived. They recall an observation of the philosopher Karsten Harries: 'the highest function of ... art is not to entertain or amuse, but to articulate a binding world view.'

In Le Corbusier's case this world view was linked to the definition of ideal types to save the industrial city from disaster. Because of political conditions in France he was not able to realize large-scale housing projects, as were his colleagues in Germany (who had socialist patronage) and in the Soviet Union (who were called upon to define the shape of a new, post-revolutionary society). Le Corbusier had therefore to insinuate his reformist doctrines into buildings of limited size — some of them private houses. To

understand this translation of philosophical ideals into particular designs it is first of all necessary to understand his idea of the city.

Even at their most generalized, Le Corbusier's urban projects were linked inextricably to Paris as economic centre, national capital and hub of a colonial system. Paris provided him with a nexus of avant-garde activity, a relatively adventurous clientele, and an urban laboratory which already contained a collage of earlier planning strategies. Despite his immigrant status and marginal bohemian position, Le Corbusier absorbed French myths of centralized power, rational planning and mandarin technocracy as means for guiding the national course. His hypotheses were worked out in reaction to pressing social problems of the immediate post-war years in France: the shortage of housing, the flood of people from country to town, the overcongestion of traffic in Paris, the need to regenerate industry and attract foreign capital, but also to accommodate radical reforms.

Le Corbusier assessed these particularly French predicaments against the backdrop of recent world events. The Great War had swept away the German, Austro-Hungarian and Ottoman Empires. Revolution in Russia had been followed by radical changes in land ownership and moves towards a new society using industrialism to achieve its ideals. Communism had become a major world force even in Europe. President Wilson's lofty international idealism in favour of a 'society of Nations' had been partly undermined by isolationists in the United States, but it encouraged imaginative leaps beyond the narrow interests of nationalism. Le Corbusier was acutely sensitive to these forces guiding the world process which touched on his own historical picture of progress towards an era of harmony. His instincts drew him towards the idea of a new international order in which capitalist ingenuity would somehow be guided towards the improvement of modern societies. The political realities of this aim remained vague, but he put great store by town planning as if the true plan had the power to improve individuals and to regulate human behaviour. 'Architecture or Revolution', he had written at the end of *Vers une architecture*, 'Revolution can be avoided'.

Between 1918 and 1921 Le Corbusier had been preoccupied with general 'laws' governing painting and architecture; he applied the same procedure to urbanism, treating it as a pseudo-science that might guide the destiny of society. Since the Sittesque days of his manuscript 'La construction des villes', he had considered the major reformist paradigms of nineteenth-century city planning and had become particularly interested in Garnier's *Cité Industrielle*. His work on low-cost housing had drawn him to the theories of the American engineer, F.W. Taylor, on efficiency in mass production, and this had helped him to outline the concept of the 'machine à habiter'. Many of his ideas came from direct observation of cities past and present. Le Corbusier was now trying to find a way of synthesizing all these elements into a single workable prototype that might have relevance to the evolving institutions and élites of the Third Republic in the turbulent years after the war.

The architect laid out the terms of this urbanistic theorem in a model and some drawings which he exhibited at the Salon d'Automne of 1922. He called the project 'A Contemporary City for Three Million Inhabitants' to stress that it might be buildable. It examined the general case of an industrial town including management, manufacturing, transport, habitation and leisure, each function in its own zone. Density was generated by building upwards using steel, concrete and mass-production techniques. The spaces left between the buildings were then to be turned over to unimpeded traffic and vast parks. The 'essential joys' of light, space and greenery were thus to be made available to all, but without resorting to suburban or decentralized development which Le Corbusier felt were anti-urban and wasteful of good land. The Ville Contemporaine was Le Corbusier's critique of the clogged nineteenth-century city, but it still celebrated centralization of government, money, resources and culture.

The Ville Contemporaine drawings showed glass skyscrapers and medium-height apartment buildings rising out of a carpet of verdure. Various earlier urban types were fused together in the plan: the utilitarian grid (Manhattan, La Chaux-de-Fonds); the city of Classical hierarchy (Paris, perhaps Burnham's Beaux-Arts plan for Chicago of 1909) and the city of symbolic, or cosmic, geometry (Peking or even ideal cities of the Renaissance). At the crossing point one did not find a temple or civic monument, but a seven-level transport terminal including railways, roads, subways and an airport on top. This was surrounded by 24 glass skyscrapers over 800 feet high, each cruciform in plan, lined up to make a monumental ensemble. Commerce and circulation were the most visible elements, and out of these Le Corbusier tried to make a formal, civic art. His image of the city as a huge machine, with cars hurtling along the axes between tall buildings, perhaps echoed Sant' Elias's Città Nuova; but the plan on which the whole thing rested was

rich in Beaux-Arts devices, and firmly in the tradition of grand French classical urbanism running back from Haussmann's boulevards, to the Champs-Elysées, even to the infinite axes of Versailles. In his book *Urbanisme* (*The City of Tomorrow*) which appeared in 1925, Le Corbusier would include a print showing Louis XIV ordering the building of the Invalides as 'Homage to a great urbanist ... who conceived immense things and realized them'.

If the plan geometry and perspectives of the Ville Contemporaine evoked 'la gloire', the section of the skyscrapers standing on stilts over multi-level circulation routes was a tidied up version of the American industrial city. From books like Hegemann's *Amerikanische Architektur und Stadtbaukunst*, Le Corbusier knew of sections through subways, streets and elevated railways, all stacked up between tall buildings. In 1915 he had himself envisaged a variation on this system, in which skyscrapers stood on piles, traffic and services passed beneath, and the floor of the city became a 'raised ground'. Individually Le Corbusier's glass towers had little in common with the eclectic towers in vogue in America — such structures as the Neo-Gothic winner of the 1922 Chicago Tribune competition. Nor did they resemble Perret's contemporary proposal for towers encrusted in ornament and linked by precarious bridges. The vertical rows of bays suggested the influence of the Chicago School of the 1890s, while the crystalline quality suggested possible knowledge of Mies van der Rohe's skyscraper projects of 1919-21. These, too, were based on a semi-transparent glass skin attached to a skeleton of stanchions and cantilevered slabs. Le Corbusier tried to give the feeling of walking through the verdant spaces of his ideal city:

'You are under the shade of trees, vast lawns spread all around you. The air is clear and pure; there is hardly any noise. What, you cannot see where the buildings are? Look through the charmingly diapered arabesques of branches out into the sky towards those widely spaced crystal towers which soar higher than any pinnacle on earth. These translucent prisms seem to float in the air without anchorage to the ground, flashing in summer sunshine, softly gleaming under grey winter skies, magically glittering at nightfall ...'

The Ville Contemporaine was for white-collar workers — managers and bureaucrats; manufacturing and the lower classes were sequestered in separate areas beyond a green belt. The middle class apartment houses were of two types: *à redent* strips, zigzagging in and out; and 'immeubles villas', which were really so many Citrohans stacked up around courtyards into communal units that looked like large filing cabinets. The *à redent* buildings recalled the layout of Versailles or some other Baroque palace, and seemed deliberately to invoke Charles Fourier's early nineteenth-century 'phalanstères', which were ideal communes. The immeubles villas were surely modelled on the monastery at Ema, which was here rethought in terms of a modern luxury hotel with centralized

facilities like heating, plumbing, a restaurant and
running tracks on the roof terrace. Each individual apartment had its own private garden alongside. Le Corbusier must often have dreamed of
such a thing in the cramped conditions of his
Parisian garret. The immeubles villas returned to
a question that had haunted him since his first
visit to the charterhouse near Florence in 1907:
how best to combine individual and community,
privacy and social life, nature and city?

Greenery was an essential element of his urban
theorem: most of the area of the city was given
over to lawns, gardens, tennis courts, boulevards
and parks. Since the days of his Ruskinian formation in La Chaux-de-Fonds he had thought of
trees as emblems of a moral order. He referred to
the park of his city as a 'lung' because it allowed
the place to breathe. Nature would provide an
antidote to the slums and soot of the nineteenth-
century city, as well as a terrestial paradise for
the hours of leisure. The search for an appropriate balance between countryside and city had
preoccupied numerous nineteenth-century political and urban reformers, including Charles
Fourier, Karl Marx, John Ruskin, Ebenezer

Howard and Frederick Law Olmsted. Le Corbusier seemed to see the question through the lens of Garnier's Cité Industrielle, which had itself been conceived as a large park. Garnier had given Garden City ideas a new interpretation using modern materials like concrete, rational zoning and Classical allusions. Le Corbusier wrote to Garnier in 1919 praising the Cité Industrielle in the most glowing terms. His own Ville Contemporaine took similar concerns to a higher pitch, in which the basic elements of mechanism, nature, geometry and modern institutions were given a new tension through juxtaposition and contrast.

Unlike present day urbanists who make a fetish of the piazza and the street defined by façades, Le Corbusier wanted to space the majority of his buildings far apart. The metaphor was one of liberation from the constriction of slums and from the choking effect on traffic of the traditional artery. Le Corbusier saw the matter in almost medical terms, as if he were cutting out a cancer. The Paris of the 1920s still had stinking alleyways and diseased areas. All that was to be replaced by a new hierarchy of circulation running from freeways for fast traffic to straight roads lined by trees in residential areas. As much as possible, cars were separated from pedestrians. At intersections there were roundabouts. Le Corbusier probably knew of Eugène Hénard's *Etudes sur les transformations de Paris* of 1903–6 which proposed similar intersections for horses and carriages, and the principle of separating levels was a fact in many nineteenth-century cities. The idea of cutting large boulevards through old fabric to ease the flow of traffic, let in air and light, and create a grand vista was intrinsic to Haussmann's Paris. The Ville Contemporaine even had triumphal arches at the end of the main axis and obelisks at some intersections. But the celebration of the automobile speeding between glass towers had a Futurist tone. Le Corbusier wrote: 'A city that has speed has success'; one might add that a city with too much success has smog.

While Le Corbusier tried to claim that his city was based on Laugier's conception of 'unité dans le détail, tumulte dans l'ensemble', most people see in it an oppressive uniformity. Since the days of his manuscript 'La construction des villes' (inspired by Camillo Sitte) he had changed direction completely. He now poured scorn on curves and meanders as 'the pack donkey's way', claiming that 'man walks straight because he has an aim in view'. Evidently he had absorbed some of the axial lessons of Baroque city planning (he seems to have studied Patte's eighteenth-century work on urbanism under Louis XV). Although he raged against the false pomposity of Beaux-Arts axial planning in *Vers une architecture*, he did not seek the urban equivalent of the subtle 'promenade architecturale': there were no 'outdoor rooms' like the forums at Priene or Pompeii. Where city planning was concerned, the Classical tradition seemed to *start* with the French Baroque: exactly where his *architectural* admirations ceased.

The focal geometries and radiating axes of the

59   The immeubles villas, 1922.

Ville Contemporaine spell out an imagery of centralized power. The élite, 'the brains of the country' — philosophers and artists as well as businessmen and technocrats — work high in the skyscrapers, surveying the theatre of daily life around them. In the distance, beyond the fields, they see factories (placed down-wind), and workers' Garden Cities. Although the workers are banished from the white-collar paradise, there is no class conflict, for each worker has a decent family house with a garden — a Dom-ino, a Monol or perhaps a Citrohan. Directives are sent out towards the compass points, while people, ideas, services, goods and money converge on the central terminus. There is no doubt that this is the capital city of the country, though of which country one cannot be sure. Despite its celebration of secular institutions, this new industrial state stands over a plan of ideal geometry like a cosmic imperial city of the past. The plan recalls that of the stockaded temple in the chapter on 'Regulating Lines' in *Vers une architecture*. The Ville poses as a mandala of social regeneration in which the leaders know what is best for all.

Le Corbusier put his faith in an élite of technocrats whose investments and energy were supposed to generate wealth and employment, but whose cultivation and public spiritedness were to edify the social realm and put restraints upon the chaos of *laissez-faire*. This curious fiction combined elements of Henri St Simon's nineteenth-century vision of a new society led by philosophical managers, with elements of Charles Fourier's 'Newtonian Sociology' of opposing forces finding an ideal equilibrium through the application of the right architectural reform. That Le Corbusier was here being overly deterministic is obvious, as if he were implying that his plans could in and of themselves bring about a peaceful revolution of values. In this scenario, the planner himself was given an inordinate amount of influence over the lives of others — rather like Plato's philosopher king who visualizes the constitution of the ideal state and paints a picture

57 (*opposite above*) 'A Contemporary City for Three Million Inhabitants', 1922.

58 (*opposite below*) Sky-scrapers in the heart of the ideal industrial city (Plan Voisin, 1925).

60 Le Corbusier and Pierre Jeanneret, Pavillon de l'Esprit Nouveau, Paris, 1925.

of it in an ideal city plan. Le Corbusier's utopianism assumed that technology, guided by the right framework, had the power to reintegrate men with a natural harmony.

Le Corbusier exhibited his next version of the modern city — the 'Plan Voisin pour Paris' — at the Exposition des Arts Décoratifs of 1925. The various national pavilions were eclectic in style, and it was at this exhibition that 'Art Déco' — a chic synthesis of exotic sources, polychrome ornament and consumerism — made its impact on the public. There were two stark departures from this luxurious scene. One was the Soviet Pavilion by Konstantin Melnikov — a dynamic display of the 'factory aesthetic', cut through by a diagonal ramp, proclaiming the progressive ideals of the new revolutionary society; and the Pavillon de l'Esprit Nouveau which Le Corbusier designed as a show-case for the Purist way of life. The Pavillon itself was a unit of the 'immeubles villas'. It had a double-height terrace with a tree passing through a hole in the roof; the apartment alongside was also double-height with a gallery slung along the back, repeating the section of the Citrohan. Either side there were curved dioramas containing models of the Ville Contemporaine and the Plan Voisin for Paris. The 'appartement-type' was furnished with Thonet chairs and Purist pictures, built-in cupboards and shelves. In

contrast to the extravagance of the other pavilions, it was restrained, even puritan. Bottles and utensils were very simple, like those idealized in Ozenfant's and Jeanneret's pictures. Instead of suave Lalique, there were simple glass flasks and pitchers taken from chemical laboratories. In his book *L'Art décoratif d'aujourd'hui* (1925), Le Corbusier criticized mass-produced kitsch, and held up dentists' chairs, folding camp furniture and utilitarian tools for emulation: 'In all ages and with all people, man has created for his use objects of prime necessity … associated with his organism and helping to complete it'. In the same spirit the Pavillon exhibited a whole range of 'purified' modern types from wine glasses up to the skyscrapers exhibited in the diaramas.

The Plan Voisin concentrated on a few square kilometres of Paris to the north of the Seine. Rows of huge glass skyscrapers rose above the rooftops with parks and avenues between. Acres and acres of old Paris had simply been bulldozed out of existence to accommodate what was, in effect, a heavy-handed intrusion of pieces of the Ville Contemporaine into an actual urban and historical setting. The glass towers were supposed to be emblems of the new economic order as well as symbols of the spirit of the times. Le Corbusier tried to argue that each age evolves its own types, and that this was now the era of the skyscraper (ironical, because he never built one). He supported his case with the argument that a drastic move was necessary to decongest Paris traffic. He also claimed that the skyscrapers would enhance land values and encourage international businessmen to place their investments and their headquarters in Paris, 'the eye of Europe'. Le Corbusier even went so far as to suggest that this would decrease the likelihood of another war, as the economic leaders would not permit the politicians in their home countries to destroy their Parisian interests.

Obviously Le Corbusier was making his bid beyond bohemia to the big business and political authorities. Beforehand he had made extensive contacts with automobile manufacturers like Citroën and Voisin, as well as with Michelin, the tyre company. Needless to say, they were happy to see city plans so uncompromisingly dedicated to automobilism. Gabriel Voisin (who also manufactured aeroplanes and took an interest in the idea of mass-produced houses) lent his name and his funds to the urban plan, and Anatole de Monzie, the Minister of Construction, visited the Pavillon. Le Corbusier backed up his exhibition with the book entitled *Urbanisme* (1925), which reiterated all the arguments behind the Ville Contemporaine and tried to explain the relevance of the same principles to Paris. He supported his ideas with lofty examples from history such as Peking and the Place des Vosges, but also made clever use of newspaper cartoons to remind the average Parisian of his constant, daily frustrations in the overcrowded city. He painted a picture of cramped, badly lit and ventilated apartments, of inadequate plumbing and sewers; of hours wasted in overcrowded métros; of the lack of decent amenities for sport, recreation and relaxation. His pitch was to all classes. The rich would get richer through an enhancement of their land values. The middle classes would have better apartments with roof terraces and parks. The poor — well, their destiny was less certain, since the equivalents to the idyllic Garden Cities of the Ville Contemporaine were not to be seen. But the new city would dispel the soot, damp and insalubrities of the nineteenth century, would bring the light and hope of the twentieth. 'Architecture or Revolution?': the Plan Voisin affirmed that revolution could be avoided.

To have focused on the decaying buildings and streets of Paris was no bad idea; to have suggested an alternative was stimulating to a high degree; but the surgery of the Plan Voisin was so drastic that it might well have killed the urban body (and the urban spirit) that it claimed to be saving. Utopian totalities — even pieces of them — do not mesh well with an urban grain that it has taken centuries to evolve. Le Corbusier's mechanistic zoning was at odds with the mixed uses and mixed incomes of a Paris that generated the very social complexity and urbanity he so admired. His simplistic diagram for urban renewal instituted grotesque clashes in scale and undermined the previous hierarchy of meaning: Notre Dame, for example, would have been dwarfed, even though the nearest skyscraper was over a kilometre away. More than that, Le Corbusier's sanitary obsession with destroying the old 'rue corridor' undervalued the role of the street as a social institution, just as his grandiose imposition of traffic arteries misunderstood the

61 Model of the centre of Paris with the Plan Voisin skyscrapers in place; note the Ile de la Cité in the foreground (from *La Ville Radieuse*).

importance of territoriality and historical memory
in the previous cityscape. His arguments could so
easily have been abused to produce real estate
profits and nothing more: one can never know for
sure, because the Plan Voisin was not carried out.

That Le Corbusier's urban model contained
basic flaws is beyond question, but some alternative to a critical urban situation was needed.
He prophesied with uncanny precision the building types and transport systems that would
dominate in the industrial cityscapes of the future
and tried to give them order and the enrichments
of nature. However, it would be a little too easy
to blame him for every banal modern downtown
full of crude highrises surrounded by wildernesses
of parking lots. Centralization, real estate profiteering by means of tall buildings, dumb urban
renewal, massive traffic schemes cutting through
old fabric — surely these would have happened
without him. Even in cases where Le Corbusier's
influence has been certain, crucial areas of his
original theorems — such as private terraces,
communal facilities, and parks — have often been
left out. As Von Moos has put it: 'Planning
policies are not determined by the influence of
one single architect, "great" as he may be, but by
socio-economic forces and interest, institutional
patterns and ideology.'

Le Corbusier's urban schemes were too
authoritarian and class ridden to appeal to the
French Left in the 1920s, and too revolutionary to
appeal to any other than marginal constituencies
of the Right. He aggrandized the new wealth
generators: automobile and aircraft manufacturers, metal and glass fabricators, engineers,
real estate people and bankers; and treated
modernization, centralization and rationality as if
they were timeless credos. All this attracted a
right-wing group called *Redressement Français*,
an 'industrial élite of intelligence, talent and
character', which supported a publication called
Towards the Paris of the Machine Age, written by
the architect in 1928. He began to speak of the
need for a new 'Authority' — a modern Colbert
— able to guide society towards the true form of
the city. But none of the magnates volunteered
themselves as patrons, even for small-scale offices
or housing, and with the 1929 crash Le Corbusier
grew increasingly disillusioned with capitalism.

Had Le Corbusier been operating in Germany
during the 1920s he would have encountered
large-scale state patronage of public housing, but
no equivalent to this funding or these policies
existed in France. The governments of both Left
and Right continued to follow the guidelines of
the Ribot Law of 1908 by which favourable loans
were given to industrial patrons of workers'
housing so long as the designs followed various
low-cost housing standards that were outlined in
detail; the worker himself would receive very
advantageous credit rates to enable him to
acquire his own home. Le Corbusier had studied
these regulations closely and had followed them
in a variant of the Citrohan called the 'Maison
Ribot', exhibited at the Salon d'Automne of
1923. A motion put forward by Messrs. Loucheur
and Bonnevoy to construct 500,000 new housing

units in ten years was carried by the Chambre des
Députés in 1921, but was still waiting Senate
approval in 1927. Meanwhile between 1919 and
1925, only 18,707 low-cost dwellings fitting the
legal prescriptions were constructed (against
over 800,000 in Germany and over 600,000 in
England). Le Corbusier was drawing up his vision
in the wrong place at the wrong time.

The one chance that he had to put his 'mass-
production' housing theories to the test was a
limited success. This was the Quartier Moderne
Frugès at Pessac near Bordeaux, designed
between 1924 and 1926. Henri Frugès was a
millionaire with interests at home and in the
colonies, in sugar and timber. He wanted to give
his workers decent places to live in that they
could afford to buy, and had read *Vers une
architecture* and seen the Ribot model at the
Salon d'Automne. Frugès was no ordinary busi-
nessman: he composed music, painted, and
designed fabrics, one of which Le Corbusier
included in the Pavillon de l'Esprit Nouveau. His
combination of paternalism, adventurousness and
artistic talent made him the ideal client for Le
Corbusier. Initially, Frugès suggested a handful
of model dwellings, but Le Corbusier soon
persuaded him to be more ambitious and even
seduced him into buying an expensive Ingersoll
Rand spray gun for applying concrete to surfaces.
At this larger scale the programme for the
'Quartier' began to touch upon one little rural
corner of Le Corbusier's grand vision of reform:
he favoured Garden Cities close to regional
manufacturing plants as a way of taking the
pressure off big cities, and of keeping rural
economies going at a time when more and more
people were leaving the land. In the Quartier
Moderne Frugès each family would have its own
garden in which to grow vegetables, relax and
enjoy a sense of belonging. Architect and client
both agreed that the housing could be a way of
stabilizing the work population.

The Pessac problem fitted neatly into a line of
prototypes that had intrigued Le Corbusier since
he had first visited workers' housing in Hellerau
near Berlin in 1911, studied Garden City ideas
and absorbed Garnier. In 1914–15, about the
time that he was preparing the Dom-ino studies,
he had read Foville's monumental *Enquête sur la
condition de l'habitation en France, Maisons-types*
(1894), which had analysed French regional
vernaculars in statistical and typological ways.
While Le Corbusier certainly had no intention of
making a regionalist statement at Pessac he none
the less intended to define a kit of relevant types,
and it cannot have been a total fluke that he
came up with five metres as the module, as
this measurement had been a rule of thumb in
numerous French peasant vernaculars. For Pessac
he visualized variations on the Citrohan and
Ribot prototypes laid out along tree-lined streets
with gardens supplemented (in some cases) by
roof terraces covered by pergolas. The basic cubic
pieces could be stacked in different ways like
sugar cubes to produce such variations as two-
storey terrace houses, and free-standing apartment blocks of four levels (referred to amusingly

as 'skyscrapers'). Frugès knew the Bastide towns of the south-west with their arcades at the lower levels, and insisted that Le Corbusier include shops in the ground floors of some of the dwellings.

The idea of 'standardizing' the pieces had all sounded very sensible, especially as local timber could be used for the formwork, but the concrete spray gun was hard to use. The local contractor lost his nerve, returning to even more expensive methods for constructing the walls. Mass-produced windows did not always fit the voids left in the structure, and by 1926 it was clear that the price per dwelling would be prohibitive for Frugès's workers. To cap it all, local authorities objected that planning permission had not been obtained in the correct way from the Mairie. Le Corbusier tried to save the day by replacing the local contractor and getting Minister de Monzie to visit the site (he did and was impressed), but the economic argument behind 'standardization' now looked like a sham.

Aside from these problems of realization, Pessac emerged as a powerful architectural idea which took its place alongside other European experiments in housing such as J.J.P. Oud's at the Hook of Holland or the Siedlungen being planned in Frankfurt. It was as if Garnier's concrete villas had been shorn of all their mouldings, leaving stark white cubic forms: a Purist

version of a vernacular. In fact, the white seemed to lack relief, so the decision was taken to paint the surfaces different colours. By this time Le Corbusier had absorbed Neo-Plasticist ideas from de Stijl on the value of coloured planes. Steen Eiler Rasmussen, the Danish architect, visited the site in 1926 and described the astonishing effect:

62 Quartier Moderne Frugès, Pessac, near Bordeaux, 1924–6.

63 Pessac today (photographed in 1985).

'Le Corbusier's architecture has, in my opinion, never been more clearly expressed than in his last work: the Pessac housing settlement near Bordeaux. The black-and-white illustrations give only a faint impression of this elegant world. The foundations of the houses are black, the walls alternately sienna brown, bright blue, bright aquamarine, white, bright yellow or grey. The various sides of the houses are not the same colour; one side for example is dark brown, the other bright green, and these colours meet directly at the corner; this is perhaps the strongest way of making the walls appear immaterial. The impression is strange and fantastic, but not chaotic. All these highly coloured surfaces with green plantings spaced in an architectonic order are placed in rows and arranged along axes. All the windows are standardized and made of the same materials. Imagine the whole settlement inhabited, the roof gardens overgrown with live vegetation, gaily coloured washing flapping in the wind of the service yards, while children run about playing. Is this then the architecture of tomorrow?'

The Pessac experiment revealed that it was not worth investing in expensive machinery for such a small number of houses (fewer than a hundred were constructed). Moreover, neither architects nor engineers had made proper provision for drainage and this cost Frugès more money and headaches. By the early 1930s some of the houses were being acquired as second homes by members of the Bordeaux bourgeoisie. The working-class inhabitants did not all agree with the architect's theoretical analysis of their needs, objecting particularly to entering via the kitchen. Colours were changed, metal windows replaced, hip roofs and ornaments added. Some see in these changes a failure of the architect's original idea; others argue that the houses have demonstrated an exemplary flexibility, and that the formal discipline of the exteriors supplies a regular armature that is happily enhanced by alterations. But it is obvious that Le Corbusier's stance as an interpreter of

64 Le Corbusier (centre) and Mies van der Rohe at Stuttgart, 1926.

65 Ludwig Mies van der Rohe, apartment house, Weissenhofsiedlung, Stuttgart, 1927.

'everyman's' tastes was highly problematic.

In 1926 the architect was invited to submit ideas for the Weissenhofsiedlung, a housing exhibition to take place in Stuttgart the following year. This was sponsored by the Deutscher Werkbund and co-ordinated by Mies van der Rohe, who organized the layout on a hill overlooking the city. The ensemble was like an Elementarist's abstract sculpture of rectangular blocks of difference sizes. It was dominated by Mies's own apartment block, with its tight plans and its reductivist interiors. A more expressionist language was employed by Hans Scharoun in a house to one end of the site, while J.J.P. Oud, the Dutch housing master, produced a well-scaled terrace row repeating a simple modular design. Le Corbusier was given two lots next to one another, with long views over Stuttgart. For these he produced two versions of the updated Citrohan, one a single house, the other a double with two units side by side. The *pilotis* under the double house were made of slender steel stanchions and exaggerated in length to an almost preposterous degree. Strip windows and roof terraces were also emphasized for their qualities of light and view. The interiors of both houses opened up to become uncluttered spaces for daytime use which could be divided at night by partitions. Compared with the 'Existenzminimum' (or 'minimal living space') designs then advocated in Germany, they gave an almost luxurious feeling of expansiveness.

Le Corbusier's Stuttgart houses demonstrated the principles of 'the 'Five Points of a New Architecture' that had been latent in the Dom-ino skeleton, and gradually clarified in the villa designs of the mid-1920s. The first point was the *piloti*, or vertical stanchion in steel or concrete, which lifted the box up into space, freeing the ground underneath for circulation or other uses. The second was the *plan libre* (free plan), whereby interior walls could be arranged at will to fit functional demands, channel movement or create spatial effects because *pilotis* were now carrying the load. The third point, the *façade libre*, also followed from the *pilotis*, as the exterior cladding was liberated from traditional weight bearing constraints, allowing openings to be arranged at will for light, view, climate or compositional needs. The fourth point, the *fenêtre en longueur* (strip window) was really a subset of the third, since the horizontal glass band was but one version of the free façade. But it was the one Le Corbusier often preferred in his villas of the 1920s where he used it to create evocative transparencies or hovering bands of glass against smooth plaster-rendered walls. The fifth point, the *toît-jardin* (roof garden) replaced land lost underneath the building with verdure open to sun, sky, trees and view (Pl.138).

When Edouard had studied Rationalist historians like Choisy and Viollet-le-Duc under Perret's

66 Citrohan variation, Weissenhofsiedlung, Stuttgart, 1927.

guidance, he had formulated the ambition of defining a language appropriate for modern times on the basis of the concrete skeleton. This would be his equivalent to the elements of construction underlying the great styles of the past. One guesses that the emphasis of *five* points was deliberate, as if he were canonizing a latter-day version of the Five Orders of Classicism. His system elevated structure to art and made the concrete frame into an instrument for societal change, generating a new living space at the scale of house or city. In his diagrams of the 'Five Points' Le Corbusier made much of the contrast between the health, luminosity and efficiency of his system, and the supposedly dark rooms, damp basements and infested attics of traditional masonry structures. Rhetoric aside, the oblong prism floating above landscape on *pilotis* was a central leitmotiv of Le Corbusier's, lying close to his image of the ideal society: a type that would be amplified, added to and in other ways transformed in his later works.

The Weissenhofsiedlung showed the world that 'the new spirit of construction and synthesis' was an international matter. Supporters saw evidence of a pan-cultural ideal and an expression of the *Zeitgeist*. But not everyone was so convinced. Critics disliked the intrusion of the factory aesthetic into the realm of the home and disapproved of the lack of regional character. Instead of healthy cosmopolitanism they saw rootless foreign intervention, and even compared the Weissenhof to a casbah in postcards which showed Arabs and camels strolling about. These hostile reactions were just a foretaste of the racist propaganda that would be directed against both non-Aryans and the modern movement in the totalitarian climate of the 1930s. They were a warning to the avant-garde that its worthy intentions did not necessarily touch the aspirations of mass society.

67   Double house on steel stanchions, Weissenhof-siedlung, Stuttgart, 1927.

68   Diagram demonstrating the principles of the 'Five Points of a New Architecture' and contrasting the lightness and airiness of the new system with traditional masonry (from *La Ville Radieuse*).

Chapter 6

Houses, Studios and Villas

'Today I am accused of being a revolutionary. Yet I confess to having had only one master — the past; and only one discipline — the study of the past.'

Le Corbusier

While Le Corbusier was preaching the virtues of mass-production dwellings and the vision of a transformed modern city, he was supporting himself with a practice based largely upon the construction of private houses, artists' studios and villas for the well-to-do. In the France of the 1920s, agencies for large-scale urban reform were lacking. Even the small-scale Pessac experiment perhaps showed that Le Corbusier's aesthetics were really more suited to 'cultured people' (as Rasmussen put it) than to workers: that the architect's universal values were more class-bound than he might have hoped. In the 1920s 'Esprit Nouveau' was to become the cultural property of upper middle-class bohemia more than any other social group.

If circumstances forced Le Corbusier to realize his domestic ideas outside the milieu at which he had aimed them, they did not stop him from using individual commissions as laboratories for architectural devices with a broader relevance. The house might even be an allegory containing the dream of the new city in miniature. His classic houses never degenerated into the flaccid International Style elegance that one associates with, say, Rob Mallet Stevens. There was always a vital tension, a striving beyond the facts of the particular case towards utopian and ideal types. Elements were discovered that might be used time and again in new combinations but without a retreat into a dull formula. To go from the boxy forms of the Villa Besnus to the assured lyricism of the Villa Stein/de Monzie four years later is to witness the flowering of a personal style, and a set of principles that would guide both Le Corbusier and later modern architects for some decades to come.

Le Corbusier's own publications about his houses, studios and villas — *Oeuvre complète*, volume 1, *Précisions, Une maison, un palais* — concentrated on the Olympian doctrines of the 'machine à habiter' — features such as the 'Five Points of a New Architecture', or the 'Regulating Lines'. Even the character of the immediate surroundings was often left out in photographs and drawings selected to present the abstract certainties of Modern Architecture. But the Corbusian vocabulary is understood more fully if one is able to understand these buildings as solutions to particular problems of programme, site, and budget too. It is important to know the ambitions of Le Corbusier's clients, the architect's precise intentions and his methods of design. Drawings show how ideas took shape and how type solutions were transformed. By penetrating each context one can sense better the interweaving of generic and particular, of ideal and circumstantial.

Le Corbusier's architectural inventions required an unusual degree of technical experimentation. After 1922 he worked in partnership with Pierre Jeanneret, his cousin, who had a firmer grasp of practicalities, and who had just worked for two years with Auguste Perret. They set up their office in the corridor of an old convent at 35 rue de Sèvres, into which it was possible to cram a line of drawing tables. To one side windows looked down into a courtyard full of trees, and at times one could hear the choir singing in the church. Edouard and Pierre gradually assembled a team of assistants, and a circle of engineers, acousticians and contractors to whom they turned on a fairly regular basis — men like Georges Summer, the Swiss engineer, Gustave Lyon, the acoustics expert, or Raphael Louis, the carpenter. As work increased drastically around 1926–9, and as the reputation became international, draughtsmen from many different countries turned up wanting to work for a master, often for little pay. This curious, dusty, monastic corridor became a training ground for at least three generations of modern architects who spread the Corbusian gospel worldwide.

To build at all an architect has to have clients. Many of Le Corbusier's early patrons were part of the art world as producers or consumers; a fair number were rootless cosmopolitans of foreign origin; some were rich Americans. They were not stuck in the rigid hierarchies and habits of French society, and were able to experiment with their style of life. They attached prestige to new ideas (some were collectors of modern art) and were willing to take risks in supporting the holy grail of modern architecture. Their individual motives in employing Le Corbusier varied from genuine excitement about his ideas to a vague feeling that this was the right man to deal with difficult requirements. Clients like La Roche and the Steins probably knew full well that their houses would become monuments in the history of art. Financial resources also varied. The Lipchitz House and Studio of 1924-5 cost about 100,000 francs. The Villa Stein/de Monzie of 1926-7 (taking into account inflation) was at least ten times that amount. Edouard and Pierre negotiated contracts of many different kinds, some based on percentage of costs, others on flat rates for each stage of a project. For the Lipchitz job, for example, they were paid between 6 and 7%.

Le Corbusier's imagination was probably haunted by an ideal vision of the modern dwelling, but his sites were as unstandardized as his clients were peculiar. At one extreme there would be the tight Planeix lot between a railway cutting, a busy Paris street and party walls; at another there would be the expansive seaside site of Baizeau with long views over the Mediterranean and the North African coastline. Such varied conditions forced Le Corbusier to adjust his typologies considerably, but in the 1920s at least, did not tempt him back to an overt regionalism. The majority of the houses, villas and studios were actually for peculiar-shaped plots close to Paris — many of them in western suburbs such as Boulogne-sur-Seine or Vaucresson. These sites were often cramped and contradictory in their demands of access, lighting, privacy and orientation. Cardinal points of Corbusian doctrine such as the free plan or the roof garden proved their common sense by opening up interiors to light and air, and by giving city dwellers a private arcadia away from the clamour of the street.

The Maison La Roche/Jeanneret of 1923–4 typifies the peculiar demands made on the architect: it is also the breakthrough building between the tentative beginnings of the Ozenfant Studio and the assured complexity of the later houses. The site is hemmed in by the back gardens of surrounding properties and occupies an L-shaped lot at the end of a cul-de-sac called square du Docteur Blanche. The design process was long and arduous. Before La Roche and Albert Jeanneret were persuaded into the affair, there were precarious negotiations between banks, landowners and possible clients. Le Corbusier often acted as his own real estate broker and this involved many risks. At one point in 1923, he seemed on the point of acquiring land on the north side of the cul-de-sac as well as at the end and on the south side. There was a scheme with houses lining both sides and an ingenious curved link, but some of the clients withdrew, and finally Le Corbusier was left with the present awkward site but two encouraging patrons who were already close to him. He attempted to unify the diverse demands behind a symmetrical façade with 'Regulating Lines', but the programme kept bulging out in awkward ways. Le Corbusier had reached the point of placing La Roche's studio across the end of the

drive as an earthbound lump when he had the brilliant idea of lifting this element up into space and curving its outer surface. The eye is immediately drawn to this hovering white box with its taut strip window running from one side to the other and its single *piloti* on axis. As well as referring to urbanist ideas (upper level for living, lower level for traffic), the elevated, curved box flows smoothly into the house and guides the meandering route on the interior. Details are linear and precise; glass is flush with the walls; the feeling is of weightless planes rather than heavy masses.

Outside, the two dwellings blend together into a single composition; inside, they contrast sharply. The Jeanneret half was actually commissioned by Lotti Raaf, Albert's fiancée (they were married in June 1923 and shared Edouard's cramped lodgings on rue Jacob for a time). The requirements were for a salon, dining room, bedrooms, a study, a kitchen, a maid's room and a garage. As the site faced north, and there were zoning restrictions against windows looking over the surrounding back gardens, it was necessary to get light in by carving out light courts, a terrace, and ingenious skylights. As one moves up through the house, the spaces seem to expand in size. The culmination of the route is the roof terrace, not unlike the deck of a ship. Interiors are treated plainly; early photographs show Purist pictures, Thonet chairs and North African rugs.

Raoul La Roche was the Swiss banker with a great interest in modern art mentioned in Chapter 4. He had met Edouard in 1918 at a Swiss dinner in Paris, and had since made a superb collection of Cubist, post-Cubist and Purist works of art. A bachelor who liked to give parties, he needed somewhere roomy, safe and well-lit to display his new and increasingly valuable collection to advantage. The architect persuaded him to construct a Purist version of a *hôtel particulier* expressly for this purpose. As a result the La Roche dwelling is more extravagant and dramatic in its use of interior space than its more domesticated neighbour. One enters a triple-height hall with landings along one side, a stair protruding on the other, and a bridge which runs at the first level just inside the glass, joining the curved studio to the rectangular parts of the dwelling. The large glazing is detailed so that surfaces flow inside and out, not unlike the elusive transparencies of Le Corbusier's paintings of around 1920-3. Walls are painted white, brown, grey and blue, and these activate the interiors still further. In 1923 there was an exhibition of de Stijl architecture at the Galerie Rosenberg in Paris, and it is possible that Le Corbusier was influenced by Neo-Plasticist ideas for generating contrast and vibration between pure colour planes. But where the Dutch architects restricted themselves to overlapping rectangles and lines, the Purist architect enriched his design with curves. In Maison La Roche formal and colouristic contrasts are dramatized by the ever-changing point of view, a procession through spaces and volumes that Le Corbusier called the 'promenade architecturale'. So effective at

69 Maison La Roche/
Jeanneret, Paris, 1923–4.

70 Maison La Roche,
interior of the studio wing.

attracting the axis of exterior approach, the curved studio wall also guides a ramp laterally along its inside surface and this rises to the upper levels. The dynamic forms have a direct, tactile appeal which draws the visitor from one vista to the next, but they also contain metaphors of movement — the ramp, stairs, bridges, veiled references to ships and cars. These celebrate the mobility of modern life (Pl.139).

The liberation of the plan at Maison La Roche relied on Cubism and concrete construction. The structure was actually a clumsy affair, an assortment of walls, piers and a *piloti*, using a concrete armature, pot-tiles, plaster and paint. It was the *image* of the mass-production house, but certainly not the reality. The finishes and details conspired to evoke cleanliness, precision and other Purist virtues of the 'machine à habiter'. But these same shifting scenes and explosions of space have recalled earlier phases in the history of architecture to some historians. Giedion remarked on 'the manner in which the cool concrete walls are divided ... in order to allow space to penetrate from all sides' and compared this to 'some baroque chapels'. More recently Kurt Forster has suggested parallels with the House of the Tragic Poet at Pompeii. Obviously it would be risky to trace Maison La Roche to a single source as Le Corbusier had already absorbed numerous lessons from Antiquity in his Jura classical houses of 1912–16, but in a general sense the building does reiterate many of the 'Lessons of Rome': subtle control of axes and sequences, compressed and expanding spaces, a clear hierarchy of intentions. Certain of Jeanneret's early travel sketches of the screen walls of Antique ruins punched with small rectangles, anticipate the planar surfaces of the 1920s houses, as if the architect wished to employ radical simplification

as a means to return to the naked structure of ancient architecture at the same time as he announced a new utopian ideal. It was in connection with the La Roche House that Le Corbusier made the leading remark: 'Here, brought to life again under our modern eyes, are architectural events from history'.

La Roche himself was fully aware of the deeper continuities with the past. On 13 March 1925, the day after the opening of the house, he wrote to his architect praising the 'various technical and planning innovations' and offering a five horse-power Citroën in appreciation of the fine work. He went on to say that he felt certain that the house would 'create an epoch in the history of architecture':

But what specially moves me are those constant elements which are found in all the great works of architecture, but which one meets with so rarely in modern constructions. Your ability to link our era to preceding ones is particularly great. You have ... made a work of plastic art.'

Le Corbusier and Ozenfant split up when they disagreed about the hanging of paintings (including their own) on the interiors, and the architect then began to preach to La Roche about the need to keep some of the wall surfaces clear for the sake of the architecture. Despite this turbulence and an exploded radiator, La Roche stuck by his architect all the way. Two years after moving in he wrote to Le Corbusier contrasting his house with other 'modern' experiments:

'Ah! Those prisms — one has to believe that you and Pierre have the secret of them, because I search for them in vain elsewhere ... Thanks to you we now know what Architecture is.'

After 1923 the French post-war economy improved, and this may be one of the reasons why Le Corbusier's commissions increased after that date. The publication of *Vers une architecture* enhanced his reputation and he continued to try and reach a general public through the annual exhibitions of the Salon d'Automne. As a rule his earliest jobs came from a small circle of people in the art world, some of whom knew each other. In 1923, for example, he was asked by two sculptor friends, Lipchitz and Miestchanninof, to design atelier/residences on the allée des Pins, a quiet back street in Boulogne-sur-Seine where they envisaged a small artists' enclave. Le Corbusier inverted the normal arrangement of the Citrohan, putting the residence above and the studio below, as heavy weights would have to be wheeled in and out. Where the site turned the corner, Le Corbusier bent the edge of one of the cubic studios into a curve, which rose to become a funnel on top. There was to have been a third unit for Canale, and a link in the form of a bridge on *pilotis* was constructed, but the client withdrew. Compared to the slightly earlier Ozenfant design, these buildings were chunkier and more massive, as if deliberately evoking the facets of Cubist sculpture.

Many of Le Corbusier's sites were extremely awkward in shape, and these required clever

71   Maisons Lipchitz and Miestchanninof, Boulogne-sur-Seine, 1923–5.

collages of external curves and rectangles, as had been used at La Roche/Jeanneret (he later called this type of composition 'pittoresque, mouvementé' — 'picturesque, eventful'). In 1924 he was approached by Paul Ternisien, a musician, who wanted a practice room for himself, a painting studio for his wife, and a small residence for the two of them, to stand on a piece of land at the other end of the allée des Pins, where it met rue Denfert-Rochereau on the diagonal. Le Corbusier exploited these peculiarities in a design which was a little minuet of curves and rectangles, a 'jeu d'esprit'. He inserted Ternisien's practice room in a pointed room with one straight and one curved wall. This fitted neatly into the wedge of the site but also wittily suggested the shape of a musical instrument or even a ship's prow (thus completing the liner analogy started in the Lipchitz/Miestchanninof stack down the allée).

In 1923 Le Corbusier's parents asked him to design them a little house on Lac Léman near Vevey. The north wall facing the vineyards (and through which one entered) was kept blank. The south façade was opened up by means of a wide strip window to make the most of the amazing views over the lake towards the Alps. In the garden Le Corbusier punched a small window through a masonry wall at the water's edge to intensify the landscape still further by framing and containing it. The device recalled the screen walls with apertures that the artist had seen and recorded in Roman ruins, while the picnic table that he attached to the wall at one end, and supported on a single leg at the other, was surely an imitation of the plank desks (held up in the same way) that he must have seen in the monastery at Ema. The idea of a vignette as a window into Mediterranean or pastoral reverie would recur in the project for Villa Meyer (1925) and on the solarium of the Villa Savoye (1928–9), where the table was also included. A variation even emerged for the porter's window at the top of the ramp of the Millowners' Building in India, twenty-five years later. This was typical of Le Corbusier's way of absorbing elements from history into his own system, then trying them again and again in different buildings.

By 1925 Le Corbusier and Pierre Jeanneret had had enough experience at translating aesthetic intentions into restricted circumstances to be able to achieve the totally accomplished Maison Cook. William Cook was a journalist who painted in his spare time, one of those 'Americans in Paris' who knew Gertrude Stein and moved on the fringes of the avant-garde. His site was again in Boulogne-sur-Seine, a stone's throw from the allée des Pins on rue Denfert-Rochereau. The Bois de Boulogne was just visible on a diagonal. The parcel of land offered enough space for small front and back gardens. It was necessary to think in terms of a façade plane continuing the building line; then to reconcile the conflicting demands of access and privacy, salon and bedrooms, car and garden, views and closure.

Le Corbusier came close to his final solution to these difficult demands in less than a week,

which suggests that the elements of the problem triggered images in his mind lying close to his picture of the ideal dwelling. He placed the main accommodations in an elegant box lifted up above the ground on side walls and on a centre line of three cylindrical *pilotis*, the foremost one visible in the front view. Le Corbusier inverted the normal plan, putting the bedrooms, the dressing room, the maid's room and the bathroom on the first level, and the kitchen, dining and living rooms on the second. This last space was actually double-height and broke up through the roof garden level, to which it was linked by another small stair leading to the library adjacent to the terrace. The *promenade architecturale* came to its end with fine views towards the trees of the Bois de Boulogne. As Le Corbusier put it: 'you are in Paris no longer.'

Maison Cook was close to being a cube, one of those ideal forms singled out in *Vers une architecture*. The interiors were sculpted into a sequence of compressed and expanding spaces in both section and plan. Curved partitions registered peculiarities of use (e.g. the many necessary points of access from the tight first-floor landing), channelled the flow of space, and modelled light and shade. The façade plane of thin stucco was cut across by horizontal ribbons of dark, semireflective glazing. A dominant symmetry was reinforced by the *piloti* on the main axis, around which voids and solids, convex and concave volumes, advancing and receding planes, were organized into a subtle play of pushes and pulls, asymmetries and secondary symmetries. Maison Cook blended together the image of the Citrohan, the principles of the Dom-ino, mechanistic analogies (such as the Farman Goliath aeroplane cockpit 'quoted' in the curved porter's lodge) and the perceptual richness born of Purist painting. As he himself wrote of the mid 1920s: 'Between

72 Sketch of framed view from the house for Le Corbusier's parents, Vevey, looking south over Lac Léman towards the Alps (Hartford, Conn., Wadsworth Atheneum).

architectural forms born of concrete and painting there was now complete agreement.'

More than that, Maison Cook was a demonstration of the 'Five Points of a New Architecture' and of certain of Le Corbusier's urbanistic doctrines. The *piloti* — generator of the new architecture *and* the new city — was presented as a cult object, focal point of all attention, lifting the box up into space. The car passed on one side, the pedestrian on the other, and to distinguish between the two Le Corbusier employed the same convention as he had used for the Ville Contemporaine: straight roads for traffic, curved for people. The 'fenêtre en longueur' and 'façade libre' were thrust at the viewer, underlined by the way the windows came almost to the edges, suggesting a weightless membrane, and by the way that the *piloti* was recessed slightly, suggesting a separation of structure and cladding. The turbulent volumes behind the façade plane were enough to imply a free plan within, and the roof terrace was clearly signalled on top. It was with some justification that the architect claimed: 'Here are applied with great clarity certainties from discoveries to date ...' The Cooks were also happy with the result: 'We are very pleased and realize full well that you managed to create not just a great house, but also a very beautiful one, with so much sun and light!'

As Le Corbusier proceeded from one design to the next he added new discoveries to his stock of inventions. Some of these were simply variations on type-solutions, such as novel ways of jointing *pilotis* to slabs. Others were schematic arrangements for plans and sections, such as contrasting curved partitions with grids, using opaque street façades and transparent rear façades, or placing small rooms low down houses and larger ones higher up. Then again there were favourite motifs such as a curved funnel to contain stairs. Taken together these all constituted the elements and rules of combination of an evolving personal style, and after 1925 the architect had a clearer understanding of the implications of his forms. This allowed him to focus on particular pieces of the 'Five Points' and to extract new possibilities from them.

In the seaside Villa Baizeau for Carthage (1927-9), Le Corbusier began to investigate the idea of the concrete skeleton as a formal generator, thinking of the building less as a box and more as a system of interlocking horizontal slabs. In the first project, double and triple spaces were spliced together in a way loosely resembling Rudolph Schindler's Lovell Beach House in California of 1922-4. But Baizeau was not convinced by his architect's gestures to the climate, as they left large areas of wall and glazing unprotected. The scheme went through various revisions including one in which curved partitions snaked back and forth within a grid of supports and between the horizontal slabs of the skeleton. In effect this was a new variation on the 'Five Points' which created a protective *parasol* on top and shaded loggias or verandas at the edges; a much simplified version of the diagram was eventually built. Le Corbusier was finding ways

of adjusting and emphasizing different elements of his system to create increasingly complex spatial effects. The Baizeau design contained the seeds of shading devices that the architect would later amplify for hot climates: the sheltering roof and the sunshading façade screen or *brise-soleil*.

The roof garden was another 'basic' element of Le Corbusier's vocabulary, related to his urbanistic ideals and his image of arcadia. In the unexecuted Meyer House for Neuilly (1925) the main volume of the building was an oblong which the architect characterized as 'smooth and unified', 'like a travelling trunk of fine proportions'. In the second version of the project the theme of a procession to the terrace was contained in a compact curved adjunct to the building, like a rethought silo, while the garden itself took on the character of a stage set for the 'high life' of 'les années folles'. Le Corbusier wrote to Madame Meyer describing his idea in words and sketches:

'From the boudoir one has come up on to the roof which has neither tiles nor slates, but a solarium and swimming pool with grass growing in the joints between the paving stones. The sky is above: with the walls around and no one can see us. In the evening one sees the stars and the sombre outline of the trees in the Folly St-James. By means of sliding screens one can cut oneself off completely ... rather as in the paintings of Carpaccio ... This garden is scarcely *à la française* but a wild shrubbery ...'

Luxurious dalliance was given a twinge of nostalgia for civilization lost: one sketch showed a table set with pitcher, glass and bowl of fruit, before an aperture looking on to a classical ruin in the landscape — a Roman memory from the trip of 1911.

It is curious to find this Mediterranean reverie cropping up in a *banlieu* of Paris, but it is yet another reminder that the classical tradition was a living force in the architect's imagination. The matter of Classical typologies with Le Corbusier is slightly obscured by his own vague use of terms. In the 1920s he called many of his houses — whether in country, suburb or city — 'villas'. This was a casual repetition of real estate terminology of the period, which used 'villa' to give allure to houses of almost any kind. He also used the formula 'une maison/un palais' — 'a house/a palace' — but by this he meant something very general: the ennoblement of a basic house type (e.g. the Citrohan) through proportion to the point where it achieved monumentality. Le Corbusier was certainly not blind to differences between 'villas' and 'palaces' in history. On the contrary, he realized that they represented two fundamental types, one rural, the other urban, in the traditions of Western architecture. He seems to have been particularly aware of French versions: the Baroque palace with wings (like Versailles) which he transferred into the *à redent* housing; the *hôtel particulier* with Rococo curved incidents behind a street façade (which perhaps influenced some of his town houses); and the elegant *pavillon* in a formal landscape (like the Petit Trianon) which was more relevant in suburban or rural circumstances. This last was not a 'villa' in the full sense, but it did draw upon a villa tradition, and did celebrate the idea of a luxurious existence in a bucolic natural setting.

If there is a single Le Corbusier house of the 1920s that really deserves the description 'une maison, un palais', it must surely be the Maison Planeix of 1924-8. This stands on the avenue Masséna, a wide and noisy street to the east end of Paris. It is a miniature urban palace in effect and in intention: with a formal, symmetrical façade, an entrance axis, a *piano nobile*, an emphasized ground level and cornice, and even, at one stage in its design, a courtyard. The site was tight, slotted between party walls, a raised garden and diagonal railway cutting to the rear, with the avenue Masséna in front — a context which made a blank, protective exterior advisable. Antonin Planeix was himself an artist, a sculptor of funerary monuments, who took an active part in the design process. In fact, he initiated that process by sending Le Corbusier a sketch showing his house with a symmetrical, tripartite façade of three bays, the central one

73 Maison Cook,
Boulogne-sur-Seine, 1926.

74 Section of Villa Baizeau,
Carthage, Tunisia, 1927.

75 Maison Planeix, Paris,
1924–8.

stressed more than those at the sides. Planeix needed an atelier as well as a residence, and over the months Le Corbusier tried out an ingenious section of varying sized spaces *en suite*, with a plan that carried the main axis through between four stalwart columns. Timothy Benton, who has researched all of Le Corbusier's domestic designs in detail, suggests that this recalls 'l'Atrio di Quattro Colonne' from Palladio's *Four Books*. More than that, it seems to me to recall the origin of this arrangement, the Roman atrium itself, especially the atrium of the 'Casa del Noce' at Pompeii with its four columns rising to the roof, which had so impressed Le Corbusier in the Voyage d'orient. This sort of foursquare heart to a dwelling behind an exclusive urban façade and preceding a more open garden façade, had been attempted in the Schwob House over a decade earlier. Indeed, the blank panel masking small side windows in the street façade of the Planeix House also echoes the blank façade of Schwob and its possible Palladian source. Evidently we here have to do with another of these basic patterns in Le Corbusier's form-making apparatus. *Cognoscenti* of the Parisian avant-garde may also have recognized an echo of the Tzara House in Montmartre of 1926 by Adolf Loos, which used a symmetrical façade but with a gaping hole for a terrace, instead of a protruding panel (Pl.137).

The *idea* of the symmetrical façade was linked in Le Corbusier's mind — and in the Classical tradition — with an axial approach towards a place of central importance. In the Villa Church at Ville d'Avray (designed between 1927 and 1929), the problem was to join a new music room and salon, and a guest wing to an existing stable and Neo-Classical block. The setting was pastoral with shaded paths, flowers and a tree-lined driveway. Le Corbusier set the main volumes diagonal to one another, emphasizing the most public of them — the pavilion containing the music room, ballroom and salon — by means of the symmetrical façade device. This also helped to draw the eye away from the old buildings towards this secondary focal point, which was used for soirées. The site was uneven, so Le Corbusier linked old and new buildings by means of a bridge threaded through glazed prisms and open terraces. Barbara and Henry Church were wealthy Americans who wanted to entertain with cultivated style. Le Corbusier gave them a building which combined some of the attributes of a luxury ship with other attributes from the *pavillon* type mentioned earlier. In Le Corbusier's mind one guesses that the salient features may have been: a cubic, well-proportioned volume among trees, a ceremonial approach, a formal landscape, a drop-off point in front of an honorific entryway, an ascent to a *piano nobile* via a vestibule, then a controlled set of movements inside offering vignettes of nature. The Villa Church had all of these qualities and in the course of the design Le Corbusier used blatantly Classical devices like formal stairs on axis and gardens as radiating *parterres*.

The Villa Stein/de Monzie of 1926-8, also known as 'Les Terrasses', was the most monu-

mental and luxurious of Le Corbusier's houses of the 1920s. He characterized it as 'une maison un palais' — 'a house, a palace', but it, too, was really a suburban villa or *pavillon* for the cultivation of mind and body: just far enough from the city limits for rural peace, yet close enough for continuing indulgence in urban pleasures. Michael Stein was Gertrude Stein's brother and a major collector of Matisse; Sarah Stein was a painter; and their good friend, Gabrielle de Monzie, was the former wife of Minister Anatole de Monzie. The Steins wanted to get away from noisy central Paris to more healthy surroundings and Gabrielle needed a new home for herself and her adopted daughter. So they decided to pool their very considerable financial resources and their households, and to have a house designed by the architect whom they considered the best in his generation. Like Maison La Roche, this would have to house a fine collection of modern painting and sculpture in a setting which was itself exemplary of the best modern architecture. There was the ambition to be great patrons and to produce a building that 'le tout Paris' would certainly come to see. The idealism of the high bourgeoisie was to be translated into a Purist equivalent of, say, the Stoclet House in Brussels by Josef Hoffmann of 1905. However, Gabrielle, Sarah and Michael had spent many pleasant summers together in an assortment of grand rural retreats. Before the war, the Steins had even frequented a Renaissance villa outside Florence. One wonders if Le Corbusier knew of this background, for his interpretation touched a number of chords in the Classical country house tradition.

The architect helped his clients to locate a long strip of land near the western suburb of Garches.

76 Sketches for Maison Planeix, 1925 or 1926 (Fondation Le Corbusier).

77   Villa Church, Ville
d'Avray, 1928, entrance to
the music pavilion.

The plot was very narrow, ran approximately
north-south and allowed plenty of room if Le
Corbusier wanted to do the obvious thing and set
the building back some way from the road. In
spring 1926 the atelier made its initial studies of
the programme, placing the garage and gardener
on the ground level, the kitchen, salon and dining
room with a terrace on the first floor, the private
suites on the second, either side of the axis, and a
roof terrace with adjoining maids' rooms on the
top. At this stage the building was a crude oblong
diagram, but between May and June a number of
plans appeared with central halls and symmetrical
wings. Above this absolutely Palladian type Le
Corbusier projected a concrete villa with a closed
north façade and a transparent south façade of
cantilevered terraces covered with greenery. In
July he exploded the whole scheme into its
garden setting as an asymmetrical sequence of
terraces and open-air rooms with sculptures
exhibited at strategic points. The servants' wing
was extended forward from the main block,
which was itself approached along a formal

driveway. Thus the decks and long windows of an
ocean liner were crossbred with a spatial complexity born equally of Purist painting and of
antique ruins like the roofless rooms in an
idyllic landscape that Edouard had sketched at
Hadrian's Villa in 1911.

This solution created many practical problems
and may have been too 'pittoresque' and 'mouvementé' for either clients or architect, so from
autumn 1926 to spring 1927 (when the building
permit was granted) things tightened up. The
final design combined the symmetry and formality of a clean block regulated according to the
Golden Section, with the meandering spatial
movement and asymmetry of the intermediate
scheme. The structural grid was laid out in a
2:1:2:1:2 rhythm with respect to the end walls,
narrow bays receiving movement from the two
main entrances or else containing stairs. At
Garches the 'Five Points' jump into yet another
combination with *pilotis* appearing only on the
interiors, where they introduced 'a constant scale,
a rhythm, a cadence of repose'. Curved partitions

of the free plan were like hieroglyphs of the human body, containing tubs, bidets, boudoirs, vestibules and spiralling stairs, in contrast to the abstract mathematics of grid and façade planes. The composition of curves within a rectangular outline puts one in mind of such paintings of the mid-1920s as *Still Life with Numerous Objects* of 1924, in which the artist succeeded in going beyond the rigidity of early Purism towards a more complex vocabulary of overlapping contours, reverse curves and ambiguous transparencies.

By spring 1927 working drawings were in process. Le Corbusier seems to have concentrated his efforts into dealing with clients and designing; Pierre Jeanneret supplied the anchor of common sense and supervised contractors; other designers in the atelier helped to test hypotheses, often producing elaborate drawings to do so. But Le Corbusier had the final say and for this commission he prepared many studies in colour. In the translation from drawing to material many others played a part. The structure was worked out by Georges Summer, using concrete *pilotis*, slabs and beams. Walls and partitions were to be of crude bricks cemented, plastered and painted so as to give the right 'machine-age' smoothness. Windows by the St Gobain Glass Company were to be inserted in oak frames by Raphael Louis, the carpenter. Radiators were standard, but many other mechanistic details had to be specially made to look mass-produced, e.g. the sliding wire and steel gate by the porter's lodge at the entrance. It is wrong to say that modern architecture rejected ornament altogether: it reinterpreted it. The details of Les Terrasses brought acute emphasis to the main lines of the forms, and also sharpened the images and associations expressing the concept of the 'machine à habiter'. A quarter of a century after completion, James Stirling caught the spirit of the iconography:

'...while Garches is not the product of any high-powered mechanization, the whole spirit of the building expresses the essence of machine power. To be on the first floor is to witness the Mumfordian end product of twentieth-century technology, "the silent, staffless power house". The incorporation of railroad and steamship fabrication is decidedly technocrat ...'

Le Corbusier had used the idea of an automobile procession up to a grand façade, followed by a sequence of curved and rectangular spaces giving on to a rear terrace and garden, in the Favre-Jacot House of 1912, and he reused it at Les Terrasses. Early photographs make much of the visual puns between cars and the forms of the house, and it is obvious that the main façade with its hierarchy of servants' and main entrances, its mild displacements of axes and clever compressions of planes, was designed to be grasped first of all from the automobile approach. It is a monumental yet weightless frontispiece packed with subdued innuendoes and visual ambiguities: the balcony at the top, signalling the main axis and posing as a benediction loggia; the canopy

over the main entrance, combining drawbridge and aeroplane wing with struts; the bands of strip windows stretched from one corner to the other, making the façade as tight as a drum; the factory glazing at the lower level, suggesting a twentieth-century equivalent to rustication. These hints and associations are held in check by tight proportions, optical illusions of advancing or receding rectangles and a rigorous outline. Classical and mechanical, plane and depth, symmetry and asymmetry coexist in a state of high tension.

To explode the form of Les Terrasses into an axonometric drawing is quickly to grasp how one level differs from another, and how real and illusionistic planes are compressed together with curved objects to make an equivalent to a Purist still life inhabitable. The route is yet another controlled ascent from car to door to vestibule, to stairs, up to the *piano nobile* where the free plan and diagonal views expand the space towards garden and terrace. The vestibule seems to restate Palladio's four columns entrance idea; the *pilotis* are oval in section, aviomorphic in image, and aligned to lead one in, then to turn one to the right up the stairs. On the main living floor curved partitions also guide the route, deflecting the eye from one sculptural event to the next. When symmetrical, the curves imply minor axes, as for the dining space at first level, or on the second level where two facing concave partitions define the axis of the entire building, as well as

78 Sketches for Villa Stein/de Monzie, July 1926 (Fondation Le Corbusier).

OPPOSITE PAGE

79 Villa Stein/de Monzie, Garches, 1926–7, view down the drive to the entrance façade.

80 (*top left*) Schematic detail of *Still Life with Numerous Objects*, 1923 (see Pl.141); (*top right*) First-floor plan of Villa Stein/de Monzie; (*bottom left*) First-floor plan of Villa Malcontenta by Andrea Palladio, 1565; (*bottom right*) Study for Villa Stein/de Monzie, spring 1926 (Fondation Le Corbusier).

81 Villa Stein/de Monzie, entrance hall with stairs.

82 (*above right*) Villa Stein/de Monzie, first-floor salon seen from the top of the stairs.

83 (*right*) Villa Church, interior with furniture designed by Charlotte Perriand and Le Corbusier.

84 (*below*) Villa Stein/de Monzie, the south garden façade.

moulding a sort of Rococo vestibule leading to Stein or de Monzie apartments. Free-plan curves contain stairs and conceal private places like bathrooms and bidets, but on the roof the curves poke through to become an entirely closed volume, a ship's funnel, originally to have contained Sarah's studio. From the decks of this noble ship it is possible to see how the driveway, paths and trees have been integrated into a single, formal landscape idea: the solemn approach of the car down a straight line on one side, the meandering path from the back terrace into the garden, on the other. Then, through the belvedere window put there for the purpose, one catches sight of the skyline of Paris.

Le Corbusier had hoped to persuade the Steins and Gabrielle de Monzie to furnish their house in a modern style. In 1928 he collaborated with Charlotte Perriand, the furniture designer, on the creation of a range of 'machines for sitting in', made from delicate steel tubes covered in chrome, and from cowhide for seats, polished leather for cushions: *le siège tournant*, for dining rooms or offices where one needed to be upright; *le fauteuil à dossier basculant*, made from strips of leather stretched over a lightweight chassis, for lounging; *le grand confort*, a formal but comfortable armchair with soft leather cushions; and *la chaise longue*, an elegant version of a dentist's chair, with a cowhide seat and backrest moulded to the human figure in a single, sinuous curve. Completing the range was a steel tube and glass table, *la table tube d'avion*. Perriand and Le Corbusier hoped to encourage the Peugeot bicycle company to manufacture the range *en série*, but failed, and instead got Thonet to put out a limited run which was exhibited at the Salon d'Automne of 1929. Like Mies van der Rohe's contemporary 'Barcelona Chair', Le Corbusier's prototypes have since become classics, but he was unable to persuade the clients of Les Terrasses to do without their fine Renaissance furniture which sat a little incongruously alongside Matisse, Picasso and slender *pilotis*. With the Churches it was different, and early views of their interiors hint at the visual interplay between the abstraction of the box and the furniture, the latter echoing both the human form and free-plan curves.

The garden façade of Les Terrasses has wider windows than the front façade, to let light deep into the structure, to open up views into the garden, and to expand the living spaces towards nature by means of cantilevered platforms and terraces. Visually the themes are now reversed: white ribbons of stucco against broad bands of glass instead of the dark ribbons of glass against wide stucco surfaces of the front. The dynamic asymmetry and hovering coloured planes of the main terrace suggest the influence of de Stijl (perhaps Rietveld or van Doesburg); equally they bring the logic of the building — horizontal slabs, and a meandering path, pulling away from a vertical, frontal plane — to a clear resolution. The extending slabs also reaffirm the potential of the Dom-ino skeleton to become a superimposed or overlapping set of layers. The outdoor room of the terrace — half inside, half outside — brings the raised garden idea of the *immeubles villas* to a splendid crescendo, a stage-set for summer scenarios or private reveries (Pl.140).

Les Terrasses was Le Corbusier's most ambitious realization yet: a synthesis of the ideas and forms which had guided him during his period of invention. In 1959 after revisiting the building, he called it 'the final flowering of the effort (modest but impassioned) of 1918 to 1925. First cycle of a new architecture *demonstrated*.' Soon after completion the house was reviewed widely in the world architectural press, traditionalists portraying it as a stark curiosity, modernists holding it up as a paradigm. Henry Russell Hitchcock, the American architectural historian, baptized it a masterpiece of the 'International Style' and exhibited photographs of it in the Museum of Modern Art in 1932, alongside other seminal works of modern architecture, such as the Bauhaus buildings of 1926 at Dessau by Walter Gropius or the Barcelona Pavilion of 1929 by Mies van der Rohe.

As well as canonizing ideals of modernism, the Villa Stein/de Monzie reaffirmed Le Corbusier's commitment to constants in tradition. The status of the clients, their artistic ambitions, the lavish budget and the prestigious site all prompted a ceremonial treatment, and the architect rose to the occasion with profundity and wit. In the 1930s he told the South African architect, Martienssen, that he had tried to recreate 'the spirit of Palladio' in his 1920s houses, and in 1947 Colin Rowe noted correspondences between the proportional system of Les Terrasses and that of the Villa Malcontenta, suggesting that both Le Corbusier and his great sixteenth-century predecessor had approached 'something of the Platonic archetype of the ideal villa ...'

From the evidence of his travel sketches, his earliest experiments in Classicism, his transactions with Perret, Behrens and Garnier, not to mention the theories and preferred images of *Vers une architecture*, it is clear that Le Corbusier's mind was stocked with lessons from many periods. He roamed up and down Classical tradition in search of the substructures, the fundamentals, as well as recurrent types and varying conventions. Whether it was ancient Greece or Gabriel, Pompeii or Palladio, Behrens or even the Beaux-Arts, the aim was the same: to abstract principles that could be transformed into the elements, rules and hierarchies of his own language. Le Corbusier transposed schemata from one context to another, discovering new connections and fusing new bonds between ideas and forms. The design sketches for his houses, studios and villas reveal his struggles as he tried to reconcile Classical symmetry with the explosions of the free plan, frontal façades with turbulent inner events, the *machine à habiter* with the archetypes of Pompeii. He stressed the *spirit* of Palladio, not the obvious attributes of his style, for, like Palladio, he knew that modernity only has value if it is rooted in the wisdom of the ancients, and that tradition is kept alive only by constant transformation.

Chapter 7

Machine-Age Palaces and Public Institutions

'Monuments are human landmarks which men have created as symbols for their own ideals, for their aims and for their actions. They are intended to outlive the period which originated them ... they form a link between the past and the future.'
Sigfried Giedion, 1944

Le Corbusier's image of an ideal city celebrated the work-place, the collective dwelling, the movement of cars and planes, physical and spiritual recreation in parks, but gave an imprecise description of public and civic institutions. Religion and the state seem to have had no public presence in his city, no clear shape in his mind. Perhaps this squeamishness reflected a lack of commitment to any particular religious or political body; or it may be that he wished to imply that a utopia made such things obsolete. Possibly he thought that the symphonic machine of the city, with its ranges of grandiose glass skyscrapers, was enough of a collective symbol on its own.

Later in the 1920s public institutions were very much on Le Corbusier's mind. He had judged the past by its temples, mosques and cathedrals, and hoped that the modern epoch would generate its equivalent. Although vague about the ideal programme, especially in an age of fragmentation and materialism, Le Corbusier was none the less committed to the traditional function of monumental architecture as a symbolic art form lending nobility and permanence to institutions and human beliefs.

In the 1920s in France, most large public buildings were still done by Beaux-Arts architects. They used the full regalia of the Classical language including figural sculpture. But the results were often pompous rather than truly monumental — at least this is what Le Corbusier felt. Certainly there were recent buildings elsewhere which made inventive use of the past, such as the Grundvig Church near Copenhagen by Jensen Klimt, the Stockholm Public Library by Gunnar Asplund or the Viceroy's House in New Delhi by Edwin Lutyens. There were also avantgarde visions for state buildings. Tatlin's Monument to the Third International of 1919, for example, tried to give shape to Marxist ideology in a spiralling abstract mechanism expressing the dialectical process and the secular religion of progress. But even if it had been buildable it might have communicated little to the public because of its rejection of conventional civic imagery.

Le Corbusier wished to define an authentic monumentality for the modern age that would avoid these limitations. He wished to make monuments that would communicate ideas about public institutions but without recourse to heavy-handed imagery or obvious historical references. He thought of such buildings as collective engines celebrating the programmes and rituals of contemporary social life over a substructure of Classical reminiscences and ordering devices. His task was to expand the language discovered in the houses to the point where it could handle problems of large size, visible hierarchy and ceremonial. It was not sufficient just to inflate domestic typologies as they stood. In making the necessary adjustments the 'house/palace' idea was useful, especially if combined with the oblong strips of accommodation hinted at in the Ville Contemporaine. 'Palace' in this instance did not mean an Italian *palazzo* around a courtyard, but something more like the Palais du Luxembourg, the Louvre or other Parisian *palais* built under the late Louis. It implied long, narrow bands of rooms punctuated here and there by monumental fixed points. These wings embraced, though they did not necessarily enclose, a formal landscape composed with axes.

Le Corbusier's first major chance to design a machine-age *public* palace came with the competition for the League of Nations, announced in 1926. The building was to stand on a wooded site outside Geneva on the shore of Lac Léman. It was to include a large auditorium for the Assembly (with enough room for 2,600 people and the press), a Secretariat for 550 offices, numerous committee rooms, a restaurant, a library and elaborate circulation, channelling delegates, functionaries, dignitaries and journalists to their respective destinations. Most people would arrive by car, so access and parking were crucial. The cost limit was set at 13 million Swiss francs and the deadline for the end of January 1927. But above these mundane requirements there was the problem of finding the right symbolism for a world parliament: an institution that was supposed to foster lofty ideals of international peace, co-operation and justice.

85 Project for the League
of Nations, Geneva, 1927.

86 (*right*) Hannes Meyer,
project for the League of
Nations, 1927.

Entries poured in from all over the world, 367
in all, representing a range of positions from
academic Classicism to the most stark functionalism. Some projects tried to express world unity
in circular forms, but did not fit well on the site
and were too obvious in their symbolism. Richard
Neutra (in combination with Rudolph Schindler)
envisaged the world parliament hovering over the
lake while Hannes Meyer placed the Secretariat
in a skyscraper and the Assembly in a factory-like
volume alongside. A Marxist with strong functionalist convictions, he wished to strip the
League of Nations of false rhetoric and élitist
'humanism'. The transparent industrial forms
were supposed to encapsulate the notion of a
peoples' parliament, open to all: an instrument
dedicated to the cause of world socialism.

Le Corbusier perceived the League of Nations
as a society of leaders dedicated to a new global
consensus above the narrow ambitions of nationalism. He celebrated this vision in a limpid
machine-age palace for the élite, combining
the principles of the 'Five Points of a New Architecture' with a deft reinterpretation of Classical
planning devices such as primary and secondary

axes, hierarchies of mundane and ceremonial, and an impressive symmetry in some of the façades. The Secretariat was laid out in slender blocks on *pilotis* so as to create lateral harbours of greenery across the site. These wings and this landscaping responded to the open 'U' shape of the International Labour Organization further along the shore. A secondary axis, running through the library, was also aligned in this direction. But the undisputed focal point of the scheme was the Assembly Chamber, distinguished from the rest by its bulk, its symmetry, and its concentrated sculptural power. Its curved section and tapered plan were conditioned by requirements of acoustics (where Gustave Lyon played a hand), visibility and structure. The resulting volume fitted neatly into a promontory jutting into the lake and could be read as the symbolic 'head' while the Secretariat formed the 'arms'. The Assembly was also given prominence by the main north/south axis passing down its middle line. This started at the car entrance to the site, ran across a formal court of honour, under a porte-cochère with seven entrances, into a vestibule, then into the Hall of Delegates — the main Assembly Chamber — a curved volume of great psychological concentration. After this the axis re-emerged, but on the lake side, under the Presidents' Pavilion. This revealed Le Corbusier's institutional interpretation as well as his capacity to inject old rhetorical devices with new meaning. The entire element was a sort of monumental portico supported on a grand order of huge *pilotis*, and in one version it was even surmounted by an equestrian group like that in San Marco, Venice, while in another study Le Corbusier showed a huge hand in a gesture of benediction. The curved flanges of the Pavilion also resembled the bridge of a ship, as if the League were a vessel of state being steered towards a peaceful future of progressive liberalism. The curve brought the energies of the Chamber of Delegates to a focus, then threw them towards the distant Alps, but it also did the opposite, drawing the setting in towards the building. It was an epic gesture, a sort of giant antenna receiving news then transmitting the decisions of the world council to all nations.

Le Corbusier's scheme was an apotheosis of the horizontal, especially when its honorific lake façade was seen across the water. The landscape flowed underneath, and on clear days it would have been possible to see the jagged Jura massif hovering above the strict line of the roof. The bands of glass and granite created multiple rhythms rising to a crescendo around the sculptural mass of the Assembly. They echoed the lake surface and introduced a dignified calm. The horizontal suggested equipoise, reasonableness, an equal footing for every representative. The Secretariat was crowned by a long roof terrace like the deck of a ship where delegates might go to chat, take the air, enjoy one of the most spectacular landscapes in Europe, then redescend to their offices. These were furnished with double-glazed windows stretching the length of the building, making the most of light and view. Luminosity was a key to the scheme — a metaphor, no doubt, for enlightened decisions cleanly made. During night sessions, the translucent walls of the General Assembly auditorium would have glowed over the water, a reassuring beacon of international co-operation. Into his League of Nations scheme Le Corbusier poured all his idealism, his noble vision of man triumphant, his hope that a new world order might come about in which human laws would harmonize with the rules of nature.

The jury consisted of both Beaux-Arts architects and men liable to be more sympathetic to modern architecture, such as H.P. Berlage (designer of the Amsterdam Stock Exchange), Josef Hoffmann, Karl Moser and Victor Horta, the Art Nouveau master (who was chairman of the committee). The Le Corbusier/Jeanneret entry excited immediate interest. After six weeks of deliberation, it was tied with eight other schemes. Then Lemaresquier, the French delegate on the committee, complained that Le Corbusier had broken the rules by submitting prints instead of the original ink drawings. He insisted on disqualification. The resulting uproar was intensified when it emerged that Le Corbusier had come in half a million francs under the budget whereas all the other finalists were well over the limit, some of them by as much as 100 per cent. Le Corbusier used every means to activate the press in support of a crusade for modern architecture. In 1928 he published a book, *Une Maison, un palais* explaining the principles behind his idea and showing up the heavy-handedness of his competitors.

Worse was to come. In the ensuing confusion the site was moved back from the lake to the Ariana Park, and the programme was expanded to include a World Library; a second, limited competition was announced. This was nothing but a front for political machinations. The provisional winners, Nénot and Flegenheim (the former was designer of the Petit Palais in Paris), were asked to develop plans further with a team of other academic architects: Broggi, Vago, Vaccaro and Franzi (all from Italy), Lefebvre and Labro from France. Le Corbusier ploughed on with a modified proposal for the new site. Then, to his astonishment, he discovered that the official team were aping his plan ideas, without acknowledgement or understanding. In 1931 he filed a 31-page lawsuit, only to receive the reply that the League did not recognize complaints from private individuals. Bureaucratic ineptitude destroyed the last illusion of grand ideals. At the end of the 1930s a ponderous pastiche of Neo-Classicism was completed in Geneva, while Le Corbusier's drawings gathered dust.

The loss of the League of Nations prize was perhaps the worst setback of Le Corbusier's career, but the furore placed the architect and modern architecture on a world stage. It was easy enough to portray the whole saga as a competition between outmoded cultural forms and the inevitable path of the future. In retrospect Le Corbusier's project is seen as a major step in the evolution of the modern movement. It takes its

87 Model of the
Centrosoyus, Moscow,
1927–8.

place alongside Gropius's Dessau Bauhaus of
1926 or the Van Nelle Factory in Rotterdam by
Stam, Brinkmann and Van der Vlugt of 1928, as
a major paradigm for dealing with the problems
of the large programme. It combined the sliding
planes and dynamic plan rotation of modernism
with a clear classical hierarchy of axes and lines
of approach; it was a sculpture in the round
drawing the landscape setting and the diagonal
route of quai du President Wilson into it, but it
also had façades. It cross-bred the spatial layering
and ambiguity of Cubism with Guadet's Beaux-
Arts methods for distinguishing 'éléments' of
'circulation' and 'surfaces utiles'. It showed how
the free plan could be exploded inside out, so
that a building became an engine of discrete parts
linked by shafts, or an organism with glands fed
by arteries. The procedure and the devices would
recur in other large schemes of the late 1920s and
early 1930s, and even in Le Corbusier's project
for the United Nations headquarters (1946).

   In the summer of 1926 Le Corbusier had been
invited by the Soviet Union of Co-operatives
(Centrosoyus) to submit a competition entry for
its new headquarters in Moscow and was eventually awarded the commission. The Centrosoyus
programme called for modern offices for 3,500
employees, as well as communal facilities like a
restaurant, lecture halls, a theatre, a club and a
gymnasium: work and leisure to be combined in

what the Soviet avant-garde of the time called a
'social condenser'. By 1926 abstract art and
mechanistic modern architecture were established
in certain Russian cities as appropriate symbolic
media of the revolutionary ethos, but there
were many competing ideas and groups. The
ASNOVA group — well represented by Konstantin Melnikov, designer of the Paris Soviet
Pavilion of 1925 — favoured a jagged and
dynamic expression evoking the energy of the
masses. Moisei Ginzburg and the group known
eventually as the OSA rejected ASNOVA as the
last gasp of bourgeois aesthetics; they required a
more impersonal and sober language supposedly
related directly to the processes and programmes
of society. The anti-monumental stance of
Meyer's League of Nations scheme stemmed
from a similar point of view in Germany known
as 'die neue Sachlichkeit' or 'New Objectivity'.
There would be much give and take between Le
Corbusier and the Soviet Union in the 1920s. His
own position was perceived as standing between
formalist and functionalist extremes, like the
work of Ivan Leonidov, a Soviet architect he
admired.

   Le Corbusier had little difficulty translating his
vision of technocratic social leadership from
capitalism to socialism. The various projects for
the Centrosoyus evoked the idea of technical
progress and mass co-operation through a lan-

guage of precisely poised slabs, glazed façades and open forums of *pilotis* linked by spiralling ramps. As in the League of Nations project, Le Corbusier made the main auditorium the 'head' of the scheme, splicing the other functions around it in a Constructivist collage which echoed the image of an aeroplane in its spreading wings and curved canopies and which responded to the diagonals of the streets. *Pilotis* were varied in size and profile to accentuate different elements within the overall hierarchy, while the façades combined double glazing through which warm or cool air was to be pushed mechanically. Le Corbusier called this double-skin system 'respiration exacte', but in Moscow it did not work well. The walls of the Centrosoyus were encased in 16-inch thick slabs of red 'Tufa' stone. These were good insulation against the extreme summer and winter temperatures of Moscow and gave the building a suitably honorific character.

The Soviet avant-garde was trying to map out an architectural and urbanistic strategy for an egalitarian, industrializing society. Le Corbusier was particularly intrigued by communal housing schemes in which a distinction was made between slabs containing rows of apartments and ancillary volumes containing communal areas such as dining rooms. Konstantin Nikolayev's student dormitory in Moscow of 1928 was of this broad type (Pl.103), while Moisei Ginzburg's Narkomfin apartment building of the same year (also in Moscow) employed an ingenious 3 over 2 section so as to combine spacious living rooms with lower bedrooms. The Narkomfin was a slender slab on *pilotis* with an interior 'communal street' running from one end to the other on upper floors; Le Corbusier would employ similar devices in his Marseilles Unité d'Habitation twenty years later. But the impact of Soviet ideas was already visible in Le Corbusier's designs for two communal institutions in Paris, each at the opposite end of the social spectrum: the Maison de Refuge for the Salvation Army (1929–33), and the Pavillon Suisse for Swiss students visiting the Cité Universitaire (1930–2). The juxtaposition of slabs with curved communal areas in both housing *and* office solutions, indicates that this arrangement was another basic leitmotiv of Le Corbusier's. Alan Colquhoun has suggested that the architect frequently used the same 'type' in different contexts and that 'this concept of type relates to a mythic form rather than to the means of solving particular problems ... as with physiognomic forms or musical modes, a number of different contents can be attached to the same form.'

While Le Corbusier was still fighting his battle over the League of Nations in 1929, he was approached by Paul Otlet, Secretary of the 'Union des Associations Internationales' with the idea of designing a centre of world culture for Geneva. It was Otlet's ambition to promote peace and progress through interdisciplinary exchange in all fields of knowledge; in other words to create a League of Nations of the mind to stand alongside the political institution: 'one point on the globe where the image and meaning of the world may be perceived and understood ...

a sacred shrine, inspiring and co-ordinating great ideas and noble deeds'. This vision of universal man above barriers of nation, caste and creed inspired Le Corbusier, as did the idea of world history as a continuum of progress. Of course the whole thing was a theoretical project, but they did decide on a real site: the slope of Grand-Saconnex looking down over Lac Léman, over Geneva — and, of course, over the League of Nations.

Le Corbusier conceived the Mundaneum in terms of both an acropolis and a temple precinct. It was dominated by the World Museum, a cross between a ziggurat and a square spiral of ramps. Around and below this were a Centre for International University Studies, an International Library (to include films and photographs as well as books and documents), a 'representation of Continents, States and Cities' devoted to 'Man living in Society, Man submitting himself to the Law of the City', a Congress Hall, and a host of other meeting places and accommodations. This 'upper city' was reached up a sacred way from the lake, a procession over platforms, courts and ramps, culminating in the 'shrine' of the Museum. The axial hierarchy of the scheme as a whole would have done credit to any Beaux-Arts trained architect, and, as Von Moos has pointed

88 Project for the Mundaneum, Geneva, 1929.

out, there are uncanny resemblances to Hemle and Corbett's reconstruction of 'King Solomon's Temple and Citadel' published in the United States in *Pencil Points* of 1925, and exhibited in Germany in 1926. Whether or not he knew of this source, it was clearly Le Corbusier's aim to return to the beginnings of monumental architecture, to Babylon, or Nineveh, or even to Saqqara where the prototypes of the Western architectural tradition — columns, walls, temples, courtyards, hypostyles, the stepped pyramid — were brought together as a grand ensemble for the first time. The Mundaneum was laid out with the help of the Golden Section, and was supposed to embody those ideal and universal values underlying all traditions, all places, all times — what Wright would have called 'that elemental law and order inherent in all great architecture'.

If the layout contained Beaux-Arts reminiscences, the buildings themselves did not: they were radiant monuments to the machine age shorn of historical trappings, yet evocative of ancient schemes of order. The World Museum returned to the archetype behind both ziggurat and Solomon's temple, the image of a cosmic world mountain. In this case corners pointed

towards the main compass directions. One ascended to the summit by elevator and then wandered down the sequence of gently sloping ramps experiencing the flow of time from the prehistoric to the modern, and at each turn the girth of the building grew wider to contain the ever-increasing body of knowledge. The 'promenade' was divided into three parallel naves, devoted to objects, places and times; works of art, scientific instruments, documents were juxtaposed with social, natural and historical contexts. It was a way of making the evolution of mankind visible: 'this chain of knowledge upon which human works unfold across the thousands of years'. Typically Le Corbusier blended a microcosm of the historical process with an organic spiral related to natural laws and mathematics.

Such grandiose pretensions towards a universal history, charting 'the spirit of man', were not to everyone's taste. Still raw from his skirmishes with the reactionary Beaux-Arts establishment, Le Corbusier now found himself labelled as a regressive, *a priori* formalist by the international Left. In an often cited critique published in *Stavba 7*, Karel Teige, the Czech architect, rejected the Museum as an unfunctional pile, and

89 (*below*) B.M. Iofan and I.V. Zholtovsky, Palace of the Soviets, second project, 1934.

90 (*below right*) Vladimir Tatlin, Monument to the Third International, 1919–20.

accused the architect of indulging in a meaningless and reactionary programme. He objected to
the claims of 'higher values' (as one might expect
a dialectical materialist to do), and accused Le
Corbusier of departing from the true way of
functionalism:

'Modern architecture was not born of abstract
speculation but from an actual need dictated by
life itself and not by the academies or officialdom … The task and the territory of modern
architecture is in the scientific design of constructions, rationally and exactly designed. Seeking
to solve metaphysical, abstract, speculative
tasks artistically in a monumental composition is
the wrong approach, the dangers of which are
exemplified by the Mundaneum.'

This was more than a criticism of a single building; it was an attack on Le Corbusier's latent
Platonism: his belief that architecture might
invoke a higher order by touching the spirit.
Teige was probably more accurate than he
realized when he claimed that for Le Corbusier

the ultimate goal of architecture was the creation
of a temple or a sanctuary. But monuments will
only be constructed if they seem to those in
power to embody the dominant ideology. The
leadership of the liberal democracies was not yet
ready for modern architecture during the 1920s,
and Soviet Communism was soon to change its
policy of support for the avant-garde. As it
happened, neither Nazism nor Stalinism would
have much use for modern architecture in the
1930s either. Abstraction was inimical to the
needs of totalitarian mass communication: realism in the visual arts, and a species of instant
Classicism in architecture, were embraced in both
Germany and the Soviet Union at the same time.

This major shift in emphasis was already
emerging in the Soviet Union by 1931 when the
competition for the Palace of the Soviets took
place. Even so, a selection of Western European
modern architects was invited to submit entries,
including Gropius, Perret, Mendelsohn and Le
Corbusier. The programme called for a complex
of halls, offices, libraries, and restaurants.

91 Model of the Palace of
the Soviets, 1931.

There were to be two main auditoria, one for 15,000, another for 6,500. The building would be used for political speeches, rallies, and mass entertainments. The site was prominent, on the bank of the Moskva River opposite the Kremlin. The Palace of the Soviets was supposed to celebrate the achievements of the First Five Year Plan (1928–33); in effect it was to be a monument to the ideas behind the Revolution — to communism and the Soviet state.

Le Corbusier read these symbolic intentions in terms of a people's forum and a celebration of technology as an instrument of social and historical change. This was reasonable enough given his years of contact with Moscow and his knowledge of the Soviet avant-garde. Ever since the heady days just after 1917, Soviet artists had tried to express the ethos of a post-Revolutionary, forward-looking society based on the secular religion of Marxism. Futurist images blending open lattices and spirals (Tatlin) had been accentuated by machine collages expressing the separate elements of function in dynamic sculptural compositions (Vesnin). After the competition for a Palace of Labour of 1924, the splayed auditorium shape had taken on an emblematic character as the container of community focus (e.g. Melnikov's Russakov Workers' Club in Moscow of 1927–8). In his project for the Lenin Library of 1927 Leonidov had placed the reading room in a glass sphere and the stacks in a slender tower supported with the aid of tension cables. A moralistic, functionalist wing had also emerged in Soviet architecture, whose values had been well echoed in Teige's critique of the Mundaneum.

In his project for the Palace of the Soviets one almost has the impression that Le Corbusier intended to synthesize these conventions and trends, and to outdo his Russian colleagues on their own expressive territory: elevating a utilitarian and structural rationale — a social instrument — to the point where it achieved a sublime expression of what he intuited as Soviet ideals. Thus his project was a studied exercise in sculptural dynamics — a glistening machine disciplined by the demands of circulation, acoustics and structure. In plan it evoked a mechano-morph with head, arms, a slender waist, and legs, if not one of Giacometti's Surrealist stick insects. The wedge-shaped auditoria (designed with the consultancy of Gustave Lyon) were visual expressions of concentration towards the stages. Fitting neatly into the bend in the river, they gathered up the energies of the surroundings and focused them towards the centre of the scheme — a rethought *agora* forming an open-air platform linked directly to the surrounding city by ramps, with a sounding board at one end of it. The auditoria shells were suspended from splayed girders, like twentieth-century versions of flying buttresses, and in the case of the larger hall, these girders were hung on wires from a parabolic arch

(perhaps drawn from Freyssinet's designs for aircraft hangars). The public spaces inside were arranged as vast hypostyles of *pilotis*. Despite its size, the project was curiously transparent, with its arches and wires rising against the domes and spires — previous emblems of power — in the Moscow skyline. In 1934 Le Corbusier compared his idea of jostling volumes on a platform to the Campo at Pisa, with the Leaning Tower playing against the free-standing objects of Baptistery and Cathedral.

Some of the other entrants to the competition blended the auditoria together into a single bulk (e.g. Mendelsohn); others played off symmetrical moves against asymmetrical ones (e.g. Perret). Le Corbusier's strategy for disposing the main pieces emerges from his design-process sketches. He began by defining appropriate forms for the main ceremonial areas, such as the auditoria, then considered a variety of alternative ways of linking them together. For the Palace of the Soviets he examined at least seven hypotheses with the auditoria this way and that way, and with asymmetrical configurations for the whole building, before he settled on the final symmetrical scheme. In each hypothesis many considerations were tested to do with access, placement in the city, sculptural coherence, and appropriateness of idea. The decisive leap to a synthetic unity of form and content defies step-by-step analysis. What Le Corbusier had to say for the League of Nations might apply equally well to the Palace of the Soviets:

'The edifice then imposed itself, as a great joy of creation, as a masterful, correct and magnificent play of forms in light, as a relation of cause to effect that reveals the intentions, as a play of the spirit in the measure of the whole, and as the simple, unambiguous clarity and purity of a crystal. In this way the palace received a dignified appearance and became imbued with the spirit of the times.'

For all its symphonic power and subtle allusions to Constructivism, Le Corbusier's scheme was rejected in favour of a Soviet entry by B.M. Iofan and I.V. Zholtovsky, adorned with a portico, columns and giant statuary. In the later (1934) version this turned into a huge wedding cake mausoleum with Grand Orders, surmounted by a statue of Lenin. Le Corbusier wrote that a 'beginning civilization like Russia requires for its people … seductive beauty: statues, columns and pediments are easier to understand than chaste, flawless lines that result from the solutions to problems of a technical gravity and difficulty previously unknown.' The regime no longer had use for the mechanistic fantasies of the avant-garde: it needed to revert to traditional images of authority to consolidate its hold. Le Corbusier's love affair with the communist state came to an end and they went their separate ways.

Chapter 8

Villa Savoye, Cité de Refuge, Pavillon Suisse.

'Architecture has to be subject to the needs of society, rich or poor; faithful to the building programme and climate; answerable to collective needs even in the construction of dwellings. It satisfies old needs and begets new ones; it invents a world of its own.'

Henri Focillon

By the end of the 1920s Le Corbusier was playing the role for which he had prepared himself for so long, that of crusader for the New Architecture. Each project was treated as if it were a chapter in a book of revelation, unveiling the correct forms for the 'spirit of the age'. In 1929 the first volume of the *Oeuvre complète* was published, making brilliant use of black-and-white photographs to present key points of doctrine and to give the impression that the work of the preceding few years had been a self-sealed episode in which ideal types had evolved towards greater and greater clarity. The hesitations of the immediate post-war years were now well in the past, and Le Corbusier was able to see ideas that had issued from the recesses of his imagination beginning to affect global realities. Photographs of him in the late twenties show him as the gaunt technician-artist with tight suit, bow tie and wire-rimmed spectacles. He peers out at the world around him like an owl, knowing full well that the click of the shutter is recording a moment in a saga. The persona has the cultivated simplicity of the briar pipe at the end of *Vers une architecture*: Le Corbusier, *'homme type'* of the machine age, oscillating between self-seriousness and self-mockery.

By the late twenties Le Corbusier had achieved an international reputation. Translations of *Vers une architecture* into a variety of languages had helped to ignite a new spirit in many quarters. The Weissenhofsiedlung had presented his work alongside the leaders of Dutch and German modern architecture and the Centrosoyus commission had involved him in the machinations of the Soviet avant-garde. The League of Nations fiasco had been fully publicized and had focused attention on the architect as a major proponent of modern architecture. In 1928 the 'Congrès Internationaux de l'Architecture Moderne' (C.I.A.M.) was founded at La Sarraz in Switzerland, and Le Corbusier was one of the first members. This organization would act as a forum of ideas for the next thirty years.

Modern architecture in its 'heroic phase' was prey to propaganda both for and against it. Supporters held up the new forms as an inevitable expression of the times, and glossed over major differences of position. Detractors tended to lump the whole thing together as 'international functionalism'. These manoeuvres left their mark on ensuing historiography which tended to work in 'isms' rather than looking at individual buildings in any detail. The architects who gathered together at Stuttgart in 1927 and at La Sarraz in 1928, and those who were gathered together in the pages of Johnson and Hitchcock's *International Style* in 1932, had widely different ideological commitments, attitudes to tradition and formal vocabularies. At the time it was probably necessary to play these differences down in order to preserve a unified front against hostile forces, but in retrospect it is striking how varied in quality and intensity the buildings of the period were. The poetic force of works by Mies van der Rohe, Le Corbusier, Rietveld or Leonidov (to mention only four) sets them apart from routine boxes on stilts with strip windows that were merely wearing the acceptable period uniform. Classic works need to be extricated from the historical categories which encrust them.

This is certainly true if one is to understand three of Le Corbusier's best-known buildings of the period 1928–33: the Villa Savoye at Poissy (1928–9), the Cité de Refuge (1929–33) and the Pavillon Suisse (1930–2). All have had a seminal influence on the work of at least four generations of architects worldwide, and have therefore fallen more than usually prey to the refracting and distorting power of later ideologies. Taken together they illustrate the complete assurance of Le Corbusier's formal system in maturity, and even hint at reasons for changes in style that were imminent. They show how the architect's *'recherche patiente'* proceeded from scheme to scheme, using and reusing similar types, but extracting new meaning from them. The Cité de Refuge and the Pavillon Suisse are both variations on the theme of the glass slab with attached communal elements at ground level, and are therefore conceptual cousins of the Centrosoyus and direct relatives of Le Corbusier's ideas for housing. The Villa Savoye is yet another descendant of the Citrohan and of the intervening canonical houses.

92 'Les Heures Claires', the Villa Savoye, Poissy, 1928–9 view towards the entrance from the south-west showing the building in its restored state.

The Villa Savoye has had a glorious career in history books but a rough time in fact. The original clients used the building only slightly in the 1930s. During the war it was used by the Nazis as a haystore, and in the 1950s was in a decayed state. Now it is a national monument with no one living in it. Meanwhile the building has taken on the character of a classic work in critical assessments. In the 1940s Sigfried Giedion singled it out as an example of his 'space/time' conception, referring (presumably) to the rich spatial effects of the villa, and the importance of changing view points. He called it a 'construction spirituelle'. The building has continued to occupy the imagination as the image *par excellence* of the 'machine à habiter' — a pristine health house open to light, sun and views over greenery. After the war Colin Rowe resurrected the villa in the context of symbolic geometry and classical values, comparing it to Palladio's four-square Villa Rotunda in the same article mentioned in Chapter 6. The Villa Savoye has thus achieved a dual status as a paradigm of modernism and as an assertion of classical values, but the former aspect has been more explored than the latter. There have been substantial transformations of the Villa's many lessons, but these are far outnumbered by the pastiches which have reduced the twenties' vocabulary to a trivial formalism.

From the moment that the first volume of the *Oeuvre complète* appeared, Le Corbusier's ideas and forms took on a new presence — parallel to the unique aura of the works themselves — in the realm of photographs and drawings. Even today there are people who pontificate on the Villa Savoye without having made the thirty-mile journey to the northwest of Paris to see the building itself. With the *Oeuvre complète* Le Corbusier created his own version of his own history, as well as a treatise. Each building was given a new context in an abstract temporal corridor removed from particular settings; other Le Corbusier schemes became the neighbours. 'Les Heures Claires' (as the Villa Savoye is also evocatively known) can be found near the beginning of volume 2, away from the other classic villas of the 1920s, and before the larger communal buildings of the 1930s. There the building lives for evermore, in the mood of a summer's afternoon, the sharp planes floating above grass and in front of trees, the undercrofts picked out by gashes of shadow. The photographs take us for an imaginative walk through a world of limpid cylinders and semi-reflecting panes of glass up a ceremonial ramp. Golf clubs and expensive gloves on the landing hint at a life of sporting chic, while in the kitchen broken bread and a Purist coffee pot suggest the sacramental. The roof terrace rides above the landscape like the deck of a well-to-do-liner. Each vignette is carefully posed.

If one approaches the villa for the first time today one sees it as a historical monument in a

carefully restored state. The house is not monochrome, but coloured like a Purist picture. White
paint on *pilotis* and on the main box stands out
sharply against the green walls of the undercroft,
the pink and blue of the curves on top. The
façade facing the drive is earth-bound in its
middle part, and this provides a strong frontal
plane which is penetrated either side by the
receding perspectives of *pilotis*. The approach is
by car and as one passes under the building (a
demonstration of urban doctrine), and follows the
curve of industrial glazing (of which the geometry

was determined by the car's turning circle), it
becomes clear that one is to be drawn into a
machine-age ritual. The plan of the building is
square (one of the 'ideal' forms from *Vers une
architecture*), curves, ramp and grid of structure
providing the basic counterpoint to the perimeter.
The section illustrates the basic divisions of a
service and circulation zone below, a *piano nobile*
above, and the celestial zone of the solarium on
top: it is the section-type of Le Corbusier's ideal
city but restated in microcosm.

A chauffeur is assumed, and one is dropped off

93 Villa Savoye, roof
terrace at first level looking
towards the salon and
solarium. Photograph taken
soon after completion.

94 Villa Savoye, plans:
(*left*) ground floor; (*centre*)
level 1; (*right*) level 2.

on axis, to proceed then into the main hall at ground level through a flanking portico of *pilotis*. The garage and servants' quarters are at this level, linked to the high life above by a spiral stair. A free-standing wash-basin poses as an industrial 'ready-made' and invites ablutions before the ascent. The honorific path is clearly signalled by the ramp which is the spine of the whole idea. Le Corbusier referred to this particular version of the *promenade architecturale* as an *Espace Arabe*. Even a scrupulous inspection of photographs and drawings cannot hope to re-create the feeling of space, the sense of rising up into an illuminated realm, or the intensive lyricism of sun-lit geometries seen through layers of semi-reflecting glass. The building imposes its own order on the senses through sheer sculptural power. To enter is to step into the fantastic world beyond the picture plane. A curve hints at a ship's funnel, recalls a Purist bottle then slips by as a servants' stair; windows, tiles, *pilotis* and other naked facts are raised to a new level of significance through an intense abstraction.

The salon/dining room, bathroom, kitchen and other living quarters are grouped together on the *piano nobile* around the roof terrace which opens to the south and lives ambiguously as an outdoor room connected to the sky. The strip windows, which appear equal on the outside, mask a variety of internal realities which are jigsawed into the plan: in places they are glazed, in other places open. They offer vignettes of super-real intensity over grass and trees. A cult of health — which architect and client may have shared — is announced by the tiled *chaise-longue* next to the bath, and the solarium at the top level. The ramp continues up towards a rectangular opening cut in the curved screen, offering stunning views over the softly rolling hills of the Ile-de-France. The architect's own description captures the atmosphere of what was intended as a summer house:

The site: a spreading grassy meadow in the shape of a flattened dome ... the house ... a box hovering in the air ... in the midst of fields overlooking the orchard ... The occupants ... found this rural setting beautiful ... who came here because they will contemplate it in its preserved state from the top of their roof garden or through their long windows facing in all directions. Their home life will be enfolded in a Virgilian dream.'

When Le Corbusier was approached with the commission for the Villa Savoye in 1928, he had reached a stage of extreme clarity in the formulation of his vocabulary. He was well-armed with *a priori* ideas, and even with ambitions to make demonstrations of his principles. The site was unusually expansive: open on all sides rather than hemmed in by surrounding buildings. The line of approach from the road corresponded with long sight-lines towards a distant landscape view. As for the Savoyes, Le Corbusier later described them as 'totally without preconceptions, either ancient or modern'. They wanted a prestigious and up-to-the-minute summer house accommodating a relatively small programme, including provision for cars, an extra bedroom, and a caretaker's lodge. Le Corbusier had almost *carte blanche* and needed to set his own limits.

It seems that Le Corbusier came up with most of the ideas for the final building early on, then went through a series of alternative studies between autumn 1928 and spring 1929, before coming back almost to the beginning. The first project seems to date from September 1928 and was captured in a series of perspectives, plans, doodles and an axonometric drawing showing the driveway approaching the building on one side, and returning to the road on the other (Pl.4). The perspectives portrayed the essential idea of a four-square building, horizontal in emphasis, supported on rows of *pilotis* and crowned by curved forms. An interior perspective visualized the view from the roof terrace, while plans examined orientation to the sun, the relationship of the structural grid to partitions and the square perimeter, and, of course, the placing of functions: these corresponded approximately to the layout of the finished building, but Madame Savoye's boudoir, bedroom and solarium were all contained together at the roof level in curves that extended the 'free plan' into space, like the stack at Les Terrasses.

95 Study of symmetrical scheme for Villa Savoye, late November 1928 (Fondation Le Corbusier).

The client wished to reduce the September scheme in order to bring down the cost, so, in early November, the architect experimented with a more compact version of the plan. The ramp was dropped altogether and replaced by a straight flight of stairs which took less room. But the decrease in area also forced the abandonment of the symmetrical, car-turn curve at ground level. Further up the building, the curved accommodations were top-heavy and uncomfortably squeezed into the perimeter. Overall the proportions became ungainly. A day later, on 7 November, Le Corbusier tried shifting around the same pieces in an even smaller plan size, with equally clumsy results.

In late November 1928 curves were dropped from the scheme altogether in a plan of an almost Palladian character, with stairs on axis, side wings at the second level, and a symmetrical mass sticking up three storeys in the middle. While this was tidier than its predecessors, and recognized something of the order of the first project, it did not satisfactorily integrate the 'Five Points' with each other, or the circulation at ground level with the *piano nobile* above. The architect needed to regain the fluidity of the initial idea while still accommodating the reduced ambitions of the client: the compromise was achieved by shifting Madame Savoye's bedroom and boudoir down from the roof to the *piano nobile*, where they were squeezed into place alongside the other spaces, which had to be reduced to fit the new arrivals in. Taking away the destination of the *promenade architecturale* did something to undermine the symbolic cogency of the ramp, but Le Corbusier needed to retain these curves for 'ideal' reasons of his own. They were a sort of 'code' for the life of enjoyment on the roof, and as such were an element of the 'section-type': traffic and ground below, living in the middle, arcadia on top. They were also a visible manifestation of the free plan attuned to the many internal pressures and movements of the building's sculptural form. In the finished work the curves appear concave or convex, planar or volumetric, as one shifts position. They also help to resolve asymmetries and to project the building's energies towards the setting.

The design process of the Villa Savoye — like the design process of his other canonical houses — reveals the way in which Le Corbusier tried to splice together schemata of different kinds in the search for an integrated form. With the Villa Savoye it was a question of channelling and containing a route inside a regular volume, but linking that route to spaces of different size and intensity. Symmetry and asymmetry were both relevant, as were closure and transparency, a disciplining grid and fragmentation of that grid, the taut planes of the box and the sensuous spaces created by curves. All this resulted in a new combination for the 'Five Points'. At the end of the 1920s he drew a series of sketches comparing the house to the Maison La Roche/ Jeanneret (noting that the compositional type was 'picturesque' and 'eventful'), to the final project for the Villa Baizeau at Carthage (the version

that looked like the Dom-ino skeleton with curved partitions inside it), and to the Villa Stein at Garches (which was the most 'difficult' but 'satisfying' because it was a pure prism). The Villa Savoye fused together the asymmetry, spatial drama and *promenade architecturale* of the first, with the skeletal character of the second, and the geometrical clarity of the third. It combined the square, the grid, the axis, the frontal plane and a turbulent drama of interior and exterior spaces, volumes and surfaces; and it managed to play these together while maintaining unity, hierarchy and an appropriate level of detail.

At Les Terrasses *pilotis* were restricted to the interior, but at the Villa Savoye they were made to play many roles inside and outside. They lifted the box above the landscape, channelled the movement of the car and accentuated the main axis. On the sides of the building they were flush with the façades, and this gave a clear reading of load and support. But on the front and back they were recessed under the slab and this engendered a hovering effect as well as a slight sense of horizontal movement in the superstructure. Inside, the grid was broken up to dramatize the independence of partitions or to receive the main pedestrian path. Thus the moment one steps inside the villa one finds a new structural rhythm taking over with the two *pilotis* flanking the door, and a square pier answering to the corner of the wall by the base of the ramp. This was another variation on the 'Four Column' entrance idea.

Details served iconographic as well as visual and practical functions, and in the Villa Savoye there was the special richness of being able to see through so many layers of the building at once: a *piloti* in the foreground might pun with a stack or the spiral stair in the background. Some accents were made expressly to create visual tensions. The *fenêtres en longueur* were varied in places to

96 Variations on the syntax of the 'Five Points of a New Architecture': 1 Maison La Roche/Jeanneret; 2 Villa Stein/de Monzie; 3 Villa Baizeau; 4 Villa Savoye.

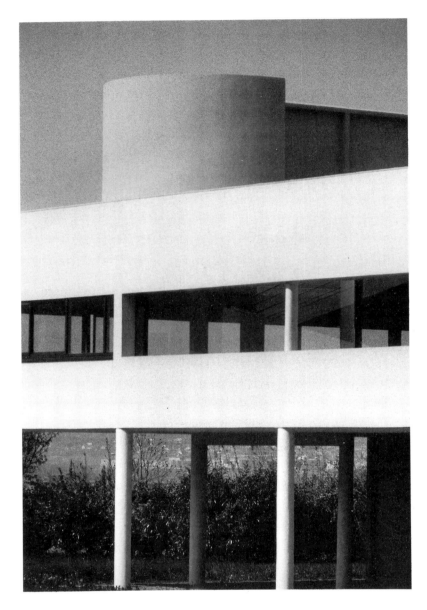

97   Villa Savoye, detail of
the south façade.

ship and the concrete frame blend into forms
born of Purist painting. The rituals of upper
middle-class existence are translated into an
allegory on the ideal modern life which even
touches upon the Corbusian typologies for the
city: separate levels for people and cars, terraces
open to the sky, a ramp celebrating movement.
The fantasy is translated into conventions that
avoid arbitrariness and that reveal Le Corbusier's
ambition to make an equivalent to the logic,
order and sense of truth he had intuited in the
great styles of the past. Rationalism was a point
of departure, but not the aim. He wished to re-
inject the ideal content that relativism and
materialism had destroyed (Pl.142).

The 'Classicism' of the Villa Savoye — like that
of Les Terrasses — is of a generalized kind:
impeccable proportions, harmony of part and
whole, the sense of repose, a just sense of hierarchy. Trabeation is given a new elemental
definition using the simplest forms of column,
slab, wall and opening. The same is true of Mies
van der Rohe's contemporary Barcelona Pavilion
which likewise echoes Laugier's reductivist hut —
the supposed archetype of the Classical language.
At the Villa Savoye the *piloti*, basic instrument of
the new architecture *and* the new urbanism, takes
on the identity of a purified column. Savoye
seems to be another mechanized Trianon in an
idyllic landscape or perhaps a 'cube house' with
Palladian innuendoes, and its section restates the
mundane base, *piano nobile*, and upper zone of
Renaissance house typology, while its ramp restates the grand central stair in a machinist mode.
But the automobile procession around to the
back surely echoes Le Corbusier's obsession with
the Parthenon, just as his ideal mathematics,
'Doric morality' and sharp profiles recall his
ancient Greek ideal:

'From what is emotion born? From a certain
relationship between definite elements: cylinders,
an even floor, even walls. From a certain
harmony with the things that make up the site.
From a plastic system that spreads its effects over
every part of the composition. From a unity of
idea that reaches from the unity of materials used
to the unity of the general contour.'

The Villa Savoye has been one of the great
form-givers of modern architecture. Imitations of
it can be found from Tokyo to Long Island.
During the 1930s it was regarded by modern
architects as a canonical work. But if it marked a
new beginning for followers, it was the end of a
line for its own creator, who never used white
forms, slender *pilotis* and ribbon windows in this
way again. Even before construction was complete, he was at work on the Villa de Mandrot for
a site near Le Pradet in Provence — a steel-
framed building with rubble walls. Le Corbusier
pursued new directions philosophically and
formally in the early 1930s. Primitivist and
regionalist strands were accompanied by intensified research into urbanism, plate glass and
metal frames. The Loi Loucheur of 1928 made
more funds available for housing and was expressly designed to revive the ailing steel in-

emphasize the anti-clockwise rotation of the car's
route: in the main driveway façade, for example,
there was absolute symmetry except for a vertical
strut that was placed to the left but not to the
right. The strip window bordering the terrace in
the south façade was so broad that it had to be
reinforced by two baby *pilotis* linking horizontal
stiffeners. Seen from the outside these delicate
cylinders hover in an ambiguous position. They
seem to be part of the façade (which they are) but
their diminutive size in comparison with the
normal *pilotis* also forces a perspectival reading
so that they are read simultaneously well within
the building. As in the Parthenon, optical distortions add vigour to the overall form.

If the Villa Savoye had been a mere demonstration of formal virtuosity it would not have
touched expressive depths. The tension of the
building relies on the urgent expression of a
utopian dream. Icons of the new age such as the

dustry. But there were many motivations behind
Le Corbusier's innovations, as one can see from
the design processes of the Pavillon Suisse and
the Cité de Refuge.

To understand the programme and imagery of
the Cité de Refuge it is necessary to grasp the
beliefs of the organization for which it was built.
The Salvation Army was founded in the 1860s in
England by William Booth to help the destitute
reintegrate with society. The movement developed in France in the late nineteenth century
under Protestant patronage, and by the early
1920s was responsible for a variety of hostels
and hospices in different parts of the country.
In 1926 Le Corbusier designed an extension to
the organization's Palais du Peuple at rue des
Cordeliers in Paris, and in the late twenties
worked on the 'asile flottant' *Louise Catherine*, a
longboat that was revamped as overnight accommodation for tramps along the Seine. The Salvation Army was reformist without being revolutionary. It mingled moral concern, charity, and
correction towards 'useful' societal norms. Much
of this appealed to Le Corbusier's idea of human
improvement through the provision of the
'correct' type of environment.

The Cité de Refuge was to stand on the rue
Cantagrel in the thirteenth arrondissement in a
poor district close to the railway running out of
the Gare d'Austerlitz. The programme combined
overnight accommodation for men and women, a
children's crèche for single or married but working mothers, a canteen for inmates or casual
visitors and ateliers for the training of labour.
The building also needed to reflect the phil-
anthropy of the donors. Chief of these was the
Princesse de Polignac, an heiress of the Singer
Sewing Machine fortune, who had already employed Le Corbusier in 1926 to make suggestions
for a house (on which she had not acted). The

98 The Primitive Hut as an
archetype of Classicism
(from William Chambers,
*A Treatise on Civil Archi-
tecture*, 1759).

princess was one of those rare philanthropists to
bridge the world between avant-garde salon and
social causes for the destitute.

There was no firm convention for a building of
this type, so Le Corbusier translated the ethos of
Christian charity and moral re-armament into the
terminology of his own reformist yearnings for
the modern city. He had already attempted to
persuade Monsieur Loucheur, the Minister of
Housing, to make the Salvation Army into a
major patron of communal house types, but
without success. The site on the rue Cantagrel

99 Ludwig Mies van der
Rohe, the Barcelona
Pavilion, 1929.

100 Cité de Refuge, Paris,
1929–33.

101 Cité de Refuge,
entrance bridge and canopy.

102   Cité de Refuge, plan of entrance level.

103   Konstantin Nikolayev, student housing, Moscow, 1927.

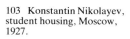

104   Preliminary project for Cité de Refuge, summer 1929 (Fondation Le Corbusier).

offered a chance to make a demonstration, to indulge in radical surgery, to cut out the choking traditional fabric, and to insert a new mechanism for generating light, space, greenery, human well-being and moral uplift. This was Le Corbusier's first chance to deal with the urban poor on a large scale, and he began to think of the building as a Salvation Army equivalent to a Soviet 'social condenser'. The first scheme of summer 1929 was for a pair of blocks (one for men, one for women) lifted up on *pilotis*, and isolated from the surroundings by a sunken garden and connecting bridge. A wedge-shaped auditorium with a curved back marked the entrance and reconciled the geometry of the street to that of the lateral slabs. These had blank end walls facing south, and fully glazed façades looking west. The image was of a crisp new *machine à habiter* combating the decayed buildings around it: Le Corbusier characterized it as a 'usine du bien' — 'a factory of goodness'.

In spring 1930, partly in response to changes of programme, partly for the sake of a clearer concept, the two blocks were swung round 90 degrees and made into a single long slab with a vast glass curtain wall facing south. Le Corbusier intended a double skin with 'respiration exacte' for heating and ventilation. The obsession with full glazing recalls the architect's enthusiasm for the 'sheer façades of bright glass and grey metal' of the Van Nelle Factory in Rotterdam, which he thought 'removed all the previous connotations of despair from the word proletarian'. In this case the glass surely had other associations as well, related to the idea of the Maison du Salut (as the Cité de Refuge was also called) as a regime of well-meaning supervision. The building took on the character of a Panopticon for improvement. Le Corbusier's moralizing technocracy was curiously appropriate to the aims of the institution. But for the inmates it was another matter: one can imagine that the average Parisian tramp had had quite enough of light, space and greenery from his life on the park bench or the banks of the Seine, and that he would really have liked windows that opened.

The entrance sequence into the Cité was like a diagram of the Salvation Army's procedures, and was clearly signalled by a series of free-standing objects arranged as a collage against the sleek backdrop of the slab. The way in was marked by a flight of steps passing into a double-height aedicule, an image of openness, shelter and reception. Here the wretched and the hungry were signed in before being sent over the bridge into the clinical-looking rotunda which was clad in white tiles, glass brick and vertical factory windows. The route was now flanked by another version of the four columns idea, but since this was approached slightly off axis one tended to take the diagonal towards the counter on the right. Here the few belongings were deposited. The counter was a long, sinuous shape directing movement towards the hall, from which one could get to the common room, the dining rooms, or the lifts and stairs up to men's and women's dormitories. The passage from street to bed had

the character of a ritual of initiation: inspection, confession, acceptance, regulation — and salvation (Pl.144).

The Cité de Refuge gave the slab idea new meanings. The public zones were like bits and pieces from the *free plan* that had been put outside a building. They resembled the pistons and valves of a disassembled engine. The architect had used cylindrical elements to channel movement in the Favre-Jacot House, and the Cité de Refuge sequence was, in effect, a clever reinterpretation of a Beaux-Arts ceremonial route. There is some evidence to suggest that Le Corbusier was directly inspired by the bastions, gate-house, moat and drawbridge of a medieval fortress. By metaphorical inversion the thick walls of past despotism became the transparent façades of supposed modern emancipation. The steel canopy with V-shaped tubes supporting it could be read as a drawbridge turned on its head.

A more certain reference is that of the ship. Liners were already a part of the architect's iconography, but in 1929 he returned from South America on board the *S.S. Lutétia* and was struck by the notion of an international, floating city in which all was healthy, regulated and clear. The nautical allusions are sensed in the long slab with its pointed prow, in the stack, the decks and much else besides. Presumably the metaphor here takes an extra point: a 'ship of salvation' rescuing the 'shipwrecked' of society from oblivion. A reviewer of the newly opened building caught the nautical allusion:

'This edifice, whose façade appears first of all like an immense glass window, has the following inscription over the entrance: 'Refuge Singer Polignac', by which its founders wish to remind us that the Princesse de Polignac, profoundly moved one winter's night by the distress of the outcasts to whom Salvation Army soldiers were giving help in front of her, donated no less than three million francs ... its architects, Messrs. Le Corbusier and Jeanneret, whose fertile originality is already well known to us, have given the building the appearance of a beautiful ship, where all is clean, comfortable, useful and gay — the turntable at the entrance, the long counter where unhappy people will come to deposit their misery as the rich deposit their valuables in a bank. In small offices, like confessionals, they confide in officers on duty at all hours, day and night. In this sort of 'central social station' or 'clearing house' one will direct them on their way ...'

The building was inaugurated on 7 December 1933 with a considerable fanfare; among the dignitaries present was the President of the Republic, Monsieur Albert Lebrun. But within months of occupation there was trouble with the 'respiration exacte' and the double-glazed façade. The summer of 1934 was exceptionally hot, and the south-facing curtain wall produced perilous greenhouse effects that turned some of the interiors into unusable ovens. The inmates and officers wanted to punch grilles in the glass and even to introduce normal opening windows. But Le Corbusier would have none of it, and in a dogmatic series of letters insisted that his 'solu-

105   Pavillon Suisse, Cité Universitaire, Paris, 1930–1. Recent photograph taken from the south-east.

tion type' was above reproach and that it was not
his fault if the building was not being run correctly. By this time analogous problems were emerging with the south-facing glass façade of the
Pavillon Suisse, and eventually shading devices
had to be worked out for both buildings. But Le
Corbusier was obsessed with the idea that the
glass slab must somehow become the normative
image for communal housing even if it meant
waiting for environmental technology to catch up.
In September 1932 he had even envisaged an
extension to the Cité de Refuge called the 'Cité
d'Hébergement' which would have extended the
slab around the corner in an indented strip like
the *à redent* housing he was simultaneously
studying for the Ville Radieuse.

The design process of the Pavillon Suisse over-
lapped with the middle stages of the Cité de
Refuge. The Pavillon Suisse is well known to
many who have never been to Paris through the
remarkable photographs and drawings of Le
Corbusier's *Oeuvre complète*, volume 2. Here it
stands a few pages after the Villa Savoye and a
little way before the urban schemes of the early
1930s, as yet another statement of mature
principle. Nearby buildings are left out, the
greenery of the site is accentuated, and soft
sunlight, more to do with Mediterranean mythology than Parisian reality, bathes the forms. The
architect presents us with a finely proportioned
steel and glass box poised on robust concrete
pilotis, facing south over a field destined to

become an athletic ground. Student rooms
conjure up that combined atmosphere of liner
cabin and monastic cell that Le Corbusier so
admired. Carefully composed groups of young
men in shirt sleeves are strategically placed so
that they may casually demonstrate the role of
the *pilotis* as liberators of terrain and circulation.
The rhetorical photographs give us black-and-
white glimpses into an ideal world of healthy
bodies and healthy minds, in which mechanization and nature run in harmony while those
'essential joys' of light, space and greenery are
made available to all (Pl.143).

The picture is filled out if one visits the site
today. The Pavillon Suisse is not an isolated
building but a terminating incident of a larger
whole — that international park to the south of
Paris called the Cité Universitaire. It stands
alongside a number of unfortunate essays in
'National' imagery from the 1920s. A diagonal
road approaches from the back, its turning circle
echoed by the curved rubble wall at ground level
containing the lounge. Above this another
concave flange contains the stair tower which
serves the main box bearing the student rooms.
Stone veneers are used extensively (they probably
weather better than white painted stucco), while
the rooms themselves face south through fully
glazed façades towards the playing fields and (in
Le Corbusier's mind, no doubt) towards the
health-giving rays of the sun. To get into the
building one passes underneath it and circles back

106 Pavillon Suisse, the
approach from the north
side. Photograph taken soon
after completion.

into the hall. This permits inspection of the *pilotis* which are different from the spindly white cylinders of the Villa Savoye, being bare concrete and extremely massive: in plan they resembled dog-bones, which is exactly what they *were* called in the atelier at 35 rue de Sèvres.

The Cité Universitaire was founded in 1921 with the intention of giving visiting foreign students decent accommodation and international contacts. In the late 1920s the Swiss community decided to build a residence. Professor R. Fueter (a mathematician from the University of Zurich) approached Le Corbusier, prompted by Raoul La Roche (the earlier client), Sigfried Giedion (the historian) and Karl Moser (the Swiss architect). The programme called for a mixture of student rooms and communal facilities. The site stood over some disused quarries, so special deep-pile foundations were necessary. A preliminary project was designed in autumn 1930, then refined and presented in January 1931. In this hypothesis all functions were lifted above the ground on slender steel stanchions. The rooms were placed in a narrow oblong running east-west, while the lounge, breakfast hall and a gymnasium (which was not called for in the programme) were clamped on to this slab in an ungainly box. The entry was at ground level through a curved, fully glazed area reminiscent of the lower level at the Villa Savoye.

The distinction between public and private areas of the programme recalls the strategy, though not the precise forms, of the Cité de Refuge and the aforementioned Soviet proto-types. The box on stilts was, of course, a generic Corbusian leitmotiv expanded here to convey the image of an ideal community floating above surrounding greenery. The scheme of 1931 embodies a new accentuation of the 'Five Points'. Strip windows are no longer dark tiers in white stuccoed walls, but bands blending with a fully glazed façade. *Pilotis* are not white concrete cylinders but steel 'I' beams supporting a steel box. These gave an appropriate directionality and perhaps betrayed the influence of Pierre Chareau's contemporary Maison de Verre (a building which Le Corbusier admired). The scheme of January 1931 gave no hint at all of 'primitivist' rubble curves or robust concrete supports of the final building.

Professor Fueter was positive about the pro-posal, praising 'the unity of conception' and claiming that it demonstrated Le Corbusier's 'mastery in striking fashion'. The committee approved of the idea of student rooms in a slab but did not like having the communal areas up in the air and hinted that they should be brought down to earth. Monsieur Jungo, Director of Federal Construction, attacked the *pilotis* and the fully glazed façade, claiming that the former were inadequate structurally (as well as being point-less), and that the latter was not a sufficient shield against the climate. The committee re-quested a second opinion from Dr. M. Ritter of the Ecole Polytechnique Fédérale in Zurich, who was even more shocked by the *pilotis*, adding that they would not react well to wind loads. He took

the scheme 'to be quite useless in its present form'. This was relayed to the architect by the diplomatic Professor Fueter.

By this time (late January), Le Corbusier had already brought the communal functions down to the ground and discovered that their rigid rec-tangular geometry did not fit well on the site. On 31 January he experimented with convex and concave curves. These were much better at recon-ciling the diagonal line of approach to the slab, and at containing and expressing interior and exterior movement. Dualities of theme between slabs and attached 'acoustic' shapes were ex-plored in the League of Nations, Centrosoyus and Cité de Refuge, but here they were given an extra complexity and richness of meaning which was surely indebted to the increasingly biomorphic forms (for example, ear shapes) of Le Corbusier's recent paintings. The contrast between oblong flanges and wavy curves was fundamental to Cubist imagery (e.g. guitars), and in the architect's hieroglyphic system these shapes had taken on multiple new associations to do with the contrast between machine and nature, stable geometry and movement, primary functions and circulation, private areas and communal spaces, the assertions of an ideal type and its accommo-dation of pressures in the setting.

The solution for *pilotis* shown in the sketches of

107 Pavillon Suisse, plan of ground floor.

108 Preliminary project for Pavillon Suisse with steel stanchions, January 1931 (Fondation Le Corbusier).

31 January was the same as the one shown in the presentation drawings. Throughout the spring months of 1931, Le Corbusier reacted to the criticisms by trying out a number of alternatives to enhance stability. He tried splay legs, grids of sixteen and thirty-two small *pilotis*, vertebrate systems of girders and beams, and squat concrete columns resembling an 'M' in plan. These practical issues were addressed at a cost. The slab looked ridiculous on a forest of matchsticks, and clumsy when supports were of varying size. Even the 'M' solution wrecked the proportions. Where the January scheme had sacrificed utility to formal effect, these studies did the opposite.

Le Corbusier needed a solution that made sense structurally, that solved the wind-load problem, that left room for drainpipes, and that fitted formally with the overall intentions of the building. He wanted *pilotis* that aligned mid-way along the slab, that were even in number, that were laterally stable, that could channel the view, that looked the same from the side, that were actually varied close-to (especially by the entrance), and that harmonized with both the circulation flow and the new 'organic' curves of the building. The resolution was at last achieved in the summer of 1931 with the *pilotis* which were variations on the 'dog-bone' shape. These did their job, looked right from all sides, and created a handsome space beneath the slab. Their complex profiles reconciled the various circulation directions and created supports that were masculine, robust and stable in form. They satisfied the structural engineers *and* the sculptor/architect and constituted another major invention which would later develop into the grand *pilotis* under the Unité d'Habitation at Marseilles.

Le Corbusier had been able to tolerate shifting the communal areas of his scheme, and had also permitted experimentation with the shape of *pilotis*, but it is doubtful that he would have done without *pilotis* altogether. On the major theme of a communal slab on posts he did not budge, even under a barrage of quite sensible criticism. The *pilotis* lay close to his central philosophical and symbolic aims, to intentions which transcended the particular case. The photographs of the Pavillon Suisse in the *Oeuvre complète* go to some lengths to show people standing, sitting or moving underneath the building. One of the captions reads:

'People without imagination still frequently pose this question: "What use are those *pilotis*?" At the festivities held in the University of Zurich in 1933, Professor *Maurin*, dean of the Faculty of Sciences for France, said to *Le Corbusier*: "I have seen the Pavillon Suisse in the Cité Universitaire. Don't you think that the *pilotis* that you have used might serve to provide the definitive solution to the circulation of traffic in a large town?" *M. Maurin*, physicist, accustomed to working in a laboratory, discovered spontaneously the rudiments of an urbanistic and architectural doctrine that Le Corbusier had expounded for ten years, without halt, in all his works and writings.'

Like some earlier and many later buildings by Le Corbusier, the Pavillon Suisse has to be understood as an exploration and demonstration of urbanistic principles. The commission was conducive to this approach as the very idea of the Cité Universitaire implied a critique of the usual Parisian slum accommodation for visiting scholars, and this particular site — with trees and athletic fields to the south — bore uncanny resemblances to the mythical landscape of Le Corbusier's ideal city. In fact, the Pavillon Suisse is a close relative of the *à redent* housing of the Ville Radieuse, which was envisaged in narrow bands lifted on *pilotis* with glazed southern façades, and which the architect began to study in 1930 (Pl.121). Le Corbusier hinted at his approach in the introduction to the second volume of the *Oeuvre complète* when he referred to the early 1930s as 'the era of large works where urbanism becomes the dominant concern' and explained that 'these buildings have played the role of laboratories'.

The clients probably did not know that their architect had given them a little fragment of his utopia, but they certainly realized that their new building had major cultural significance. The final report of the committee referred to the frankness with which the Pavillon Suisse expressed the means of construction, and to the way in which it crystallized 'the aspirations of the epoch which tend towards a new ideal'. Professor Fueter, who had supported the architect through thick and thin, forecast (correctly) that the building would 'mark an era in human development' while giving 'our country the greatest honour'. Later on, when he had seen the Pavillon Suisse complete, he wrote a more personal letter to Le Corbusier in which he said that he was 'bowled over' by it, that he thought it 'perfect in every way', and that he felt it possessed 'enormous artistic value'.

Taken together, the design processes of the Villa Savoye, the Cité de Refuge and the Pavillon Suisse reveal a great deal about the inner workings of Le Corbusier's vocabulary in maturity. All three were conceived at a time when the architect was still confident that the machine age might be on the brink of a millennium. The forms were sustained by the force of this social vision and by the ambition of defining ideal types. The architect found the right shape for each building by extending and testing well-tried solutions, yet the new programmes, sites *and* intentions presented him with unprecedented conflicts and stimuli, stretching his categories to reveal new contradictions. These were resolved by inventing new forms or, at any rate, variations on old ones. Even then, further modifications were necessary as individual elements were adjusted to harmonize with the hierarchy of each building's guiding ideas, with what Le Corbusier later called 'the rules of the game' of the new creative organism. An order had to be created which transcended any mere addition of earlier formulae by blending parts and whole, content and form into a new and indivisible unity.

109 Pavillon Suisse, detail of rubble wall.

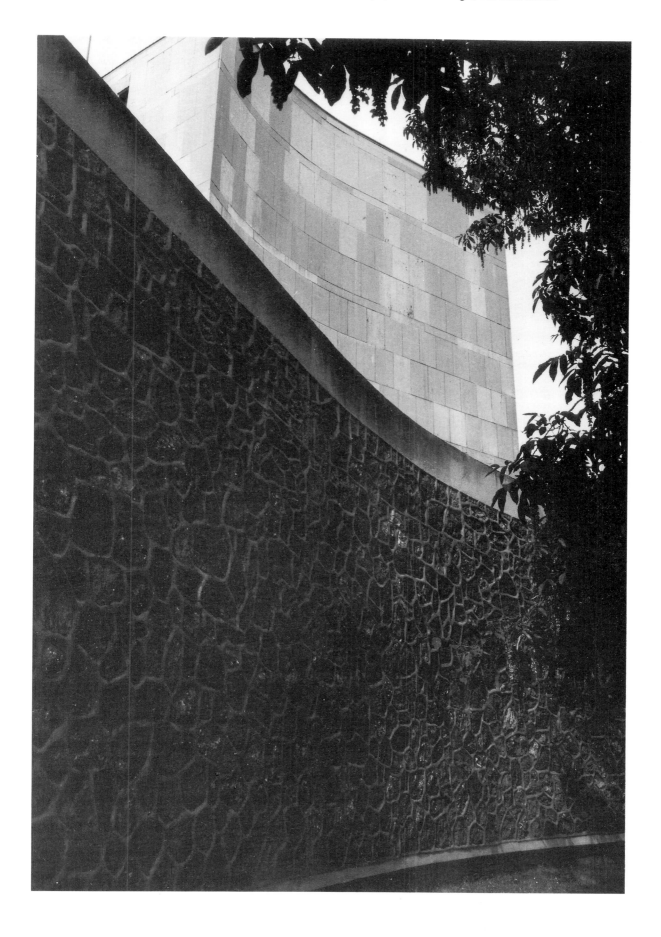

Chapter 9

Regionalism and Reassessment in the 1930s

*'It involves, basically, resolving the debate
between impersonal, international and standardized architecture and localized vernacular
architecture ... But then are the two tendencies
really antithetical?'*

Marcello Piacentini

The 1930s was a decade of mixed fortunes for
modern architecture and for Le Corbusier. The
new forms crossed frontiers to countries as far
apart as Mexico, South Africa, Japan, Finland,
the United States and England, but also ran into
a totalitarian wall close to their places of origin,
especially in Germany and Russia. Nazi criticism
treated the modern movement to a string of racist
insults and identified it with the corrosive effects
of international communism. Italian Fascism was
able to tolerate the new architecture so long as it
genuflected to nationalism and the classical
tradition. Stalinist rejections caricatured the
abstract forms as examples of 'bourgeois formalism'. Totalitarianism required the full rhetoric of
monumentality for its state institutions, and, in
Germany at least, encouraged an obvious regionalism to express the myths of blood and soil.

These shifts in the international configuration
of beliefs affected Le Corbusier in a number of
ways. The choice of a heavy-handed classical
design as winner in the Palace of the Soviets
competition was a strong hint that the time was
up for modern architecture in Russia. Attacks
against him by the critic Alexandre von Senger,
identifying him directly with communism, were a
warning of the style that later Nazi criticisms
of modernism would take. Even in the liberal
democracies, Neo-Classicism continued to be
favoured for official and state commissions. Le
Corbusier's chances were further eroded by the
Depression, which had its greatest impact on the
French construction industry around 1935. By
then the flow of commissions into the atelier at
35 rue de Sèvres had been reduced to a trickle.
The architect came near to closing down completely and had to rely increasingly on book
royalties, lecture fees and the sale of paintings.

While Le Corbusier endured these frustrations
his international fame continued to grow. As a
leading figure of the C.I.A.M. organization
(Congrès Internationaux de l'Architecture
Moderne) he had contact with the international
élites of modern architecture. In 1935 he was
invited by the Museum of Modern Art to lecture
in the United States and was treated as a culture
hero of modernism. Still no commissions materi-

alized. Le Corbusier threw his energies into
quixotic urbanistic studies for world cities such as
Buenos Aires, Paris, Antwerp and Algiers, and
continued to preach the supposed universal
values of the Ville Radieuse to a world lurching
inevitably towards war. After a period of political
engagement with the Syndicalist movement in the
early 1930s, he was drawn to desperate and
dangerous right-wing ideas in the beginning of the
following decade (see next chapter).

On the positive side was his marriage to
Yvonne (née Jeanne Victoire Gallis) which took
place in 1930. They had known one another since
the early twenties. She was the perfect antidote
to Edouard's self-seriousness. A couturier from
Monaco, dark, lively and iconoclastic, she
appealed to the unsystematic side of his nature.
Her preposterous sense of humour extended to
placing rubber insects under the plates of notable
guests. The relationship was kept extremely
private, and well away from the projection of the
artist's persona. One does not know how much he
shared his inner musings with Yvonne, but she
certainly provided a psychological anchor through
the most difficult fifteen years of Le Corbusier's
life. Early on they decided not to have children:
Edouard's monk-like devotion to art left no room
for them; besides, Yvonne was in her late thirties
when they married.

The relationship between an artist's inner,
imaginative life and external events is anything
but straightforward. It would be unwise to try and
erect a simple equation between Le Corbusier's
private life or the turbulent events of the 1930s,
and his changes in style. He responded to some
stimuli but not to others, and effects were not
always immediate. A cactus sketched on holiday,
a work of art, a ride on a ship, a political idea —
each or all could cause tremors in the form-
generating mechanism. A shift from mechano-
morphic to biomorphic forms was already evident
in some of Le Corbusier's paintings of the late
1920s. Large-scale commissions forced him to
extend some levels of his early language, as has
been shown in the design process of the Pavillon
Suisse. He saw no need to make a recipe out of
the villas of the 1920s, as many of his imitators

were to do in the following decade. The 're-cherche patiente' identified weaknesses in the earlier propositions — for example, streaking and cracking in plaster walls — and sought new and better solutions. In the early 1930s Le Corbusier would extend the steel-frame vocabulary of the Pavillon Suisse in a number of apartment designs which had the function of laboratories for his housing ideas for the Ville Radieuse. At the same time, the rubble walls and bone-shaped *pilotis* anticipated a sequence of buildings rejoicing in natural materials. Contact with rural sites and hot climates as well as failings in 'respiration exacte' forced Le Corbusier to reconsider the dogmatism of the international box. He opened himself once again to the old problem of regionalism, and turned to an inspiration familiar since youth — peasant vernaculars. Thick turf roof, fat pier and pro-tective stone wall took their places in his vocabu-lary, as did the sun shading screen or *brise-soleil*. There was a shift away from the taut skins and hovering volumes of the 1920s towards the textured façades and massive forms that one associates with the 1950s.

The 1930s have never been given a fair deal by historians of modern architecture. Sigfried Giedion, Nikolaus Pevsner and Henry Russell Hitchcock were perhaps too intent on defining the generic characteristics of the 'International Style' to accommodate buildings that deviated from this whitewashed and plastered unified front. It was precisely because Le Corbusier's transitional works of the 1930s were so played down that critics were so shocked by Ronchamp in the mid-1950s, accusing the architect of having abandoned his position; they associated this 'position' with his buildings of the 1920s, and failed to realize that he had already abandoned some of it by 1931. To understand the late works properly it is necessary to investigate the 1930s in detail, including projects and paintings as well as finished buildings.

Painting continued to be a means for trans-forming the outer world into a private hiero-glyphic system. Increasingly it allowed Le Corbu-sier to probe forces within himself and to unearth images from the subconscious. In the 1930s, forms became more complex and elusive, bound-aries and contours taking on a life of their own. A transition had been underway throughout the 1920s, with outlines becoming freer. A major shift beyond the rigidities of early Purism seems to have occurred around 1927, with the intro-duction of organic forms, the human figure and such 'objets à réaction poétique' as bones, shells and pebbles. Increasingly these fetishes with some magical resonance accompanied or dis-placed the 'objets-types' of machinism. Pene-trating the mysterious secrets of natural structure was nothing new to a student of L'Eplattenier, who years before had dissected pine-cones, trees and fossils in his drawings. Surrealism revealed a new pattern of oddities to Le Corbusier, just as Picasso and Léger unlocked the power of chiaro-scuro and monumentality in the handling of a wider range of emotions and impulses.

By the end of the 1920s, objects in Le Corbusier's paintings were no longer enmeshed in tight layers of proportionally controlled planes: they lumbered about in a fuller space, colliding in bizarre juxtapositions. One can see this in a painting such as *Sculpture et Vue* of 1929, in which a glass, a bone, a matchbox and a buxom nude line up alongside one another in a strange clash of magnitudes. Each object is abstracted just enough for one to grasp purely visual puns between the outlines of a figure and that of a glass, but the images are still identifiable enough for one to feel a jarring contrast between the mechanical and the natural. A favourite motif from the 1920s — the glass with stem — is now portrayed as a squashed oval, pneumatic in character, whereas in the classic days of Purism it would have been treated as a circle over a stereometric shape, like a regulated engineering drawing. The transition recalls that between the cylindrical *pilotis* of the villas and the sinuous, double-curve profiles of the *pilotis* of the Pavillon Suisse.

By the early 1930s Le Corbusier had assembled a rich stock-house of shapes which had a life of their own, independent of any descriptive or functional purpose. Surrealism encouraged him to make elaborate 'double-entendres' in which a curve might refer simultaneously to the outline of a woman and that of a landscape. The translation from painting to architecture continued to be anything but straightforward, but the increased complexity of the painting syntax surely allowed Le Corbusier the architect to make more daring juxtapositions and to attempt more fluid transitions in buildings. Iconographically too he now had a deeper grasp of 'montage', whereby two images seen side by side might generate a new meaning. This too would help him manage contrast, wit and irony in his architecture.

110 Le Corbusier and Yvonne in the south of France, early 1930s.

111 *Sculpture et vue*, 1929.
Pencil and watercolour.

The flirtation with Surrealism became a full-blown affair in the Beistegui apartment designed for a roof-top on the Champs-Elysées between 1929 and 1931. This was the last luxurious gasp of the Purist style. Beistegui was a fun-loving millionaire who wanted to transform this prime piece of Parisian real estate into a pleasure pad, and to do so with the help of an architect who had just achieved international fame. On 5 July 1929, in response to the client's initial approach, Le Corbusier wrote that 'my game has been played for twenty years. Today it is won. I am recognized and people know what I do.' It was, he added, a 'vedette' commission: a 'star' commission — a question of doing a 'Le Corbusier building' for a client keen to collect chic avant-garde creations.

The architect responded to these curious conditions with a retrospective commentary on the discoveries made in the villas of the 1920s. The main theme was a 'promenade architecturale' up a spiral stair on to a series of roof terraces, delimited by high walls just allowing crucial landmarks such as the Eiffel Tower or the Arc de Triomphe to show above the parapet. The idea of the 'machine à habiter' was turned into an exquisite game, with hedges that slid up and down, powered by electric motors, and a rotating periscope poking out of a funnel shape to allow a voyeur's inspection of Paris. There were other elaborate contraptions, including a pop-up film projector with screen on pulleys, and a spiral stair

unfolding around a glass screw-shaped column. The top roof terrace was arranged as an outdoor room. 'Verdure' — the great moral emblem of Le Corbusier's ideal city plans — here became an absurd carpet rendered in grass. At one end there was a false Rococo fireplace, on the mantelpiece of which the Arc de Triomphe seemed to sit like an *objet trouvé* turned into a clock. Of course, Beistegui's sophisticated guests would have recognized the reference to Magritte's Surrealist paintings immediately they arrived on the roof, drinks in hand.

The Beistegui penthouse mannerized the Purist language, placing its characteristic elements in ironical quotation marks. The 'Maison Outil', aimed ten years earlier at the problem of mass housing, ended up as a rich man's toy. Paris, the city into which Le Corbusier had hoped to drop the heart of his ideal city, grinned back — its historical monuments turned into mantelpiece ornaments. Utopia became an introverted commentary upon its own means: the redemptive images of the machine age were reduced to elegant impotence. Was this a wry commentary on the architect's own failure to carry his plan into the public realm, or on the mores of a society that reduced reformist critique to the level of chic consumption? Perhaps the parody cut deeper still, a reminder that the fragments of the ideal city are destined themselves to become elements of a historical montage.

The Maison Clarté apartment building in

Geneva of 1931 was an earnest creation by comparison. The client was Edmond Wanner, a Geneva industrialist, who also acted as contractor, and this ensured a very high standard of realization, especially in the electric welding of the steel. The Clarté rises out of the complex street pattern like a stranded ocean liner. The lower-level shops and entryways introduce a satisfactory street scale. The impact of the block is blunted by a curved podium with a façade of plate glass set into glass bricks. The slab itself is formed from a steel armature of standardized elements, yet the building still makes a less memorable claim on the *ideal* of standardization than its much less standardized 1920s precedents, let alone its more polemical cousins, the Pavillon Suisse and the Cité de Refuge. The apartments are double-height and have terraces made from cantilevered extensions of the slabs. These introduce a theme of horizontal stratification like that envisaged in the Secretariat of the League of Nations five years earlier. The slabs in turn protect the façade from the elements and support coloured awnings against the rays of the sun. There was a tentative beginning here of the idea of a sun-shade façade.

The other main apartment scheme dates from 1933: the building containing Le Corbusier's own apartment on rue Nungesser et Coli, near Porte Molitor, Paris. In this case the site was hedged in between tall façades, but there was a sports field opposite. As with the Pavillon Suisse, this was a reminder of the conditions of the Ville Radieuse and he used the commission to study relevant techniques in glass and steel construction and fabrication. To make the most of the splendid views over light, space and greenery Le Corbusier conceived the building as a much enlarged Maison Cook, around a central *piloti* and extending floor slabs in concrete. Instead of using stucco (by now it was already clear that the standard 1920s finish weathered very badly), he employed Nevada glass bricks and large plate glass windows. This way light was brought deep into each apartment. Le Corbusier had been impressed by Pierre Chareau's Maison de Verre, designed for Dr Dalsace, which made poetic use of similar materials. In the *Oeuvre complète* Le Corbusier claimed that: 'Once the building was inaugurated, the tenants spontaneously declared that a new life had started for them, thanks to the glass wall and certain common service facilities.'

On top of the building Le Corbusier placed an apartment for Yvonne and himself. This was organized on two levels, with a roof terrace and small guest room at the upper one, and the main body of the apartment below. The kitchen, living room and bedroom faced east through the street façade, towards the skyline of Paris. At the back, beyond the light court, was Le Corbusier's studio under a high vault supported on splayed beams. Light came in from the top and at the sides. The party walls in brick and rubble made a bizarre contrast with the machined steel and glass blocks of the rest of the building, a juxtaposition like that of the rubble wall and glass box of the Pavillon Suisse. The studio was a more massive

112 Beistegui apartment, Paris, 1929–31, roof terrace with the Arc de Triomphe in background.

version of the ateliers he had visualized for 'Maisons d'artistes' in 1919–20, and a reinterpretation of a project of 1929 called simply 'Ma Maison', in which the studio had had huge hooded vaults. It became his *sanctum sanctorum* — private retreat. Perched above Paris, he could let his mind roam freely, and concentrate on broad principles away from petty distractions. Each day Le Corbusier devoted a few uninterrupted hours to painting, contemplating and sketching. He would then cross Paris to the narrow atelier at 35 rue de Sèvres to intervene in the design process of his assistants and collaborators.

The combination of steel and rubble had actually emerged first of all in the context of a low-cost housing experiment of 1928–9 known as the 'Maison Loucheur'. The Loi Loucheur of 1928 made finances more easily available for cheap housing and encouraged the use of steel, and after the mixed blessings of the cement gun at Pessac, Le Corbusier probably realized that it was best to rely on a mass-producible, dry assembly system, that could be combined with materials found close to a site. The Maison Loucheur plans were as compact as ships' cabins, and contained sliding partitions and folding beds so that they could be adjusted between night-time and daytime use. But Le Corbusier was not successful in finding a patron to construct such dwellings. He therefore reverted to the old pattern of trying out a low-cost housing idea in an individual commission of some luxury.

Appropriately enough, the client was Madame de Mandrot, who had hosted the first C.I.A.M. congress at her castle in La Sarraz, Switzerland, in 1928. She wanted a holiday house for a site outside Le Pradet, near Toulon, in the south of France. The land was on a slight hill, surrounded by vineyards and less than a mile from the Mediterranean. A white cube would have violated the spirit of the place, and Le Corbusier had other ideas in mind, that harmonized better with the materials of the region. Neighbouring buildings were some distance away on other low hills, and most were made of local stone. Le Corbusier organized the house as an oblong on a plinth, providing terraces and a processional stair. He opened up the plan and the façades with the help of a metal frame, so as to make the most of breezes, light and view. For a feeling of stability and protection, he followed the hints of the neighbours and used masonry walls. The strategy was far less doctrinaire and shrill than that attempted (with limited success) at Pessac six years earlier. The de Mandrot House made a rich montage of the factory aesthetic and the primitive. In this version of 'regionalism', the mass-produced was brought in from the outside and then juxtaposed with customary objects of local practice.

In 1930 Le Corbusier also designed the Errazuris House for Chile to go on another rural site, but one he would never see. Machine-age posing was out of the question because of the

113 Clarté apartments, Geneva, 1931–3.

114 Clarté apartments, view up stairwell.

115 (*opposite*) Porte Molitor apartments, rue Nungesser-et-Coli, Paris, 1933.

116 Maison de Mandrot,
Le Pradet, near Toulon,
1929–32.

impossibility of transporting modern materials.
The architect was forced to think in terms of local
stone, timber, climate and landscape. He gave
the *piloti*, the roof garden, the free plan and the
ramp an entirely new roughness and solidity. The
Errazuris House was held up on thick logs and
stone piers; the ramp was also made of local
boulders, cut to conform to the geometry. The
roof rose above the ramp in a violent silhouette,
unlike the rigorous horizontal line of machinism.
It was coated in a dense cover of turf — a modern
version of a primeval sod cabin. The turf roof
idea reappeared soon after in a house by Antonin
Raymond for Japan, and in Aalto's Villa Mairea
at the end of the 1930s. Other sensibilities were
also probing beyond the limitations of the International Style, and looking back at the question
of regional identity via the abstraction that had
been one of modernism's discoveries.

The house at Mathes (1934–5), on the Atlantic
coast of France, was also designed without a visit
to the site. The budget was very limited and it
was a case of following local contracting practice
and materials. Photographs of the sand dunes on
the property were sent to Paris. Le Corbusier decided on a position that would make the
most of Atlantic views and create shelter against
wind. Considerable rainfall could also be expected. It was a holiday house in which the inhabitants would want to sit outside or, at least, on
half-sheltered terraces. The solution was an
armature of rugged stone walls with a secondary
system of wooden posts, floors, beams, windows
and verandas. The roof was made to slope and
drain in towards the centre line as a 'V' shape and
was made from corrugated asbestos. This simple
shed was lent a certain dignity by careful control
of proportion, solids and voids. 'And thus a
house was created without a fault, without
supervision — by a small village contractor,

honest and conscientious — and on an unbeliev-
able budget.'

'Honest and conscientious' might well be used
to describe the attitude to materials, especially
after the elaborate artifice of the 1920s villas.
Again memories of Le Corbusier's Ruskinian
formation seemed to be resurfacing: after all,
the earliest houses in La Chaux-de-Fonds had
attempted to combine timber and rusticated walls
in a direct and honest manner. The return to the
solid wall as a spatial container was a major shift
in emphasis after the *pilotis* and slabs of most of
the 1920s houses, but these solid lateral walls
were handled as abstract planes in a way that was
quite different from Arts and Crafts usage. The
diagram of the house at Mathes — its underlying
type — was to resurface fifteen years later in
India, where the scoop roof idea would recur in
the High Court at Chandigarh, and the pier/
veranda concept would be rethought in the
Sarabhai House in Ahmedabad.

Le Corbusier's 'patient search' was a gradual
experimentation with well-tried forms. Some
levels in his language altered, others remained
much the same, and on occasion he even looped
back to earlier phases to reconsider old types,
devices or elements in quite a different context.
In the translation from one setting to the other,
the 'substructure' of the idea would be given new
levels of meaning and new possibilities for future
use. Sometimes Le Corbusier would return to a
form which had been in a drawn project unbuilt
for many years, and bring it back to life. In the
same spirit he often carried about old sketches
and doodles for paintings with him on his travels,
which he used as a springboard for inspiration.

The Petite Maison de Weekend of 1935 was a
reworking of the 1919 Monol theme of a house as
a low, vaulted structure. But what had started life
as a proposal for 'mass-production houses' now

turned into a rustic retreat for a well-to-do client on a suburban site to the west of Paris. The sophisticated primitivism inherent in making a cave out of modern materials like concrete and glass bricks was emphasized by the thick turf roof climbing from the ground, the rough brick smoke stack, the neolithic stone circle in the garden, and the plain wooden panelling of the interiors. The plan seemed to contain some hidden erotic imagery: the rubble wall receiving the car was unquestionably womb-like. The house itself was formed from swelling curves. Le Corbusier contrasted the angular forms of the Citrohan and the absorbing curves of the Monol type in terms of gender: 'in the one, strong objectivity of forms ... *male* architecture; in the other, limitless subjectivity ... *female* architecture.'

The furniture designed by Le Corbusier and Charlotte Perriand in the late 1920s already delighted in a suave, Surrealist confrontation of mechanical steel tubes, polished chrome and rough cow hide. The Beistegui apartment derived part of its fascination from tongue-in-cheek reversals of the natural and the artificial. The paintings of the early 1930s collided bones with bottles, rough with smooth, the 'primitive' with the 'modern'. The Petite Maison de Weekend combined these conflicting allusions into a play of tensions, best characterized by Vincent Scully who described the building as 'this elegant

cavern, this ironic grotto half underground.'

'One says ironic because there remains a kind of intelligent distance, especially apparent in the furniture, a marvellously active collaboration of the popular, the primitive, the high tech and the *en série*. During these same years the work of Frank Lloyd Wright was also exhibiting an exotic and consciously primitive character — very straight and serious. With Le Corbusier there is more comment and a marvellous pictorialization. A sense of ironic play still persists ...'

The Errazuris, Mathes and the de Mandrot Houses had all been designed for countryside sites where it had been advisable to use local materials. The primitivist stance of the Petite Maison — in la Celle St-Cloud, a few miles from the Villa Stein/de Monzie — was frankly ideo-logical: the expression of convictions at variance with the ideal of a universal application of machine-age types. From his travel sketches and writings one realizes that Le Corbusier was becoming fascinated by folk forms in North Africa, Spain and Greece. In 1931 he visited Morocco and Algeria, particularly the Mzab. Here he was captivated by the harmony between people, buildings and the landscape, as well as by the ingenuity of the vernacular in dealing with local materials and the hot climate. The low houses blended with their natural setting and

117 Petite Maison de Weekend, Celle-St-Cloud, 1935.

118 Sketches illustrating the principle of the *brise-soleil*, late 1930s.

used shaded courtyards, ventilation holes, thick mud walls and careful orientation to keep out glare and heat. In 1935 he would even write: 'I am attracted to the natural order of things ... in my flight from city living I end up in places where society is in the process of organization. I seek out primitive men, not for their barbarity, but for their wisdom.

This did not mean that Le Corbusier was about to retreat into the desert or into a cult of peasant crafts, but it did mean that he needed to blend together old and new, universal and regional in a way that avoided the twin dangers of bogus folk-lore and inappropriate modernity. 'Regionalism' was a matter much discussed in Europe of the 1930s, but it only too often degenerated into a superficial play with vernacular motifs — hip roofs, wooden beams, deep-cut eaves, etc. — in the belief that this would lead to a 'popular' imagery. Much Nazi regionalism was of this kind, where it was confected as a Nationalist 'Heimat-stil', an antidote to 'rootless' modernism. Le Corbusier's approach to the problem was far more penetrating. He realized that vernaculars produced 'type-forms' every bit as rigorous as those praised in *L'Esprit Nouveau*, through a process of adaptation and tradition. He needed to find adequate ways of blending the sub-structures of the vernacular — their principles of organization — with the rules of his own vocabulary. The Petite Maison perhaps needs to be seen in the broad context of a reassessment of the balance between country and city: in 1934 Le Corbusier had proposed a 'ferme radieuse', an agricultural community with vaulted buildings.

Another result of the crossbreeding of inter-nationalist and regional solutions, of modern technique and rural wisdom, was the *brise-soleil* or sun-breaker. In 1929 Le Corbusier had written arrogantly that the 'machine-age' solution of 'respiration exacte' would allow the same house to be built anywhere, but in the early 1930s he soon changed his tune. The Baizeau House for Tunisia had already revealed the potential of the Dom-ino skeleton to provide a shaded veranda at the building's edge. In 1932, in a scheme for low-cost housing for Barcelona, he organized his dwellings as a tight-knit modern version of a casbah, and treated the façades to moveable louvers, the roofs to thick turf protection.

The search for a viable sun-shading element was accelerated by the architect's repeated trips to North Africa. The unbuilt Ponsich apartments of 1933 for Algeria showed how a tall building could combine glass façades and a honeycomb of protective louvers. In making this innovation Le Corbusier was careful to preserve the integrity of his frame vocabulary, while reaching out for a modern equivalent to the wooden screen 'mash-rabyas' of Arab buildings or the brick louvered 'claustras' he had seen in Morocco. He wrote:

'... so out of simple deference to imperative local conditions a 'North African' architectural style appears ... Remember the Moroccan window openings arranged like a pack of cards set up at right angles in the depth of the wall: the same sculptural and architectural results can be achieved with modern techniques. Unity, regional style ...'

Thus a new element was added to the 'free façade', but its regionalism was not so much cultural as climatic. In 1936 Le Corbusier had the role of consultant to Lucio Costa and Oscar Niemeyer in their design for the Ministry of Education in Rio de Janeiro, which was a sky-scraper clad with louvers on its most exposed façade. It was typical of Le Corbusier's method that he should gradually have coaxed new effects and meanings from his new 'architectural word'. In a multi-purpose block for Nemours, the *brise-soleil* took on the character of deep-cut loggias and verandas, lending weight and texture to the façades. In a project for the Law Court Building, Algiers (1938), this new sense of sculptural weight was used to confer civic monumentality and human scale simultaneously. And in the huge skyscraper for the Quartier de la Marine, Algiers, of 1939, the *brises-soleil* were integrated with the structure, creating a woven density of light and shade, as well as a vocabulary able to distinguish interior uses and to maintain unity and multiple scales simultaneously. All these lessons would prove useful over a decade later in India. They contributed to a broad shift in style away from the weightless skins of the 1920s buildings towards the massive perforations of the 1950s. But as usual, innovations took place within the context of well-established 'rules' of the Corbu-sian vocabulary.

One can see this transposition of inventions from one context into another if one traces Le

Corbusier's various projects for museums. In 1931 Le Corbusier wrote a letter to Christian Zervos, editor of *Cahiers d'Art*, explaining his idea for a Museum of Modern Art that would start as a small nucleus, then grow gradually as needs demanded or funds permitted, into an expanding square of parallel halls based on a module. In effect this was a flattened out version of the World Museum from the Mundaneum of 1929. In the 1930s Le Corbusier became fascinated with the ideas of Matila Ghyka on proportion in nature (*Le Nombre d'or*, Paris, 1931), and it seems likely that he must have known about D'Arcy Thompson's classic work, *On Growth and Form*, which described growth and transformations in nature in mathematical terms. In 1939 the 'Museum of Unlimited Growth' incorporated a system of structure, bays and lighting, over a square spiral plan: the geometry of a shell in rectangular terms. Meanwhile, in 1935, the architect had submitted plans for a museum for the city and state of Paris, to stand just across the road from the right bank of the Seine. For this context, the ideal type of the World Museum was modified in another direction. Le Corbusier this time took the stepped section and set it down either side of a raised courtyard with views towards the Eiffel Tower. The plan was vaguely reminiscent of Michelangelo's Campidoglio in Rome — with side wings creating an outdoor room — but the classical overtones were not enough to guarantee Le Corbusier a commission. When it came to the 1937 Paris exhibition his *Pavillon des Temps Nouveaux* was constructed using a pragmatic steel truss and tent system. But the 'idea type' of the museum did not desert him. In the museums for Ahmedabad, Chandigarh and Tokyo, designed in the 1950s, he would revert to the paradigm of

the Museum of Unlimited Growth, but transform it to a different climate, construction and programme.

If the early 1920s was a period of invention in which Le Corbusier laid down many of the ideas, types and elements that would guide his life's work, the 1930s was a period of transition in which he submitted these earlier architectural discoveries to a rigorous reassessment. When devices were found lacking they were rejected or modified, or else new ones were found in their stead. But these new inventions still had to blend conceptually and formally with the basic grammar that was found satisfactory, and that the architect tended to regard as natural and unassailable. Le Corbusier's architectural language had internal rules of its own.

One glimpses here an imaginative universe populated by conceptual and formal molecules undergoing different reactions to produce new compounds — or, if one wants a biological metaphor — an evolving set of species adapting to the demands of changing environments: as when the *brise-soleil* was invented to make the principle of the free façade tenable in a hot climate. The 1930s was a crucial phase of transition during which the basis of Le Corbusier's late works was laid. The distance from the Monol House of 1919 to its descendant the Sarabhai House of 1951–4 was made that much shorter by the Petite Maison de Weekend of 1935; the Surrealist paintings and doodles of the 1930s contained the seeds of the forms of Ronchamp; the unexecuted textured tower for Algiers was the key to the post-war *brise-soleil* façades at Marseilles and at Chandigarh. But there was one other key to this transition: the urbanistic inventions of the 1930s which, likewise, extended and transformed those of the 1920s.

Chapter 10

Politics, Urbanism
and Travels 1929 – 1944

*'The creative artist is by nature and by office the
qualified leader in any society, natural, native
interpreter of the visible form of any social order
in or under which we choose to live.'*
                          Frank Lloyd Wright

When Le Corbusier had exhibited the Ville
Contemporaine in 1922, he had been an unknown
artist from the Latin Quarter trying to capture the
attention of the Parisian public with the image of
an ideal city. France was pulling herself back to
prosperity after the dreadful impact of the First
World War. The architect had put excessive faith
in capitalism as a means to generate a better
future. Ten years later Le Corbusier found
himself assembling the plates and text for another
utopia, the Ville Radieuse, published in 1935 in a
book of the same name. He was now an acknowledged leader of the international modern movement, with contacts from South America to the
Soviet Union. He had even built fragments of his
ideal city in buildings like the Pavillon Suisse.
France was reeling from the delayed impact of
the world economic depression. Extremists of
Left and Right snarled at one another over a
shaky Parliamentary system. Fascism was safe in
Italy, Nazism on the rise in Germany, Stalinism
in control in Russia. Le Corbusier had left behind
the safety of the drawing board for the politics of
pamphlet and street: in 1930 he became an active
member of the Syndicalist movement. The Ville
Radieuse was now being proposed as a blueprint
for total social reform in the face of total break-
down.

The transition from Ville Contemporaine to
Ville Radieuse was affected by Le Corbusier's
international contacts with other planners,
especially in Germany and the Soviet Union. In
1928 at Madame de Mandrot's castle La Sarraz,
near Lausanne, the Congrès Internationaux de
l'Architecture Moderne (C.I.A.M.) had been
founded with Le Corbusier, Karl Moser, Sigfried
Giedion and Walter Gropius as senior members.
This round table of architectural knights embark-
ed upon a collective crusade to ameliorate the
modern city through large-scale rationalized
planning. The foundation document spoke of
architecture being put back 'in its true sphere,
which is economic, sociological and altogether in
the service of humanity'. The 1929 C.I.A.M.
meeting was at Frankfurt, a city which had given
major public support to housing, and the subject
was the 'Existenzminimum' ('minimum habita-

tion'). At Brussels the following year, C.I.A.M.
III focused on the relative values of high- and
middle-density housing.

In the late 1920s Le Corbusier was in continuous contact with Moscow. Inevitably he was
embroiled in debates between those who believed
in centralized cities and those committed to
'disurbanization'. His sympathies were with the
former, but one model for rationalized decentral-
ization fascinated him. This was the linear city,
first proposed in the late nineteenth century by
Arturo Soria y Mata, then converted to communist doctrines by the Soviet planner Milyutin
in the 1920s. A linear city was a continuous belt
of parallel roads and railways, with housing,
factories, terminals all along its length. It brought
country and city into close proximity, avoided any
central nucleus of power, and was expandable. It
therefore seemed an appropriate metaphor for an
egalitarian society experiencing rapid growth, in
which it was an avowed aim to demolish the
difference between peasantry and proletariat.

The Soviet disurbanists attacked Le Corbusier's
plans of the 1920s as mechanisms of capitalist
profiteering rooted in class distinctions. In 1930
he wrote a reply called 'Réponse à Moscou' in
which he endeavoured to demonstrate that his
joyous plans were for the good of all. He illustrated his text with seventeen plates showing a
considerably modified layout from the centric
Ville Contemporaine. This was his new ideal city:
the Ville Radieuse, later expanded upon in the
book of the same name. The basic idea of free
circulation and greenery through high density was
still dominant, and the constituent types were still
skyscrapers and collective apartment houses but
the plan was no longer a mandala of centralized
power. Instead it spliced together an extendible
linear city with the abstract image of a man:
head, spine, arms and body. The skyscrapers of
the Ville Contemporaine were rearranged away
from the city centre at the 'head', and the 'body'
was made up of acres of *à redent* housing strips
laid out in a stepping plan to generate semi-courts
and harbours of greenery containing tennis
courts, playing fields and paths. These all faced
south through glazed façades like so many Pavil-

lons Suisses laid end to end. They were raised on *pilotis* so that the entire surface of the city was a co-extensive, fully public space. Child care centres, communal restaurants, central heating and plumbing were all supplied, and on the roof tops there were running tracks, sandy beaches and swimming pools. Le Corbusier had been impressed by the decks of a luxury liner during his 1929 visit to South America, and in his book *La Ville Radieuse* suggested that similar features be supplied in modern housing. The apartment units steered a middle way between the luxurious *immeubles villas* and the 'minimum habitations' being proposed in Germany and Russia. Everyone lived in the same type of building: class distinctions were not acknowledged in the realm of property. The *à redent* housing fused together ship, *phalanstère*, and the utopian leitmotiv of the glazed box on stilts in a cogent imagery for an egalitarian yet technocratic society. The Ville Radieuse was dedicated to the idea that harmony could be found within industrialism by finding the right balance between individual, family, and the public order of the state; between built form and open space; between city and nature.

Were the egalitarianism and expandability introduced in an attempt at seducing the Soviets into giving Le Corbusier a major urban plan? This is possible: by 1930 droves of Western European planners were swarming eastwards to help construct the cities of the Five Year Plan. But 1930 was also the year that Le Corbusier joined the Syndicalist movement, and the new emphases of his Ville Radieuse did illustrate some aspects of Syndicalist doctrine — at least as these stood in the late 1920s, and as Le Corbusier understood them in his own, idiosyncratic way. Syndicalism had been born in the 1880s and 1890s as a coalition of anarchism and socialism and had played a central role in the French Union Movement. The Syndicalists were opposed to centralized capitalism, but not to industrialization. They rejected parliamentary democracy as a tired relic of a lost liberal age, but valued representation. They therefore dreamed up a meritocracy like a pyramid, with its base in the shop floor and the fields, its middle in regional assemblies of elected managers, its pinnacle in elected cadres of leaders. The general strike, rather than total revolution, was to be the instrument of change, and one aim was the collective control of the means of production. By the late 1920s Syndicalism was attractive to intellectuals who saw capitalism failing, who feared Fascism but also recoiled from the idea of 'the dictatorship of the proletariat'. Among them was Le Corbusier.

In the late 1920s the architect had had a brief flirtation with a right-wing organization called 'Redressement Français' which combined authoritarian and technocratic leanings. Each week he played basket-ball with one of the members, a certain Dr Pierre Winter, who may have had some influence on the architect's obsessions with athleticism, sunlight and fresh air. Another member was Georges Valois, a French Fascist who openly admired Mussolini. Le Corbusier was tempted by the idea of a strong leader as a means to realize the true plan, but troubled by a system that might destroy individual liberty. At the same time he could not accept communism, perhaps sensing that it might interfere with his élitist stance as philosopher-artist and that it might disallow his cherished urban ideals to flourish. If he was to build the Ville Radieuse he needed access to power or, given his failures with the status quo, potential power, and for this Syndicalism seemed to hold out some promise. Its doctrines were an eclectic mixture of élitism and egalitarianism, technocracy and organicism, conservatism and progressive thought. Between 1930 and 1935 Le Corbusier was an active member on the editorial staff of two Syndicalist journals: *Prélude* and *Plans*. These were full of

lofty pronouncements on the need for a 'new European order' and there was a nebulous conception of a society based on 'natural laws'. The Syndicalist idea of the hierarchy of authority implied regionalist delegation and there were even allusions to cultural groupings which ignored old national boundaries — e.g. a Mediterranean federation. Syndicalism supplied Le Corbusier with a vague political framework that settled comfortably over the contradictions that were already thoroughly embedded in his largely intuitive beliefs and dogmas.

The Ville Radieuse was a grandiose theorem for a flat site with nowhere in particular in mind, but it was only one of the planning models considered by the architect in the early 1930s. In 1929, in response to hilly ports like Rio de Janeiro and Montevideo, he had begun to work out an entirely different configuration based on linear viaducts treated as vast landscape sculptures. He travelled to South America as a guest of Los Amigos del Arte, and was astounded by the sumptuous hills and and luscious vegetation of Brazil, especially as he was able to experience these from a zeppelin and an aeroplane. The 'bird's-eye view' encouraged him to think of urbanism in terms of a 'fifth façade' — from above, and (in 1935) to write a small book, *Aircraft*, on the new world revealed by flight. He flew with Mermoz and Saint-Exupéry (the latter a poet of the aeroplane) over the Amazon, and sketched the snaking bends of water beneath. Flight revealed the works of man in a huge cosmic context of geological folds and rippling coastlines. He translated his landscape studies into a simple, curved hieroglyph: 'the law of the meander'.

Cities such as São Paolo, Montevideo and Rio de Janeiro were developing with astounding speed as the resources of the hinterland were exploited. Le Corbusier's viaduct idea was to absorb the pressure of increased population and to facilitate the rapid flow of people and goods to and from the points of exit. He envisaged a new type of urbanism for ports abutting mountains. 'From far away, I saw in my mind the vast and magnificent belt of buildings, crossed horizontally by a super highway flying from mount to mount and reaching out from one bay to another', he wrote in response to Rio. Apartments were to be slotted into the 'constructed sites' underneath, and office buildings would be blended in as rectangular incidents along the way. Typically, this idea fused a number of sources. In 1910, Edgar Chambless had proposed 'Roadtown', a sort of continuous snaking palace with a railway in the basement, houses at middle levels and roads on top. Le Corbusier was fascinated by Matté Trucco's Fiat Factory in Turin, with its car test track on the roof, and by Milyutin's linear city idea. In effect, the South American proposals rejuggled the pieces of his own urbanism — freeways, strips of housing, skyscrapers — into a sculpture evoking at the same time his sinuous sketches of the landscape and the image of a machine-age Roman viaduct.

In December 1929 Le Corbusier returned to

121   Le Corbusier inspecting a model of *à redent* housing.

L'AVENIR.

Perspective d'un Phalanstère ou Palais Sociétaire dédié à l'humanité.

Europe on board the ocean liner *Lutétia*. A luxury cabin was put at his disposal in which he exhibited sketches made during his lectures. He attended a costume ball where he sat next to Josephine Baker, in fancy dress; he drew her on the back of the invitation with the heaving hummocks of the Rio skyline in the background. Le Corbusier always carried small pocket-size sketchbooks with him on his travels. These served as diaries and records of things seen. Fragments of invention occur among telephone numbers or doodles of plants, people and boats. On one sheet of his 1929 sketchbook he drew Josephine Baker nude. On another he jotted down his vision of the new Rio in blue crayon: an auto-route leaping from wooded slope to mountains, with the liner at anchor in the foreground.

Le Corbusier used the voyage home to compose a book: *Précisions sur un état présent de l'architecture et de l'urbanisme*. This summarized general doctrines like the 'Five Points', the box on stilts and the idea of a high-rise city liberating greenery, and included poetic recollections of South America, its landscapes and its people. With the suspension from activity afforded by the ship, he also evoked the Villa Savoye in a lyrical description, and did sketches of an ocean liner alongside a skyscraper frame and the League of Nations. One gets a glimpse here of Le Corbusier's extraordinary power of metamorphosis, his magician's talent for lifting an *objet trouvé*, then transforming it into the terminology of his own fantasies. The image of the ship — already important in the context of Purist forms and *Vers une architecture* — was now associated with a picture of the ideal community. In the book the *Ville Radieuse* he used postcards of liners to make analogies with the *à redent* houses, and even included a section of a steamship from a Cunard poster. The relevance of nautical imagery to the Cité de Refuge was mentioned in Chapter 8.

It was thus curiously appropriate that the 1933 meeting of C.I.A.M. on the 'Functional City' should have taken place on board the *S.S. Patris* as it steamed from Marseilles to Greece and back. Against the stunning landscape background

of the Peloponnese the group put together its charter for a new, more enlightened European urbanism. The ship stopped at Athens and they went ashore to pay homage to the Parthenon. As well as architects and planners there were painters like Fernand Léger and Laszlo Moholy-Nagy, art critics like Christian Zervos, and the future semi-official historian of the modern movement, Sigfried Giedion. Le Corbusier played a major role in the proceedings and some of his urbanistic ideas were adopted uncritically being dangerously removed from the poetic vision of which they were part. It was the more diagrammatic and absolutist aspects of his planning ideas which seem to have been transferred to his associates, and many of these were later incorporated into the *Charte d'Athénes* (1943), a document which Le Corbusier himself edited and which was to have a huge impact on planning thought and action after the Second World War. Moreover, the 1933 discussions seem to have concentrated on the free-standing slab for housing — thereby neglecting a variety of terrace, courtyard and *à redent* housing types that had been either projected or else employed by the architectural avant-garde of Europe during the previous fifteen years. Reyner Banham has speculated about the possible impact of this exclusive approach

'The Mediterranean cruise ... was clearly a welcome relief from the worsening situation of Europe and in this brief respite from reality the delegates produced the most Olympian, rhetorical and ultimately destructive document to come out of C.I.A.M. ... its air of universal applicability conceals a very narrow conception of both architecture and town-planning and committed C.I.A.M. unequivocally to: (a) rigid functional zoning of city plans, with green belts between the areas reserved for different functions and (b) a single type of urban housing expressed in the words of the charter as 'high, widely spaced apartment blocks wherever the necessity of housing high density populations exists' ... at the time it had the power of a Mosaic commandment

122 Charles Fourier, the Phalanstère, as illustrated by Victor Considérant, *c*.1834.

and effectively paralysed research into other forms of housing.'

Le Corbusier's numerous urban projects of the 1930s show how he attempted to modify his abstract typologies to a variety of pre-existing topographies and cities. For Nemours in North Africa (1933), he proposed eighteen residential unité blocks (instead of *à redent* strips) oriented north-south against the mountain backdrop; the roadways linking them to the port and base below were sculpted into a network of curves. For Zlin in Czechoslovakia (1935), he designed the Bata works as a variant on the linear city idea, while for Buenos Aires in 1938, he tried to introduce a series of converging axes to liberate congestion and bring all forces to focus on a platform in the harbour on which he placed a monumental ensemble of skyscrapers. Throughout the 1930s the atelier produced other detailed studies for cities as varied as Antwerp, Barcelona and Paris, usually without being solicited by city authorities. Obviously Le Corbusier hoped that he would be hired, but his plans were so drastic that they were hot potatoes politically, even for those well-disposed towards the architect. None the less these activities spurred on local groups and laid the basis for future action. The spread of the

123 Transformations of the ocean liner and the palace, 1929 (from *Précisions*).

modern movement was much more than just the expression of the 'International Style': it was also the implantation of urbanistic and sociological critiques which would bear fruit in the transformed conditions of the post-Second World War world.

The single city to preoccupy Le Corbusier the most during the 1930s was Algiers, for which he made a series of town-planning proposals between 1931 and 1942, none of which was constructed. He was invited there in spring 1931 by Les Amis d'Alger, to lecture on urbanism in a series marking the Colonial Centennial. Major changes were in the air and there was talk of replanning. Le Corbusier's two lectures were packed out, and in the audience was the progressive mayor of Algiers, Brunel. The architect extended his stay two weeks in order to grasp the shape of the city and the terrain. At the time Algiers had a population of about 250,000, two-thirds European and one-third Muslim. It was the administrative capital and industrial centre for all of French North Africa. It consisted of two distinct sectors: the old Turkish casbah where most of the Arabs lived, and the 'Nouvelle Ville' with broad boulevards and buildings that might have come from the south of France. Le Corbusier called the site 'the most beautiful in the world'. Turning its back to the hinterland of the Kabyle hills and Atlas mountains, Algiers stretched out in a langorous curve along the coastline. A focal point was created by the casbah, the Fort de l'Empereur and the pile-up of buildings and hills behind the port.

Although Le Corbusier was not officially invited to submit plans for Algiers, he decided to try his luck, knowing full well that the mayor was interested, and that other architects were jockeying for positions. Major changes were needed to accommodate a growing population and the flow of trade. The problem was to define an order capable of growth and change, but with certain fixed points of monumentality appropriate to Algiers's increasing importance in the French colonial order. It was also necessary to come to terms with the casbah (which some Europeans wanted to demolish) and with the expected growth of the Muslim population. Le Corbusier revealed his epic vision of the future role of Algiers as a capital city in a letter to Brunel, the mayor, which contained a 'regionalist Syndicalist' assumption that a new Mediterranean culture was on the point of emerging: 'you govern a city of destiny ... races, tongues, a culture reaching back a thousand years ... truly a whole'. He illustrated his idea of Algiers as a fulcrum of world events by means of a diagram marking P, B, R and A — Paris, Barcelona, Rome and Algiers — then went on to imply that 'Algiers would cease to be a colonial city'. Quite how or when this would happen he did not say, but he implied some new, vague political grouping: '... Algiers becomes the head of the African continent, a capital city. This means that a great task awaits her ... a magnificent future too. This means that the hour of city-planning should strike in Algiers.'

Strike it did in December 1932 when Le Cor-

124 Sketch of nude, Algiers, 1931 (Fondation Le Corbusier).

busier unveiled his 'Plan Obus' in an exhibition organized by Les Amis d'Alger. 'Obus' means 'explosive shell', and the plan did resemble the curved trajectory of a projectile shooting in a shallow curve along the coast, then exploding into fragments around the old city and the hills. The Obus consisted of four main elements orchestrated into a sculptural whole: the *cité d'affaires* by the water in a pair of giant, indented slabs; the enclave of convex and concave apartment buildings for the middle classes on the slopes of Fort de l'Empereur; an elevated roadway linking these two instruments of the colonial presence in a north south axis and leaping above the casbah which was thus 'preserved' but also surveyed; and a long, snaky viaduct running for miles along the coast with a freeway on top. This was over a hundred metres high and had walkways, shops, and small house cells for the less well-to-do plugged into its Dom-ino structure. To stress the pluralism of his housing solution, Le Corbusier illustrated façades with horseshoe arches and Moorish details alongside others in a modern style. ·

The Obus plan was a transposition of Ville Radieuse principles into a particular cultural and landscape context in which it was necessary to accentuate the idea of organic growth on the basis of a cellular module. Skyscrapers, freeways and *à redent* housing were now crossbred with a linear city, and with the meandering viaduct idea from the South American schemes. The rigid, orthogonal geometry was superseded by a sinuous abstraction of both landscape and female contours, not unlike the curved outline of the *chaise longue*, but also recalling the waving terrace walls of the Favre-Jacot site plan twenty years earlier. In 1931 Le Corbusier had done precise, erotic drawings of two nude girls in the casbah, and he

had later transformed these into looping and interweaving lines not unlike his ideograms of meandering rivers and hills. They re-emerged a few years later in a mural that he painted at Cap Martin. He had also compared the 'efficient stratification of terraces' in the casbah to the bland boulevards of the Nouvelle Ville, and noted arcades by the port with houses inserted into the arches. In the summer of 1931 he had visited the oasis cities of the Mzab which had impressed him for their tight-knit coherence and for their harmony with climate and natural setting. He seemed to be in search of emblems to contain the sensual, fecund magic of Algeria, and the mystical calligraphics of his sketches (not unlike Arab script) were now compressed into the plan Obus. An ecstatic hymn to the Mediterranean dream, Le Corbusier's Algiers project evoked a new social order, in which men would supposedly be liberated by their pantheistic fusion with nature. Mary Macleod is probably right in seeing here an idealization of the regional Syndicalist utopia: an integrated society announcing the 'total symbiosis of man, architecture and the landscape'.

But behind this pantheism were cold facts concerning the class structure and colonialism. Obus glorified the élite in their sumptuous curved redoubts, their cars always at the ready for a quick spin to the office, Arabs kept at a safe distance below. The cells in the long spine were only fourteen square metres each, while the luxury apartments on Fort de l'Empereur were four times as large. As much as images of integration, the roads were instruments for rapid control and the equally rapid transit of goods and materials produced with cheap labour. The axis hurtling southwards into the distance over the uneven terrain was seeking out mineral wealth

125 Plan Obus, Algiers, 1932.

126 Mural at Badovici Villa, Cap Martin, 1938.

and probing for trade. The casbah would be kept, but as a sort of folklorist curiosity. For all the rhetoric of the time in favour of the 'integration' and 'union' of the two cultures, for all Le Corbusier's symbolism of a *cité d'affairs* between the two communities, the Plan Obus spoke of the imposition of a foreign order as clearly as had the Roman cities of North Africa's past.

To have had a chance of realizing the Plan Obus Le Corbusier would have needed the support of those in power. Behind the scenes he approached Marshall Lyautey and Mayor Brunel, requesting a 'simple decision of authority'. Brunel pointed out that he was requiring dictatorial powers over both property and the rights of citizens. But the majority of *colons* regarded Le Corbusier's Obus as an implausible daydream, and the scheme was rejected. Although not requested or employed to, the architect came back with a modified version, Obus B, in which the curved viaduct was left out, and the *cité d'affaires* became more monumental: a sky-scraper based on a tensi-structure and an H-shaped plan. Obus C followed in spring 1934, this time just the skyscraper, but with the outline of a 'civic centre' to the east of it. Jean Cotereau, a journalist, called it 'a new bombardment of Algiers'. Le Corbusier tried all he could to publicize the plan and its supposed feasibility, but in 1936 Brunel was defeated and so was the Plan Obus. A right-wing mayor, Rozis, took over in Algiers.

During the 1920s Le Corbusier had translated the imagery of modern transport — automobiles, aeroplanes, ships, travel trunks, railway sleeping cars — into the forms and details of his buildings. In the 1930s he used the plane and the ship as means of providing a special vantage point over the shape of the city. Air views offered the equivalent of an Olympian vision for the future and stimulated soaring insights into the basic relationships between human settlements and natural forces. Ships allowed a different sort of drama in which the image of a city could none the less be caught in its totality. Some of Le Corbusier's most stunning sketches of Algiers and Rio de Janeiro were done over the rail with davits in the foreground, the long line of the seashore in the middle ground, and the city against the turbulent backdrop of hills in the background. So it was again when he visited the United States for the first time in 1935, and described the violent silhouette of Manhattan's skyscrapers rising out of the early morning mist as the ship drew into harbour. And with each new place another aspect of Le Corbusier's well-formed urban typologies came into focus. For the United States it was the skyscraper as urbanistic tool which became the predominant obsession.

Le Corbusier's American lecture tour was partly sponsored by the Museum of Modern Art, the organization which had put together the exhibition entitled 'The International Style' in 1932. This exhibition and its accompanying catalogue had done much to make the European modern movement palatable to the American public, but it had concentrated on aesthetic and

127 Edgar Chambless, 'Roadtown', 1910.

stylistic aspects of the architecture at the expense of social content. In 1932 an article on Le Corbusier's urban ideas had appeared in the *New York Times*, but this had portrayed the architect as a Futurist utopian, a dreamer interested in new kinds of glass skyscraper. The 'International Style' was beginning to catch on in America, and there were even sound and elegant buildings like the PSFS skyscraper in Philadelphia by Howe and Lascaze to prove it. Wright and the West Coast architects like Schindler and Neutra were, from the vantage point of an East Coast coterie, valuable but not central appendages to a new spirit. Whether he knew it or not, Le Corbusier was being invited as a celebrity of European modernism, a culture hero, to delight college audiences and museum groups, and perhaps to stimulate the spread of a 'modern style' in schools of architecture.

This is not what Le Corbusier, the 'Colbert from the Old World' had in mind. He was coming to America to preach salvation from the excesses of capitalism through the bible of the Ville Radieuse. His myth of the United States had begun with those 'first fruits of the New Age', silos and concrete factories. This was the promised land of the European avant-garde with its skyscrapers and freeways. Here was the industrial country with all the right equipment to build the Ville Radieuse, but with the wrong mentality because it lacked the *plan*. In his months in America Le Corbusier visited Manhattan and Chicago and was both appalled and amazed by these skyscraper cities with their sprawling networks of railway tracks and roads running out into miles of suburbs. He poured his ambivalence into a book *Quand les cathédrales étaient blanches* (1937), referring to New York as both 'the work-

Er la rue? On avait oublié la rue!

une biologie entière un être raisonnable

north

south

re-formation cellulaire de la ville

128 The Cartesian skyscraper as a salvation for the American city, late 1930s.

operating in new complexes like the Rockefeller Centre, Le Corbusier planned large glass curtain walls. He called the type the 'Cartesian skyscraper'. In plan it was like a hen's foot, with three main wings disposed to catch light and sun. This would be the instrument to let the city breathe and allow countryside to come up to the urban heart by absorbing the suburban populations back into the centre of the city. Le Corbusier's doodles of American cities made much of the congestion brought on by canyon streets with traffic lights at every corner, of the chaos of the higgledy-piggledy setback skyscrapers ('Romantic') and the 'cancer' of the suburbs. The 'Cartesian skyscraper' would cure all these ills in a single surgical stroke.

Americans were absolutely charmed by this dapper gentleman from France with his horn-rimmed spectacles, his reels and reels of sketches (he drew in coloured crayons as he talked), his witty aperçus and his hopelessly impractical sounding suggestions. The East Coast establishment insisted on seeing Le Corbusier as just an architect, and (one guesses) may have been a little protective of their own turf. Le Corbusier did not meet Frank Lloyd Wright, who was just then proposing the opposite, decentralized model of 'Broadacre City', with as little success in persuading authorities to take it seriously; nor, so far as one can tell, did he have direct contact with the Public Works department of Roosevelt's New Deal Administration. A potential link between the reformist content of modern European planning and the reformist policies of the United States government was lost. To the private sector — real estate developers and big business clients — the 'Cartesian skyscraper' idea must have seemed hopelessly untenable as it threw away so much potentially profitable land for 'useless' parks.

For all his efforts — over two dozen lectures and thousands of miles of travel — Le Corbusier received only one commission. This was for a house for a college president in the Midwest, and the sketches showed a design closer in spirit to the intermediate studies for Garches nine years earlier than anything he had done recently. But this too fizzled out. The Soviet Union had shown itself unworthy of his plans; so, after a brief show of interest in 1934, had the Italians; now struggling American capitalist democracy made the same mistake. Le Corbusier and America failed to make lasting contact, signals being misunderstood on both sides.

The architect returned empty-handed to a Europe deep in crisis and lurching inevitably towards war. In 1936 the Popular Front came to power in France. As this leftist coalition was committed to parliamentary democracy the Syndicalists found themselves on the side-lines. *Prélude* had ceased publication the previous year and Le Corbusier virtually withdrew from his previous commitments. He was in a tighter and tighter corner, with no real commissions, and with less and less tangible link between his urban plans and solid means for realization. He dreamed up a 'National Centre for Collective Festivals

house of the new era' and a 'fairy catastrophe'.

Le Corbusier hit the headlines immediately on his arrival in New York when he declared that the skyscrapers were too small and too close together. He later tried to explain that the suburb was the great problem of the United States because it swallowed up useful land with low-density buildings, wasted time and energy in the sprawl of roads and railways, and failed to produce the arcadia that was intended. This analysis must have seemed quite curious to members of the American middle classes enjoying the seclusion, greenery and fine architecture of places like Winnetka or River Forest close to Chicago. After all, many of Frank Lloyd Wright's *and* Le Corbusier's best houses had been for suburban lots. Instead Le Corbusier preached the value of the centralized high-density city. Realizing that the *à redent* model would not be compatible with American land values, he proposed huge glass skyscrapers to contain either apartments or offices. Large spaces would exist around the buildings into which parks, freeways and freeway intersections could be inserted. Having seen successful air-conditioning systems for 100,000 People' — an enormous stadium facing a stage — but it remained unclear what rallies, celebrating what ideas, would take place there. In 1938 Le Corbusier planned a monument to Vaillant-Couturier, the left-wing mayor of Villejuif, with a huge slab supporting a sculptural bust, an open book and a gesturing hand of comradeship. This was about the nearest that he came to socialist realism, and the idea of the Open Hand would recur — in a quite different guise and meaning — at Chandigarh.

Meanwhile Le Corbusier had not forgotten about Algiers. In fact he put more and more eggs into this single basket. Through the efforts of P.A. Emery, his collaborator, and those of Georges Huissmann, director of the Ecole des Beaux-Arts, he was appointed to the Comité du Plan Régional for Algiers in February 1938. He proposed Obus D, which was more or less the same as C, but with a Y-shaped skyscraper. In March 1939 he unveiled Obus E, the scheme with the textured skyscraper of *brises-soleil* alluded to in the last chapter. This was situated on the point of the Quartier de la Marine, its narrow ends facing sea and land, north and south. In plan it was a lozenge, a shape well suited to accommodate a core of elevators, which also gave the building the character of a wing, or even a ship's prow, ploughing towards the water with the lower buildings of the civic centre in its wake. The public lower levels of the building met the sloping

land on a series of terraces which penetrated the base, bringing in different sorts of circulation. Above this base, which was amplified in scale by means of huge windows and monumental concrete sun screens, the bulk of the building rose in three main bands. Again these were protected by *brises-soleil* integrated with the façades as an enormous trellis of different sizes to express varying interior functions. The *brises-soleil* created loggias and protected terraces at the edges of the offices, and channelled the view in quite a new way. Their depths were arranged to admit winter (but exclude summer) sunlight. On the exterior they gave the skyscraper a powerful plasticity and monumentality, multiple rhythms and scales. The façade may have been influenced by American Beaux-Arts skyscrapers, such as Albert Kahn's First National Bank Building in Detroit of 1922 (Le Corbusier had taken the trouble to illustrate this example in *L'Art décoratif d'aujourd'hui*), but the Algiers skyscraper went deeper than just a surface pattern. Le Corbusier compared the hierarchy of core, structural floor, lattices and smaller louvers to that of a tree, with trunk, branches, twigs and leaves. Again we notice him returning to his La Chaux-de-Fonds days, in the search for an organic analogy. The skyscraper for the Quartier de la Marine was a powerful image of the state, and its Muslim loggia vocabulary was continued at a smaller scale in the neighbouring public

129 Skyscraper for the Quartier de la Marine, Algiers, 1939.

structures as a new civic language. He called this a 'pure North African architecture', 'a palace and no longer a box — a palace worthy of reigning over the landscape'. None the less the plan was vetoed.

In 1938 Le Corbusier had published a plea for the peaceful use of mass-production entitled *Des Canons, des munitions? Merci. Des logis S.V.P.* (*Canons, Arms? No Thanks. Housing Please*). In autumn 1939, just after the declaration of war he at last received a commission from the French Government — for a munitions factory! When France fell in June 1940, Le Corbusier and his wife fled to the Pyrenees where they installed themselves in the small town of Ozon. He had become a French citizen in 1930 but his defective eyesight and age (he was 52) excused him from military service. Did he perhaps continue to look at the destiny of France as a total outsider? Like many other Frenchmen, he was not sad to see the collapse of the Third Republic, though the prospect of a Nazi Europe must surely have disturbed him. A number of moral choices were open to him, including escaping the country or eventually becoming involved in the resistance. Pierre, his partner and cousin, eventually chose the latter course. Edouard felt that his first duty lay with architecture and urbanism. He decided to try and function within the framework of a defeated country. With the emergence of 'Free France' after the Armistice, he sought out old friends from *Redressement Français* and the Syndicalist movement who were now installed in the Vichy regime under Marshall Pétain. Among these were technocrats who dreamed of a New Economic National Plan, but they had to compete with members of the Old Right who revived the idea of a France of medieval *corporations* or guilds. Within months Le Corbusier found himself on a committee (with his friend François Pierrefieu) responsible for making urbanistic and architectural initiatives for what remained of France and the Empire.

In the weird atmosphere of Vichy, the architect began to conceive a new planning hierarchy headed by a single individual with enormous powers to control the architectural destiny of France. He formulated his ideas for the future of the country in two books which appeared in 1941, *Destin de Paris* and *Sur les quatre routes*. He had always said he was haunted by the shadow of Colbert, and now the shadow took on ominous proportions. Armed with these delusions of grandeur he tried to push his Algiers plans through but soon succeeded in alienating friends and in irritating functionaries at Vichy. In July 1941 he was informed that his services were no longer needed. But he did not give up, attempting to speak to Pétain directly (he was not granted an interview) then ploughing on with the final plan for Algiers, the 'Plan Directeur'. This dispensed with the pan-Mediterranean myths of Obus A and concentrated on the idea of Algiers as a 'meeting place' of European and Muslim cultures. The textured tower was shifted east to Bastion 15 where it proclaimed without ambiguity the dominance of the surrounding European quarter. Lower buildings close to the Quartier de la Marine and the casbah were to contain a Muslim Cultural Centre. In the accompanying text Le Corbusier examined the history of the city and projected its future for decades, referring to it in Nationalist terms as 'the Phoenix of France'. This bit of phoney patriotism was soon knocked flat by an article of Alexandre von Senger's that was reprinted in an Algiers newspaper in spring 1942 (it had originally appeared in 1934), linking Le Corbusier to Bolshevism and an international Jewish conspiracy. It was all that the architect's enemies needed to have the Plan Directeur vetoed. He returned to Vichy, packed his bags and retired to the Pyrenees.

To treat Le Corbusier's behaviour over Algiers as a case of straight opportunism would be to miss the complexity of his situation and his motives. Of course he wanted to build, the more so as he was now in his fifties, and had not had a major commission for a decade. But his actions were also influenced by his self-image as a prophet, his crude environmental determinism, and his historicist belief that a new era, the 'second machine age' — separated from the chaos of the 'first machine age' by the 'time of troubles' (the Depression) — was about to dawn. In this scale of utopian values, the first duty lay in the realization of the plan, because this was for the greater social good over a long period: it did not occur to Le Corbusier that a pact with the devil might besmirch him and his architecture. Robert Fishman has put it well: '... this self-absorption in the plan ... was his integrity — but also his failure. He had reduced politics to a simple yes or no to the plan, and he was willing to support any regime that said yes ... In his concern for the administrative state he had lost touch with the just state.'

One wonders if Le Corbusier let these troubling thoughts penetrate his consciousness in his mountain hideaway between 1942 and 1944. He threw himself into painting and writing, producing *La Maison des hommes* (with Pierrefieu), the *Charte d'Athènes* and *Entretiens avec étudiants des écoles d'architecture* in 1943; *Les Trois Etablissements humains* and *Propos d'urbanisme* in 1944. These books contained insights on a range of subjects from peasant vernacular architecture to the role of linear cities in a new Europe. Le Corbusier also found the time to chair various committees of A.S.C.O.R.A.L. (a research affiliate of C.I.A.M.) which examined a number of French cities in detail. For it was now increasingly clear that the allies would win the war and that a massive reconstruction would take place under some unknown political and economic order. But for all the sweeping range of his new plans, Le Corbusier would never again state with the same confidence that a total city, a work of art, might bring about a new era of harmony. The Ville Radieuse slipped into the past — another paper utopia. In his drawings and sculptures the artist returned time and again to the theme of Ubu Roi — Alfred Jarry's preposterous, strutting king whom no one would take quite seriously.

130 Sketches exploring the
analogy between the fir tree
and the skyscraper with
brise-soleil, early 1940s.

131 Maison Fallet, La Chaux-de-Fonds, 1905–7.

132 Watercolour study of a house for La Chaux-de-Fonds, probably Maison Stotzer, end of 1907 or beginning of 1908 (Bibliothèque de la Ville, La Chaux-de-Fonds).

134 Maison Favre-Jacot, Le Locle, 1912, view towards
the main entrance and *cour d'honneur* from the end of the
drive.

133 (*opposite*) Maison Jeanneret, La Chaux-de-Fonds,
1912.

136   Villa Schwob, general view from the north-west with
kitchen wing in the foreground.

135 (*opposite*) Villa Schwob, La Chaux-de-Fonds, 1916,
detail of canopy and columns.

138 Double house, Weissenhofsiedlung, Stuttgart,
1926–7.

137 (*opposite*) Maison Planeix, Paris, 1924–8.

140   Villa Stein/de Monzie, Garches, also known as 'Les
Terrasses', 1926–7, close-up view of the rear, garden
façade from the first-level terrace.

139 (*opposite*) Maison La Roche, Paris, 1924, view down
the ramp in the curved studio.

141　*Still Life with Numerous Objects*, 1923. Oil on
canvas, 45 x 57½ in. (114 x 146 cm.). Fondation Le
Corbusier.

142 Villa Savoye, Poissy, also known as 'Les Heures
Claires', 1928–9, view across the meadow towards the
south façade.

143 Pavillon Suisse, Cité Universitaire, Paris, 1930–1, view from the east showing *piloti*.

144 Cité de Refuge, Paris, 1929–33, view from the vestibule towards the entrance bridge and canopy: note the *brises-soleil* attached to the glass façade in the background.

145 Unité d'Habitation, Marseilles, 1947–53, raking view of *pilotis*.

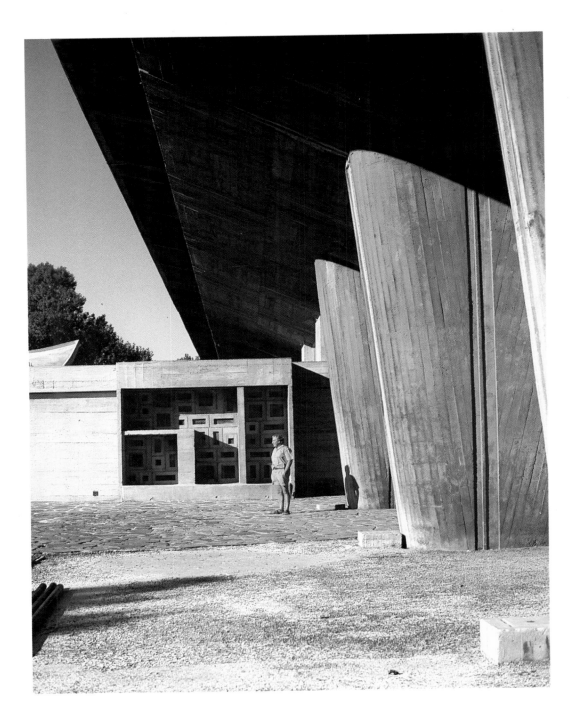

146 Unité d'Habitation, Marseilles, west façade.

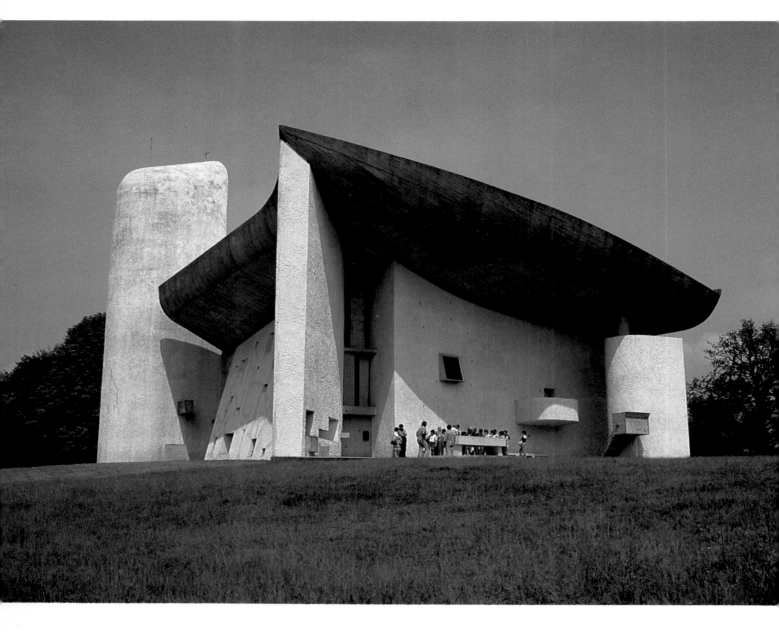

147 Chapel of Notre Dame du Haut, Ronchamp, 1951–3.

148 *Taureau II*, 1953. Oil on canvas, 63¾ x 45 in. (162 x 114 cm.). Fondation Le Corbusier.

150 Chapel at Ronchamp, the 'prow'.

149 (*opposite*) Monastery of La Tourette, Eveux-sur-
l'Arbresle, 1953–7, view towards pyramidical roof of the
Oratory through *ondulatoires* in the lower walkway.

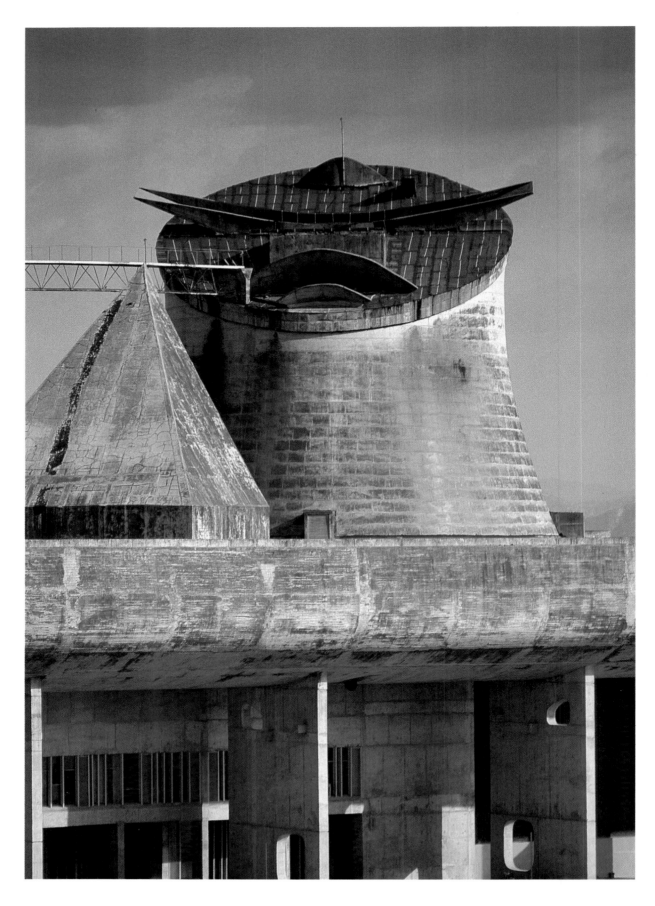

151 Parliament Building, Chandigarh, India, 1951-63,
detail of roofscape showing crescent forms on the funnel.

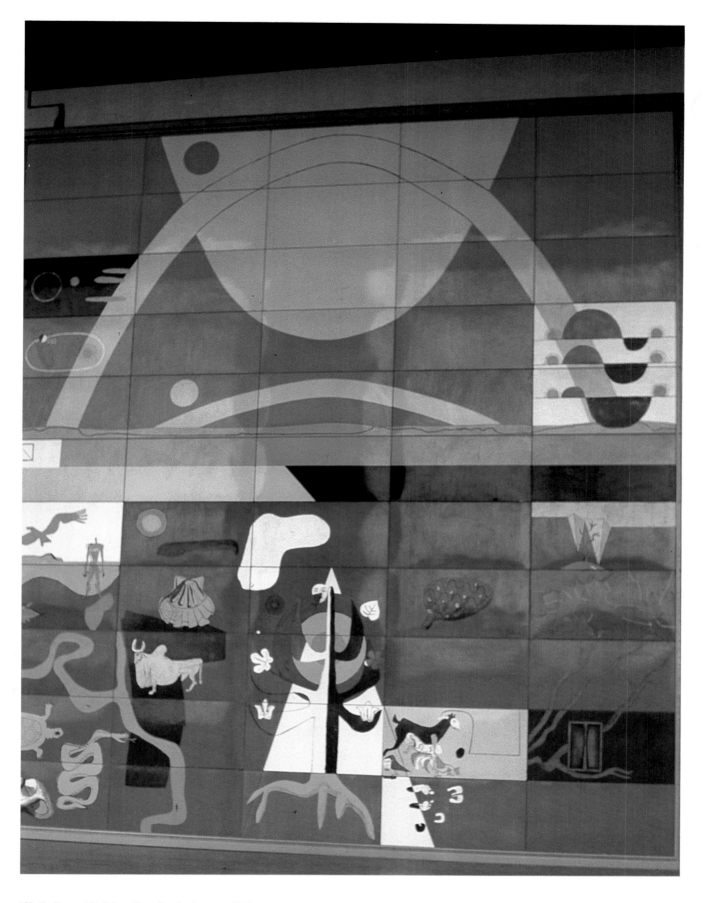

152 Parliament Building, Chandigarh, the enamelled
door decorated with solar symbols.

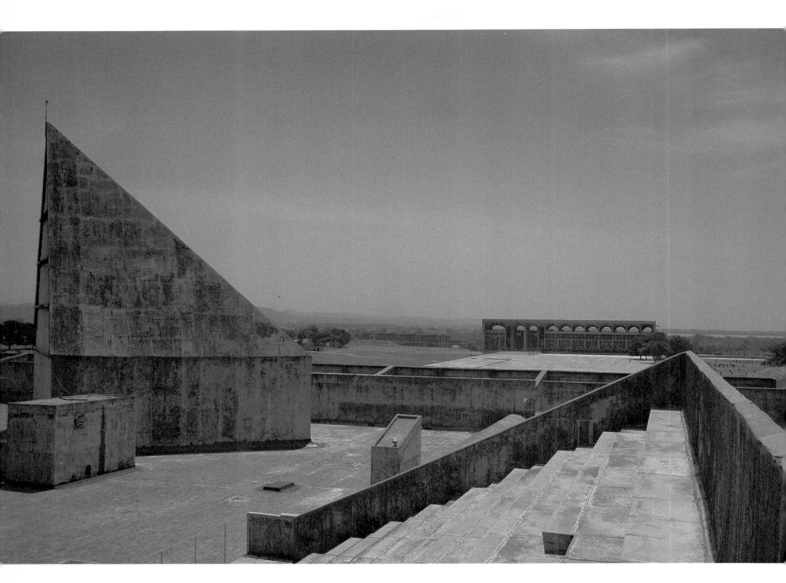

153 Chandigarh, view from the roof of Parliament to the
High Court.

154 Sketch of pyramids and Sphinx, Giza, Egypt,
Sketchbook F25, 1952 (Fondation Le Corbusier).

155 Millowners' Associ-
ation Building, Ahmedabad,
India, 1951–4, rear (east)
façade.

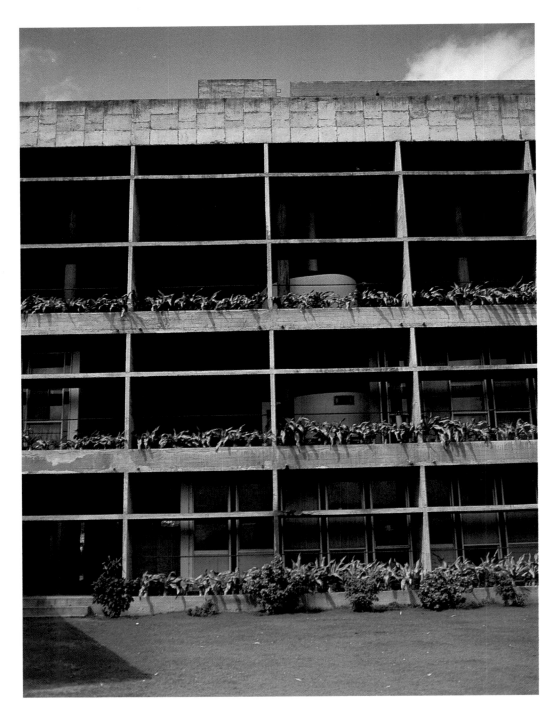

156 (*opposite above*) The Yacht Club, Chandigarh, 1962.

157 (*opposite below*) Sarabhai House, Ahmedabad,
1951–5.

158 The Museum, Chandigarh, 1957, galleries on level 1.

159 Shodhan House, Ahmedabad, 1951–4, view from the
terrace towards the garden through the *brises-soleil*.

160 Heidi Weber Pavilion, Zurich, 1963–5.

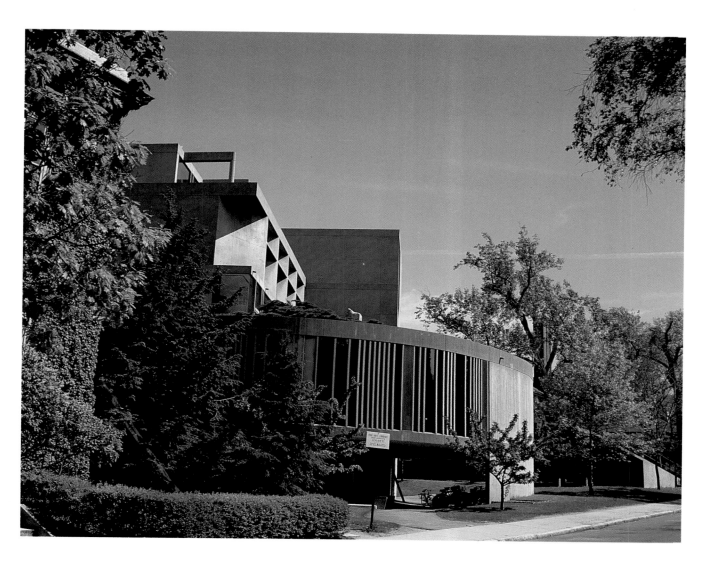

161 Carpenter Center for the Visual Arts, Cambridge,
Mass., U.S.A., 1959–63, seen from Quincy Street.

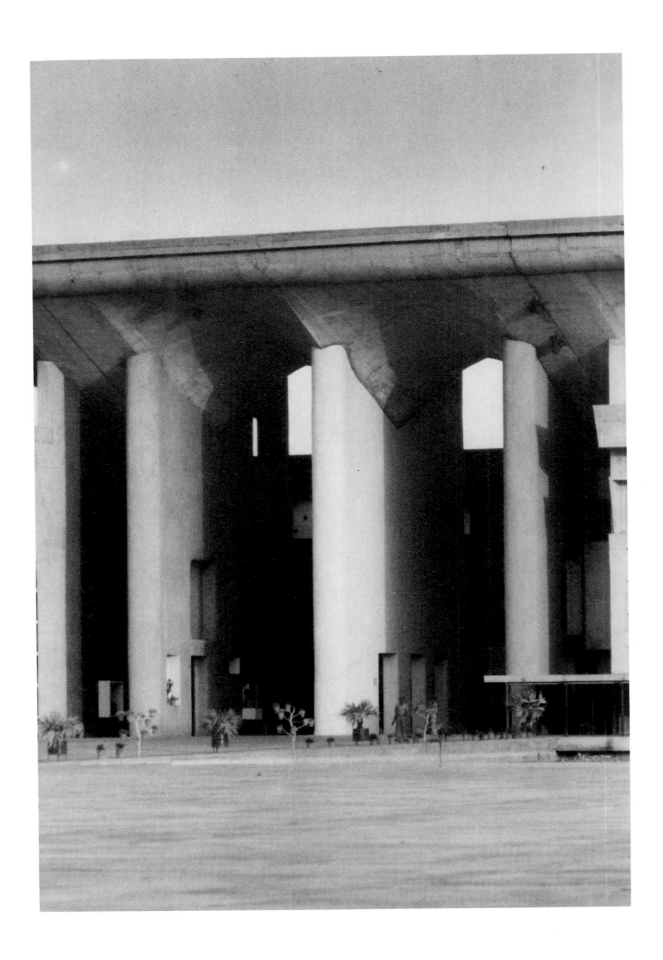

PART III
THE ANCIENT SENSE: LATE WORKS 1945 – 1965

Chapter 11

The Modulor, Marseilles and the Mediterranean Myth

*'Over the years I have felt myself becoming more
and more a man of everywhere but always with
this firm attachment to the Mediterranean: queen
of forms under light. I am dominated by the
imperatives of harmony, beauty and plasticity.'*
Le Corbusier

Throughout the 1930s Le Corbusier had clung to
the idea that history was evolving towards a new
era of equilibrium. Instead the world had experienced political chaos, destruction and war. His
utopianism had even taken him into a moral
impasse. In 1945 Europe lay in ruins. The pseudo
religion of progress and the cult of the machine
had a tarnished air. One did not find the middle-
aged Le Corbusier — fifty-seven at the end of
hostilities — declaring a 'new spirit of construction and of synthesis' as he had done a quarter of
a century earlier with the arrival of peace.

His urban projects had been conceived as
instruments to generate a new civilization and
had relied upon an unlikely marriage of capitalism, radical reform, nature and art. Their liberal
idealism made no sense in an era of political
extremes: too conservative for revolutionaries,
they were too revolutionary for conservatives. Le
Corbusier had been left clutching at ideological
straws. After the war the context was entirely
different. The modern movement emerged
triumphant as the accepted architecture of liberal
democracies and welfare states. With the Marshall Plan of 1947, funds poured into the European reconstruction. Old members of C.I.A.M.
were waiting in the wings with ideas that seemed
to embody the right mixture of rationalism and
humanitarian sentiment. But the rows of clinical
housing slabs which now rose out of the rubble
were often a travesty of all that Le Corbusier had
stood for. The integrity of his urban vision was
precariously reliant upon the action of his own
poetic sensibility and sense of order. Without
these, the Ville Radieuse could become a banal
set-piece of the bureaucrat and the traffic
engineer: a diagram rather than a town.

Throughout the war Walter Gropius, Mies van
der Rohe and other European immigrants had
kept the modern movement alive in America. But
the diaspora of forms changed their meaning and
by the early 1950s the International Style was
already spread thin. Capitalism was content to co-
opt the rhetoric and even the images of modernist
planning so long as these served the programmatic aims of business — nature, reform and
art were dispensible elements of the original

theorem. Modern architecture very easily became
a thin veneer over the utilitarian box or the
developer's financial calculations. Now that
society was at last ready to adopt modern architecture on a broad scale, it also devalued it.

The enemy had once been fake revivalism.
It was now fake modernism. The task of Le
Corbusier's works was to reaffirm the values that
had guided him from the start, but in forms
adjusted to the post-war reality. The architect
had patiently evolved a wide range of new
solutions in the previous fifteen years which took
him well beyond Purism, and which he was now
ready to put into action. He had explored a new
archaic mood and sensed its relevance to the
existential conditions of a war-torn France. Like
Alvar Aalto in the same period, he wished to
investigate the overlaps of modern probity and
the ancient sense. The search for constants,
emphasized in *Vers une architecture*, now went on
with less concern than ever for an imagery of
machinism.

Le Corbusier's first period of invention had
occurred in a France that had just won the Great
War, that stood at the head of an empire, and
that created conditions in which an avant-garde
could flourish temporarily. The France of 1945
was a very different place. It was pulling itself
clear of defeat, occupation, corrupt rule and
severe bombardment. Its global role was dimin-
ished, and its calculations now had to be made
between the emergent giants of the United States
and the Soviet Union. The colonial system within
which Le Corbusier had tried to function was
rickety. Within a decade there would be a host of
new independent nations — a situation which
would make the question of post-colonial identity
an important one for architecture. As usual, Le
Corbusier was quick to grasp this larger picture.

In the late 1940s the French reconstruction was
uppermost in his mind, as it had been for some
time *before* the Liberation. Early in the war he
had proposed self-built dwellings of mud and logs
('Maisons Murondins') to deal with the housing
emergency. In his books in 1943 and 1944 he
began to plan in pan-European terms, envisaging
linear cities between major centres of population

162 (*previous page*)
Chandigarh, India, The High
Court, 1951–5.

from Paris to Moscow. In the book *Les Trois Etablissements humains*, the analysis shifted to agricultural units, linear industrial towns, and 'radio-centric' cities of culture and political power. A.S.C.O.R.A.L. had collected data on French towns even as the fighting continued. When the armistice arrived Le Corbusier was ready to move.

One does not know how the architect avoided possible charges of collaboration — perhaps his rejection by Vichy was a blessing in disguise — but within months of the Liberation he was approached by Raoul Dautry, Minister of Reconstruction, who wanted him to study housing for Marseilles with a view to establishing relevant prototypes for French mass-housing. The resulting Unité d'Habitation took seven years to complete and announced with full force both the architect's urban philosophy and new devices like the *brise-soleil* and *béton brut* (bare concrete). In retrospect one realizes that the Unité, along with Mies van der Rohe's very different but nearly contemporary glass and steel towers, was one of the major parent buildings of the post-war modern movement. The Unité drew together a lifetime's research into the ideal community, but expressed these insights in a vocabulary linked to Le Corbusier's other experiments of the late 1940s as painter, sculptor, theorist, architect and planner. Before looking at it in detail it is as well to have these other researches in mind.

Le Corbusier's most immediate task after the Liberation was to set his house and his studio in order. Edouard and Yvonne returned to rue Nungesser et Coli to find wild sycamores popping out of the planting boxes and briar roses entwined around the metal garden chairs. The last entry in the drawing register at 35 rue de Sèvres was dated June 1940. Jerzy Soltan, a Polish architect who arrived to work there in August 1945 (staying four years), recorded his impression of the old Jesuit monastery, the courtyard, the dank stairway leading up to the second-level landing, the little door into Le Corbusier's world:

'Eighty to ninety feet long and ten to fifteen feet wide, the atelier was in fact a section of a long white dead-end corridor. A row of large windows was on one side, and a blank wall faced them ... Sometimes ... a Bach fugue or a Gregorian chant trickled in from the church into the atelier ... Old drafting tables, broken stools and chairs, creaking easels, broken and half-broken architectural models in various scales, rolls of drawings, drafting utensils — all these competed for space ... and of course, covering everything was a thick layer of dust. Dust had been gathering there ... since the beginning of the war and the decay of the atelier into a *débarras*. It was awakening at this time to its new, post-war life.'

Pierre Jeanneret and Le Corbusier had split up over their different political views on the war. The few temporary assistants who came to work part-time in the atelier in 1945 did so for virtually nothing. In 1946 matters improved when Le Corbusier got projects for La Rochelle and St-Dié, the latter a small town in the east of France

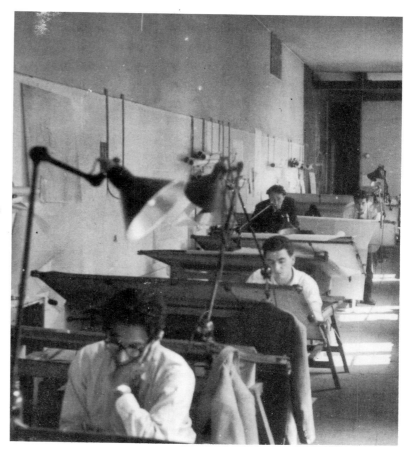

that had been damaged in the German withdrawal. Le Corbusier proposed eight unités d'habitation flanking a civic centre planned as a sort of acropolis including public buildings, a museum and administrative offices. It was as if the Mundaneum had been exploded open and made available to a small town community. Although the urban plan was not carried out, the project did allow Le Corbusier to experiment with urban monumentality and enclosed civic space, two issues that had been underplayed in the Charter of Athens and which would preoccupy C.I.A.M. in the late 1940s and early 1950s. He also received a modest commission from a St-Dié bonnet manufacturer by the name of Jacques Duval to build a factory. This was Le Corbusier's first construction for over ten years. The factory was a simple, oblong box with a stair tower and an internal structural grid. As suggested in certain schemes for Algeria, *brises-soleil* were attached to the façades as crates. Concrete surfaces were left bare or else painted in bright colours, and Le Corbusier tried out a new proportional system called the 'Modulor'.

The Modulor was supposed to be 'a harmonic measure to the human scale, universally applicable to architecture and mechanics'. A six-foot man with his arm upraised was inserted into a square which was in turn subdivided according to the Golden Section. Smaller dimensions were generated by the Fibonacci series and in later

163 The atelier at 35 rue de Sèvres, Paris, in the early 1950s.

164 The Modulor.

versions two scales of inter-spiralling dimensions were introduced (the Red and the Blue series). The Modulor was to give harmonious proportion to everything from door handle to heights to the widths of urban spaces, and Le Corbusier even hoped to encourage industry to use it to standardize products. He liked to quote Albert Einstein who told him that the system made 'the bad difficult and the good easy'. In fact, Le Corbusier never hesitated to ignore the Modulor if it got in the way of a proportion that his eye told him was just right, and was furious when he found some of the less talented members of the atelier justifying atrocities on the grounds that they were 'Modulor'. He even took the drastic step of banning the use of the system for some months.

The Modulor brought together the Purist obsession with defining absolutely beautiful measures with the idea of architecture as a microcosm of natural laws governed by mathematics. Its elaborate range of harmonies probably suggested a tactile equivalent to music and there can be no doubt that the dynamic and telescoping proportions were well suited to the spatial ambiguities, complex curvatures and rhythmic, textured façades of Le Corbusier's late style. It was after the war that he began to use the term 'ineffable space' to denote the ravishing effect of abstract proportion and sublime ratios in great architecture. Moreover, the Modulor pulled together a range of other obsessions from the standardization of types to his youthful romanticization of Pythagoras as a 'grand initié' (viz. Schuré's, book) revealing a higher order to the base world below. Typically these Olympian pretensions were combined with humour. The Modulor man was built like a Greek *kouros* statue with bulging thighs and a slender waist, but he had obviously just come from a few hours vigorous cycling around a rooftop gymnasium track. He might have stepped out of the pages of a French advertisement, as familiar and easy to recognize as his much tubbier automobile relative, the Michelin man.

Le Corbusier was flattered by the serious scholarly attention given his publications *Le Modulor* (1948) and *Modulor II* (1957). In 1951 at a conference 'On Divine Proportion' in Milan he heard the views of historians like Rudolf Wittkower on Vitruvian, Renaissance and other systems of proportion. Long before this he surely knew of Leonardo da Vinci's illustration of Vitruvian man inscribed in a circle, and was at least intuitively aware of concepts of symbolic representation through cosmic geometries in past architecture. Like so many of Le Corbusier's other late inventions, the Modulor drew together various periods of the architect's earlier researches. Modular systems had been studied by the Werkbund theorists before the First World War as a means to 'civilize' the brute facts of mass production, and in *L'Esprit Nouveau* and *Vers une architecture* Le Corbusier had treated geometry as one of the keys to higher order. His fascination in the 1930s with Matila Ghyka's somewhat mystical interpretations of mathematics (*Le Nombre d'or*, 1930) coincided with a renewed interest in structures underlying nature that echoed the Ruskinian lessons of his youth in La Chaux-de-Fonds. The Modulor was more than a tool; it was a philosophical emblem of Le Corbusier's commitment to discovering an architectural order equivalent to that in natural creation. One of his major breakthroughs about the Modulor occurred in the thoroughly Nietzschean setting of a storm. He was on board the *S.S. Vernon S. Hood* in 1946 in mid-Atlantic when the ship ran into a gale. As he always carried a grimy strip of paper marked with experimental Modulor proportions with him, he decided to use the time in the hold to good purpose, and came up with a little sketch in his sketchbook of the Modulor man with his arm upraised.

This was one of the many journeys that Le Corbusier made in the ill-fated adventure of the United Nations project. Earlier in the year he had been invited by the French government to join a commission studying the idea of a United Nations headquarters to stand somewhere in the United States. He had flown to New York immediately. After the gloom and rationing of France, Manhattan was rich and bustling. Le Corbusier set up a studio on the twenty-first floor of the RKO building and began to study the problem with the other architectural delegates, including Oscar Niemeyer, his Brazilian associate on the Ministry of Education in Rio ten years earlier. Various sites were considered near San Francisco and New York, for a sort of United Nations township. Le Corbusier began to think of including a spiral World Museum as he sniffed

the opportunity that had evaded him in the
League of Nations fiasco twenty years earlier.
Then the Rockefellers made available a few acres
next to East River at 40th Street, on the flank of
Manhattan.

It was clear that the United Nations would now
be a high-rise scheme, and Le Corbusier reacted
to the new constraints in a series of sketches
covering sixty-one pages of his pocket notebook
between 25 January and spring 1947. He put the
Secretariat in a flat-topped skyscraper raised on
pilotis. It stood out, a sombre sentinel of peace,
against the backdrop of frenzied Manhattan
silhouettes. The Assembly was placed alongside
in a curved 'acoustic' volume and linked it to a
long hovering horizontal by the riverside, containing lounges and press galleries. General
agencies were included in a subsidiary slab to the
north end of the site. He intended that the spaces
between the buildings should be planted like a
park and that the Secretariat should have *brises-
soleil* laid out according to the Modulor. Memories of the harbour of greenery in the League of
Nations project of 1927 were fused with the
researches for the Admiralty tower in Algiers,
and with the experience of designing a *brise-soleil*
skyscraper with Costa and Niemeyer in Brazil in
1936. 'Project 23-A' (as Le Corbusier's scheme
was called) was a demonstration of Ville Radieuse principles for the Americans, and an
example of the 'correct' morphology for the
skyscraper.

Le Corbusier probably thought that he would
be hired. Instead 23-A became the property of a
technical committee that took on Wallace Harri-
son to carry out the design. Le Corbusier later
claimed that his sketchbook containing the sixty-
one pages of studies was stolen while he was in
Boston. True or not, he does seem, in effect, to
have been robbed of his own idea. The buildings
that stand next to the East River are pale imitations of what might have been, though there are
fine details such as the textured green curtain
wall. The United Nations has been acerbically
described as the origin of the 'international hotel
style'. The lobbies in particular are full of period
clichés. The scheme as a whole lacks the formal
force and *gravitas* that Le Corbusier would have
given it.

If 23-A had been built as intended it would
have revealed a new set of environmental and
sculptural devices in the *brise-soleil*, just at a time
when America was about to embark on an
unprecedented skyscraper boom at home and
abroad. As it was the Miesian glass and steel
formula triumphed and became the standard
image of the multinational corporation. Within
years of the United Nations, Skidmore, Owings
and Merrill designed the Lever House on Park
Avenue, a refined slab hovering above a horizontal podium topped by a roof terrace (an idea
that was not without Corbusian overtones). Le
Corbusier returned embittered to Europe where
steel was out of the question in post-war conditions. In France and India he used rough
concrete, bare bricks and forms of primeval force
to define a new archaic sensibility. One wonders

165 Project 23-A for the
United Nations, New York,
1947.

if things would have been different for America
and for his late style had he been given the
United Nations job.

The primitivism of Le Corbusier's late works
had already been prepared in the 1930s, but it
was reinforced by his experiences in painting,
sculpture, tapestry and mural designs after the
war. The years of withdrawal in the Pyrenees, the
sense of futility at destruction, seem to have sent
the artist deep into his subconscious in search of
totemic images. The 'Ubu' series contained this
sense of the absurd, while a doodle of an open
hand anticipated a post-war emblem of hope and
co-operation. Le Corbusier let his mind wander
in free association. One day in the Pyrenees (in
1942 or '43) he was looking out of the window at
oxen moving back and forth. He had recently
picked up a stump of dead wood and a pebble in
a gully. As he drew and redrew, the 'objets à
réaction poétique' blended with these and the
'Taureau' was born. Like Picasso's Minotaurs,
the 'Taureaux' became an obsessive motif in Le
Corbusier's prints, paintings and drawings, and at
Chandigarh the bull shapes were even abstracted
into the forms of architecture (Pl.148).

Le Corbusier seems to have carried in his
imagination certain formal configurations with a
deep emotional appeal which could represent a
variety of different subjects, and even refer
simultaneously to a series of images. On one
occasion in the early 1950s he was travelling to
India in a plane with a publication of his early
drawings on his lap. He looked down and saw a
still life of bottles and glasses (done in the 1920s)
on its side. Seen in this way the original representation was lost, but the outlines touched the
Taureau category in his imagination, and a new
variation, in which the bottles turned into horns
and a head, came into being. This transposition
of forms into ideas, and ideas into forms, suggests
an imagination able to make extraordinary
analogical leaps between shapes and images.
Eduard Sekler has shown how the outlines of

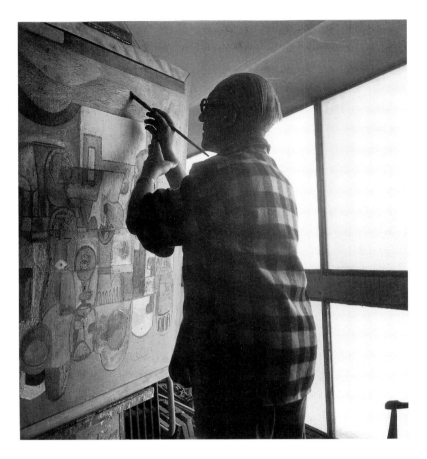

Composition, Spirale logarithmic of 1929 gradually evolved, over the years, into a quite different subject in a different medium: the wooden sculpture *Totem* of the late 1940s. The artist described this manner of using and reusing shapes:

'Le Corbusier carries within himself and with himself ideas of a formal ('plastique') nature which go back ten, fifteen, twenty years or more: they are drawings, sketches which fill drawers at his home and some of which he takes on journeys. In this way contact is immediately re-established between a new stage and an earlier one.'

In 1931 Le Corbusier had transformed naturalistic sketches of the girls he had drawn in Algiers into wiry pen and ink studies of interweaving, curved contours. Around 1938 he had translated these into a large monochrome mural on the ground-floor terrace of Jean Badovici's villa at Cap Martin on the Côte d'Azur (Pl.126). The ambiguous flux of figure and ground, as well as the monumental figure style, owed more than a little to Picasso's *Guernica*. Le Corbusier continued to research a similar theme after the war on an outdoor wall next to his own cabin at Cap Martin. *Alma Rio* (1949), which hung for some years above the dining table in Le Corbusier's apartment, also drew upon the raw material of his travel experiences. The looping curves brought together the sketches of South American rivers seen from the air and the snaking viaduct proposals of 1929, with the elegant silhouettes of women's shoulders which he had admired, then drawn, during his second South American trip of 1936. Behind his hieroglyphs there were many levels of private association which he strove to contain and 'objectify' in abstract forms. This procedure of blending memories also operated in Le Corbusier's buildings, and was an essential part of his power to transform precedents into a new order.

In 1949 Le Corbusier decorated the wall of the lounge in the Pavillon Suisse with a monumental mural of mythological figures and female deities, including one illustration of the curious image from Mallarmé, 'keep my wing in your hand'. The same goat-like goddess recurred on the cover of Le Corbusier's short book *Poésie sur Alger* (1950). The repeating obsessions would crop up at all scales and in new media, for in the early 1950s Le Corbusier was invited by Pierre Baudouin (an expert on weaving at Aubusson) to design tapestries. The artist called tapestry 'the mural of the nomad'. The lumbering volumes of his early 1930s style gave way to broad areas of colour combined with arabesques. These linear pictograms were easily transferable into enamels, tapestries, photo-montages, even *bas reliefs* in concrete. Le Corbusier's aim seems to have been a reinvigoration of painting as a public art attached to buildings. At Chandigarh he would illustrate cosmic themes on huge tapestries that were hung in the High Court.

Around 1944 Le Corbusier began collaborating with Josef Savina, a Breton cabinet-maker, in the creation of bold, polychrome wooden

sculptures based on the biomorphic forms of
paintings and drawings. The individual pieces
were carved roughly with the marks of the chisel
left showing, and were collided together in
bizarre assemblages. Some of these resembled
phantasmagoric vegetables with pods and stems,
others were like Surrealist anatomical study
models in which certain glands had grown absurd-
ly out of proportion. The 'Ozon' sculpture of
1946 was in the shape of a huge distended ear
lunging towards the surrounding space. Le
Corbusier explained that he was exploring 'an
acoustic component in the domain of form' and
that his assemblages could 'emit' and 'listen'.
He would use similar gestural shapes in the
light towers at Ronchamp or the roof scoops at
Chandigarh. The rough surfaces of the sculptures
also revealed the value of coarse textures that
would find their equivalent in the bare concrete
and crude brick finishes of the late works.

But it would be wrong to disassociate Le
Corbusier's forms from the network of associations which gave them their symbolic purpose.
Between 1947 and 1953 he put together *Le
Poème de l'angle droit*, a prose poem weaving
together favourite Corbusian obsessions to do
with the transubstantiation of natural forces —
sun, moon, water, shadows, etc. — into myths.
The text was illustrated with a sort of *iconostasis*
of tableaux laid out symmetrically like an abstract
tree of life in a vaguely cruciform pattern. In the
top row were such symbols as the 'S' signifying
the rise and fall of the sun, the serpentine curves
illustrating the 'law of the meander', the interlocking of night and day, engineer and architect,
shadow and light. Lower down, the Modulor
appeared alongside a concrete skeleton and a
section of the Unité d'Habitation showing the
parabolic paths of the sun at solstice and equinox,
and demonstrating the principle of the *brise-soleil*
whereby rays would exclude summer glare but let
in winter heat and light. There was also a row of
panels obscurely related to the 'anima' or female
principle in the universe, and an individual panel
of the 'Open Hand' (see Chapter 13). The *Poème*
relies on a contrast between opposites, in a way
already anticipated in the drawing Le Corbusier
had done for his book (written with Pierrefieu)
La Maison des hommes (1942): this had shown a
grimacing Medusa on one side, a radiant sun on
the other. Such symbols belonged to the artist's
private religion. Perhaps they were painfully self-
conscious attempts at echoing the exotic heresies
of his Catharist ancestors.

By 1949 the atelier at 35 rue de Sèvres was
getting back into full swing as work continued on
the Unité for Marseilles. A new commission
arrived from South America to design a house
and surgery for Dr Currutchet in La Plata,
Argentina. The site was next to a fine Neo-
Classical building looking over the park, and at
the back it shifted on to an awkward diagonal. Le
Corbusier separated the office from the dwelling
but placed both behind a screen of *brises-soleil*,
linking the spaces inside by a ramp and stairs.
The section was very complex with a slot of open
air at the heart and a hanging garden at an upper

level. The *brises-soleil* handled the glare, channelled the view, and gave the whole building an
honorific façade that was still punctured enough
with shadow not to interfere with the neighbour.
In effect, many of the discoveries of the 1920s
houses were here re-stated in a sub-tropical
mode; a similar transposition would be attempted
in the Indian houses a year or two later. Soltan
recalls the difficulties of co-ordinating the section
with a cranked plan shape:

'Distributing spaces (open and enclosed) on the
numerous levels, connecting them with ramps and
staircases, and covering them with different types
of roofs, ceilings, and flying slabs became the
main themes of the spatial game. The relations
between solids and voids, orthogonal and slanting
were very complex indeed. To develop these
relationships on paper using standard projection
techniques was impossible ...'

If Currutchet was a house conceived as a large

168 Le Corbusier and Josef
Savina, Wooden Sculpture,
'No.5', 1947.

166 (*opposite above*) Le
Corbusier painting in his
studio, early 1950s,
(probably re-working *Still
Life with Numerous Objects*,
1923, Pl.141).

167 (*opposite below*)
Taureau, line drawing from
the *Poème de l'angle droit*,
Pl.149.

169 Le Corbusier, project for Roq and Rob holiday housing, Cap Martin, 1949.

170 Currutchet house, La Plata, Argentina, 1949, section.

trellis of greenery, the unrealized Ste-Baume and Roq and Rob schemes of the same period were variations on the cave. The former was a shrine where it was believed that Mary Magdalene had spent her last years, and Le Corbusier organized the sacred place as a procession through landscape culminating in a subterranean grotto top-lit through light shafts. The pilgrims' houses were like troglodyte dwellings, but with curved partition walls echoing prehistoric types. 'Roq and Rob' was for holiday housing on the Côte d'Azur. The drawings evoked the image of a primeval settlement attached to the hillside. The idea was to halt suburban sprawl by increasing density, but in a way which harmonized with the area. Roq and Rob was a sort of stepped unité, a type of casbah in modern materials. Individual units combined the vaults of the Petite Maison de Weekend with the 2:1 section that Le Corbusier preferred. Interiors relied on steel trusses on a cubic module. Roofs were covered in turf and straggling Mediterranean plants. This was 'regionalism' at its best: combining old and new, responding to climate, site, vegetation, views and local precedent. Le Corbusier explained the idea behind the scheme:

'... the landscape which is to be seen must be preserved, not built on in a haphazard fashion. A wise plan should provide the resources of nature: architectural forms of great sculptural value must be created. Excellent precedents were offered by ancient small towns standing on the higher parts of the coast. In these the architectural site is made up from houses crowded together, but with "eyes" (windows) looking towards the infinite horizon.'

Behind these intentions was a passionate attachment to the Midi, which was in turn linked to a larger myth of the Mediterranean. This had first been nurtured in the Voyage d'orient when it had been a matter of ruins facing the sea and of peasant folklore. Le Corbusier's obsession with Mediterranean ancestry contributed to it, as did the writings of Cingria Vaneyre. The houses of the 1920s contained many links with the south, from white forms in light, to open terraces, to sketches of antique ruins seen through strip windows. In the 1930s the cult had been reintensified through the love affair with Algiers, city of the sun. In the 1940s and 1950s, 'Mediterraneanism' embraced both a love of the archaic and a sort of solar paganism. Cézanne, Matisse, Picasso supplied an honorable pedigree in the search for a mythological classical landscape to be translated into modern terms.

Le Corbusier's links to the Mediterranean were reinforced by his regular summer visits to Cap Martin not far from Monaco. Here he constructed himself and Yvonne a log cabin, with another shed nearby to which he could retire to think and draw. He used the cabin for experiments with furniture and details: the *aérateur*, a pivoting ventilating door with attached insect screen (used in many of the late works) was pioneered there. At Cap Martin Le Corbusier could become the noble savage: sunbathing, swimming, painting, entertaining informally. His friends remember him in shorts, a Pastis in one hand, perhaps enthusing about the limpid undersea world he had seen that morning, telling preposterous stories or arguing some fine point of the Modulor. At Cap Martin the bitterness and defences were laid aside in favour of the art of friendship.

In the late 1940s the atelier was dominated by the huge scheme for the Unité d'Habitation at Marseilles. Le Corbusier's initial studies called for three separate buildings to stand at La Madraque near the Old Port (an area badly damaged by Nazi dynamiting and then later during the allied landings of 1944). In 1945 he investigated the idea of a '*unité de grandeur conforme*' (unité of the proper size). This was an abstract prototype containing the optimum number of people (about 1,600), a variety of apartment sizes, a middle-level shopping street and other communal facilities such as a public roof terrace. The hypothesis reflected years of rumination on collective living. For example, the apartments were to have double-height living rooms linked to single-level bedrooms and kitchens by an overhanging gallery, an arrangement descending from the immeubles villas of 1922.

Indeed the Unité as a whole was a chance to demonstrate the theory of a 'vertical Garden City' for industrial society, in which high density would allow liberation of the soil for nature, and in which the essential joys of light, space and greenery would be made available to all. Le Corbusier worked his way towards a seventeen-storey block with twenty-three different variations on the basic apartment type to accommo-

date individuals or families of up to six people. The section was to allow staggering of dwellings so that each would pass through from one side to the other, and access corridors could be limited to one every three floors. The basic diagram was of a slab on stilts with a core of vertical circulation linking three main horizontal areas of public space: the area under the *pilotis* (continuing the ground plane), the raised street half-way up, and the upper terrace on top.

This rationale began to suggest a form much like an enlarged version of the Pavillon Suisse: a slender slab on muscular *pilotis*. The idea of

171 Le Corbusier working at Cap Martin.

172 The 'cabanon', Cap Martin; note the vertical slot of the *aérateur*.

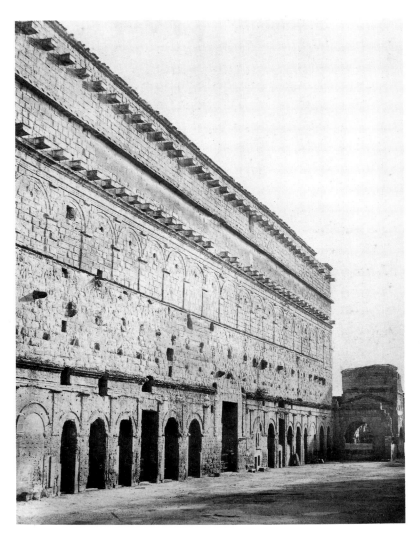

173 The Roman theatre,
Orange, first century A.D.

174 Unité d'Habitation,
Marseilles, 1947–53.

raised walkways echoed the Algiers viaduct,
while the shading terraces recalled the textured
skyscraper of 1938–42 for the same city. It is
likely that the ingenuities of an overlapping
section were originally inspired by Soviet 'social
condensers' like Ginzburg's Narkomfin building
in Moscow of 1928. Haunting the unité idea were
older collective archetypes such as Fourier's
phalanstère, with its communal street and
surrounding nature; the monastery at Ema (*the*
paradigm of harmonious resolution between
private and collective, and also an inspiration in
its framed views over a paradisiacal nature); as
well as, of course, the ocean liner (which Le
Corbusier had been studying for nearly a quarter
of a century). In the organization of the Unité
these schemata are so completely fused that it is
pointless to harp on them too fully: however, it is
the image of a ship, with funnels, decks, cabins
and public walkways which seems to be most
telling at Marseilles.

In 1946 Le Corbusier was asked to restrict
himself to a single unité off boulevard Michelet,
south-east of the Prado. The site still contained
olive trees, cypresses and boulders. The slab was

angled to the street so that its longitudinal axis
ran exactly north-south. Each apartment had
double exposure and so could enjoy morning sun
and landscape views to the east, evening sun and
views of the sea to the west. *Brise-soleil* depths
were calculated to exclude hot summer sun and
glare but to let in winter rays. Formally the
problem was to bring this vast block to life in a
way which made the hierarchy of public and
private areas legible from afar. Individual apertures needed to maintain identity and contribute
to a harmonious and dynamic whole, seen close
to or far away. Months of work went into façade
studies using the Modulor to help regulate the
relationships between large and small elements.
The resulting composition was a subtle blend of
opacity and transparency, massiveness and
hovering planes. Extra richness was supplied by
touches of primary colour on terraces and, of
course, by the different textures of bare concrete.

The architect compared the structural concept
of the building to a bottle rack into which
standardized bottles are inserted. Individual
apartments were to be dry-assembled, lined with
lead for sound insulation, then hoisted by crane
and slotted into the structural frame. Le Corbusier might well have used steel at Marseilles, but
the material was in very short supply in post-war
France, so he decided to work the whole thing
out in concrete. Many different architects contributed to the design, among them André
Wogenscky, Roger Aujame and the Russian-born
Vladimir Bodiansky, an engineer and aircraft
designer. They worked out a concrete frame that
would rest on enormous tapered *pilotis*. Plumbing
and electrical wires were to be threaded through
sleeves, run along a raft over the *pilotis*, then
brought down to the ground through the structural shafts (an arrangement loosely reminiscent
of the Pavillon Suisse).

These were the hard technological facts of the
collective *machine à habiter*, but partly out of
necessity, partly out of choice, the imagery of
the building was to express an almost archaic
character. Le Corbusier discovered that it would
only be possible to construct the Unité using
many different groups of contractors, that some
of the work would be crude, and that it made no
sense to expect smooth transitions in the concrete
work. He therefore decided to make roughness
an aesthetic virtue, to exploit the imprint and
grain of the formwork planks as if they were the
chisel marks of one of Savina's sculptures. 'Béton
brut' ('bare concrete') as it came to be called,
was superbly sensitive to light and shade, and
could be sculpted to lend the whole building a
heroic force like that of Paestum or some other
Antique ruin. Le Corbusier confided to Andréini
that he wanted to make the most of contrasts
between naked concrete and machine-age
materials like steel and glass, and that he was
thinking of 'béton brut' as a natural material like
stone. A generation of 'Brutalists' got hold of
rough concrete and turned it into a glum period
cliché, but at Marseilles the finishes are vibrant,
the profiles tense, the joints precisely placed.
Seen from a distance the Unité d'Habitation is

175 Unité d'Habitation, Marseilles, the interior street.

176 Unité d'Habitation, Marseilles, sections.

like a vast, textured cliff, which echoes the stone outcrops in the foreground and rocky Provençal mountains in the background (Pls. 145, 146).

The celebration of the Mediterranean setting reaches its apotheosis on the public roof terrace. Here the nautical references — stacks, railings, deck games, etc. — are unmistakable. The para-

pet is just high enough to block out the urban surroundings and just low enough to include vignettes of the sea, the chain of rocky islands by the port, and the hills to the rear. It is the same trick as the Beistegui roof terrace, but on a much larger scale, and in a Homeric mode of severe concrete. There are even small landscape mounds in concrete, and these pun with the crags five miles away. The ventilating stacks echo the shape of the *pilotis* beneath the building and the children's crèche is a small Corbusian piece on slender supports approached by a ramp. It hovers half over a pool where infants can splash in sun or shade. The panorama is exhilarating, as is the direct contact with sky and sea. A running track circulates around the whole deck, a cross between a deck game and an ancient gymnasium. Marseilles was a Greek colony centuries before Christ and the region was part of the Roman empire. The classical undertones of Le Corbusier's Mediterranean myth are not foreign to this context.

The Unité opened in October 1952, having survived ten changes of government and nearly as many Ministers of Reconstruction. It had been attacked from the start by other architects jealous of the way that Le Corbusier was allowed to flout building codes. Another group claimed that the building would cause mental illness (to this day some Marseillais still call it the 'maison du fada' — the 'house of the madman'). But at the opening, Le Corbusier was awarded the Legion of Honour by Eugène Claudius-Petit, Minister of Reconstruction at the time, and a friend of the architect. An even grander event took place on the same deck in 1954, when C.I.A.M. held its conference at Aix-en-Provence. This time the parties were bacchanalian with shepherd bards in fur costumes and an elaborate striptease (the latter shocked the prudish Dutch members who staged a walkout). Perhaps the elder members recalled *S.S. Patris* twenty years previously — the voyage on which they had hatched the ideas that became the Charter of Athens. The Unité took the Catechism and gave the word invincible aesthetic form. And it did this in a rugged vocabulary that also appealed to a younger generation fed up with the diagrammatic planning of 'official modern architecture', wishing to give shape to a new, post-war state of mind.

Even before it was finished, the Unité began to influence architects around the world. There

177 Unité d'Habitation, Marseilles, living–dining room.

would be competent imitations like Roehampton Housing Estate near London, and intelligent critiques like Denys Lasdun's Bethnal Green Clusters of 1954. These accepted the ideas of high density, modern services, fresh air and the image of an ideal community but replaced the absolutist block by a shape better suited to marry with the existing city. Similar strategies were suggested by the theorists and practitioners of 'Team X', the group which superseded C.I.A.M. in the 1950s. As they saw it the problem was to preserve the ethical stance and many of the devices of the unité, but to cross-breed these with local typologies and contexts. An example of this approach was José Luis Sert's Peabody Terraces (graduate student housing) at Harvard (1961–3), which restated such Corbusian principles as the concrete tower, the roof terrace, the complex section, the upper street and the *brise-soleil*, but in ways that blended with the collegiate courtyard tradition and with the colours and textures of that particular bend in the river. This project demonstrated how it was possible to extend Le Corbusier's ideas without devaluing them or slavishly reproducing them.

The more usual story was one of bastardization. All over the world blocks of public housing popped up which could boast density and little else: no communal areas, no greenery, no terraces, no scale and no architecture. As Banham has put it: 'the tawdriness of the consequences has become a byword for the failure of modern architecture'. But it is really too facile to blame the banality of imitations upon the prototypes that they imitate: by this logic one ought also to blame Palladio for every mock-classical suburban house using fake columns and pediments. Assessments of the unité *theorem* need to bear in mind that both atrocities and fine housing

have been developed from this particular cluster of ideas. Even the precise *model* of the unité — i.e. a slab highrise on stilts with terraces and a park — has been appropriate in some circumstances.

As for the particular Unité that stands on boulevard Michelet, it must be judged in its singular conditions as well as in its role as exem-

178 Cunard poster of an ocean liner (reused by Le Corbusier to illustrate collective living).

179 Unité d'Habitation, Marseilles, the roof terrace pool.

plar. The usual roster of criticisms is that the apartments are too narrow, that the approach corridors are too dark, that the middle-level street cuts off this community from the world outside. To these one must now add that the concrete on the roof terrace is weathering poorly in the salt air. But the present inhabitants of the building seem to have surmounted these problems, and are in the building by choice, because they find it a pleasant place to live. Marseilles is a congested, noisy city with a decaying housing stock, and the Unité allows proximity to the city centre but without the concomitant disadvantages. The alternative would be to move out to the suburbs. In that respect the grand Corbusian theorem of the 'vertical Garden City' fits the local situation far better than it would most. The park and the views towards mountains and sea are appreciated. In fact, the inhabitants have formed a co-operative to keep the place up, and express a certain pride in living in a building by Le Corbusier. These do not seem to be symptoms of a major failure.

Buildings slip away from their creators, assuming a texture and life of their own. It is interesting to visit the Unité between five and six in the evening in the autumn, when it is still hot enough to wear shorts and thin cotton dresses. People flood in from work and school, leaving their cars under the trees; they dawdle by the banks of cypresses, or play tennis, or shop in the upper street. On the roof terrace old men chat, catching the last of the afternoon sun while their grandchildren splash in the pool. The crags, in reality miles away, hover like models on the parapet ledge, their shadows turning from Cézanne blue to deep mauve. A ship pulls away from the port, dark against a shimmering sea, as in Le Corbusier's Algiers sketches. The textured oblong, broods like an Antique viaduct above the trees, its bold mass and mighty legs evoking the great wall behind the Roman theatre at Orange. In the tawdry imitations skill, philosophy and poetry are absent. The Unité takes a patiently worked out urban theorem and renders it in the terminology of a Mediterranean dream.

Chapter 12

Sacral Forms, Ancient Associations

'We must return to the source, to the principle and to the type.'

Ribard de Chamoust

As well as demonstrating Le Corbusier's theories of housing, the Unité d'Habitation at Marseilles laid out the elements of his late style. Concrete was used to create massive forms, textured façades and profiles of complex curvature. The abstraction of the Modulor was synthesized with a robust primitivism. Discoveries of the 1930s such as the Surrealist roof terrace and the *brise-soleil* as a loggia were given a powerful sculptural shape. Between 1950 and 1955 Le Corbusier would have ample opportunity to extend these devices further because he was at last swamped with work. The buildings of this period are marked by an archaic mood. The Roq and Rob scheme of 1949 revealed his late procedure: old ideas such as the Monol housing or the Petite Maison de Weekend were 'rethought' in the terminology of an ancient Mediterranean settlement.

The Maisons Jaoul in Neuilly of 1951 to 1954 also reflected an obsession with the vernacular roots of architecture and also drew upon the Monol typology. Two suburban houses for clients who were related to each other, these were fitted on to a tight lot surrounded by trees through an ingenious insertion of garages beneath, and an equally clever handling of openings to preserve privacy. The heavy wooden slats in the window panels and the extensive use of husky brick ('materials friendly to man'), confirmed the orientation suggested in Le Corbusier's regionalist exercises of the 1930s. With their boldly expressed concrete frames, Catalan vaults and touches of contrived irregularity they were (as Smithson put it) 'on the knife edge of peasantism'. James Stirling, the English architect, encapsulated the confusion felt by the architectural community when he contrasted Jaoul to Garches: the latter 'a monument, not to an age which is dead, but to a way of life which has not generally arrived'; the former 'built by and intended for the status quo'. He hymned the steam-power imagery and nautical detailing of Garches and lamented the romanticism of handicraft at Jaoul: 'Algerian labourers equipped with ladders, hammer and nails'. There was puzzlement about the lack of engagement with mechan-

ization, actually, ideologically and symbolically in Le Corbusier's recent creation.

While the architect had jettisoned something of his religion of the machine, this did not mean a retreat into art for art's sake. The primitivism of the late works needs to be seen in the ethical perspective of a search for the roots of architecture, an attempt at touching upon the basis of psychic experience, and the old obsession of harmony with nature. The commissions which Le Corbusier received in the early 1950s stimulated these concerns. India awoke a vein of mysticism and confronted him with a living folklore, while the programmes of the Monastery of La Tourette and the Chapel of Notre Dame du Haut at Ronchamp forced him to reflect upon the role of the sacral in past and present architecture, and to penetrate the institutional basis of types with an ancient pedigree. Both were also for remote rural sites where his cult of nature could have free rein.

The Chapel of Notre Dame du Haut at Ronchamp stands on a hilltop in the foothills of the Vosges not far from the Jura. It can be seen for miles around with its white thumb tower against the sky, and the dark hull of its roof riding over the evergreens. The curves echo the folds and silhouettes of the surrounding ridges, an effect which is intensified when one mounts the pilgrims' path to the summit. North and west walls are concave and closed; south and east bend in to admit light and receive long, distant views. As the plan shows, the three hooded towers blend with the sinuous wall surfaces that curve inside and out to form top-lit chapels or else to define slots into which sacristy and confessionals are set. Given the complexity of the experience, the formal means are surprisingly economical: concave and convex pieces of similar shape are juxtaposed, fused or separated to create a building unequalled in its spatial mystery in the modern age. One has to go back to Borromini or even to the Small Baths at Hadrian's Villa to find anything remotely comparable.

The basic elements of walls, hooded towers, curved roof and different-sized apertures are enmeshed in a play of complexities and contradictions. The south wall (seen in the first view from the path) is in tense opposition to the main tower which reads from this angle as a swelling volume; soon it will be seen as a thin plane wrapped around the interior space. The wall itself is detailed to appear thick and massive by the door, thin and light towards the peak where it meets the roof. The apertures of various sizes set into the wall recall gun slots and seem to be random, but are actually placed according to Modulor proportions. They continue the game of affirmations and denials, being detailed in one case to reinforce the thickness of the wall, in another to reinforce its planarity.

As one moves clockwise past the bulging west wall the roof is lost from view but a gargoyle pokes through the parapet, spewing rain water through its nostrils towards a tank filled with prisms of rough concrete. The wall then curves up and round to become another tower (demarcated by a joint in the surface), which meets back to back with its twin. Read together they make a major cleft and signal the usual entrance. The white, pebble-dashed surface — sprayed on to disguise a variety of structural armatures in concrete with rubble between them — is curiously like meringue. The same surface is used inside as well. This treatment reinforces the general theme whereby insides become outsides, and outsides become insides. The rest of the north wall is treated to more slots and to a slender stair with a steel railing, a collagist's touch of mechanization alongside the rustic flank of the walls. As the wall surface comes to the corner, the roof reappears to cantilever out over the eastern end of the building where concavity again dominates, creating a covered place for an outdoor chapel, complete with altar and pulpit.

The transition into the interior at Ronchamp is

180   Chapel of Notre Dame du Haut, Ronchamp, 1951–3, looking east along the south wall.

181   Chapel at Ronchamp, site plan.

dramatic. One enters an otherworldly cave, a catacomb. The architect called it 'a vessel of intense contemplation and meditation'. Light pierces the south wall and touches rough curves, chunky wooden benches and the smooth stone of altar and steps. As the eyes adjust to the crepuscular dimness, one grasps that the interior has no strict symmetry, that walls, benches, altar and roof are in dynamic, diagonal tension, that the space compresses together aspects of a centralized church with aspects of a longitudinal one. The roof sags downwards in a curve, like a heavy tent, and the floor slopes, funnelling attention to the altar at the east end. But there is a chink of light along the top of the wall, so the apparently massive ceiling seems to hover. Where the ceiling meets the towers on the interior, it slices into them: another reversal, since on the exterior the towers poke through the roof.

An effigy of Our Lady is embedded in the east wall above the altar in a glazed niche surrounded by pinpoints of daylight which evoke stars, and perhaps ideas of the Virgin as *stella maris* (Star of the Sea) and *regina coeli* (Queen of Heaven). The niche is two-sided and the statue rotates so that the pilgrims who flock to Ronchamp in their thousands twice a year can see her when they gather on the grassy platform to attend open-air mass. Here the concave exterior of the east wall reveals its potential, as it focuses attention on the outdoor altar and throws the voice of the priest outwards; at the same time it gathers up the energies of the setting and ties the building to the distant hills. It is what Le Corbusier had in mind when he pointed out how the Pavillon Suisse curved wall 'gives a suggestion of tremendous extent, seems to pick up, by its concave surface, the whole surrounding landscape'; it is also what he meant when he spoke of 'acoustic shapes' in his sculptures, which 'emit and listen'. The remaining 'walls' of the outdoor chapel at Ronchamp are the horizons themselves. The inside/outside idea is brought to a crescendo which conveys the feeling of an Early Christian gathering in a landscape, while touching on the artist's

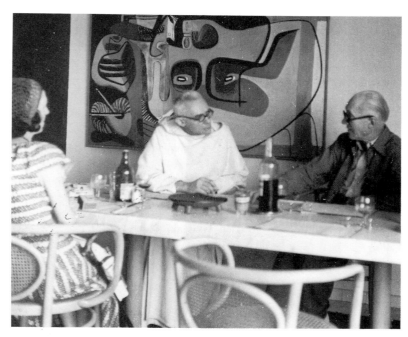

private agenda of a mystical cult of nature.

To one end of the outdoor sanctuary, a single concrete pier holds up the corner of the roof in a hint at the actual construction. It emerges from a curved element which is like a sliced-off tower and which acts as a spatial rudder to the building, while summarizing ambiguities between plane and volume. The curve of the east wall continues to become the *inner* surface of the south wall, except for a slight gap into which a third entrance, linking interior and exterior chapels, is set. Roof and wall cease to debate and at last conspire together in the pointed peak of the building. Throughout the procession, Ronchamp's curves have demonstrated that they are no merely arbitrary graphic trick. They carry intentions into three dimensions (in fact four) with tension and precision. They address the

182 Chapel at Ronchamp, distant view from the southeast.

183 Le Corbusier, Father Couturier and Yvonne in the apartment at rue Nungesseret-Coli (the painting is *Alma Rio*, 1949).

horizon, model light and shade, channel interior and exterior movement, and resolve the internal and external pressures (Pls.147, 150).

When architects and critics flocked to Ronchamp in the mid-1950s to see the finished building, they returned home with mutterings about 'a new Baroque' or 'a descent into irrationality'. Nikolaus Pevsner, the historian who had written *Pioneers of Modern Design*, was puzzled by what he took to be a departure from the true way. Stirling wrote of 'the rationale and the initial ideology of the modern movement … being mannerised and changed in a conscious imperfectionism'. Ronchamp was contrasted with the supposed 'rationalism' of the architect's earlier works and with the mechanistic precision and industrial standardization of American modern architecture of the 1950s, especially that stemming from the example of Mies van der Rohe. These reactions perhaps tell more about the preoccupations of the period than they do about Ronchamp. Notre Dame du Haut was far from being a clean break. It had roots in the artist's earlier paintings, sculptures, buildings and urban schemes, as well as in his analyses of a number of vernacular and monumental structures from the distant past.

Le Corbusier was approached to design the chapel in early 1950 by Canon Ledeur of Besançon on the recommendation of Father Alain Couturier of Lyons. Both had been pioneering the idea of a renaissance of Church art and architecture. Couturier was even editor of a journal called *Art Sacré*, which, since the 1930s, had published reformist opinions. They argued that traditional images and types were in a state of decadence, and that the Church must turn to the most vigorous creators of modern art and architecture to set this right. Realist objections against abstract art were countered with the expressionist argument that intense arrangements of form might stimulate spiritual concentration and thus elevate the quality of communication to the faithful. Couturier played a part in the commissioning of Matisse for the Chapel at St-Paul-de-Vence and would also steer the job of designing the Monastery of La Tourette towards Le Corbusier. In the turmoil surrounding the reception of the unorthodox Ronchamp design, Couturier guarded building and architect against attacks.

When Le Corbusier was first approached he recoiled, claiming that the Church was a 'dead institution'. This ludicrous retort perhaps had to do with his bitterness over the recently rejected scheme for a shrine to stand at Ste-Baume near Aix-en-Provence — the supposed resting place of Saint Mary Magdalene in her last years. Equally it was the reaction that one might expect from a social theorist who had never indicated places for churches in urban plans and who perhaps regarded the official clergy with some suspicion despite his highly romantic ideas about monkhood. But while Le Corbusier had no particular religious creed for affiliation, he was not without a sense of 'higher things'. He had been brought up as a Protestant, and both his mother and his Aunt

Pauline had been devout. A feeling for moral and spiritual questions had been gradually transformed into the language of Ruskinian poetics and of Idealist philosophy, and into a commitment to social and moral improvement through the amelioration of the environment. Le Corbusier's Rousseauesque confidence in the inherent good of man and in the harmony of nature's 'laws' put him at odds with the Catholic doctrine of the Fall and with the idea of Original Sin. But he was not a materialist. Le Corbusier tended to see nature and architectural order as material manifestations of some vaguely defined spiritual presence. When questioned about his beliefs in relation to Ronchamp he replied: 'I have not experienced the miracle of faith, but I have often known the miracle of ineffable space ...'

When Le Corbusier first visited the site in 1950, he was quick to grasp the many layers of memory in the place. The Romans and, before them, sun-worshippers had held the Ronchamp hill sacred. In the Middle Ages a cult of the Virgin had developed around an effigy with supposed miraculous powers. During the Reformation these powers were credited with stopping heresy from spreading from the east. (What an irony that Le Corbusier's ancestors were among these heretics, and that he even cherished his links to the earlier Catharist heresy too!) In 1944 the hill was bombarded in the German withdrawal from France. Ronchamp was associated with the Free French Forces and with the Liberation. The rebuilding of the church was not without patriotic overtones. Le Corbusier immersed himself in books which Couturier gave him about the Catholic liturgy, and began to reflect on religious spaces throughout history that he had found moving, but it was the *genius loci* itself, the sacredness of the spot and its special relationship to the surrounding landscape which dominated his imagination: particularly the resonance which he sensed between the hilltop and the distant ridges on the horizon. Two weeks earlier, he had passed Ronchamp on a train and glimpsed the ruins of the old church, remarking in his sketchbook that the silhouette of the new building would need to be smaller to be in scale with the hill. In his reflections on the landscape he perhaps recalled his youthful, Alpine walks with L'Eplattenier, and even the occasion on which they had had the curious idea of erecting a temple to the mystical cult of nature on the Jura mountain-tops. Surely he also recalled the processional path up the Acropolis, the diagonal views of the Parthenon, the circuitous processional path to the back entrance, and the way that curved stylobates and columns in entasis linked building silhouette to far landscape. His earliest study doodles (now lost) dealt with the address to the four horizons and with the path of the sun. Such metaphysical reflections were complemented by hard practical demands. There was little water on the site and a collecting device was necessary (the eventual sluice roof responded to this need); and the difficult climb made it sensible to reuse the rubble of the old church.

Le Corbusier's design processes proceeded in anything but a rational, straightforward way. He moved back and forth between general ideas and particular observations. Analogical leaps of thought were crucial in the creation of hypotheses. Many links between form and form, form and idea, idea and idea were made in the unconscious during a period of incubation. Of the design process he wrote:

'When a job is handed to me I tuck it away in my memory, not allowing myself to make any sketches for months on end. That's the way the human head is made: it has a certain independence. It is a box into which you can toss the elements of a problem any way, and then leave it to 'float', to 'simmer', 'to ferment'. Then one fine day there comes a spontaneous movement from within, a catch is sprung; you take a pencil, a charcoal, some coloured crayons ... and you give birth on the sheet of paper. The idea comes out ... it is born.'

The generating idea for Ronchamp was born in the late spring of 1950 in one of Le Corbusier's sketchbooks. The ensuing string of pen and ink sketches (one of them dated June) already anticipated the finished forms in some detail. They implied a turbulent sculpture in the round gathering up the energies of its setting. The sketches also offer clues concerning the roots of the new idea in Le Corbusier's earlier style and in a variety of historical sources. He probably had no fixed conception for a church, and his client positively discouraged him from returning too literally to traditional layouts which would have required symmetry. But Le Corbusier had only recently designed a religious space for the Ste-Baume scheme. This had been a pilgrims' cave with light dropping in from the top. In other works, auditoria and places of assembly were often contained in 'acoustic' curves which modulated sound and expressed something of their function. But the closest anticipation of the Ronchamp plan is to be found in the concave and convex curves, echoing landscape, of apartment buildings from the Algiers project twenty years earlier. Analogies with Le Corbusier's late paintings also abound, as they do with the 'Ubu' and 'Ozon' series of sculptures. When he published Ronchamp, he let the model be photographed alongside these 'acoustic' forms to reinforce the connection. As usual nature played a part: there are various sketches of shells examining the way that outside surfaces become inside ones, and inside ones become outside ones.

Le Corbusier's style provided him with a range of ways of dealing with new problems and with a hieroglyphic system for absorbing and transforming *objets trouvés*. The Ronchamp roof supplies an example of this metamorphosis. It may have been inspired by: a crab's shell picked up on Long Island, ships' hulls, memories of sluices and ski-jumps, the profile and structure of aeroplanes' wings. In the inner landscape of Le Corbusier's imagination, poetic correspondences existed between such diverse things. Some of the links probably had to do with analogies of function (e.g. a roof and a crab's shell) or to do with

184 (*opposite above*) Chapel at Ronchamp, interior view towards the altar.

185 (*opposite below*) Chapel at Ronchamp, the outdoor altar in front of the east wall.

186 Chapel at Ronchamp,
view from the north-east.

the flow of water (boat, sluice and crab's shell). Others probably arose from formal and structural similarities. Even resonances of language may have played a part: in French 'coquille' means shell and 'coque' means the hull of a boat. As in a dream, bizarre connections might actually constitute a new structure of truths in which

187   Boat and shell,
Sketchbook B6, 1931
(Fondation Le Corbusier).

hermetic levels of meaning would be combined. In Le Corbusier's mind there was perhaps a connection between these sources around the general unifying ideas of a 'vessel of contemplation', a spiritual container, a ship of salvation riding over the waves of the landscape.

The lighting towers at Ronchamp have a no less intriguing pedigree. The most important influence was the top lighting system of the Serapeum at Hadrian's Villa, that Le Corbusier had sketched forty years earlier during the Voyage d'orient, and which he had attempted to employ at Ste-Baume. The exterior massing, hooded shape, and little cross on top of the main tower recall a sketch that the architect had made of a small rural church in Spain when travelling there in the 1930s. Greek island vernacular sources have also been feasibly suggested. The perforated south wall seems traceable to the mosque of Sidi Brahim at El Atteuf in the Mz'ab, Central Algeria, a region that Le Corbusier had visited enthusiastically in the same period. He had also been struck by the rippling, curved walls in whitewash or mud of the North African vernacular. The lighting slots obviously resemble fortification gun apertures — perhaps a wry reminder of the Second World War history at Ronchamp. And so lists of sources could continue, adequately supported by documentation, except that this approach would leave the impression that invention consisted of simply making montages of beguiling fragments. The remarkable thing about Ronchamp — or about any successful work for that matter — is the way the influences have all been transformed into a new compound of form and meaning from which it is impossible to subtract an element without destroying the whole.

To trace the sequence of drawings and models

from mid-1950 up until 1953, when construction began, is to see how Le Corbusier discovered an appropriate articulation for his guiding ideas. The walls were bent in three dimensions, not just two, and detailed to maximize tensions and ambiguities. The roof was thought of as a sluice and in one sketch (done while he was flying over Crete) he compared the rush of water to the action of a ski-jump. His temple to nature required that sun, light, wind and rain be endowed with cosmic overtones. The gargoyle in the west wall was detailed to resemble the nostrils of one of his mythical 'Taureaux', while the cistern beneath was set about with triangular prisms suggesting some occult aquatic symbolism.

Ronchamp bears superficial resemblances to certain Expressionist schemes of the 1920s but avoids overstatement: its forms are tight, its curves precise embodiments of intentions. There are also similarities with the totemic abstractions of contemporary artists such as Robert Motherwell or David Smith. Like Le Corbusier, they too were concerned to blend the Surrealist appeal to magic with devices derived from Cubism in a search for images with a direct appeal to the subconscious. But Ronchamp is rooted in Le Corbusier's own preoccupations and discoveries. It even harks back to his Ruskinian upbringing under L'Eplattenier ('only nature is true'), and to the *fin de siècle* fantasy of a Wagnerian *Gesamtkunstwerk*: a total work of art in which painting, sculpture and architecture would be integrated as an expression of a unified societal ideal. Le Corbusier intended that there should also be electronic music on the hill at Ronchamp, rumbling and emitting strange sounds at selected times of day.

Despite the pretensions towards the archetypal, Ronchamp has not had an entirely positive reception. The conservative clergy found that the building departed too far from religious norms. More recent, 'progressive' opinion has reacted against the 'aesthetic Christianity', regarding it as high-camp spiritualism. There is, certainly, a

pantomime aspect to some of the details at Ronchamp, such as the sickly-sweet coloured glass decorations which reek of Miró or Léger at their most saccharin. However, the effect of the forms in their setting, of the changing patterns of light and shade, of the intense interiors, is most likely to lead to agreement with the praise of the Abbé Ferry: '... in the mid-twentieth century, the chapel assumes in its turn the totality of Christian mystery, ... one finds there the moving atmospheres of earlier ages, like those of the catacombs, the ancient basilicas and our old Romanesque churches.'

While Ronchamp was still in the late stages of design, Le Corbusier received the commission for the Dominican Monastery of La Tourette, to stand on a slope near Eveux-sur-l'Arbresle, a few miles to the west of Lyons. Father Couturier again played a major role in securing the commission for Le Corbusier and in explaining the rudiments of monastic life to him. Not that the architect needed much encouragement on the subject given his early passionate interest in the charterhouse at Ema, a building which had made him 'conscious of the harmony which results from the interplay of individual and collective life when each reacts favourably on the other. Individuality and collectivity understood as a fundamental dualism'. Despite the fact that La Tourette was destined for the Dominican Order of Preachers, Couturier encouraged him to visit and to study the Cistercian monastery at Le Thoronet in Provence, arguing that this was the quintessential expression of the monastic ideal. He even suggested that the issues did not vary much from period to period — an implication of 'constants' that must have appealed to Le Corbusier. With his letter (written in June 1953), Father Couturier included a sketch of the typical Cistercian plan with communal facilities attached to a cloistered courtyard which was, in turn, clamped to the side of an oblong church.

Le Corbusier's abstraction of these and other monastic prototypes is best understood if one first

188 (*above left*) Sketches of the lighting system, the Serapeum, Hadrian's Villa, Tivoli, recalling observations made during the Voyage d'orient.

189 (*above*) Roof and gutter of the Chapel at Ronchamp, Sketchbook E18, 1951 (Fondation Le Corbusier).

190 The Monastery of La Tourette, Eveux-sur-l'Arbresle, 1953–7, view from the north-west.

191 La Tourette, curved side chapels protruding from the north wall of church.

has the finished La Tourette in mind. The usual approach is from the north, and the first view is of a blank rectangle of concrete which turns out to be the side of the church. This is surmounted by a cross and punctured low down by a curved protrusion containing side-chapels. The ear-like shape with its battered walls recalls Ronchamp, but here light comes in from the top through a series of sloped 'light cannons'. The blank wall is a forceful and enigmatic expression of a closed and exclusive institution. Only when one draws level with it does one realize how subtly this vertical plane plays against the slope while drawing in long diagonal views over the valleys and hills to the west. In fact the top line is not horizontal, but slopes down towards the east end, engendering an illusion of compressed perspective while adding life to the volume of the church inside and out. Rowe has hinted at the brooding presence of this wall: 'a great dam holding back a reservoir of spiritual energy'.

A few more steps and one passes the other wall of the church, to perceive a rectangular vignette of landscape between it and the rest of the building. The monastery is revealed as a rectangular 'U' embracing a precinct: the Le Thoronet diagram rethought and reassembled. But at La Tourette there are cells (rather than a communal dormitory), and there is no habitable courtyard

192 (*top left*) La Tourette, plan at level of church.

193 (*above left*) Cistercian monastery of Le Thoronet, 12th century, plan.

194 (*above*) La Tourette, view from the main entrance along the south wall of the church.

195 La Tourette, the courtyard: the pyramid stands over the Oratory.

reached from a cloister. The old type has been recast in the form of a flat-topped communal concrete jetty floating out over the landscape on piers. The ideal society blends the images of a precinct and of a transparent box floating above the terrain. An assemblage of glazed walkways, skylights and prismatic objects punctuate the basic moves of the design.

Variations in fenestration, sculptural weight and transparency signal changes of use. The private cells of the monks run around the top two floors on the exterior rim of the building, each marked by a sun-shaded balcony: the individual is blended into the communal order. Access corridors to the rooms run along the inside surfaces of the court and are lit by thin horizontal slits at eye level. The entrance is beneath the double stack of cells and is reached from the outside over a bridge parallel to the oblong of the church, a device recalling the bridge at Le Thoronet as well as the entrance sequence into the Cité de Refuge. The most public functions — the novices' library and seminar rooms — are on this level. So is the Oratory, which is experienced as a pyramid over a cubic volume. La Tourette was to be a teaching institution for the Dominican Order of Preachers; correspondingly the entrance level is treated in an open, inviting way. The access deck is a relative of the street-in-the-air at Marseilles, but here it runs along the inner edge of the court and is given a complex pattern of glazing and opaque panels. The seminar rooms on the outer perimeter are treated to full floor-to-ceiling glazing divided by unevenly spaced concrete mullions called 'ondulatoires'. Between some of the struts vertical, pivoting ventilating doors called 'aérateurs' are inserted. The combined fenestration system was laid out by the musician/architect Yannis Xenakis according to Modulor proportions to create 'musical glazed rhythms' (Pl.149).

These ondulatoires come fully into their own on the next floor down, that containing the monastery's own communal functions, such as the Chapter House, the Refectory and the glazed walkways linking to the church. There is no courtyard/cloister in the full sense at La Tourette: the site would not have allowed it without expensive excavation. The promenade on top of the building, and the lower walkways (laid out in the form of a cross) are set aside for contemplative strolls and for the reading of the Office. The ondulatoires in the walkways dramatize the actual movement behind them and ripple into sculptural action as one passes by. When seen on the diagonal, they evoke the receding planes of light and shade of the traditional cloister's arcading. The bare concrete forms in taut proportions echo old aspirations towards a pure abstraction in stone: light, music and mathematics had been used by the Cistercians as the means for touching on the Divine. The elegant serenity and poverty of La Tourette's finishes are not without moral associations.

Le Corbusier was adept at distorting, inverting and contradicting the order suggested by an ideal type. As one spirals down La Tourette, one glimpses bizarre juxtapositions of forms: the pyramid over the Oratory breaks into the court and rhymes with the tilted diagonal of the atrium roof; the cylinder of the 'medieval' spiral stair echoes its modern factory counterpart, the kitchen stack, and resonates with the curious curved cubicles for visitors by the entrance; the low lump of the Sacristy, with its rows of 'light guns', collides with the church wall, and plays against the cruciform walkways. The result is a marriage of different shapes, identities and associations. But these contrasts are minor compared to the collision between the horizontal layers of the monastery and the vertical box of the church. The resulting tension is particularly rich when seen across the meadows. The play of major mass against void, of light against shade, is reinforced in a minor key by smaller ratios and intervals of varying depth, texture and transparency. The tension between, and resolution of, individual and collective — central to Le Corbusier's interpretation — are carried through into smaller parts.

La Tourette embodies a variation on the old Corbusian theme of a box on stilts. But the 'Five Points of a New Architecture' have been enriched and extended to allow new elements. Piers of various sizes, shapes and profiles channel the space on the outside; cylindrical pilotis of various dimensions articulate the public spaces inside. Church and cells are highly concentrated rooms. Façades are textured by ondulatoires and aérateurs, conceptual cousins of the fenêtre en longuer, the pan de verre and the brise-soleil, in that they too embody the Rationalist ideal of a grammar appropriate to the reinforced concrete skeleton. It was typical of Le Corbusier's approach that he should have sought a different form for each function: the fixed panes between the ondulatoires are there exclusively to light, the vertical aluminium doors of the aérateurs (recalling aeroplane flaps), exclusively to ventilate. The old functions of the window find themselves recast in a new language of 'type-elements' which Le Corbusier felt were archetypal.

When Le Corbusier went to the trouble of inventing new elements it was usually because the old ones had failed, and/or because he was faced with an unprecedented situation. Since the early 1930s he had had trouble with fully glazed, sealed façades. Some of the environmental problems had been handled by the various sorts of brise-soleil. He evidently valued the idea of full floor-to-ceiling glazing and the idea of natural cross-ventilation. Moreover, he had gradually discovered that an intermediary texture between the sculptural crates of the brise-soleil and the machine-age smoothness of pans de verre was needed for expressive reasons. Ondulatoires fitted into this agenda nicely. The basic moves of La Tourette — overhanging cells on top and piers underneath, but with public spaces needing views between — may have encouraged the search for a façade solution that was textured enough to allow a vertical transition from piers to cells, and dynamic enough to allow horizontal movement in response to the stepping layers and the idea of a

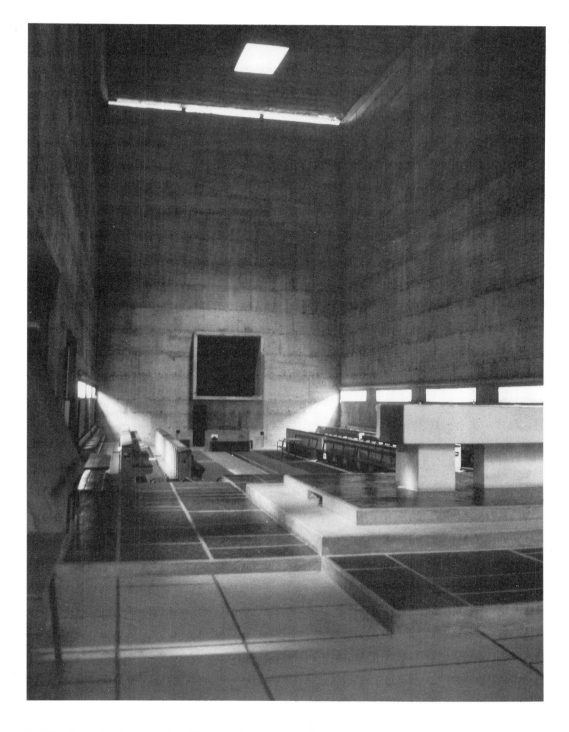

196 La Tourette, interior of church looking west from altar to choir.

building hovering towards its setting. *Ondula-toires* solved such problems adeptly. Xenakis has described the agonies that went into establishing a hierarchy of rhythms between the struts which harmonized with the composition, reflected interior uses and conformed to the numerology of the Modulor. The *ondulatoires* enriched the interiors too by slicing up views into intriguing vignettes while giving a slight sense of enclosure. Seen on the diagonal in cross light, they gave a mysterious opacity to the fenestration, and revealed themselves to be relatives of Classical mouldings. To

their author they perhaps recalled the perceptual ambiguities of rows of fluted columns seen in raking views of Greek temples. Combined with the overhanging 'cornice' of the cells, and the forceful plasticity of the piers, the *ondulatoires* of La Tourette aspired towards the 'spiritual mechanics' which Le Corbusier had praised in the tight profiles of the Parthenon.

On the interior, materials were handled with equal directness, the cells being pebble-dashed like Ronchamp — small, spare rooms of intense concentration, looking out on to little rectangles of sky, trees and hills. Pipes and ducts were left bare in corridors. This modern, functionalist austerity may be construed as monastic in intention, but it is as well to remember that the budget of La Tourette was slashed in two. Floors in the walkways were bare concrete, patterned according to the Modulor to create a 'dallage' echoing masonry paving. Bold touches of primary colour enlivened the surfaces, as at Marseilles and in Chandigarh.

The sequence through La Tourette takes one into spaces of varying psychological character, from the enclosed mystery of the little pyramid Oratory to the open luminosity of the atrium, to the formality of the Chapter House and Refectory. The last has four fine *pilotis* passing through it, defining a main axis and side slots for tables. Consistent with the overall collagist strategy, the size, weight and texture of structure are varied from place to place. La Tourette creates a medieval warren in concrete: a closed city of the spirit enlivened by stunning views over nature. The plan was determined by the Rule of the Dominican Order, a programme of daily routines with long historical sanction:

'I have tried to create a place of meditation, study and prayer for the Order of Preachers. The human requirements of that problem have guided our work ... I imagined the forms, the contacts, the circuits which were necessary so that prayer, liturgy, meditation and study should be at ease in this house. My work is to house men. It was a question of housing friars and trying to give them silence and peace, which is so essential in our life today. The friars ... please God in this silence. This monastery of rough concrete is a work of love. It does not show off — it is from the interior that it lives. In the interior the essential takes place.'

Perhaps the path through La Tourette from the secular world outside, over the bridge, through the novices' zone, down into the communal areas, on into the church, and finally into the curved bulge of the side-chapels where Mass is said by the ordained monks (the same protrusion seen in the earliest view) has the significance of a rite of passage towards the priesthood. The church which culminates the route is a space of chilling gravity, force and discipline which the *Oeuvre complète* describes as 'd'une pauvreté totale' ('of a total poverty'). The choir stalls occupy the west end; a few public seats the other; the altar stands between on a raised plinth. Light creeps in through low slots by the stalls (surprisingly adequate for reading), through a crack at the top between roof and wall (the slight depression of the ceiling breeds an eerie tension), through a vertical slot in one corner, or else through the aperture to the side-chapels in the curved extension. The 'light cannons' illuminate the side altars clearly, while the smaller variants over the Sacristy are even aligned to the sun's angle at the equinox. The main church space is a cross between a Corbusian *boîte à miracles* ('miracle box') and a stark church interior from the Middle Ages or earlier. Like Ronchamp, it suggests a

return to beginnings. In *Vers une architecture* Le Corbusier described Santa Maria in Cosmedin in terms of 'the Primitiveness of the Early Christian Chapel': '... a church for poor people ... set in the midst of ... luxurious Rome, proclaims the noble pomp of mathematics, the unassailable power of proportion, the sovereign eloquence of relationship. The design is merely that of the ordinary basilica, that is the form in which barns and hangars are built.'

La Tourette blends old Corbusian themes like the box on stilts and the flat-topped urban structure pulling away from a hillside (e.g. Montevideo 1929) with more recent inventions like the interior street, *béton brut* and the textured façade. It fuses Ema with Le Thoronet in overall organization and even in certain details. The sloped cloister of Le Thoronet is found in a new form in La Tourette; so are the ideas of a linking bridge, an upper walkway, a pyramid and a church with level changes. Le Corbusier did not mimic his sources directly but transformed them, holding on to the elements that he thought retained validity or value. Attracted to the intruding polygon of the fountain in Le Thoronet, he made equivalent staccato incidents with the Oratory and spiral stairs at La Tourette. At a deeper level still he sensed in Cistercian architecture an elemental purity of formal expression transcending period and style. After visiting a church constructed by the Order he wrote of the poetry of light and shade in 'this architecture of truth, calm and strength'.

Even the conception of an ideal community suspended above an idyllic landscape was an amalgam of Le Corbusier's own utopian typology and old memories from the Voyage d'orient. The monasteries at Mount Athos in Greece were perched above the hillsides with elaborate outriggers extending the cells at incredible heights. Tops were flat, bottoms extended downwards to meet the irregular slope, and one entered from high ground at the back. Courtyards had chapels and shrines dotted around in them. In the young Jeanneret's own words: '... a large, alluring fortress wall ... A vast horizontal crowned the quadrilateral of buildings, guiding the eye far away towards the sea ... cells with their galleries open to the sea, high up in the sky.'

Like the Unité d'Habitation at Marseilles, La Tourette draws sustenance from Le Corbusier's youthful Mediterranean dream. The blank north wall with restated court evokes old European religious echoes, and even resonates with the vernacular patterns of the Midi in which windowless north walls face up to the chill of the Mistral while social life and sunlight live within. Le Corbusier had hoped to address his conceptions of the ideal life to the modern city, but had to be content with the piecemeal unités, and to watch their devaluation in grotesque housing slabs worldwide. It was somehow central to his predicament that his vision of societal harmony had to evade mass society to remain intact; and that this vision should have been realized in a remote rustic spot for the social programme from which it had originally sprung: the community of monks.

197 La Tourette: cell balconies and *ondulatoires* in the south façade.

Chapter 13

Le Corbusier in India: The Symbolism of Chandigarh

'Architecture has its public use, public buildings being the ornament of a country: it establishes a nation, draws people and commerce, and makes people love their native country, which passion is the origin of all great actions in a commonwealth.'
Sir Christopher Wren

It was consistent with the other twists and paradoxes of Le Corbusier's late career that his grandest monumental designs and most complete urban plan should have been realized far from the industrial countries of the West towards which he had directed his architectural gospel. Neither the United States nor France, the most likely candidates, offered the architect a major public building, and the fiasco over the United Nations only confirmed his already well-formed (and well-founded) suspicions of public patronage. By contrast, India — poor, technologically backward, making the first tentative steps after independence — welcomed Le Corbusier with open arms and a wide range of commissions: the urban layout of Chandigarh, four major government buildings including a Parliament and High Court, two museums, and a number of institutional and domestic projects for Ahmedabad (the subject of the next chapter). Only Paris and La Chaux-de-Fonds can show as many Corbusian buildings as these two Indian cities, and the Parliament building at Chandigarh must be counted one of the architect's masterworks.

Family resemblances can be found between the Indian buildings and Le Corbusier's contemporary European projects. There is a similar sculptural weight, and intensity in the use of light and space; natural analogies and cosmic themes underlie imagery; materials like brick and bare concrete are used in a deliberately rough way to evoke archaic and primitivist associations. Façades tend to be highly textured with intervals controlled by the Modulor, and new elements like the deep-cut *brise-soleil*, the *ondulatoire* and the *aérateur* are employed with thick directional piers. But Le Corbusier was not simply exporting a global formula: his usual type-solutions were modified to the limitations of local technology, the strengths of regional handicraft and the demands of a searing climate. He was quick to realize that he was dealing with an old civilization evolving rapidly towards modern democracy yet also trying to rediscover roots after the colonial experience. Glib modernity and the slush of nostalgia were equally to be avoided. The situation demanded largesse, vision and insight into what was relevant in India's spiritual and material past.

If India and Le Corbusier seem right for one another in retrospect, their initial convergence was anything but straightforward. Chandigarh was born out of the massacres, tragedies and hopes that attended partition and the creation of Pakistan. In July 1947 the Independence Bill was signed and British rule in India came to an end. When Pakistan came into existence the following year the State of the Punjab was cut in two, millions of refugees fled in both directions, blood was spilt in great quantities and the old state capital of Lahore was left on the Pakistani side. Temporarily business was run from Simla, the British hill station, but this was practically and symbolically inadequate. It was obvious that a new city must be founded to anchor the situation and to give refugees (many of whom were Hindu or Sikh) a home. P.L. Varma, Chief Engineer of the Punjab, and P.N. Thapar, State Administrator of Public Works, considered a number of sites before settling on a place between two river valleys, just off the main Delhi to Simla line, a safe distance from Pakistan and at a point where the huge plains began to fold into the foothills of the Himalayas. Transport, water, raw materials, central position in the state were all practical considerations, but Varma still insists that an intuition of the *genius loci* played its part. The place felt auspicious: they chose the name after 'Chandi', the Hindu goddess of power.

From the outset it was clear that Chandigarh would be no mere local venture. Pandit Nehru and the central government felt the Punjab disaster keenly and realized the importance of cementing new institutions and housing in place. New Delhi agreed to cover one third of the initial costs and Nehru himself recommended Albert Mayer, an American planner whose acquaintance he had made during the war, to lay out the new city. Matthew Nowicki, a capable young architect who had once worked with Le Corbusier, was selected to concentrate on architectural matters, including the design of the main democratic institutions on the Capitol. A modern and efficient city, with up-to-date services, sewerage and transport was envisaged by the government. Nehru spoke of clean, open spaces liberating Indians from the tyranny of the overcrowded and filthy cities, as well as from the confines of agricultural, village life. Chandigarh, then, was to be a visible and persuasive instrument of national economic and social development, consonant with Nehru's belief that the country must industrialize or perish. It was to be a showpiece of liberal and enlightened patronage, and he would later eulogize Chandigarh as a 'temple of the New India'.

Mayer's plan of 1950 organized the city into sectors around a hierarchy of green swards and curved roads. The commercial zone was at the centre, the industrial area to the south-east, and the Capitol to the top or north-easterly extremity, separate from the residences and on the verge of open countryside. Nowicki's few extant sketches show that he thought of the Capitol as a series of objects separated by wide, open spaces. He began to experiment with a vocabulary of columns and screens for some of the buildings. The Parliament was expressed as a spiral ziggurat, obviously but skilfully modelled on Le Corbusier's Mundaneum project of 1929. Mayer

was a major proponent of Garden City thinking in America, and his picturesque roads and green spaces set about with low-rise buildings conformed to this point of view, as well as extending the British tradition of suburban residential zones on the outskirts of numerous Indian towns. But the overall shape of Mayer's plan, as well as the placing of the city of affairs as a separate 'head', also loosely recalls Le Corbusier's Ville Radieuse.

Fate intervened in spring 1950 when Nowicki was killed in a plane crash in Egypt. Again Thapar and Varma set out to find a new chief architect. They continued to feel that there was no one in India remotely capable of handling such a thing (scarcely surprising given the habits of professional training under the Raj). They went to London and spoke to Jane Drew and Maxwell Fry, who had experience designing in the tropics but who hesitated to take the whole job on and recommended Le Corbusier. The delegation went to Paris and the master turned them down, especially when he heard that they wanted him to move to India and realized how low the fees would be. But gradually he came round, declaring that the necessary work could be done mainly in Paris. Finally he agreed to be chief

198 Chandigarh, India, 1951–65, view from the south-east across the Capitol towards the Parliament Building and Secretariat.

architectural consultant for the city as a whole
and exclusive designer of the Capitol buildings.
He accepted a modest monthly salary and agreed
to make two month-long visits a year to India.
Jane Drew and Maxwell Fry were to be employed
on three-year contracts, concentrating attention
on the design of all facilities for residential
sectors, and then forming teams of young Indian
architects to carry on the work (eventually under
Pierre Jeanneret). Poor Mayer was to continue as
planner, but he would be no match for the far
more powerful personality of Le Corbusier, a
man who had reflected on the nature of cities for
forty years, who saw no real division between the
functions of architect and planner, and who now
firmly intended to lay down the law.

In spring 1951 Le Corbusier went to India and
met the rest of the team in a rest-house on the
road to Simla, where they worked together for
about four weeks. But the guiding principles of
the new Chandigarh plan were laid down in four
days. In principle it followed Mayer's, as the
contract had suggested that it should. But both
Fry and Le Corbusier had found the curved roads
flaccid, so Le Corbusier returned to an orthogonal grid while Fry sneaked in a few curved
lateral roads for variety. The anthropomorphic
diagram — head, body, arms, spine, stomach,
etc. — of the new plan was accentuated by major
axial routes crossing towards the centre; it
reverted more closely to the form of the Ville
Radieuse. But the elements making it up were
quite different. The skyscrapers of the technocrats were replaced by the shelters of democracy
at the head; the communal medium-rise apartment houses of the main body were replaced by a
gradation of different house types (eventually
fourteen in all) catering for manual labourers at
the bottom social rung up to judges and high-
level bureaucrats at the top. There would be
variants on terrace houses and magnificent
modern bungalows but (it was eventually
decided) no high-rise buildings. Le Corbusier
realized that his usual housing models had a
limited relevance in a place where there was
plenty of land and where people were used to

living half outside. He confided to his sketchbook
that the basic unit in the Indian city was 'the bed
under the stars'.

Each rectangular sector of Chandigarh measured about 4,000 by 2,600 feet and was to be
regarded as a largely self-contained urban community. Sectors were linked — and separated —
by a grid of different-sized roads varying in size
from small bridle (or rather bicycle) paths within
the sectors, to residential arteries, throughways,
and finally the grandiose Jan Marg running up the
centre of the city towards the Capitol. In all seven
main types of circulation were worked out;
typically these were canonized 'les sept Vs' (short
for 'voies' or 'ways'). Evidently Le Corbusier
was anticipating a time when motor traffic
might become a major force in India. In other
respects too the plan followed old Corbusian
prescriptions: the separate zoning of living,
working, circulation and leisure; the fusion of
country and city through the planting and provision of trees and parks; rigid geometrical
control and delight in grand vistas and processional axes; a sense of openness rather than of
enclosure; a lingering hope that urban order
might bring social regeneration in its wake.

Much of this runs against the planning fashion
of the moment, which is squeamish about any
form of environmental determinism, nervous
about the grand plan, and committed to spatial
enclosure and the cultivation of visual variety.
But before the dictates of the present are imposed on Chandigarh it should be born in mind
that a bold statement of order embodying the
idea of a beneficent but stabilizing state was a
virtual demand of Le Corbusier's clients. The
élite with which he had contact was cosmopolitan
and often Western-educated; it probably did not
see itself living in some higgledy-piggledy
Orientalist version of 'Indian Life'. Le Corbusier's mandate came in part from Nehru, who
later spoke of Chandigarh as 'reaching beyond
the existing encumbrances of old towns and old
traditions' and as 'the first large expression of our
creative genius, founded on our newly earned
freedom'. There was little room in this vision for
Gandhi's spinning-wheels or for his idealization
of the village as the moral core of Indian life;
indeed the construction of Chandigarh entailed
the destruction of a number of villages.

Of course there is no divine rule which says
that grids and axes are the only appropriate
metaphors for the rational and modernizing
powers of government, but in Le Corbusier's
mind such associations probably did exist. It
was as if he wished to give to the New India its
symbolic equivalent to the Raj's New Delhi. He
studied and admired the grand axes and main Raj
Path of that city, as well as the monumental
approach to Lutyens's Viceroy's House. Like his
English predecessor he too hoped to synthesize
the Grand Classical and Indian traditions with a
statement of modern aspirations. But obviously
the task of crystallizing the ethos of a liberated
and democratic society was quite different from
that of expressing foreign domination and imper-

199   Town plan of Chandigarh, 1951.

ial power. Le Corbusier's belief that the city as a whole should carry symbolic values took him back to old fascinations: the axis between the Arc de Triomphe and the Louvre; the superb iconographic clarity of the plan of ancient Peking; perhaps even to the ancient Hindu theoretical texts on urbanism, the 'Shilpas' in which cities were sometimes described as centric diagrams with main roads intersecting at their centre. It is rather doubtful whether Le Corbusier studied these theoretical precepts, but he certainly knew a relatively modern incorporation of them: the early eighteenth-century city of Jaipur, which was laid out on a grid of wide streets. If Le Corbusier had taken a greater interest in the urban qualities of the commercial centre at Chandigarh he might have found relevant lessons at Jaipur for the shaded linkage of public courtyards; unfortunately he did not.

Thus, despite the rhetoric of Nehru, the past was not banished at Chandigarh; rather it was examined critically for relevant lessons of organization. The housing by Fry, Drew and Pierre Jeanneret used concrete, brick and modern plumbing and equipment, but the architects also tried to respect custom and caste in the house plans and to transform vernacular prototypes in the provision of loggias, sleeping terraces, territorial walls and shading. Le Corbusier's Indian sketchbooks brim over with rustic enthusiasms. He sketched the simple yet ancient tools of the peasants, returning time and again to the robust forms of bull-carts. Gandhi crept into his

musings through the back door as he revelled in village folklore and the apparent harmony of people, things, animals and nature. Thus the sophisticated foreign primitivist intuited links between his own contrived pantheism and the deeply rooted cosmic myths of India's ancient religions: the 'delights of Hindu philosophy', the 'fraternity between cosmos and living beings'. And all this seemed substantial, rich and vital alongside the anaemic and trivial values of modern industrial life. Gradually India settled into Le Corbusier's mind as a country that must avoid the voracious industrialism of the 'first machine age' by forging a new culture on a firm moral base involving equilibrium between the religious and the secular, the rustic and the mechanical.

While Le Corbusier was absorbing the human content of the Chandigarh problem he was also reflecting on the best ways of dealing with monsoons and extreme heat. He studied or sketched vernacular structures, colonial verandas, the loggias of Mogul pavilions, the shaded walkways of Hindu temple precincts, and tried to distil the basic lessons from them. These in turn he sought to blend with the fundamentals of his own architetural system: the skeleton of the Dom-ino or the low vaults of the Monol. In his search for a basic, modern 'Indian grammar' the North African projects from the 1920s, 1930s, and 1940s were obviously pertinent, especially for dealing with the sun.

Le Corbusier's guiding ideas for the Governor's

200 The High Court seen from the Parliament.

201 Plan of Chandigarh Capitol, 1952 (Fondation Le Corbusier).

Palace, the High Court, the Parliament and the Secretariat developed with astonishing rapidity in his portable atelier, the sketchbooks. The unifying theme and leitmotiv of the Capitol was established as the *parasol* or protective, over-hanging roof, supported on either arches, piers or *pilotis*. This device would shelter the buildings from sun and rain while remaining open at the edges to catch the cool breezes and allow a variety of views. The *parasol* was also capable of a multiplicity of meanings, and Le Corbusier soon discovered poetic and cosmic possibilities in sketches which showed water sluicing off roofs into basins. The idea could in turn be modified to create loggias, verandas, scoops, porticoes, and curved or rectangular roofs hovering above deep undercrofts of shadow. *Brise-soleil* screens of various kinds could be suspended, attached or built up in front, generating openings and entries or allowing the eye to penetrate to the depths of buildings or even beyond them to mountains and sky. Le Corbusier was to discover that the *parasol* could also resonate across time, recalling a number of symbolic motifs in the history of Indian architecture.

Le Corbusier placed the Governor's Palace at the head of the Capitol, and the Parliament and High Court lower in the hierarchy facing one another but slipped slightly off each other's axis; they flanked the view to the Palace and expressed the idea of a balance of powers between the judiciary and the executive. The Secretariat was lodged behind and to one side of the huge hieratic box of the Parliament. It was as if Le Corbusier had re-adapted the devices for dis-tinguishing ceremonial from workaday aspects of government from his League of Nations scheme years before, but exploded them across a huge platform. Throughout its evolution the plan of the Capitol bore comparison with the rectangles and flanges in tension of an early Mondrian or else with the sliding objects and subtle axial shifts of a Mogul palace or garden. Among Le Corbu-

sier's earliest Indian sketches were ones of the eighteenth-century garden at Pinjore that used clever effects of illusion to compress together terraces of water with the rugged outlines of the landscape. As his ideas for the spaces between the monuments developed he incorporated hillocks, trenches for vehicular circulation, water basins, ramps and (eventually) a panoply of signs and symbols illustrating the philosophy behind the city. These were all orchestrated into a surreal landscape in which foreground and back-ground were ingeniously compressed to produce bizarre illusions of size and scale.

While Le Corbusier was weighing up the over-all shape of the Capitol he was also trying to establish appropriate forms and symbols for each institution, always on the basic theme of the *parasol*. A variant emerged in the project for the Governor's Palace (1951–4), eventually not built because Nehru found it undemocratic. It would have dominated the site from afar with its intri-cate silhouette standing out against the blue haze of the hills. It was preceded by ramps, pools and sunken gardens, and approached off-axis by car along a valley route; a similar means of access was worked out for all the buildings. The image was dominated by the upturned crescent on top. This was lifted up on four supports, creating a small theatre for nocturnal events above and a shelter for afternoon receptions underneath. The shape seemed to gesture up towards the planetary realm and would have answered similar shapes in the neighbouring constructions. Many images were compressed into it. Among Le Corbusier's travel sketches are some comparing bulls' horns to tilted roof structures open at the edges to let air pass. The bull was related to old animist themes in Le Corbusier's paintings (stemming ultimately from the Surrealist obsession with Minotaurs) as well as perhaps to Hindu icono-graphy since Nandi the bull was a vehicle of Shiva; in this case, surely, the image also had to do with Le Corbusier's nebulous belief that

India's future lay in a fusion of traditional rural values and modern progressive ones — in another part of the Governor's Palace a curious sculpture was proposed which blended the bulls' horns with an aeroplane propeller. But the *parasol* was in turn an ancient symbol of state authority, found on top of Buddhist stupas and in a much later domical or arched form in Islamic monuments. The Governor's Palace, portrayed at the end of its pathways and pools, silhouetted dramatically against the sky, experienced both frontally and in torsion with its surroundings, recaptures something of the spirit of the Diwan-I-Khas at Fathepur Sikri, a site that the architect had seen and admired. In this example, *chattris* or domical variants on the *parasol* were lifted at the four corners of the roofline on slender supports through which the sky could be seen.

202 (*above left*) Karli Chaitya Hall, India, 2nd-1st century BC: the Buddhist parasol.

203 (*above*) Sketch of the Governor's Palace, Chandigarh, 1952 (Fondation Le Corbusier).

204 (*far left*) Diwan-I-Khas, Fathepur Sikri, India, late 16th century.

205 (*left*) Bulls' horns and tilt roof, from Indian Sketchbook F26, 1952 (Fondation Le Corbusier).

Le Corbusier was certainly aware of a much later attempt at a 'beneficent' imperial eclecticism: that of Lutyens in the Viceroy's House in New Delhi. The main dome of this building declared the power and tolerance of the Raj through the fusion of stupa and Classical dome, rather as the city layout declared respect for the past by careful alignments with the various ancient Delhis. The imperial hat was then impishly turned on its head in other parts of the building to become a scoop or water basin; in the gardens at the back a pretty Edwardian version of Mogul landscaping continued the aquatic theme. But the dome would not have been an appropriate emblem for Chandigarh even if Le Corbusier had not regarded the form as defunct. So it was transformed into a counter-shape, a form that did not compress its forces downwards, but that sprang upwards, open and free. This was the emblem for the new, democratic, liberal and liberated India — a shape that echoed the gesture of the 'Open Hand', Le Corbusier's symbol of international peace, transcending politics, caste, religion, race. It was the very symbol that he hoped to erect adjacent to the Governor's Palace where the two silhouettes could be appreciated simultaneously. In transforming certain buildings within the Indian tradition it was not the architect's aim to make obvious references to particular creeds and periods but to create a truly pluralist imagery touching on universal human themes. The foreign and the indigenous, the new and the old were in this case blended into an imagery for the new Indian identity around pan-cultural ideals that were the opposite of tyrannical.

Variations on the sheltering roof idea were used in the other buildings as well. The High Court, for example, was conceived as a huge open-sided box under a giant roof standing on a 'grand order' of concrete piers. These formed a portico marking the asymmetrical entrance where they were slightly curved in plan recalling the subtleties of the Pavillon Suisse *pilotis* or the heroic supports under the Marseilles Unité. The Supreme Court was to the left of the entrance on its own, while the other courts spread out to the right under the *parasol* behind a secondary system of sun-shading grilles. Massive ramps zigzagged their way laterally through the structure linking to upper-level offices and offering vignettes of the Parliament in the distance between the piers (eventually the three supports at the entrance were painted red, yellow and green). The underside of the *parasol* was arched in a manner recalling sketches that Le Corbusier had done forty years earlier of the Basilica of Constantine. The huge *parasol* was intended to convey the 'shelter, majesty and power of the law'. Under the entrance Le Corbusier placed an odd little sculpture of a snake rising from a water basin: his own curious interpretation of a coiled serpent embodying the principle of spiritual power.

Le Corbusier's dabblings in cosmology and researches into tradition would have been all for nought if he had not had the means to transform ideas into sculptural forms of prodigious force and presence. From the start he thought in terms of concrete. The material was far from perfect for high temperatures but local know-how and materials did exist. Construction would be labour-intensive, and over the years the 'prophet of the machine age' would be treated to the sight of hundreds of Indians swarming over wooden scaffolding tied with ropes, or wheeling tiny loads of concrete up rickety ramps before packing the stuff into place between rough planks. The resulting crudities were turned into richnesses in the creation of an instant patina that gave the buildings an archaic feeling appropriate to Le Corbusier's intentions. If the rude and powerful shapes recall Marseilles and La Tourette they have equally to be seen in terms of the indigenous mud architecture which the architect admired close to Chandigarh. It was typical of him that he should have sought to combine the vitality of folk craft with the abstract fastnesses of courtly monumental traditions. Concrete allowed him to sculpt with broad ochre surfaces gashed by openings of shadow. In the bold creative moves made in sketches between 1951 and 1953 a new language of monumentality was invented that went well beyond the spindly limitations of the International Style but without regressing into ersatz historicism. The finished Chandigarh monuments have the air of buildings that have stood there for centuries: an architecture 'timeless but of its time' (Pls.151–4).

The High Court was the first structure to be erected on the Capitol and so served as a trial in the realization of ideas. In parallel Le Corbusier evolved the most complex of the designs, that for the Parliament. This began life as a large, inward-turning, shaded box preceded by monumental arches and by an even larger arched portico. Ancient Roman sources again come to mind (the Pont du Gard, the basilicas), but gradually the idea was simplified towards a trabeated solution with the sides behind *brises-soleil* and the front facing the plaza as a scooped portico. This appeared to gesture across the Capitol and also acted as a huge gutter to sluice the monsoons. The plan extended an old Corbusian pattern: a free-plan grid of supports with the main functional organs set down into it as curves. Le Corbusier was on the alert for ritual. He wished to give shape to the dominant role of the Assembly Chamber and to the dialogue between it and the Senate. Public involvement might be implied through surrounding forums in the hypostyle and through the portico linked to the setting as a sort of shaded stoa.

As at Ronchamp and La Tourette, Le Corbusier explored the mythical qualities of light and darkness in the Parliament Building. Early sketches showed rays of sunlight and moonlight penetrating the interiors in a dramatic way; there were even obscure references to 'nocturnal festivals'. As problems of lighting and ventilating the Assembly Chamber came to the fore, the architect broke the room up through the roof as a tower (Pl.3). In one version he added a spiral walkway as a stair for the window cleaners, but this surely had a symbolic role too. The spiral

206 High Court, Chandigarh, 1951–5.

207 Diwan-I-Am, Red Fort, Delhi, early 17th century.

208 Parliament (or Assembly) Building, Chandigarh, 1951–63.

209 Parliament Building,
Chandigarh, roofscape.

210 (*above left*) Jantar
Mantar, Delhi, early 18th
century.

suggested growth and aspiration, and perhaps
echoed Tatlin's Monument to the Third International (1919) or various revered minarets in
the history of architecture (e.g. Samarra, Ibn
Tulun). Later the tower was modified to take on
a hyperboloid geometry inspired by cooling
towers that Le Corbusier saw in Ahmedabad.

To observe the design process of the Parliament is to see customary elements of the architect's vocabulary invested with fresh levels of
meaning. The reference to a cooling tower might
be seen as an appropriate image for Nehru's
policies of modernization and industrialization,
but these twentieth-century myths were blended
with ancient sacral images. In some of his
sketches Le Corbusier compared the Assembly
space to the dome of Hagia Sophia with rays of
light streaming down. Celestial connotations in
his rethought dome were reinforced by the idea
of having a single ray of light hit a column of
Ashoka (the first Emperor of India) on the

Speaker's rostrum on the occasion of the annual
opening of the Parliament. The axis of the room
was aligned to the cardinal points, and so twisted
from the geometry of both building and city.
These solar gestures were supposed to remind
man that he is 'a son of the sun'. There is an echo
of the Pantheon — a microcosm linked through
its oculus to the planetary order — but the idea of
a ray of light bringing its renewing power to the
darkness and touching a shaft of stone is also
found in Hindu temples. In the Parliament the
path through the main ceremonial door (with its
various solar diagrams) takes one through a zone
of transition into a hall of columns and then
around the base of the Assembly funnel in a
clockwise direction recalling ritual circum-
ambulation in ancient Indian religious architecture. One other association may have floated into
Le Corbusier's memory in his search for an
appropriate image of congregation: the funnel-
like chimneys of Jura farmhouses of his youth,
into which the whole family would climb.
Through a prodigious feat of abstraction old and
new were compressed together in a single
symbolic form (Pls.151, 152).

A similar procedure of analogy and transformation is sensed in the design of the top of the
funnel with its tilted plaque, its up-turned
crescent and its downward-turning curves. Le
Corbusier let it be known that he wanted the top
to be equipped for 'the play of lights', that he was
thinking of it as a sort of observatory. This
suggests that he may have been inspired by the
extraordinary abstract constructions at the Jantar
Mantar in Delhi which had prompted him to
exclaim in his sketchbook: 'The astronomical
instruments of Delhi ... They point the way: relink men to the cosmos ... Exact adaptation of
forms and organisms to the sun, to the rains, to
the air etc. this buries Vignola ...' Planetary
crescent paths can be found traced in stone in
these prototypes, and Le Corbusier's studies for
reliefs, enamels, tapestries and monumental signs
indicate that he was fascinated by the curves of
the sun at solstice and equinox. The crescent
curve undergoes metamorphosis: it echoes the
Open Hand, the Governor's Palace silhouette,
bulls' horns, the chassis to carry the planets in
their cycles. Time and again in the sketchbooks
he returns to the form of the bull-cart wheel with
crescent-shaped suspension resting on the hub.
Like the *parasol*, the wheel was an ancient image

211 (*far left*) Oxcart wheel, India, Sketchbook K45, 1956 (Fondation Le Corbusier).

212 (*left*) Le Corbusier in India, sketchbook in hand.

of complex religious and political meaning that did indeed touch on cosmic and solar themes; it was also a modern Indian Nationalist symbol.

The plan of the Parliament is an ideogram rich in intentions. It seems to be modelled on that of the Altes Museum in Berlin by Schinkel; at least both are variants on a fundamental type where a stoa or portico precedes transition towards a domical space and where the hierarchy between ceremonial spaces and more mundane functions at the fringes (at Chandigarh the offices) is clearly marked. But Le Corbusier rejects Neo-Classical symmetry in favour of a turbulent contrast between symmetry and asymmetry, rectangular and curved, funnel and pyramid, box and grid. The roof volumes mark the main chambers and enter a spatial dialogue that reaches out to mountains and sky. Within they battle with the grid, compressing space in a way inconceivable without the plastic intensity of Cubism. The day-to-day entrance is to the Secretariat side, two levels below plaza level (a valley allows these buildings extra accommodation downwards). The ramps slice back and forth in section, allowing diagonal views of the funnel descending into the hypostyle, whose concrete mushroom columns are lit soberly from mysterious side sources. One enters the main chamber and the space expands upwards but in a manner that does not detract from the function and focus of the room.

The portico of the Parliament blends the crescent themes with the functions of sluice and frontispiece. Once again the gestural action of this shape reveals its capacity to lunge over great distances, in this case towards the High Court 400 yards away. Seen obliquely, it points to the mountains. Head-on, the turbulence ceases and it becomes a wide, low horizontal. Like Ronchamp, the Parliament is a sculpture in the round that

213 (*above left*) Parliament Building, Chandigarh, plan.

214 (*below left*) Karl F. Schinkel, Altes Museum, Berlin, 1827, plan.

215 The Secretariat, Chandigarh.

216 (*opposite above*) The commercial centre in Sector 17, Chandigarh.

217 (*opposite below*) Housing in Sector 20, Chandigarh.

Even then its sheer bulk had to be lessened by lowering the ground level through excavation. The resulting slab was nearly 800 feet long and contained eight sub-units. The construction joints between them were hidden behind a continuous screen of *brises-soleil*. The Modulor and the recent experience of Marseilles were both a help in balancing unity and variety, monumentality and the human scale. The fourth sub-block was varied in its façade treatment and amplified in its apertures to express the presence of the minister-ial offices. The full fenestration system comprised *ondulatoires*, *aérateurs* with insect screens as well as the *brise-soleil* fins. Movement of air was encouraged by fans, but air-conditioning was considered too expensive. Besides, Le Corbusier probably wished to demonstrate his natural devices for dealing with the climate. In truth these have been only partly successful. This enormous office building had to deal with the daily shifts of a huge labour force. Lifts and stairs were complemented by curved ramps sticking out from the slab like ears or handles. There was also a roof terrace affording sheltered places from which to enjoy the long views over landscape, city and Capitol.

It was Jane Drew who initially suggested to Le Corbusier that he should set up a row of signs symbolizing his architectural and urbanistic philosophy: the harmonic spiral, the signs of the Modulor, the S shape signifying the 24-hour rise and fall of the sun, curves showing the path of the sun at equinox and solstice and, of course, the Open Hand rising above the curious 'valley of contemplation'. In addition Le Corbusier envis-aged a curious sculpture of a broken Classical column with a tiger advancing upon it: an image of the collapse of British rule and the reassertion of Indian identity. When the Governor's Palace was rejected, Le Corbusier decided to replace it with a 'Museum of Knowledge'; later still he conceived a 'Tower of Shadows' to stand between Parliament and Justice — his twentieth-century version of the Jantar Mantar for registering sun angles on different-sized *brises-soleil*. At the time of writing, this last contraption and the Open Hand are in the process of construction, so the Capitol is in essential ways incomplete. But similar signs adorn both the boldly coloured tapestries that Le Corbusier designed for the High Court and the large enamel ceremonial door under the portico of the Parliament.

Intended as a popular art, the signs come very close to magniloquent kitsch. The reverent see in the Open Hand a pan-cultural significance, a cross between a Buddhist gesture for dispelling fear and a hovering Picasso Peace Dove. The cynics see a grotesque baseball glove and 'the fiction of a state art with no state religion behind it'. But Le Corbusier took it very seriously as an emblem of universal harmony representing, among other things, the belief that India might lead a moral regeneration. The form had a most complex genesis perhaps going back as far as the Ruskinian moral symbolism attached to fir trees in his youth. Le Corbusier is reported to have described the Open Hand as:

emits entirely different sensations from different points of view. The frontal approach suggests less a Classical portico than a Mogul audience chamber of the sort that Le Corbusier had observed in the Red Forts of both Delhi and Agra. These were defined by grids of supports open at the edges for cross-ventilation and shaded from sun and rain by deep overhangs. Le Corbu-sier's solution responded to analogous issues with equal formality but in the terminology of his new 'Indian grammar'. He bridged the gap between East and West, ancient and modern, by seeking out correspondences of principle.

For the Chandigarh Secretariat Le Corbusier originally intended a skyscraper. In its second version this was like the tower he had suggested for Algiers — textured with deep crates of *brise-soleil* which also functioned as balconies; the recently rejected United Nations Secretariat would have employed a similar system. But despite the architect's eagerness to demonstrate at last the 'correct' form for the skyscraper it gradually became clear that this was not the right place as a tall building would have dwarfed the ceremonial buildings. So the block was put on its side where it could act as a terminating barrier to the Capitol and as a backdrop to the Parliament.

... a plastic gesture charged with a profoundly human content.

A symbol very appropriate to the new situation of a liberated and independent earth. A gesture which appeals to fraternal collaboration and solidarity between all men and all the nations of the world.

Also a sculptural gesture ... capable of capturing the sky and engaging the earth.

By the late 1950s there was enough above ground at Chandigarh for Le Corbusier and the world architectural press to begin to judge what the finished buildings might look like. Along with the other late works they played their part in encouraging a reaction against the steel and glass clichés of the previous decade: in the 1960s bold concrete porticoes and piers became standard fare in city halls and cultural centres in many parts of the world. Meanwhile Le Corbusier turned to smaller buildings in Chandigarh such as the Museum and Yacht Club (Pls.156, 158). The former was a red-brick box lifted up on *pilotis* and top-lit through light troughs. Ramps rose to one side of the double-height lobby, guiding the visitor through the exhibition sequence. The building was a close relative of the museums for Ahmedabad and Tokyo. Like them it descended from the Museum of Unlimited Growth of the 1930s. At Chandigarh slight refinements such as the alternating system of piers and oval *pilotis* (creating bays and a free plan simultaneously) were enhanced by sober lighting and tight proportional control. The Yacht Club was even simpler, being a distillation of the 'Indian grammar' into a delicate, concrete-framed pavilion with free-plan partitions playing against the grid. The site was to one end of the lake that P.L. Varma insisted be built.

With its long, wide esplanade, its views to the mountains and its glimpses of the distant

218   Sketch of the Open
Hand, Chandigarh.

silhouettes on the Capitol, this must be counted among the most beautiful spots in Chandigarh.

It is still too early to come to conclusions about the urban qualities of Chandigarh: for most criticisms there is an answer. If one side claims that it is an ill-begotten toy of neo-colonialism another replies that it is the benchmark by which later Indian planning must be judged; for some-one who points to uniformity and rigidity somone else can be found to point to the shaded streets of the better-off sectors or to the splendid views of the mountains; the moan that the streets are too wide is countered with the observation that Chandigarh is easily able to absorb its growing traffic; vague charges of being 'un-Indian' are met with the reminder that the place offers welcome relief from the filth and overcrowding of the traditional population centres. There is almost universal agreement that Le Corbusier's principle of discrete zoning is singularly ill-matched to the complex mixed uses and mixed economies of Indian life, and almost universal condemnation of the vapid, sun-baked spaces of the commercial centre in sector 17. What was intended to be a modern version of a 'chowk' or bazaar area has come out as a bleak no man's land flanked by dead-pan rows of *pilotis* and brutally propor-tioned balconies. It seems odd that Le Corbusier should not have devoted time to the 'stomach' of his anthropomorphic city; Fry was shocked to return later and discover how bleakly these spaces had turned out.

Whatever its faults, the extraordinary thing is that Chandigarh exists at all: the expression of a huge collective effort that was launched after strife and tragedy. In its early years of growth the city has far outstripped the initial figure of 150,000 to approach the intended final population of half a million. It has played a central role in the economic transformation of the Punjab into one of the richest areas of India, a process

achieved partly through industrialization and the mechanization of farming. This success brings problems in its wake. If the city goes on expand-ing as an industrial centre there is the danger that its positive qualities will be undermined by speculation, bureaucratic graft and laissez-faire construction. The growth has also had its political stresses. In 1966 the Punjab was again divided, and the new state of Haryana now occupies half of the Parliament Building. At the time of writing Sikh aspirations towards independence are stimulating unrest in the Punjab with the threat of further divisions. As the idea of a pluralist, secular state takes increasing buffeting from various religious extremisms, the Open Hand still lies in prefabricated fragments, rusting in the grass, its messages dimly heard.

Le Corbusier's 'Indian grammar' has not always been a success in others' hands, and at Chandigarh the vocabulary has been spread very thin. Yet the master's work and presence have founded a modern Indian tradition of real worth, containing architects of calibre like Balkrishna Doshi, Charles Correa and Raj Rewal. To them, and to an even younger generation, Chandigarh is a bold beginning whose lessons need transforming still further to the complexities of Indian reality, especially at the urban scale. Admiration for a forceful statement of philosophy is tempered by suspicions of absolutism, and scepticism about the values of the Oxbridge élite that brought Chandi-garh into being. In their search for regional identity they look for a greater accommodation of social and spatial ambiguities. The webs of streets in villages and the tight-knit structures and spaces of Jaisalmer have become the revered urban models.

Like the city as a whole, the Capitol monu-ments excite ambivalence. Those squeamish about monumental statements of power are naturally left uneasy; they revert to facile gestures for filling the spaces between without realizing that this would destroy a place that has a sort of magic in relation to mountains and sky. Arguably the buildings themselves are too grand to house the functions of a mere state capital. But then the original client was not just the local bureaucracy, nor even just Nehru, it was a newly emergent national consciousness which chimed with the hints of a new, post-colonial world order. Le Corbusier chose to celebrate this mood in quasi-sacral terms transcending limited political rhetoric and chauvinism. The ideology that brought the

Chandigarh programme into being has slipped away, but the artist saw beyond these transient conditions to themes of longer-range human relevance. The Chandigarh monuments idealize cherished notions of law and government with deep roots: they span the centuries by fusing modern and ancient myths in symbolic forms of prodigious authenticity. Although recent in fabrication they possess a timelessness that will insure them a major place in the stock of cultural memories.

219 The Museum, Chandigarh.

Chapter 14

The Merchants of Ahmedabad

*'The Millowners' Building is a little palace,
genuine evidence of an architecture for modern
times adjusted to the climate of India. With the
other Ahmedabad buildings ... it will be a true
message towards an Indian architecture.'*
                                    Le Corbusier, 1953

Within weeks of his arrival in India in the spring
of 1951, Le Corbusier was invited to Ahmedabad,
the textile centre in the north-west of the country.
The mayor wanted him to design a new Museum
and Cultural Centre for the city, and a residence
for himself. The architect also received word
from the President of the Millowners' Association
requesting a house. Thus began a stormy relationship with one of India's most sophisticated and
most forward-looking urban élites. Not all the
original commissions worked out, but new ones
emerged. In the end Le Corbusier built four
buildings in Ahmedabad: the Museum, the Millowners' Association Building, the monumental
dwelling for Shodhan, and the restrained house
for Mrs Manorama Sarabhai.

These designs occupied Le Corbusier between
about 1951 and 1956, a period of peak concentration in his mid-to late sixties when he was also
working on La Tourette, Ronchamp, the Maisons
Jaoul and the monuments in Chandigarh. Ahmedabad offered him relatively modest commissions in which he could pioneer his 'architecture
for modern times adjusted to the climate of
India', then transform the lessons to the larger
and more arduous projects of Chandigarh. But he
did not relegate Ahmedabad to the status of a
side-show. His patrons were a unique and
demanding group. The city possessed a rich
cultural and architectural legacy of its own: there
was an identifiable ethos to which an artist might
respond.

Ahmedabad was founded in the fifteenth
century on the east bank of the Sabarmati river
by the Sultan Ahmed Shah. An entrepôt for the
exchange of goods and fabrics, it also stood at the
crossroads of ideas and forms. Gujurati architecture fused imported Islamic types with formulae
and craftsmanship indigenous to both Hindu and
Jain traditions. The city was absorbed by the
Moguls, then by the Maharastras, but managed to
keep the East India Company at bay. In the mid-
nineteenth century, the millowners mechanized
early, so avoiding the devastating impact of
British textile industrialization on the local
handicraft trade. Despite his negative views on
mechanization, Gandhi based his Ashram in

Ahmedabad; between the wars the National
Congress rallied in the city. The Ahmedabadi
élite played its part in the liberation from British
rule. After independence the city could even
be portrayed as a model of 'the New India',
combining progressive views, modern technology
and a judicious sense of tradition.

The millowners who became Le Corbusier's
clients formed a close-knit group of families. As
part of a strategy of communal self-preservation
they oscillated between competition and co-
operation. The majority were Jain and therefore
belonged to a sect with roots at least as old as
Buddhism, which stresses the inviolability of all
forms of life. Traditionally they had concentrated
their expertise in trade and finance, surviving as a
small minority through an agile but limited
accommodation to dominant groups. Surplus
wealth went into teaching institutions and temple
construction. Superb buildings like those at
Ranakpur and Mount Abu were elaborate
cosmological diagrams of Jain beliefs. In the
twentieth century, the philanthropic drive was
diverted into more secular channels — educational institutes, libraries and museums.

In the Ahmedabad context, the Jain patronage
of architecture allowed a nice balance between
personal displays of prestige and the edification
of the city. Modern Medicis, the merchants of
Ahmedabad wished to convert their money into
the more elevated currency of art. They may even
have nurtured the ambition of reviving something
of the city's past architectural glory. Visual
quality was a daily concern in their textile
businesses, and they were entirely open to
technological and conceptual inventions. They
wished to turn the 'Manchester of India' into a
centre of culture, and knew that Le Corbusier
could give their enterprise immense prestige. For
his part, it must have been flattering to have all
this attention after years of neglect in Europe.

Like Palladio's patrons in Vicenza, Le Corbusier's in Ahmedabad mostly knew one another;
many were even related. At the top of the
pyramid of local wealth was Kasturbhai Lalbhai,
a Jain millowner who supported the Ahmedabad
Education Society. Four of Le Corbusier's

commissions were linked to two of Lalbhai's nephews, and a fifth to his sister. Chinubhai Chimanbhai, the mayor, was one nephew, and he used his post to further public works like a stadium and libraries. He commissioned Le Corbusier to design the Museum and Cultural Centre, as well as the Mayor's residence. Surottam Hutheesing, president of the Millowners' Association, was another nephew of Lalbhai's. He wrote to Le Corbusier in the Punjab requesting a design for a residence. The connection later developed into another commission, for the Millowners' Association Building. Manorama Sarabhai was Lalbhai's sister. She too commissioned a house from Le Corbusier. Shyamubhai Shodhan, who eventually took over the Hutheesing House design, was also related to the group.

The position of Le Corbusier's sites in the overall geography of Ahmedabad says something about his clients' aspirations. The old city, with its markets, *pols*, mosques, gates and dusty, narrow streets, was on the east side of the Sabarmati river. Many of the millowners had family townhouses there. In the nineteenth century the mills developed to the north, but still on the east bank, where they had access to river water and railways. In the early twentieth century the city began to spill westwards, on to the other bank, where it was less crowded, dirty and noisy, and there were trees and breezes. In the early 1950s, a certain social *cachet* was attached to the acquisition of a free-standing villa in a garden — a way of life that, ironically, duplicated that of the British cantonments. These buildings were usually exotic bungalows dressed with a few mouldings imitated from local monuments. All of Le Corbusier's completed buildings in Ahmedabad have plenty of space around them. He did not have to deal with the problem of inserting modern architecture into the traditional Indian urban fabric.

As his buildings were free-standing objects, they had to address the problems of a stringent climate through orientation to prevailing breezes and through adept placing of apertures and shading devices. The chief difficulties of the local weather were listed in a letter of 1951 from Gira Sarabhai to the architect:

'During the rainy season, Ahmedabad is wet and warm, the rainfall in 3 months from June to August being about 50 inches. There have, however, been instances of 24 inches of rain within 24 hours. This was, however, very, very exceptional. It may occur once in 20 years. The temperature during the monsoon is about 90 degrees.

It is the winter season which is dry and cool and very pleasant. The temperature goes down to about 70 degrees.'

She might have added that in the hot, dry season, the temperature was capable of touching 120 degrees, and that the prevailing wind was from the south-west; whereas in the cool months, the prevailing wind was from the north-east.

As has been shown for Chandigarh, Le Corbusier's strategy in dealing with these climatic extremes was to adjust type-solutions from his own earlier hot-weather experiments (Algeria, Tunisia, South America) to lessons that were already well-tried in Indian traditions of building. His general conception of an 'Indian grammar' received inspiration from historical examples of many periods that he saw in and around Ahmedabad. Whether timber or stone, these worked with deep reveals, overhanging ledges and window frames, fret-work screens of various kinds, and combinations of pillared halls and courtyards to encourage the flow of breezes. The merchants' houses in the old quarter of the city employed delicate lattices and balconies. The Gujurati mosques fused the complex pillared halls of earlier temple architecture with open courtyards. Water was often integrated as a visual and cooling device: the stepped wells in and around the city were monumental stairways of complex section and intricate spatial character descending to subterranean pools. To the west was the palace, mosque and tomb complex of Sarkej with pillared pavilions open to a tank. Some of these fifteenth-century structures illustrated the *parasol* principle quite clearly.

Le Corbusier's design for the Ahmedabad Museum was one of his first experiments with the *parasol* idea. The exhibition spaces were placed in a blank brick box lifted clear of the ground on *pilotis*, and approached from the courtyard at the heart of the scheme by a ramp rising past a pool. Light was introduced indirectly through baffles, under the edge of the roof slab, and via the windows in the courtyard. The whole building was shaded by a horizontal slab with a line of shadow beneath it: in effect this functioned as a cornice, but it also echoed similar ledges in Ahmedabadi monuments which had façades of hovering horizontals and shaded reveals. A water garden of troughs and tanks was laid out in a geometrical pattern on top of the slab. The water was supposed to help cool the spaces underneath and to provide a twentieth-century version of a Mogul garden. In Le Corbusier's project there were shrubs and floating flowers of different colours. Planters around the base of the box were to spread tendrils over the façades, shading them and softening them visually. Unfortunately these landscaping ideas — essential to the concept — were not carried through.

The site for the Museum was just west of the Sabarmati river, at a point where there was room to create a park. Le Corbusier included appendages for natural history, archaeology and anthropology as well as an open-air theatre in his project. He perhaps thought of the programme in terms of the unity of the arts and human sciences; in India it was also possible to foster links between folk crafts and contemporary means of expression. The industrialized textile business already made extensive use of village designs. The Museum might become an institution for visual literacy combining many media, and explaining the context within which forms emerged. Such ideas had been evolving in Le Corbusier's mind for more than twenty years, having been central to the Mundaneum and to

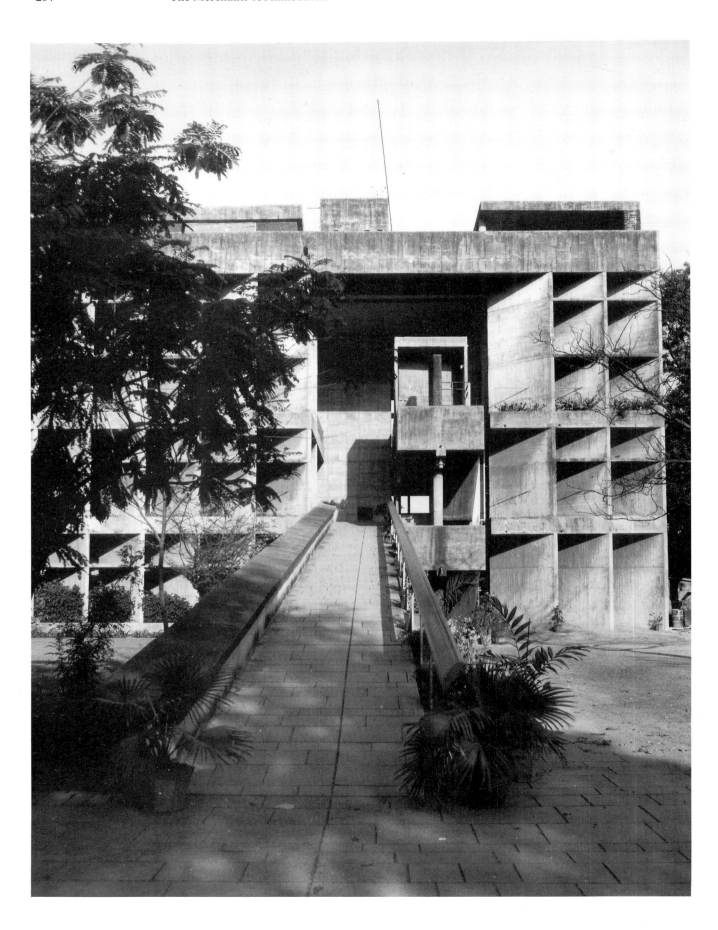

the Museum of Unlimited Growth of 1939. In effect, the Ahmedabad building was a rough-cut version of this 'machine à cultiver', but adjusted to the Indian climate. The Cultural Centre and other appendages were axed, and the Museum was built on its own. The realized work lacks the clarity and bold elegance of its cousins, Le Corbusier's Museums for Tokyo and Chandigarh.

The site for the Millowners' Association Building was three-quarters of a mile north of the Museum, also on the west bank, but at a point opposite the old city. The Association had been founded in 1891 to provide a loose framework for caste connections and family ties. The practical programme for the new building was never very precise. Really it was to be an exclusive club suitable for business meetings, receptions and lectures. It therefore had to contain an auditorium, a dining room, offices, seminar rooms, and a lot of generalized space for parties or exhibition displays. It was implicit that the building should embody the social prestige and power of the millowning élite.

From the start Le Corbusier thought of the building as a monumental house cut through by a ramp and a ceremonial route. It was the old theme of 'une maison, un palais', but stretched in the direction of 'un palais'. An early scheme with a large aperture framing a western-facing terrace was replaced by an idea using diagonal *brises-soleil* to keep out the afternoon sun and to lend an air of grandeur to this, the street façade. The side walls (north and south) were made almost entirely blank, brick outside, rough stone veneer inside. Attention was therefore channelled to the rear (east) façade, with its opportunity of views towards the river and the city. These were maximized by opening the building out to the setting, and by placing the screen of slender *brises-soleil* normal to the façades where they would obstruct the eye the least. A duality was implied between the dense street side and the open river one. Perhaps this was Le Corbusier's response to the ambiguous stance of the millowning group — both exclusive and philanthropic. From their processional platforms and shaded halls of pillars the millowners could see the old city opposite, and the dyers at work in the muddy pools of the Sabarmati below — a reminder of the source of their own wealth. On the street side the ramp and the exclusive ranks of *brises-soleil* left little doubt about the gulf separating the inner circle from the rest.

The rows of diagonal fins and varying slabs signal that the Millowners' Building has floors of varying height, while the ascending ramp and protruding stair hint at the *promenade architecturale* which is later threaded back and forth through the free plan of the interior. As one rises up the ramp, the *brises-soleil* dissolve away and the eye is able to penetrate the structure to rectangles of sky on the other side. A concrete plane, punctured by the shaded rectangle of the porter's window, bars the way and forces a rightward movement — a device recalling the disguise and surprise of Mogul palace transitions. The *piano nobile* of the first level contains offices,

221 Millowners' Association Building, east façade.

222 (*above*) Pavilion at Sarkej, near Ahmedabad, India, late 15th century.

223 (*left*) Millowners' Association Building, plan of level 2, with curved auditorium.

220 (*opposite*) Millowners' Association Building, Ahmedabad, India, 1951–4, west façade.

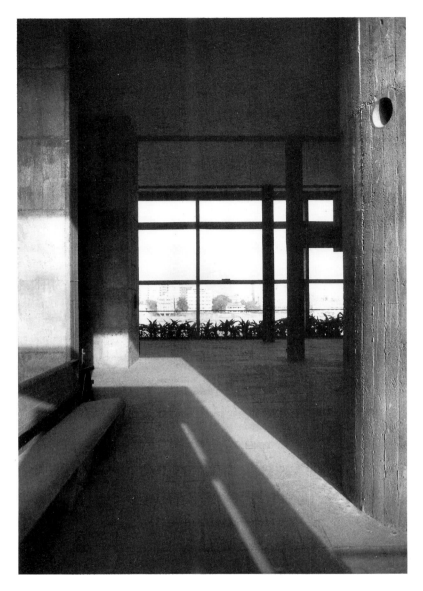

224 Millowners' Association Building, level 2 looking towards the river.

back over a half-level balcony before breaking in reverse direction through the slab to the roof terrace. This final flourish puts one in mind of the whimsical stair rising through the levels of the Panch Mahal at Fathepur Sikri. Like the lobby, it is incomplete without the ruffle of saris, the chatter of the powerful, the knowing nods and glances of the initiates.

The jagged rectangles and diagonals of the main façade give no hint of the curved climax to the route: the auditorium at the top of the building. This is treated as the cult space of an obscure rite. In plan the room is a curl shape in which the ends do not touch, but overlap, leaving a gap between curved planes for an entrance. Similar shapes are to be found in many of Le Corbusier's late paintings, but here they are embedded in the themes of a building where delight is taken in tense contrasts between curved objects, horizontal slabs, a grid of structure, diagonal planes, and a nearly square plan. Curves in the Millowners' channel the flow of movement, compress and expand the interior space illusionistically, and generate an intense plasticity through the play of light and shade. They receive diagonal paths and deflect the eye through the rear screen towards the vignettes of the city. Focal points of human activity, the curves are also used with considerable wit. The lavatories at the first level are contained in two curl shapes laid back to back which separate women's and men's entrances. Limited in height, they allow the ceiling slab to pass overhead without interruption. The bar on the second level is yet another version, but this time it is surmounted by a curved balcony which flows on to become a straight plane bordering the middle-level balcony. Variations of function and shape are orchestrated around a single theme.

In the auditorium all the stops are pulled out at once. The walls lean inwards like the battered walls at Ronchamp and explode through the roof slab in a way recalling the funnel at Chandigarh. The curved ceiling sags downwards in the middle, in a variant of the crescent motif, expressing the weight of water above: again Le Corbusier had hoped to utilize a roof reservoir. At the edges light reflects in under the soffits, shaded by the *parasol* effect of the overhang. The resulting 'acoustic' sculpture is one of Le Corbusier's most complex. Close to the entrance one senses the auditorium as both an object in a space and a space in an object — an effect that would not have been foreign to a Mogul architect or even a Hindu temple designer, even if it is here couched in a post-Cubist language of form.

The bare concrete and textured façades of the Millowners' Building relate it to Le Corbusier's other late works, but many earlier schemata are also compressed into it. The duality between a blank street façade and a transparent garden one emerges as a theme in Maison Schwob, 1916, and is reinterpreted with the help of the free plan in numerous villas of the 1920s. If the idea of zigzagging movement between parallel walls and past curved objects inserted in a grid recalls Garches, the notion of a sequence culminating in an expanded space (with a little extra stair to the

the meeting hall, and the elevator entrance, all linked by an open channel articulated by columns. Shadows are almost tangible, the sculptural play of volumes is intense, and one is drawn to the river side where the network of *brises-soleil* cuts a dark plaid against the light.

The rightward shift puts one on the axis running back to the stairs, and these take one to the grand lobby above (over 1½ times the height of the first floor), through a free-standing portico with a swivelling door. The space flows around the curved volume of the auditorium to the left, and again expands over the river to the back. A theatrical note is struck by the curved cocktail bar to the right of the entrance point, a cross between a Maharaja's pavilion and an industrial stack — though, in the context of a building like a huge concrete loom, perhaps it should be read as a monumental bobbin or spool. The playfulness is reinforced to the south-east corner of this floor, where an adventurous stair without a railing cuts roof) echoes Maison Cook. The ritualistic ascent of the Villa Savoye is recast in rougher materials on a new site, but with the ramp turned inside out as an institutional icon.

The pure slabs and columns of the Millowners' Building — especially seen as horizontal shelves in the rear façade — mark a return to the elemental definition of trabeation implicit in the Dom-ino skeleton. In the 1920s Le Corbusier had consolidated parallels between this structural archetype of modern architecture and certain essentials of Classicism. In the Indian works — and especially in the Millowners' Building — consonances were found with the open pillared halls and shaded overhangs of Indian tradition. The noble prism next to the Sabarmati river is a worthy descendant, for modern industrialists, of Indian pleasure pavilions with their steps, ramps, and platforms linked by subtly shifting axes, their views and clever involutions of geometrical themes. At Sarkej there is even a palace with blank side walls and a thin screen of columns affording views over the water. Tradition is reinterpreted at the level of underlying spatial structures, not at the level of mere motifs, then rethought in terms of a modern system of construction and expression. Le Corbusier himself referred to the Millowners' Building in a letter as 'un petit palais' — 'a little palace' (Pl.155).

The designs for the Chimanbhai and Hutheesing residences (for the Mayor and the President of the Millowners' Association respectively) also explored the 'house/palace' theme by ennobling the domestic programme to the point where a monumental presence was achieved. Both were variations on the same basic ideas: cubic volumes eroded by deep apertures for shade and air, and hovering horizontal *parasols* for protection from sun and rain. The *brises-soleil* were laid out according to Modulor proportions and were detailed so as to read as honorific screens. The lower parts of the dwellings were low, shaded and cave-like. But as one moved up through the levels there was expansion to sky and setting. Elaborate spatial sequences of contrasting light and shade were assembled around ramps, platforms and views through the crates of the *brises-soleil* towards verdant gardens and pools. The terraces were placed to make the most of prevailing breezes and to serve as sleeping porches for the summer months. The designs maximized the duality between solid walls and deep perforations, between orthogonal geometries and meandering routes, between vertical penetrations and the horizontal layering of space.

The architect had spent three hard years working on the Mayor's residence, even reaching the point of choosing coloured marble inlays for the interiors, when the commission ran into trouble. The Chimanbhais seemed to think of the building in the most conventional of terms and tried to get Le Corbusier to change features that

225 Millowners' Association Building, level 1, curved lavatories and *brises-soleil* in the east (river) façade.

226 Maison Shodhan, Ahmedabad, 1951–4.

227 (*opposite*) Maison Shodhan, view from the roof down to the terraces and garden.

were integral to his conception. There were also squabbles over the late payment of fees and travel expenses. The Hutheesing commission encountered similar difficulties, and it became clear that the client did not wish to proceed. The architect sometimes had to wait months for cheques to come through, but this was more a function of obtuse foreign exchange regulations than of exploitation. None the less Le Corbusier felt slighted. He assembled a circular letter of grievances to embarrass all concerned, and threatened to take the matter to the Prime Minister. His vision of India as a highly moral country was a little shaken by these day-to-day troubles. He portrayed himself to Bajpay (the Prime Minister's secretary) as a man of principle dispensing his wisdom against considerable frustrations and odds: 'I do not come to India to make money. I bring to this country a doctrine of architecture and urbanism, technical know-how, a certain philosophy ... in a word, the fruit that a man of 65 can bring to bear after a long career.'

The Sarabhais stuck with their architect, even chiding him for having included them in his sweeping condemnations. They helped to mend the relationship between Le Corbusier and Ahmedabad. The commission for the Mayor's

house sank, leaving only the trace of a page or two in the *Oeuvre complète*, but the Hutheesing project was salvaged when Shyamubhai Shodhan, yet another millowner, agreed to take it over without altering it in any way, despite a change in site. The new lot was in Ellisbridge on the west side of the river only about a mile from the Millowners' Building, on a suburban tract next to railway yards, and with street access from the west. There were no distinctive views or forces in the context to be preserved (as there had been with the Millowners') so Le Corbusier's main considerations were sun, wind and the relationship to approach and landscaping. He placed the cubic volume diagonally with respect to the perimeter with its somewhat blank north-east and south-east façades excluding the sun and the noise of trains. The other two façades were more open to the garden, and were armed with *brises-soleil* against the worst of afternoon glare: these could catch the prevailing summer breezes, functioning like giant radiator grilles. The diagonal position allowed one to perceive the building in a three-quarter view when coming up the drive. Before sweeping round to the monumental concrete portico, one had a glimpse of the spatial acrobatics to come later on. The

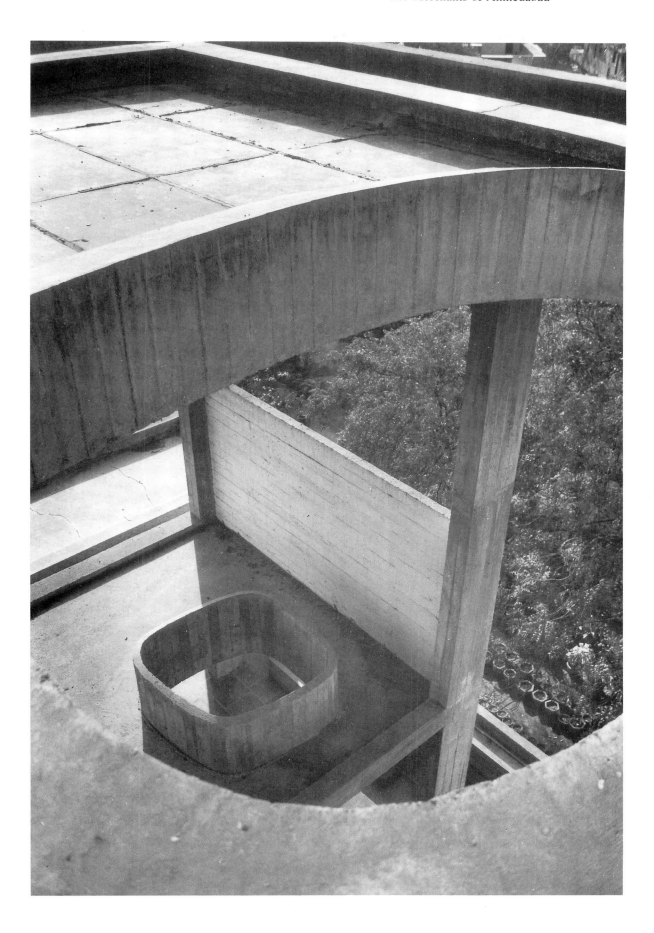

landscaping of the site was handled by means of curved mounds, one of them with a pool set into its crest. These helped to link the sculptural object of the building to the setting, while contrasting with its sharp rectangles.

The composition of the Shodhan House is capped by the protective *parasol*. This is supported on slender concrete piers which rise through the structure. The crowning horizontal hovers clear of the walls and rhymes with the lateral planes of the *brises-soleil*. Like the Millowners' Building, the Shodhan derives part of its vitality from the juxtaposition of single, double, and even triple volumes in section. At ground level, the double-height living room gives on to the garden: Serenyi has rightly compared this room to both the double-height space in the Citrohan and the tall entrance halls of the old Ahmedabad houses (including the ancestral Shodhan residence). A lateral ramp takes one to the upper levels where bedrooms are grouped around the triple-height terrace in a way that is loosely reminiscent of Garches. The terrace is the *pièce de résistance* of the whole idea: its explosive planes recall both de Stijl constructions and the elusive spatial ambiguities of Indian miniature paintings. It embodies Le Corbusier's 'Arabian Nights' fantasy for his original, fun-loving bachelor client. In the same miniatures, the architect had been intrigued by the portrayal of a courtly life of hedonism played out on little stages looking over paradisiacal gardens (Pl.159).

The oval aperture in the lower slab rhymes with a hole of similar shape cut into the *parasol* slab above, and the sky is glimpsed through both as through a magnifying lens. The same shapes pun with the oval pool in the garden, and this similarity draws the exterior closer, giving the surrounding nature a super-real intensity as it is glimpsed in vignettes through the *brise-soleil* apertures. The path to the roof constitutes another precarious and whimsical spiralling of landings and steps. Looking down it is possible to grasp how the rectangular geometry of the building is set off against the curved sweep of the drive, the subsidiary volume of the servants' quarters and kitchen extension, and the mounds. A rain spout sticks rigid from the slab, poking towards the soft, female shape of the pool in its grassy hummock. It fulfils some private erotic agenda of the building's meaning. During the monsoons it throws water dramatically clear of the façade into the garden below.

The Shodhan House has a long pedigree in Le Corbusier's *oeuvre*. It is a suburban cousin of the Currutchet House of 1949 and a descendant of the Baizeau House for Carthage of 1928 which also explored the idea of a complex section under a sheltering roof slab. The *Oeuvre complète* states that the plan of Shodhan 'recalls the ingenuity of the Villa Savoye ... in a tropical and Indian setting'. More than that, it explores the contrast between the Dom-ino skeleton and the cubic compactness of the Maison Citrohan. Le Corbusier characterized the Citrohan descendants as 'male' architecture, standing square and rigid against the landscape. The Monol lineage, on the

other hand, was 'female', with low vaulted spaces blending into the setting. The Sarabhai House in Ahmedabad belongs to this latter tradition. It is formed from a series of vaulted, parallel bays oriented to catch the breezes. On the roof is a dense turf garden with gurgling water troughs. The brick piers support rough concrete beams and the vaults are tiled. The interiors are low but airy, and at the edges the piers make shaded verandas under concrete hoods. The site is in the verdant 'Retreat' at Shahibag, enclave of the Sarabhai clan. The house is so overrun with greenery that it almost disappears. The one showy touch is a slide which descends from the roof garden to a pool, but this also acts as a subtle divider between the territories of mother and eldest son.

The client, Mrs Manorama Sarabhai, had only recently been widowed, and wanted a quiet place for herself and two sons. Le Corbusier caught the right mood in an understated building that interfered as little as possible with the superb vegetation. Perhaps in this respect for nature he was registering something of the Jain point of view. The low ceilings and hooded views give the house the air of garden pavilion with noble proportions but humble materials: it seems to idealize the simple life in harmony with a natural setting. But this particular 'primitive hut' contains Western works of art that would not look out of place in the Museum of Modern Art, and is air-conditioned in some areas (an extreme luxury for the India of the 1950s). Mrs Sarabhai was the sort of Indian client to have chickens and cows in the garden, but also to own an up-to-date Chrysler automobile.

The programme for the Sarabhai House was articulated as much in discussion as in writing. The building was fashioned around Manorama's precise needs. Gira, her sister-in-law, and Gautam, her brother-in-law, also helped in the dialogue with the architect, even visiting him and some of his works in Europe. Gira had studied with Frank Lloyd Wright and knew about con-temporary developments in Europe and America; Gautam was later to be a major force behind the creation of the National Institute of Design in Ahmedabad. Both helped to smooth the way for Le Corbusier in the various crises, and both were aware of the art-historical significance of a design from his hand. The architect usually stayed with the Sarabhais during his trips to Ahmedabad. Manorama was a deeply committed client: in the late stages of the design she consulted with the site architect Jean Louis Véret often and wrote to Le Corbusier frequently, including Modulor dimensions of details, and tactfully indicating conflicts in the design.

The basic themes of the Sarabhai House were discovered in late 1951 and early 1952: a series of bays oriented to catch the prevailing breezes in both directions and to channel movement from the public to the private sides of the site. In the first scheme, a carport was included behind the slide, as if the Indian motor owner's natural destination after a hot drive was a cool swimming pool entered via a slide from the roof. Eventually

228 (*opposite above*) Maison Sarabhai, Ahmeda-bad, 1951–5, garden façade.

229 (*opposite below*) Maison Sarabhai, interior looking towards the garden.

the garage was amalgamated with the servants' and kitchen block to one side of the entrance court. Le Corbusier varied pier placements on the interior to create a rich flow of space laterally and diagonally. Initially he tried to express the vaults on the outside and to exclude the glare with wooden or concrete grilles modelled on the ones he had seen in old Ahmedabad houses. The exposed vaults were rejected because they would look too much like a factory, the screens, because insects might eat the wood and monsoon rain might be driven through the lattices. So the architect came up with the idea of rectangular concrete hoods which gave a protected feeling to the interiors and introduced a rich formal contradiction between vaults and trabeation. Le Corbusier used this small commission to investigate new variations on the protective roof idea. The terrace was made into a deep pad of soil with water troughs running across it (a far more successful insulation than a concrete *parasol*). The ends of the bays were treated to wood and glass swivelling doors which could be swung open to aid natural ventilation (already occurring through vertical slots), or swung closed to seal part of the house for air-conditioning. Small apertures punched through the wood afforded ravishing fragments of greenery and flowers to anyone looking out.

The Sarabhai House has many other relatives than just the Monol in Le Corbusier's earlier work. The immediate first cousins belong among his transformations of Mediterranean and North African folk architectures: the Roq and Rob project and the Fueter House of 1949, or the Maisons Jaoul of 1953. The Petite Maison de Weekend of 1935 already explored the idea of low vaulted spaces surmounted by a turf roof, while the house at Mathes of the same period investigated the transition of pier and wall planes into a veranda vocabulary. In the Sarabhai House the lateral pier was cross-bred with the *brise-soleil* to create a structural type for a hot tropical climate. The sluice roof ideas of Chandigarh and Ronchamp were restated in the gurgling water troughs and the slide, and the roof garden became a dominant theme related to Le Corbusier's celebration of natural forces — the rain, the vegetation and the sun, and even the moon, since he hoped that roofs would be used at night. The spirit of the house is conveyed by a phrase the architect attached to another project, that for a 'Residence inside an agricultural estate near Cherchell, North Africa' of 1942, in which vaulted spaces, lush walled gardens, water troughs and pools were woven together: 'En bâtissant moderne on a trouvé l'accord avec le paysage, le climat et la tradition!' ('Building in a modern way one has found harmony with countryside, climate and tradition!')

Like Le Corbusier's other Indian buildings, the Sarabhai House has its own touchstones in Indian tradition. The deep-cut embrasures and low, shaded spaces suggest inspirations from both peasant vernacular sources and the utilitarian PWD bungalows built by the British, while the rough brick and concrete echo similar usages in Ahmedabad's textile mills. The vision of a pavilion looking out from shaded spaces towards water and greenery recalls the Royal Apartments from the Red Forts of Delhi and Agra, while the veils of shade on the interiors evoke the otherworldly mood of a shrine. The slide has an uncanny resemblance to the azimuth triangle from the Jantar Mantar, though astrological geometry gives way to a catching and playful image of 'the high life' (Pl.157).

To treat the Sarabhai House as an isolated, luxury commission is to miss much of its point, and to misunderstand its enormous influence. For Le Corbusier this little building was a 'regionalist hypothesis', an exploration of a language appropriate to modern Indian conditions in general. Its elements are to be found again in the vaults, piers, shading devices, troughs and flat *parasol* of the High Court at Chandigarh; but they are also to be found in the architect's studies for the cheapest possible houses: his 'Indian grammar' had to be capable of serving both peasants and judges to be considered valuable. For all its privacy, the Sarabhai House has had a wide influence in India. Many imitations using brick piers and concrete beams have been clichés, but there have been deeper transformations too. The Gandhi Ashram (1960) in Ahmedabad by Charles Correa fuses ideas from the Sarabhai House with the pavilions of Kahn's Trenton Bathhouses, yet the building has a life of its own. The meandering sequence of pavilions with views across planted courts to the river evokes the spiritual search and calm of the Mahatma, while the low-key vocabulary echoes the old Ashram bungalows nearby and conveys an appropriate mood of humility and discipline. The 'Sangath' studio of Balkrishna Doshi (1980), another architect who worked with Le Corbusier, indicates that Le Corbusier's 'Indian grammar' is capable of rich transformations a full thirty years later. In this case it is the turf platforms and shading vaults of the Sarabhai House that haunt Doshi's solution.

Le Corbusier's robust Indian buildings opened up a new set of expressive opportunities and attempted to deal with the dilemmas of postcolonial identity by forging links between old and new, but without regressing into nostalgic sentimentality. The relevance of this inquiry lay in its forging of alternatives to the glossy clichés of a debased International Style, and in its demonstration of a method for reading tradition at the level of underlying types. Le Corbusier's Indian realizations need to be seen against broad horizons of the period, including Barragan's abstract evocation of Mexico's ancient heritage, and Japanese attempts at fusing modern technology with lessons abstracted from traditional timber architecture. Even now, thirty years later, the implications of the processes of thought behind Le Corbusier's Ahmedabad buildings have yet to be developed. His 'true message towards an Indian architecture' was directed at a question that is ever more relevant in the Third World: 'how to become modern and return to sources; how to revive an old dormant civilization and take part in universal civilization.'

Chapter 15

Retrospection and Invention: Final Projects

*'Styles, like languages, differ in the sequence of
articulation and in the number of questions they
allow the artist to ask ...'*
                                     E.H. Gombrich

By the time he reached his seventieth birthday in
1957, Le Corbusier was considered by many to be
the world leader of the modern movement.
Awards, medals, dedications, retrospective
exhibitions were showered upon him. But the
position of architectural pope brought with it
problems as well as privileges. From his lofty
pedestal the architect saw his gospel reduced to a
check-list of clichés and his urban philosophy
made banal. The eyes of the architectural world
were on his every move and he was pursued by
journalists. They did not quite succeed in turning
him into a performing clown (as they tried to with
Picasso), but the standard attributes of his
persona — everything from his hornrimmed
spectacles to his Modulor-like hands — became
public property in the media. Le Corbusier
looked upon fame with considerable ambivalence, especially as it wasted so much valuable
time. Genuinely touched that Royalty awarded
him the R.I.B.A. Gold Medal (in 1959), he still
regarded the cultural establishment, that now
wished to claim him, with suspicion. His caution
is revealed in a telling doodle from the sketchbook in which he recorded the award of an
honorary degree from Cambridge University in
1959. He drew himself and Henry Moore (also
being honoured) striding pompously in long
robes. Out of a nearby window a student was
shown hollering 'Down with the Academy'. In
fact this did happen; perhaps Le Corbusier
recorded the event because it reflected his own
mixed emotions towards academic respectability.

Le Corbusier had always hoped to found a
tradition, and in the 1950s it was clear that he had
succeeded. But this very success also contained
dangers. His breakthroughs of the 1920s had
stimulated architects of the order of Aalto and
Terragni to their own high level of invention, but
had also spawned meaningless clichés of strip
windows, aeronautic curves and *pilotis*. Much the
same thing happened with the late works. There
were fine extensions of their principles by architects such as Kahn, Barragan, Tange, Lasdun and
Rudolph, but there were also all those Corbusian
parodies using pointless *brises-soleil*, scooped
porticoes and acres of crude rough concrete.

Worse than that were the caricatures of Le
Corbusier's urban ideas, especially in the realm of
public housing and skyscraper construction.

The self-conscious role of leadership, and the
realization that his ideas were being reduced to
travesties, encouraged Le Corbusier to go on
cutting new paths, but this impulse was accompanied by the need to reaffirm basic principles of
his life's work. The buildings of 1950–5 were a
hard act to follow even for himself. He did not
suffer the loss of direction of the ageing Gropius
or the regression into feeble mannerism of
Wright, but he never again matched the Parliament Building at Chandigarh either. The 'angois-
ses de la création' — 'pains of creation' — as Le
Corbusier himself called them, did not get less
with age. Soltan has even suggested that they
increased, and that this had to do with 'the
growing sense of responsibility, of expectation of
permanent excellence ... of fear that the previous
success was the last one'.

It is likely that both social and personal factors
had an influence on Le Corbusier's slight loss of
intensity in his last years from 1957 (when La
Tourette was finished) until his death in 1965.
One has the feeling that the post-war years of
European privation and Indian political idealism
were much more stimulating to him than the
increasingly fat consumerism of Europe and
America from the late 1950s onwards. The programmes — their social meaning — gripped him
far less. Then there was the death of Yvonne.
This took place in 1957 after a long period of
deterioration in her health. It was a big shock,
and according to some of his friends he was not
the same after it. While his fame increased, so did
his sense of isolation.

If Le Corbusier's followers had trouble transforming his discoveries into cogent statements, so
on occasion did he. In his late years he could
survey his own *oeuvre* as a sort of lexicon, and
this sometimes took him close to self-caricature.
The late unités are shadows of the first heroic
statements; the Maison du Brésil (1957– first
project Lucio Costa) pales next to the utopian
probity of the Pavillon Suisse close by, and the
sports agora at Firminy is the Ville Radieuse gone

230 Heidi Weber Pavilion, Zurich, 1961–5.

stale. If the Firminy church is ever completed it may prove to be the exception to this stricture — an ingenious fusion of the funnel idea from Chandigarh with the top-lighting effects of Ronchamp, in which the volume starts from a square plan then tilts and becomes curved as it rises.

Le Corbusier did not restrict his researches to concrete and rough brick, however much one may associate these materials with his late years. In the Phillips Pavilion for the Brussels World Fair of 1958 he employed steel tubes and tension cables to create a dramatically pointed tent with curving surfaces. This suitably 'technological' building contained sound-and-light shows (designed with the help of the composer Xenakis). For the Heidi Weber Pavilion (1961–5), to stand on the lake shore in Zurich and contain a small collection of Corbusiana, Le Corbusier turned back to an old idea from the 1930s: a sequence of spaces under a steel truss umbrella roof. In the final version, bright-coloured porcelain enamel panels are juxtaposed with plate glass in dynamic Modulor proportions. The whole thing has the character of a shining toy and seems to anticipate 'High Tech'. Around 1963 Le Corbusier was asked to extend the Jaoul Houses, and proposed a light steel tubular attachment in a quite different and deliberately contrasted aesthetic much closer to Jean Prouvé or to the pre-war Maison de Verre, than to the husky primitivism of the houses themselves (Pl.160).

Le Corbusier left a number of projects incomplete and unbuilt at his death. One of the strongest ideas was that for Venice Hospital. The site was near the station and Le Corbusier respected the skyline of the city, conceiving the building as a series of low boxes matted together in a complex pattern of overlapping walkways, platforms and spaces, extending over the water on piers. This form abstracted and intensified the neighbouring urban structure of Venice with its canals, bridges, rios, small piazzas and paths. The response to the programme of a hospital was efficient yet grim: patients were sequestered in top-lit rooms without a view. The drawings showed black Modulor men laid out on slabs as if the whole thing were a necropolis or city of the dead. Colquhoun observed that the scheme was pervaded by a 'ritualistic seriousness' and 'gravitas' at odds with the transient values of mass society.

Le Corbusier's detractors have never ceased to bicker about his supposed insensitivity to urban context. But both Venice Hospital and the Roq and Rob scheme (ten years earlier) were based on the reading of underlying typologies in existing towns in terms of both buildings and spaces between. These patterns of adapation and memory were then translated into standardized modern systems of construction, arranged in a cellular fashion to evoke growth and change, as in the vernacular, or in the patterns of nature. Such preoccupations would be central to Team X in the 1960s, but Le Corbusier beat the younger generation to the mark with a contextualist solution that avoided the other danger of sentimental imitation of old buildings. Where skyscrapers were concerned, admittedly, Le Corbusier remained committed to the idea of a strong vertical gesture without subtle linkage to the setting: one can see this only too clearly in the contemporary 'Cultural Centre for quai d'Orsay, Paris' of 1963.

Time and again in his final projects, Le Corbusier investigated ways of creating tension and ambiguity between buildings and their surrounding field. The project for the French Embassy in Brazilia, of 1964, juxtaposed a quasi-cylindrical Chancellery with a low rectangular Residence, using screens of *brises-soleil* to relate the two. Ritual and representation were handled through formal façades and processional routes around and through the structures. Screens of *brises-soleil* were adjusted to enhance ambiguities of scale between the two main functions, maximizing contrasts and tensions. A large aperture cut under a portico in the Residence functions as a lens, framing views in both directions to and from Chancellery and lake. The accommodations within the cylindrical screen do not touch the edges at all points, engendering vital sculptural variations between container and contained: in the Millowners' Building it had been curved objects in a rectangular frame; here the positions were reversed.

In his early seventies Le Corbusier could look back over fifty years at a stock of solutions which he could now manipulate with an almost Manner-

ist delight in virtuosity. Eduard Sekler has suggested that '... self-quotations, often modified from earlier unbuilt projects or from non-architectural works ...' were part of this pattern. Obviously it was an approach which ran the risk of facile self-imitation; equally it was possible to research new combinations in a lexicon of devices to which Le Corbusier gave an almost immutable status individually. The unrealized Olivetti research plant (for an autostrada site at Milan-Rho) of 1963 combined the curved ramps and roads of the Algiers Obus studies with organic shapes from the late paintings and a new inflexion of the glazed-box typology. The client had a distinguished record as a patron of modern architecture in the work-place, and Le Corbusier translated this ethos into a mechanistic palace of research penetrated by humane naturalistic metaphors; this was surely his answer to Marcel Breuer's curved UNESCO building in Paris of a few years earlier. The Strasbourg Congress Hall of 1964 (also not built) seemed to return to the dramatization of curved external ramps attempted in the Centrosoyus schemes of 1927, but the roadway rising up and cutting through the box was here emphasized by rippling *ondulatoires* like those used in the cloister of La Tourette. Both the Olivetti and Strasbourg projects seemed to imply a new lease of life for the 'Five Points' in which curved elements were exploded outwards from grids or boxes to become elusive landscape or traffic circulation sculptures. They illustrated Le Corbusier's contention that: 'The quality of ... circulation is the biological discipline of the work'.

The Carpenter Center for the Visual Arts at

231 Project for Venice Hospital, 1963.

232 Carpenter Center for the Visual Arts, Cambridge, Mass., U.S.A., 1959–63, view of the Quincy Street or 'demonstration' façade. Note the *ondulatoires* and *aérateurs* on the curved studio.

233 Project for Olivetti Research Centre, Milan-Rho, 1963.

Harvard University (1960–3), one of the last buildings to be brought to completion in Le Corbusier's lifetime, belongs to the same family. In fact it is a little earlier in date, and some of the devices just discussed were discovered in the course of its design. At the heart is a cubic volume from which curved studios pull away from one another on the diagonal. The whole is cut through by an S-shaped ramp which rises from one street and descends towards the other. The Carpenter Center breaks boldly with the orthogonal geometry of its Neo-Georgian setting. The layers and levels swing out and back from the grid of concrete *pilotis* within, making the most of cantilevering to create interpenetrations of exterior and interior, as well as a sequence of spatial events linked by the *promenade architecturale* of the ramp. Appropriate to its function as a visual arts centre the building embodies a *synthèse des arts majeurs*: painting, sculpture and architecture. The ramp allows one to inspect Le Corbusier's architectural elements, as well as studio activities within the building.

The organic analogies of the plan, the free sculptural expression of movement, the ambiguities of figure and ground, of mass and space, relate the Carpenter Center to the other late works: the angled *brises-soleil* are like those at Chandigarh, and the ramp passing into the building recalls the Millowners' Association Building. But the smooth cylindrical *pilotis* and clean-cut slabs, including the full orchestration of the 'Five Points' (in addition there are later 'Points' like the *brise-soleil, ondulatoire* and *aérateur*) introduce a retrospective note. Le Corbusier seems to have returned to the spirit of the Dom-ino — the archetype of his concrete systems — and rigorously reconsidered the fenestration elements and spatial ideas appropriate to it. The *Oeuvre complète* rightly states that the building embodies 'a demonstration of Le Corbusier's theories', and that 'numerous of his typical elements find their way into it'.

The many intentions and levels of meaning in the Carpenter Center become clearer if one reconstructs the design process. Le Corbusier was approached in 1959 to create a suitable setting for the visual arts at Harvard by José Luis Sert, Dean of the Graduate School of Design, a friend and previous collaborator, who had also been a President of C.I.A.M. Alfred St Vrain Carpenter, an alumnus of the College, had given a tidy sum of 1.5 million dollars for this purpose in response to President Pusey's fund drive of the late 1950s. It was a period in which many élite American universities were building art centres and adorning their campuses with works by internationally famous designers. Cambridge, Massachussetts, had a special link to the modern movement as both Walter Gropius and Sigfried Giedion had taught at Harvard before Sert. It was a Harvard convention that each department should have a unique identity and stand in its own building. Over the years the university had employed representative architects of various styles and epochs such as Charles Bulfinch, Henry Ware and William Van Brunt, Henry Hobson Richardson, Richard Morris Hunt, and Walter Gropius. The 'Le Corbusier' building needed to take its place in a miniature museum of architecture, crystallizing the best of contemporary expression (Pl.161).

The idea of working in the United States touched raw nerves in Le Corbusier. He had always admired the country for its technical potential but it had turned deaf ears to the redemptive message of the Ville Radieuse in the 1930s. American 'gangsters' had then added injury to insult by 'stealing' his resplendent United Nations idea and debasing it. All this produced a profound distrust of American officialdom. Le Corbusier haggled over the Harvard contract and took his patrons to the brink of humiliation. He demanded higher than usual fees and insisted that 'an American architect' should execute the building from preliminary plans. This was Sert's cue, and he took it, volunteering to safeguard Le Corbusier's plans and carry them through to the letter.

The site was cramped between Neo-Georgian buildings, and when Le Corbusier first inspected it in 1959 he shrugged, saying that this was 'such a small commission from such a large country'. But there was breathing space in the direction of 'Harvard Yard', an arcadian precinct of formal buildings on axes, with trees and diagonal routes threaded between them. Le Corbusier was intrigued by the flow of people through this space between classes. The programme appealed greatly to the architect. It recalled his own education in the Arts and Crafts and touched on lofty intentions to do with harmonizing the head and the hand. The synthesis of the arts, of form and feeling, was linked to larger ideals of cultural regeneration in Le Corbusier's framework of

beliefs. At a more mundane level this was a chance to design flexible studio spaces linked to green terraces and disposed to make the most of variable lighting conditions.

Le Corbusier's normal procedure on acquiring a new commission was to study the site and programme in depth, with the help of crude models. While a problem was gestating, he

234 First sketch of the Carpenter Center, Sketchbook P60, 1 April 1960 (Fondation Le Corbusier).

235 Coloured crayon study of the spiral ramp idea for the Carpenter Center, 7 April 1960 (Fondation Le Corbusier).

236 Carpenter Center, first project, June 1960, presentation plan, level 3 (Harvard Archives).

continued his daily Parisian routine. In his late years he devoted mornings to painting and to concentration in solitude. Then in the afternoons he went to the atelier from 2 p.m. onwards, to hand over doodles to collaborators, and to react to other explorations of earlier promptings. During this stage of incubation an embryo of ideas and forms, a new entity fusing new and old expressions, gradually came into being. When it was ready, it came to the surface of his mind.

The first idea for the Carpenter Center actually emerged in writing as a short prose poem in his sketchbook. Circulation was the generating force: '... the spiral from the roof of the museum must become a track of gardens and dense rockeries in the landscape and forming landscape.' This literary response to the paths in the Yard which had captured his attention in Cambridge was given an alternative, three-dimensional shape in the first sketch for the Carpenter Center, which appeared in Notebook P60 on 1 April 1960. This showed the Arts Center as a curved, free-form sculpture on *pilotis* with the ramp passing through at the third level. Cantilevered curves either side contained the sculpture and painting studios, while a round space on top was for exhibitions. The transparent edges of the building were treated to *ondulatoires* in musical Modulor proportions. Outside space passed inside, and inside, outside. The ambiguities of Ronchamp or the auditorium of the Millowners' Building were combined with a grid of *pilotis* and a complex sectional idea, with layers of floor extending back and forth from the double-height volume around the ramp. The 'Five Points' were accentuated in a new way: as if the Villa Savoye had been exploded inside out, with ramp and curved partitions extending to the environment.

When Le Corbusier visited the atelier in the afternoons he hovered back and forth between his little cubicle at one end and the trestle tables of his assistants. He sometimes intervened with bold crayon or charcoal sketches that were intended to capture — or recapture — the guiding impulse of a scheme. Collaborators then took these rough hypotheses and translated them into drawings that could test the building against impending realities. For the Carpenter Center he chose Jullian della Fuente, a Chilean whose first job was to study the ramp gradients. It was hard to fit the slope between the streets while preserving the legal limit of 10 per cent, and on 7 April Le Corbusier intervened with a bold coloured crayon sketch on a large sheet of tracing paper which reverted to the original spiral ramp idea. The curved studios were now contained in elliptical outlines laid on top of one another at 90 degrees.

Many symbolic references seem to be compressed into these shapes. The ellipses — as in the reliefs, enamels and tapestries at Chandigarh — surely referred to the orbits of the sun at equinox and solstice. The ramp had an uncanny resemblance to a freeway intersection. During his trip to the United States in 1935, Le Corbusier had singled these out as essential tools of the Ville Radieuse. He had even praised the parkways around New York for their combination of automobile movement and greenery. In his 'one American Building' Le Corbusier seemed to be digging into past associations related to his hope that America would accept the harmony of nature and industrialization implicit in his urban message.

But the spiral ramp was found to be impractical. A compromise between centralized and longitudinal schemes for the building was evolved: an S ramp running between gland-shaped studios. Formally this was a counterpoint to the curves; practically it improved gradient, entry and linkage to the site; symbolically it drew, like the spiral, on Le Corbusier's fund of cosmic signs. The S signified the rise and fall of the sun: the basic natural rhythm. In the Preface to the English-language version of the record of his American travels — *When the Cathedrals Were White* — he had dedicated the sign (and its attendant doctrines) to the American élite: 'This is the measure of our urban enterprises.'

In mid-April 1960, the idea continued to crystallize in superb coloured crayon sketches, and a cubic form emerged at the heart of the scheme. For Le Corbusier freehand drawings were not just records of functional accommodations: they were like seismograms of intentions rooted deep in the artist's mind. When he insisted time and again that 'the secret labour' of painting was central to his architectural creations, he did not mean to say that he came up with pleasing shapes that he then just transferred from the easel at rue Nungesser et Coli to his assistants' drawings the same day at 35 rue de Sèvres. Rather he meant to say that painting was a means of scanning the inner landscape of the imagination. The anguish of each new scheme consisted, partly, in avoiding facile patterns, in the search for a deeper content appropriate to the new situation. As Jerzy Soltan has recalled, Le Corbusier was only too aware of the difference between a false ease and a difficult resolution in making a drawing. When his imagination was flowing freely — released by the morning's spiritual exercises and painting — his eyes would turn inward: the hand would register a genuine configuration rich in half-conscious associations.

Some of the drawings executed for the Carpenter Center in April and May have this character of ideographs. The aerial view of 1 May showed all the levels at once, distinguishing them from each other by the use of coloured crayon outlines; colours were also used to identify fenestration and walls, to show which parts of the façade would receive direct sun and to indicate greenery. The overlapping flanges, guitar and musical instrument shapes recall Cubist pictures. Le Corbusier could treat a site as a field analogous to the area of a canvas, then build up planes upon it until an intense plasticity and rhythm were achieved. The Carpenter Center's configuration of curved studios attached to the shaft of the ramp echoes the biomorphic surrealism of the artist's 'Ubu' and 'Ozon' sculptures; in this instance the analogy with lungs seems most compelling. These were discussed by Le Corbusier in *The City of Tomorrow* and had metaphorical relevance to the ideal plan for a city as they implied the liberation of the town, the free circulation of traffic and air, the provision of greenery — a city able to 'breathe'. In the Radiant City and unité plans, similar curves were often used to codify nature in contrast to the orthogonal rigidities of the slabs. Again, the plan forms of the Carpenter Center reflect Le Corbu-

sier's *urbanistic* intentions.

Once the guiding shape of a scheme had been established, Le Corbusier was loath to change it. A concept of sufficient depth was capable to some degree of secondary adjustment without threat to kernel meanings. The presentation model and drawings for the Carpenter Center were well received by the client and committee in summer 1960, but in the autumn conflicts were discovered between internal ramps and lifts, and between *ondulatoires* and the *brises-soleil* necessary to protect them from the glare. Matters were not helped when the client insisted on moving the offices and the main entrance to the ground floor from the third, eroding the significance of the ramp. The story of the scheme between autumn 1960 and early 1961 was one of a series of collisions and conflicts in the design itself, which necessitated some major alterations. In January 1961 the main curved studios were rearranged so that the third-level one was shifted to the back, and the second-level one to the front; in turn they were both made the same shape.

Le Corbusier used each design process to test new ideas and to refine old ones. For the Carpenter Center he investigated piers and beams before settling on a solution of smooth slabs and cylindrical *pilotis* of different sizes for the structural skeleton. *Ondulatoires* and *brises-soleil* did not mix well in the fenestration, so he decided

237 Carpenter Center, Prescott Street side from the north-east.

to keep them apart. After trying out *brises-soleil* like aeroplane flaps on struts, the architect reverted to the well-tried Chandigarh and Ahmedabad solution of concrete fins set diagonal or normal to the building edge. In Cambridge, of course, glass had to be inserted. A heating and ventilation system was recessed in the slabs, and combined with pivoting *aérateurs* for air. There were some teasing contradictions, as in the Quincy Street façade where plate glass appeared on third and fifth levels while *brises-soleil* appeared on the fourth. This illogical combination handled the varying view and lighting needs of the interiors, and happened to look best. But the arrangement also responded to the guiding ideas of the design: especially to Le Corbusier's intention of showing off all his fenestration devices in a single elevation.

This conception of the Carpenter Center as a memento and manifesto of architectural elements was uppermost in Le Corbusier's mind in 1961, when details were sent across the Atlantic to Sert for conversion into working drawings. Here was a unique situation in which a devoted previous collaborator and refined American contractors could be relied upon to give exact shape to Le Corbusier's demands. Even the final presentation drawings of April 1961 were referred to pompously as 'the crystallization of my relative ideas on the architectural drawings of our epoch': they presented the pure geometries of the building in pale ochre for the concrete, blue for the glass and red for the structure, and evoked the old definition of architecture as 'the magnificent, knowledgeable and correct play of volumes under light'. They were carefully regulated according to the Modulor. In style they were quite different from the late paintings and the design process sketches, as if the architect wished to return to the ideal mathematics of Purism. He said that they gave the architectural sensation 'pure et simple'.

Immense care went into the detailed definition of the concrete skeleton. Le Corbusier hoped to use steel formwork but was told it would be too expensive, and it was therefore necessary to use cardboard 'Sonotube' cylinders. Photographs of trial castings were sent to Paris. The architect rejected those versions that had even the slightest spiral incisions from the moulds. He wanted pure cylinders and pure slabs, absolutely smooth and clean. His letters imply that he was thinking of this skeleton as a sort of absolute definition for concrete, a point that invoked old Rationalist credos stretching back beyond even the Dom-ino idea to Perret and Viollet-le-Duc. However, the Rationalist structure (which was actually anything but easy and rational to construct) had also to be elevated to the level of a 'construction spirituelle', a tightly proportioned work of art, a revelation of the Ideal. He wrote to Sert: 'Everything has been greatly simplified. The structure is limited to round columns of variable thickness, bearing parasol slabs *without capitals*. It is the key to the solution for reinforced concrete ...'

To go with his canonical solution for the skeleton, Le Corbusier proposed wall and fenestration definitions with equal absolutism. He said that he wanted the concrete to be smooth, insisting that 'béton brut' was not 'béton d'une brute' ('concrete produced by a brute') but merely *bare concrete*. He proposed that the skilful American contractors (William Tucker of Boston) achieve refined finishes and narrow joints. Quarter-inch ridges were proposed for rectangular wall and *brise-soleil* surfaces on the exterior. These would catch the sun and form a thin line of articulation. Curved walls were to be formed from vertical battens laid side to side. Eventually it proved necessary to import boat builders from Nova Scotia to construct the formwork for the irregular curves.

Openings for the Carpenter Center were of four main kinds: full floor-to-ceiling glazing (*pans de verre*); *brises-soleil* (which were also conceptual relatives of walls); *ondulatoires* (which gave the cleanest definition of an opening as a wall simply discontinued in places); and *aérateurs* (the last named being vertical pivoting doors with attached insect screens). Taken together these constituted a grammar of the façade which was Le Corbusier's updated version of the free façade principle from the 1920s. The idea was that each element should serve a particular function, and that each should embody and symbolize that function. Le Corbusier explained to Sert:

'Having arrived at the most perfect of proportions possible for the building my intention is to choose materials which, after fifty years of research, have become the typical materials for reinforced concrete.

Thus panes are fixed, sealed in the concrete: they are there exclusively to light.

The *aérateurs* are there to supply fresh air by physical means of exchange through gravity and orientation.'

In the Carpenter Center, Le Corbusier assembled a sort of *summa* of his discoveries; the results of his life-long quest for principles. The *piloti*, slab, *brise-soleil*, *ondulatoire*, *aérateur* and other parts of the architect's language for concrete were given their quintessential definition. Perhaps they were his modern answer to the certainties of the Classical language: elements rooted in construction, but elevated above the mundane, and approximating the status of natural facts. In the Carpenter Center they could be seen inside and out from the ramp, and all together in the 'coup de poing' ('punch'), or demonstration façade looking out towards Harvard Yard. Arranged in moving, plastic compositions and rich variations, ennobled by the Modulor, they transcended the practical, touched the heart and achieved the level of Architecture.

In *Vers une architecture* Le Corbusier had written that a plan might be an abstraction 'containing an enormous quantity of ideas'. The drawings of the Carpenter Center are ciphers to many-levelled intentions, and bring us closer to the mythical landscapes of the artist's imagination, a world in which American freeways could fuse with a cosmic sign of solar harmony, and in which lung forms and the Modulor could blend

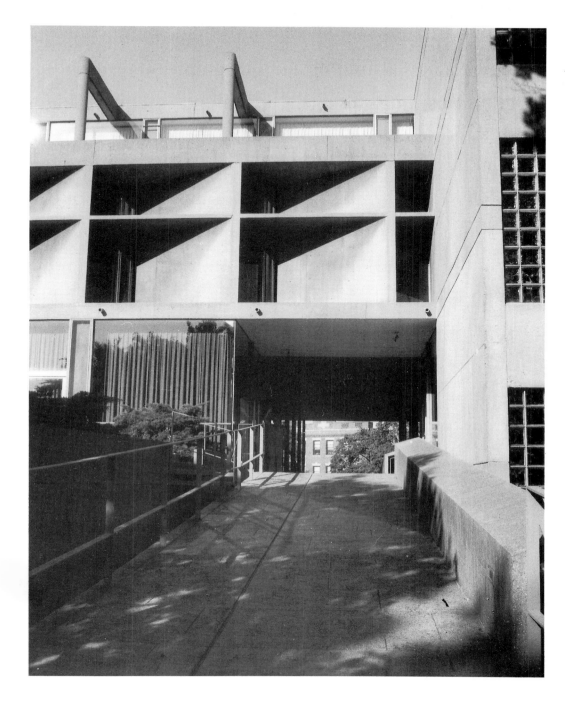

with the principles of the Dom-ino skeleton. The Carpenter Center is a 'synthesis of the major arts' — painting, sculpture and architecture — but also alludes to the central Corbusian theme of the city itself as a work of art: a token and instrument of the integrated society. The S, the cube, the lung-shaped curves supporting greenery, are surely a metaphor for an old urban dream in which man, machine and nature were to live in harmony.

Le Corbusier never built his ideal city in fact and was therefore forced to build it in fragments or else to refer to it through symbolic emblems. A memento of an artist's transactions with a continent, his one building in the United States is also a private diary of life-long themes written in a half-veiled code. Utopia — unrealizable and perhaps no longer desirable — finds only hermetic fulfilment in the hieroglyphs of a small building plan. The city of the future becomes a museum-piece to be studied by scholars like an obscure text in the university library. Le Corbusier's architectural language — far from effecting world reform — becomes a curio, a collector's item, another performer in the saga of styles and symbols. The stance is poignant: as if the old man were already looking back on his own life as a complete work, a chapter of history that was closed.

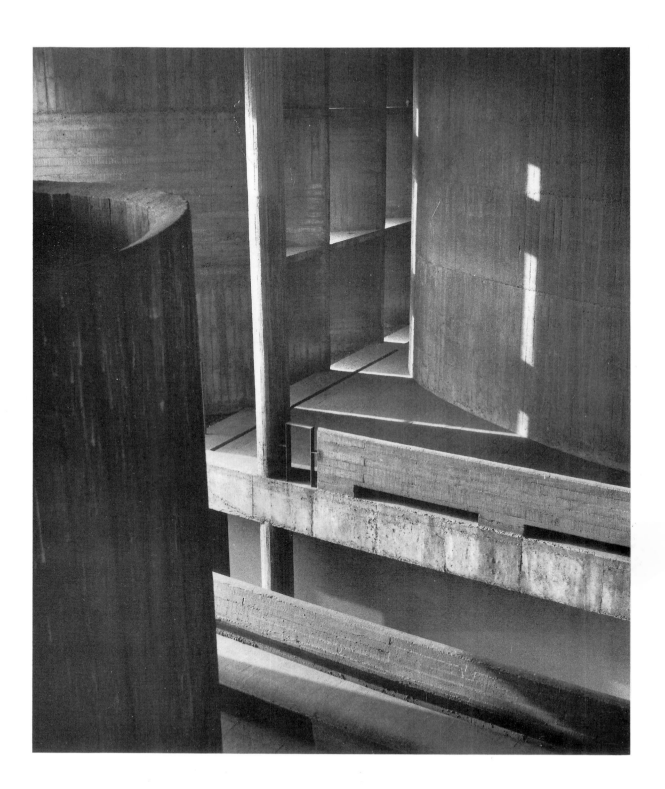

CONCLUSION
Le Corbusier: Principles and Transformations

*'To be modern is not a fashion, it is a state. It
is necessary to understand history, and he who
understands history knows how to find continuity
between that which was, that which is, and that
which will be.'*

Le Corbusier

Le Corbusier died in the sea at Cap Martin on
27 August 1965, probably from a heart attack.
The coffin was laid in state in the church of La
Tourette and then in the atelier at 35 Rue de
Sèvres in front of one of the artist's favourite
tapestries. At 9.30 pm on 1 September in the
cour carrée of the Louvre, André Malraux, the
Minister of Culture, read out a funeral oration
that reflected upon Le Corbusier's genius. The
state that had given him relatively few public
works and no major monumental commissions
added him to the roll-call of French culture after
his death. A delegation of Greek architects sent
soil from the Acropolis, and the Indian government water from the Ganges, to be scattered on
the remains. On 3 September Le Corbusier was
buried alongside his wife at Roquebrune in the
grave that he had designed in 1957. With its
inclined rectangle next to a cylinder on a terrace
platform, the tomb looks down over the bay
where the architect had spent some of his best
days and come to his end. The last exit and
resting-place were fitting for his Mediterranean
cult.

Le Corbusier's departure left a major void in
world architecture. More than just a collection of
individual works, he bequeathed a universe of
forms, ideas, images, sagas, cities, visions of the
future and perspectives on the past. No other
architect grappled so comprehensively with the
range of problems confronting the modern epoch.
Like any creator of new paradigms, he altered the
basis of future discourse. There is scarcely a
twentieth-century designer of note who has not
drawn upon his example, and there are many
others who have simply taken his discoveries for
granted. Walter Gropius may yet prove to have
been correct in suggesting that Le Corbusier
created 'a new scale of values, sufficiently profound to enrich generations to come'.

Le Corbusier is just distant enough to stand
clear from the standard shibboleths of modernism, but not yet far enough away to emerge as a
historical totality. Current judgements of his
work are still coloured by contemporary ideological commitments: many can agree on the
stunning poetry of his forms but debates still rage

about their relevance to the moment. At one end
are those who treat Le Corbusier as a paragon
of modernism, often missing deeper historical
dimensions, and coming close to a trite formalism. At the other are those who associate him
directly with the ugliness and banality of many
modern townscapes, as if he had single-handedly
invented the worst aspects of industrialism.
Meanwhile his work is quietly extended, assessed
and transformed worldwide by architects who
admire the force of his seminal buildings, but who
seek more subtle accommodations to context and
region.

Le Corbusier disturbs with the beauty and
probity of his forms but also by the frankness
with which he dealt with the paradoxes and conflicts of an increasingly technological age. He
refused to escape industrialization, feeling that
this could only lead to a Luddite cul-de-sac.
Instead he tried to reconcile the machine with
nature, modern man with fundamentals drawn
from tradition. In his urban plans he accepted the
emerging transport systems and building types of
the white-collar metropolis — freeways, skyscrapers, apartment blocks — and tried to give
these mundane functions a lyrical form. Le
Corbusier's various interwar *villes* assumed an
unlikely co-operation between capitalist ingenuity
and liberal reform, and were precariously reliant
upon the sensibility of a single artist, for all their
pretences at being normative: the artist-hero, part
social scientist, part Messiah, was supposed to
intuit the true 'spirit of the age' and to give this a
proper shape which would also be a blueprint for
the ideal society of the future. Yet despite the
dictatorial determinism and the dubious historicism, there was still something remarkable about
the way that Le Corbusier looked at the city
afresh, considering such basics as housing for
the largest number, work and leisure, public and
private, transport and greenery, visual order
and the expression of power. He foresaw with
amazing clarity the typical patterns of the industrial towns of the future and tried to give the
inevitable a more coherent and (so he hoped)
more humane form.

Le Corbusier never built his utopia of course,

239 Millowners'
Association Building,
Ahmedabad: 'this magnifi-
cent, knowledgeable and
correct play of volumes
under light'.

and probably never could have. After the Second World War it was scarcely possible to think that mechanization would automatically bring about a better future, and he avoided his earlier apocalyptic tone. Yet it was precisely in the reconstruction and economic boom of the 1950s and 1960s that his ideas and images had their greatest impact on actual construction. What was built was a grotesque caricature of the Ville Radieuse or the unité, without many of the devices that Le Corbusier had considered essential, such as parks and roof terraces. Mass society produced the very problems he had warned against, and on the largest scale. Profiteer and social engineer constructed arid diagrams and forgot about nature and the art of architecture. Le Corbusier's critics blamed him directly for bland urban renewal and the destruction of old towns. He became a convenient scape-goat for ugliness and lack of urbanity that reflected only too clearly the limited aims and instrumentalism of modern corporate states and socialist bureaucracies.

Le Corbusier's urbanism is identified overeasily with his most sweeping and absolutist plans: the Plan Voisin for Paris hangs around his neck like an albatross. It tends to be forgotten that he considered a variety of linear city ideas, various forms of acropolis (Mundaneum and St-Dié), and also revealed his sensitivity to context (Roq and Rob, Venice Hospital). When he did have a chance to lay out a whole town, at Chandigarh, he modified his abstract propositions considerably to deal with site, climate, culture and tradition. The Capitol space is almost cosmic in scale, but Le Corbusier did not leave an exemplary twentieth-century version of a piazza in his *oeuvre*. Current urbanistic ideologies in advanced industrial nations are directed at the problems of knitting together the old fabric; they do not find much support from Le Corbusier's tirades against the street or from his apparent negligence of the 'outdoor room'. But in the third world, where populations and cities are expanding beyond control, the planner has to think in the broadest terms of industrialization in relation to the rural base. Some of Le Corbusier's hypotheses are being modified and regionalized: the worthy lineage of fine housing descending from the unité (see Chapter 11) suggests that it is possible to learn from Le Corbusier's example without just repeating his mistakes.

Le Corbusier's elevated powers of conceptual and formal resolution seem to me to be beyond dispute: buildings with the spatial richness and symbolic resonance of the Villa Savoye or the Parliament in Chandigarh are altogether rare in the history of architecture. But he does seem to have been negligent over finishes and materials. Some of the 1920s villas needed serious repairs only a few years after completion, and the concrete of the Millowners' Building and the Marseilles roof terrace is already in a bad way. Similarly, Le Corbusier's pursuit of novel technological solutions sometimes led him to neglect comfort and commonsense, as seems to have been the case with the curtain wall at the Cité de Refuge. Perhaps anticipating the deterioration of the actual fabric, the architect made sure that each building was photographed in its pristine state: ideal intentions were preserved forever in the black and white photographs of the *Oeuvre complète*.

Corbusian academies gloss over his faults, ape his forms and miss his real strengths, whereas the best extenders of Le Corbusier's examples subject the errors to scrutiny, embrace the lasting qualities and transform the principles. To do this they need to go beyond the obvious aspects of style to the deeper levels of organization. That is why this book has relied only slightly upon such tags as 'Art Nouveau', 'Neo-Classicism', 'International Style' or 'Brutalism'. Instead it has concentrated upon the basic conventions and types of Le Corbusier's vocabulary and on his own transformations of nature and tradition. A personal language lives within the recesses of an artist's mind as a set of schemata and potentialities: one can get glimpses of its internal order and connections from sketches, paintings and design process drawings. Each time he created a new building Le Corbusier mobilized his family of forms, discovering new relationships between the various members and, occasionally, introducing new devices or elements.

Taking Le Corbusier's *oeuvre* as a whole, it is possible to discern some general patterns. During his formative years up to about 1920, he naturally drew upon a range of contemporaries and near predecessors such as L'Eplattenier, Perret or Viollet le Duc, but he also looped back far into the past to establish the dimensions of a private myth. Crucial impressions from the ancient classical, medieval and Islamic worlds were embedded in memory and continued to haunt him for the rest of his life. With the plan of the Favre-Jacot House, the skeleton of the Dom-ino or the section of Maison Schwob, young Jeanneret began to discover strategies that were really his own. It took Paris and Purism for Le Corbusier to lay down the formal and intellectual structures of his full synthesis. By the time he had written *Vers une architecture* and formulated both the Citrohan and the types of his ideal city, the architect was ready to spell out the forms he felt appropriate to the machine age.

The period 1922 to 1930 was one of peak invention in which Le Corbusier explored and refined his vocabulary, mainly in houses. By the mid-twenties, in such buildings as Maison Cook, he had succeeded in fusing together the potentials of concrete, the spatial ideas of Purist painting and his social vision of a new way of life in a single, accomplished statement. The classic houses, Stein/de Monzie and Savoye, followed in quick succession, each enriched by qualities abstracted from the classical tradition. In the League of Nations and the Mundaneum he broached the problem of modern monumentality; in communal schemes like the Pavillon Suisse or Cité de Refuge he expanded the 'Five Points of a New Architecture' to address urbanism. His vocabulary shared elements of period style with such contemporaries as Gropius, Mies van der Rohe or Rietveld, but the underlying images were his own. Beyond individual buildings it was Le Corbusier's intention to create the generic elements of an authentic modern architecture that would be as incontrovertible as the great styles of the past.

The 1930s was a period of reassessment in which Le Corbusier modified some of his type-forms to respond to region, topography and hot climates, but in which he also explored ways of translating the increasing anthropomorphism of his paintings into the larger scale of architecture and urbanism. He became cautious about the idea of a universal machine architecture, examining once again the primary lessons of adaptation to be learned from peasant vernaculars. The bold masonry walls of the houses at Le Pradet and Mathes, the turf roof of the Petite Maison de Weekend and the sinuous forms of the Algiers viaduct reflected a major shift in sensibility that could be accounted for in various ways: modifications in ideology, new stimuli, self-criticism, altered intentions. In the 1930s Le Corbusier extended the range of his vocabulary, introducing

variations on old elements (such as the *pilotis* of the Pavillon Suisse) but also adding new inventions like the *brise-soleil*.

Although most of the architect's discoveries of the 1930s remained on paper, they none the less provided the basis for the late works. The period 1947 to 1954 was as fruitful as the 1920s had been, but the obsessive, forward-looking utopia was now replaced by a mellow assessment of timeless values and an obsession with the harmony of nature. In his late paintings, sculptures and architectural metaphors, Le Corbusier articulated a private cosmology to do with sun and moon, male and female, the machine and the Mediterranean myth. The Unité d'Habitation at Marseilles drew together a lifetime's reflections on the ideal community, but expressed these through a rugged imagery, using *béton brut*, Modulor and *brise-soleil*. Ronchamp and La Tourette evoked the beginnings of their respective institutions, while the Indian works touched on basic types within the architectural traditions of the subcontinent. With the wind-battered

240 Le Corbusier's tomb at Roquebrune: the themes of a lifetime.

forms of the Chandigarh monuments we sense a heroic posturing towards the most magnificent creations of the past. Le Corbusier here seems to have grappled with problems of immortality while, perhaps, admitting to himself that his ambitions towards universality could never have an adequate societal base.

The forms and finishes of Le Corbusier's different phases betray a multitude of shifting meanings, but there are also recurrent schemata which lie near the core of the vocabulary. Some of these passed through all the different stages, for example the 2/1 section of the ideal dwelling. Inspired by the cells of Ema and used in the Maison Schwob, this became the basic housing unit from the Citrohan and the immeubles villas to the unité thirty years later. There were also rcurrent leitmotivs such as the hovering box on *pilotis* and the vaulted structure on piers which cropped up in numerous guises, materials and sizes, collecting new levels of meaning along the way. Certain repetitions were almost 'grammatical' in kind, as when relevant positions of windows, walls, partitions and *pilotis* were suggested by the rules of the 'Five Points'. Others were closer in spirit to the preferred configurations in his paintings, as when ear shapes were repeatedly attached to oblong slabs or funnel-shaped objects were set down into grids. Then there were basic themes like the automobile procession up to an opaque façade followed by a pedestrian route over levels towards a more transparent rear façade. These favourite devices were rarely determined by function. A curve that began life containing stairs in a house of the 1920s might metamorphose to contain an assembly chamber in a public building of the 1950s.

Individual elements of Le Corbusier's vocabulary such as the *piloti*, the *brise-soleil* or the rampwere more closely determined by particular functions and had a more predictable relationship to each other. In fact he tended to treat these as if they had some immutable or irreducible status, like the 'standards' of the Greek temple in *Vers une architecture*. In this he betrayed his debt to the Rationalist tradition and, above all, to Perret, who thought that it might be possible to generate an entire vocabulary on the basis of the concrete skeleton; but there was also the Idealist's obsession with defining the perfect type for each problem (support, lighting, opening, etc). The Dom-ino structure took on the status of a modern primitive hut from which the basic elements of architecture might all eventually be derived: the principles of the 'Five Points' were rooted in this archetype, as were much later discoveries such as the *ondulatoire* or the *parasol*.

An individual device like the *piloti* was evidently capable of numerous forms, juxtapositions and meanings. As well as being the Corbusian equivalent to the column it was also a tool for urbanism. It might serve to lift the body of the building into space, to define a route, to introduce a cadence to an interior; it might be round or oval in plan, parallel-sided or tapering in elevation, smooth or rough in finish. And, depending upon the weights to be borne and

complex of intentions surrounding its use, the *piloti* might evoke different references. In the entrance hall of the Villa Stein/de Monzie the four oval *pilotis* suggest simultaneously the idea of a classical vestibule (Palladio's four-column idea) and the notion of aviomorphic struts; in the Chandigarh Parliament, the grid of giant mushroom columns recalled an ancient hypostyle. In a similar way, each of the elements of Le Corbusier's vocabulary could be modulated to take on new meanings within each complex of ideas and forms. Schapiro has rightly suggested that a personal style is like 'a language, with an internal order and expressiveness, admitting a varied intensity or delicacy of statement'.

In his paintings, too, Le Corbusier used and reused a limited number of shapes and relationships between motifs, ever discovering new representational, expressive and compositional possibilities. A set of curves which first emerged as the outline of a guitar might later occur as the profile of a woman's shoulder; the lines used to describe bottles and glasses might later, when turned on their side, evoke the image of a bull. Ideas would suggest forms but forms would also suggest ideas. One can see this too in certain curves of Le Corbusier's architecture. The concave President's Pavilion of the League of Nations gestured towards the mountains like a huge antenna, a combination of portico and ship's bridge. Needing another image of state authority for the Governor's Palace at Chandigarh twenty-five years later, Le Corbusier turned the curve on its side to become a crescent which now gestured towards the sky. In its new context and position the shape combined the images of open hand, planetary path, bulls' horns, and ancient *parasol*.

Designing a new building was never just a case of sticking pre-existing types into a new assemblage; rather it was a matter of 're-thinking' customary elements to fit new intentions, and then of embedding them in an emerging new synthesis. Le Corbusier's creative procedure relied upon a period of subconscious immersion in which unprecedented links were made. To judge from his sketchbooks, he oscilated back and forth between raw impressions of the world and the sorting of perceptions into categories. His mind contained an elaborate mythical structure in which objects were stolen from their customary niches and reused for his own bizarre purposes. A crab's shell might rhyme with an aeroplane wing and the hull of a boat to become a chapel roof (Ronchamp); memories of a ruined Roman basilica might fuse with the type of a *diwan* and a *parasol* in concrete to express the idea of the sheltering power of the law (the High Court). The process recalls Freud's analysis of dreams:

'Such of those elements as allow any point of contact between them are condensed into new unities. In the process of transforming the thoughts into pictures, preference is unmistakably given to such as permit this putting together, this condensation. It is as though a force were at work which was submitting the material to compression and concentration ... one element in the manifest dream may correspond to numerous elements in the latent dream thoughts …'

If a single form could collect many images, a single image could also take many forms. One such recurrent icon was the ocean liner, which possessed overtones of cleanliness, rigour, mobility and internationalism. In the houses of the 1920s references were occasionally made to funnels, decks and railings. At a larger scale the liner took on the significance of ideal community or new kind of city. The Cité de Refuge ploughs its hull through the old fabric of working-class Paris to open up light, space and greenery to the poor; it is also a ship of salvation run by a firm captain and crew. In the Unité at Marseilles the nautical analogies are cross-bred with the leit-motiv of the collective box hovering above an ideal landscape on *pilotis*. The ship is here recast as a major actor in the artist's Homeric drama of the Mediterranean in which the avowed aim is to return machine-age man to the roots of Western civilization. The articulation is accordingly archaic.

Such manipulations of imagery were not undertaken for their own sake but to condense together numerous ideas relevant to a particular programme. Symbolic forms were the very means through which Le Corbusier interpreted and idealized the processes and institutions of society. The stunning funnel shape containing the Assembly space in the Parliament at Chandigarh repeated an old syntax pattern: the curved object rising out of a box with a grid inside it. But here the arrangement combined multiple associations to do with top-lighting, a dome, a power station cooling tower, an Indian observatory and childhood images of assembly inside a chimney-shaped room. By creating a multivalent symbol, Le Corbusier tried to reconcile the many polarities of the societal task: East and West, ancient and modern, cosmic design and secular rule.

Many of the substructures of Le Corbusier's vocabulary were laid down early in his life when he learned to 'penetrate the cause' behind natural appearances. Nature suggested a vast system of purposeful forms each with its proper place in the order of things. The architect tried to emulate this appropriateness in his own 'species' and types. He also drew direct analogies — between lungs and the circulation of a town, for example, or between the trunk, branches and twigs of a tree and the core, structure and *brises-soleil* of a skyscraper. Nature provided a bedrock of certainties beyond the arbitrariness of taste and convention. When Le Corbusier tried to translate the inner laws and harmony of nature into mathematical terms, as in the Modulor, his overall purpose was to relink man to the larger order which included the action of organisms and plants, and the movement of the planets. He would surely have agreed wholeheartedly with Palladio's suggestion that the architect should follow 'that which the nature of things teacheth', emulating 'that simplicity which appears in the things produced by her'.

Along with nature and geometry, Le Corbusier's other great inspiration was tradition, his 'one master'. Here too he tried to penetrate to the generating principles, often using sketches as a means to simplify what he had seen and to store it away in his memory. During his early travels he treated buildings like the House of the Tragic Poet at Pompeii or the cells of the monastery at Ema as if they were archetypes, and the Parthenon became a paradigm of formal excellence. Young Jeanneret made his entrance into architecture at a time without firm conventions: even Art Nouveau, which seemed to answer the call for a new architecture, soon slipped away. Looking back with scorn over the arbitrariness of the various nineteenth-century revivals, he followed Viollet le Duc in seeking out the quality of 'style' in general. In his formative period he worked his way through Gothic, Romanesque, Islamic, Byzantine, Classical, Renaissance, Neo-Classical and contemporary examples, trying to distill certain essential values from all the different periods and then to translate these into a modern vocabulary. This sort of fusion of global sources into a new amalgam would have been inconceivable to an architect a century and a half earlier; in that sense he gained from the pluralism and widening historical scholarship which accompanied the 'battle of the styles'.

In later life, Le Corbusier's mind was thoroughly stocked with impressions from the past. He was adept at juggling types from one context to another — Baroque palace plan into *à redent* housing, ziggurat into World Museum; he was also witty in his confrontations, as when the villa was cross-bred with a liner at Garches or the medieval drawbridge was inverted to become the entrance canopy at the Cité de Refuge. In the 1930s he studied the vernaculars of North Africa for their wisdom in dealing with the climate, and in the 1950s managed to grasp very quickly what was essential about a number of eras of Indian architecture. Beyond the particular example he tried to see the type; behind the individual experience to construct the ideal form. Towards the end of his life he tried to penetrate to the archetypes behind such institutions as church, monastery and hall of justice. He avoided pastiche by transforming all these lessons into a vocabulary with a rigour and appropriateness of its own.

To Le Corbusier the adventure of modernism was that it allowed one to portray an ideal future *and* return to roots. He tried to replace the weary aesthetic conventions of the late nineteenth century with something more basic and durable. Armed with a pan-cultural ideal, he roamed freely about the architectures of the world in search of universals. Beyond the incidentals of personality, period, region and style he hoped to unearth a primary language of forms rooted (supposedly) in some inherent structures of the mind. These were the 'constants' that it was the business of the modern architect to reinvigorate.

At present, Le Corbusier is revered and imitated by some, rejected and hated by others. He has been compared to the designer of a concentration camp and upheld as 'the architectural touchstone of the age'. He means one thing in India, another thing in France, and each person concentrates on different phases or features of his work. His buildings have now taken on the character of international exemplars which have to be negotiated by friend or foe. Le Corbusier is himself part of tradition and has even altered the perspective on the distant past. As he slips further into history, his modernity matters less and less: it is the timeless levels in his art which have most to give to the future.

242 The High Court from
the roof of the Parliament
Building, Chandigarh: the
ancient sense.

Bibliography

The following bibliography concentrates on books which are cited frequently in footnotes. For more comprehensive treatment see Lamia Doumato, *Le Corbusier, A Selected Bibliography*, Monticello, Illinois, Vance Bibliographies, 1979; Peter Serenyi, *Le Corbusier in Perspective*, Englewood Cliffs, N.J., Prentice-Hall, 1975; exhibition catalogue, Palazzo Strozzi, *L'Opera di Le Corbusier*, Florence, 1963; Russell Walden, ed., *The Open Hand, Essays on Le Corbusier*, Cambridge, Mass. MIT Press, 1977 (in footnotes); Maurice Besset, *Who was Le Corbusier?*, Geneva, Skira, 1968; Jean Petit, *Le Corbusier: Lui-Même*, Geneva, Rousseau, 1970. See also Carmen Gregotti, *Le Corbusier Bibliographia Generale* in catalogue Feltrinelli, Milan-Rome, and Maurice Besset, 'Le Corbusier', *Encyclopedia of World Art*, Vol. IX, N.Y., 1964. Extremely effective catalogues have been assembled in the libraries of the Fondation Le Corbusier, 10 square du Docteur Blanche, 75016, Paris, and at the Graduate School of Design, Harvard University, Cambridge, Mass. 02138.

Books on Le Corbusier cited frequently in text

Paul Venable Turner, *The Education of Le Corbusier, A Study of the Development of Le Corbusier's Thought 1900–1920*, Harvard Thesis, 1971, New York, Garland Press, 1977.

Mary Patricia May Sekler, *The Early Drawings of Charles Edouard Jeanneret (Le Corbusier) 1902–1908*, Harvard Thesis, 1973, New York, Garland Press, 1977.

Martin Steinmann and I. Noseda (eds.), *La Chaux-de-Fonds et Jeanneret (Avant Le Corbusier)*, Niederteufen, Arthur Niggli, 1983 (exhibition catalogue).

Giuliano Gresleri and Italo Zannier, *Viaggio in Oriente, Gli Inediti di Charles Edouard Jeanneret, Fotografe e Scrittore*; Venice, and Fondation Le Corbusier, Paris, 1984.

Stanislaus Von Moos, *Le Corbusier, Elements of a Synthesis*, Cambridge, Mass., MIT Press, 1979. (Originally published as *Le Corbusier: Elemente einer Synthese*, Frauenfeld and Stuttgart, 1968.)

Peter Serenyi, *Le Corbusier in Perspective*, Englewood-Cliffs, N.J., Prentice-Hall, 1975.

Maurice Besset, *Who Was Le Corbusier?*, Geneva, Skira, 1968.

Russell Walden, (ed.), *The Open Hand, Essays on Le Corbusier*, Cambridge, Mass., MIT Press, 1977.

Colin Rowe, *The Mathematics of the Ideal Villa and Other Essays*, Cambridge, Mass., MIT Press, 1976.

Kenneth Frampton (ed.), *Oppositions 15/16 and 19/20*, special double issues of magazine on Le Corbusier, New York, Institute for Architecture and Urban Studies, 1978 and 1980 respectively.

Max Risselada (ed.), *Le Corbusier and Pierre Jeanneret, Ontwerpen voor di woning*, Delft, 1980.

William Curtis, *Le Corbusier, English Architecture 1930s*, Milton Keynes, Open University, 1975.

Robert Fishman, *Urban Utopias in the 20th Century: Ebenezer Howard, Frank Lloyd Wright and Le Corbusier*, New York, 1977.

Brian Brace Taylor, *Le Corbusier at Pessac*, Cambridge, Mass., Harvard, Carpenter Center, 1972.

Tim Benton, *Les Villas de Le Corbusier et Pierre Jeanneret 1920–1930*, Paris, Editions Sers and Fondation Le Corbusier, 1984.

Brian Brace Taylor, *Le Corbusier, La Cité de Refuge, Paris 1929/1933*, Paris, 1980.

William Curtis, *Modern Architecture Since 1900*, Oxford, Phaidon, 1982; Englewood Cliffs, N.J., Prentice-Hall, 1983.

Reyner Banham, *Theory and Design in the First Machine Age*, London, Architectural Press, 1960.

Sigfried Giedion, *Space, Time and Architecture*, Cambridge, Mass., Harvard University Press, 1941; fifth ed., 1967.

Danièle Pauly, *Ronchamp, lecture d'une architecture*, Paris, 1980.

Norma Evenson, *Chandigarh*, Berkeley University, California, 1966.

E.F. Sekler (ed.) and William Curtis, *Le Corbusier at Work, the Genesis of the Carpenter Center for the Visual Arts*, Cambridge, Mass., Harvard University Press, 1978.

Publications Containing Useful Primary Material

Eight volumes of the *Oeuvre complète* (all translated into English and other languages) entitled:
Le Corbusier et Pierre Jeanneret followed by span of dates, thus:
1910–1929, Stonorov and W. Boesiger, Zurich, Editions d'Architecture, 1937; *1929–1934*, W. Boesiger, Zurich Editions Girsberger, 1935; *1934–1939*, Max Bill, Zurich, Editions Girsberger; *1938–1946*, W. Boesiger, Zurich, Editions Girsberger, 1946; *1946–1952*, W. Boesiger, Zurich, Editions Girsberger, 1953; *1952–1957*, W. Boesiger, Zurich, Editions Girsberger, 1957; *1957–1965*, W. Boesiger, Zurich, Editions Girsberger, 1965; *1910–1965*, Boesiger-Girsberger, Zurich, Editions Girsberger, Zurich, 1965. See also *Le Corbusier Dernières Oeuvres*, W. Boesiger, Zurich, Editions d'Architecture, Zurich, 1970.

H. Allen Brooks (ed.), *The Le Corbusier Archive*, N.Y., Garland, and Paris, Fondation Le Corbusier, 1982 (32 volumes of drawings).

A. Izzo and C. Gubitosi, *Le Corbusier Drawings*, Rome, Officina, Editioni, 1978.

A. Wogenscky (Preface), M. Besset (Introduction), F. de Franclieu (Notes), *Le Corbusier Sketchbooks*, Cambridge, Mass., MIT and New York, Architectural History Foundation, 1981, 4 volumes: Volume 1, 1914–1948; Volume 2, 1950–1954; Volume 3, 1954–1957; Volume 4, 1957–1964.

Le Corbusier, *Oeuvre plastique, peintures, dessins, architecture*, Paris, Editions, Morancé, Paris, 1938.

Selected Works by Le Corbusier

C.E. Jeanneret and A. Ozenfant, *Après Le Cubisme*, Paris, 1918.

C.E. Jeanneret and others, *L'Esprit Nouveau* 1-28, 1920–1925, reprinted N.Y., Da Capo Press, 1968.

Le Corbusier, *Vers une architecture*, Paris, Vincent, Fréal, 1923; translated into English by Frederick Etchells in 1927 as *Towards a New Architecture*, and republished frequently thereafter in many languages.

Le Corbusier, *Urbanisme*, Paris, Vincent, Fréal, 1925; translated into English as *The City of Tomorrow*.

Le Corbusier, *L'Art décoratif d'aujourd'hui*, Paris, Vincent, Fréal, 1925.

Le Corbusier, *Une maison, un palais*, Paris, Crès, 1929.

Le Corbusier, *Précisions sur un état présent de l'architecture et de l'urbanisme*, Paris, Vincent, Fréal, 1930.

Le Corbusier, *La Ville Radieuse*, Paris, Editions de l'Architecture d'Aujourdhui, 1935; translated as *The Radiant City*.

Le Corbusier, *Quand les cathédrales étaient blanches*. Paris, 1937; translated as *When the Cathedrals Were White*, N.Y., 1947.

Le Corbusier, *Modulor*, Paris, Editions de l'architecture, 1948; translated as *The Modulor*, Cambridge, Mass., 1954; *Modulor 2*, Paris, Editions de l'architecture, 1955.

Le Corbusier, *Le Livre de Ronchamp*, Paris, 1961.

Le Corbusier, *Creation is a Patient Search*, N.Y., 1960.

Notes

Books and authors already listed in bibliography are referred to in abbreviated forms. Le C = Le Corbusier; CEJ = Charles Edouard Jeanneret; OC = *Oeuvre complète*; VUA = *Vers une architecture*.

Preface

p.8 History as master: Le C, *Précisions*, p.34.
Frank Lloyd Wright, 'In the Cause of Architecture', *Architectural Record*, 23, March 1908, p.158.

Historians of modern architecture: Henry Russell Hitchcock and Philip Johnson, *The International Style, Architecture Since 1922*, N.Y., Museum of Modern Art, 1932; see also Giedion, *Space, Time and Architecture*.

Introduction: Notes on Invention

p.11 Motto: Eugène Viollet-Le-Duc, *Discourses on Architecture*, Boston, 1876.

p.12 Plan ideas: Le C, *VUA*, p.45 where he writes: 'Faire un plan, c'est préciser, fixer des idées' (In these footnotes I have used 1958 French edition).

Caption 4: Henri Focillon, *The Life of Forms in Art*, New Haven, Yale, 1949.

Chapter 1. The Home Base

p.16 Motto: André Malraux, *The Voices of Silence*, trans. Gilbert, N.Y., 1953, p.281.

Formative years: the most useful primary sources are in the Bibliothèque de la Ville, La Chaux-de-Fonds (early correspondence, sketches and travel photographs) and the Fondation Le Corbusier, Paris. Secondary sources of value: Maximilien Gautier, *Le Corbusier ou l'architecture au service de l'homme*, Paris, 1944; M.P.M. Sekler, *The early Drawings of Charles Edouard Jeanneret*; P. Turner, *The Education of Le Corbusier*; Le C, *L'Art décoratif d'aujourdhui*; Petit, *Le Corbusier: Lui-Même*; Von Moos, Le Corbusier, *Elements of a Synthesis*; Steinmann (ed.), *La Chaux-de-Fonds et Jeanneret (Avant Le Corbusier)*; Allen Brooks, 'Le Corbusier's Formative Years at La Chaux de Fonds', *The Le Corbusier Archive*, Vol.1, p.xv ff. *Synthesis*; Steinmann (ed.), *La Chaux-de-Fonds et Jeanneret (Avant Le Corbusier)*; Allen Brooks, 'Le Corbusier's Formative Years at La Chaux de Fonds', *The Le Corbusier Archive*, Vol.1, pp.xv ff.

p.17 Le C, *The Modulor*, p.182.

p.18 Mother's advice: *OC 1910–1965*, p.6, letter by Le C dated 5/9/60.

Summits: Le C, 'Confession', *L'Art décoratif d'aujourdhui*, p.198 (author's translation).

School report: M.P.M. Sekler, *The Early Drawings*, p.11; for philosophy of Ecole d'Art see Luisa Martina Colli, 'Jeanneret und die Ecole d'Art', in Steinmann (ed.), *La Chaux-de-Fonds et Jeanneret*, p.16 ff.

p.19 Early clients: Jacques Gubler, 'Die Kunden von Jeanneret', Steinmann (ed.) op.cit., pp.33-7.

Ruskin and trees: see M.P.M. Sekler, 'Le Corbusier, Ruskin, the Tree and the Open Hand', in Walden (ed.), *The Open Hand*, pp.42 ff.

p.21 Fallet design process: M.P.M. Sekler, *The Early Drawings*, pp.530 ff.

Art movement: letter CEJ to L'Eplattenier, 26/2/1908, cited M.P.M. Sekler *The Early Drawings of CEJ, p.249 (author's translation)*.

p.22 Jeanneret early readings: see Turner, *The Education of Le Corbusier*, for detailed analysis of contents of architect's library and impact of 19th-century Idealism on him.

Mantegna drawing: letter CEJ to L'Eplattenier, early November 1907, M.P.M. Sekler, *The Early Drawings*, p.212.

Chartreuse: card CEJ to parents, 14/9/07, Allen Brooks, 'Le Corbusier's Formative Years …', p.xix. (author's translation). CEJ uses the phrase 'la solution de la maison ouvrière type unique' which is ambiguous. Brooks suggests 'the answer for individual worker's housing'.

p.23 Jaquemet and Stotzer: Gubler, 'Die Kunden …', for details of client. Also E. Chavanne and M. Laville, 'Les Premières Constructions de Le Corbusier en Suisse', *Werk 50*, 1963, pp.483-8.

p.24 Nuremberg: for detailed reconstruction of CEJ's travels, M.P.M. Sekler, *The Early Drawings of CEJ*, pp.178 ff.

Nature is true: Le C, 'Confession', *L'Art décoratif d'aujourdhui*, p.198 (author's translation).

Chapter 2. In Search of Personal Principles

p.26 Motto: CEJ card to parents, 17/6/1911, on exhibition in Bibliothèque de la Ville, La Chaux-de-Fonds, Summer 1983.

Rationalism: see J. Summerson, *Heavenly Mansions*, London, 1949; Viollet-Le-Duc, *Discourses on Architecture*, Chapter 10. For details on Perret, Peter Collins, *Concrete, the Vision of a New Architcture, A Study of Auguste Perret and his Precursor*, London, 1959.

p.28 Skeleton: cited by P. Turner, 'Romanticism, Rationalism and the Domino System', Walden (ed.), *The Open Hand*, p.25.

Paris: in the Bibliothèque de la Ville, La Chaux-de-Fonds, there is a collection of Jeanneret's early photos of Paris including Versailles, the Eiffel Tower and the Galerie de Machines. These were probably taken in 1908–9.

p.29 Letter: CEJ to L'Eplattenier, 22/10/08, see Petit, *Le Corbusier: Lui-Même*, pp.34-6. For early readings, P. Turner, 'The Beginnings of Le Corbusier's Education, 1902–1907', *Art Bulletin*, June 1941, pp.214-44.

p.30 Jura chimneys: the connection with the Chandigarh is made by Allen Brooks, 'Le Corbusier's Formative Years at La Chaux-de-Fonds', p.xv.

La Construction des Villes: unpublished manuscript analysed by H. Allen Brooks, 'Jeanneret and Sitte: Le Corbusier's Earliest Ideas on Urban Design', Helen Searing (ed.), *In Search of Modern Architecture: A Tribute to Henry Russell Hitchcock*, Cambridge, Mass., MIT, 1982.

p.31 Report on Germany: CEJ, *Etude sur le mouvement d'art décoratif en Allegmagne*, La Chaux-de-Fonds, 1912.

Hermann Muthesius: 'Wo stehen wir', 1914, this passage translated Banham, *Theory and Design*, p.73.

Wright's influence: subtle connections suggested by Paul Turner in lecture at MIT, November 1981, later expanded in 'F.L. Wright and the Young Le Corbusier', *Journal of Society of Architectural Historians*, XLII, 4, Dec. 1983, pp.350-60. See letter Le C to H.T. Wijdeveld, 5/8/25 in which Le C refers to seeing Wright work around 1914 and thinking it 'si épurée et si novatrice'. See also Thomas L. Doremus, *Frank Lloyd Wright and Le Corbusier, The Great Dialogue*, N.Y. Van Nostrand, 1986.

Alexandre Cingria Vaneyre: *Entretions de la Villa du Rouet*, Geneva, 1908.

p.32 German grip: discussed by Turner, *The Education of Le Corbusier*, p.85. (author's translation). CEJ uses the word 'l'etau' which could be translated as 'vice' as well as 'grip'.

p.33 Voyage d'orient: see Gresleri, *Viaggio in Oriente*, for extensive reproduction of sketches and photographs made by Jeanneret, as well as detailed reconstruction of his trip.

Albert Jeanneret: letter to parents, 18/5/1911, Bibliothèque de La Ville, La Chaux-de-Fonds. For father's scepticism, see Monsieur Jeanneret's diary (BDLV, LCDF), entry for 4/4/11: 'When will the day arrive that my sons settle down somewhere?'.

Folklore: Jeanneret's observations were first made in articles for *La Feuille d'Avis*, La Chaux-de-Fonds, between July and November 1911, then published posthumously as *Le Voyage d'orient*, Paris, 1966.

Masonry cubes: Le C, 'Carnet de Route, 1910, Les Mosquées', *Almanach d'Architecture Moderne*, Paris, Crès, 1925, p.61 (author's translation).

Parthenon: marbre pentélique, Ernest Renan, *Prière sur l'Acropole*, Athens, N.D., pp.1-2.

p.34 Parthenon: comparison to machine, see Turner, *The Education of Le Corbusier*, p.101.; supreme mathematics, Le C, *Voyage d'orient*, p.166.

Acropolis: Le C, *VUA*, caption, p.166. (Etchell's translation).

Occidental Europe: for CEJ's reaction, CEJ to parents, 7/10/11; he also reports having had diarrhoea at Delphi and successfully stopping it by eating Italian pasta!

Antiquity: The Renaissance historian is James Ackerman.

p.35 Casa del Noce: Le C, *VUA*, pp.148-49. (Etchell's translation). Rudolf, Wittkower, *Architectural Principles in the Age of Humanism*, London, Warburg Institute, 1949, p.63.

p.36 Italy: graveyard and Colossea etc.: CEJ letter to William Ritter, posted 1/11/11. See Eleanor Gregh, 'The Dom-ino Idea', *Oppositions 15-16*, Cambridge, Mass., 1979, pp.61 ff. Gregh's study is very valuable in reconstructing the period 1911–15 in Jeanneret's life.

Chapter 3. A Classicism for the Jura

p.37 Firs, harsh country: letter CEJ to William Ritter, 25/11/11, cited by Gregh, op.cit.

Favre-Jacot: details of client from Gubler, 'Die Kunden … von Jeanneret'.

p.39 Jeanneret circular letter: Bibliothèque de La Ville, La Chaux-de-Fonds, exhibited at Musée des Beaux Arts, Summer 1983.

Nouvelle Section: see CEJ, *Un mouvement d'art a La Chaux-de-Fonds*, La Chaux-de-Fonds, 1914 and M.P.M. Sekler, 'Un mouvement d'art a La Chaux-de-Fonds, a propos de La Nouvelle Section de l'Ecole d'Art', Steinmann (ed.), *La Chaux-de-Fonds et Jeanneret*.

p.40 Jeanneret Dittisheim design: for this and early studies of Favre-Jacot and Jeanneret houses see *Le Corbusier Archive*, vol.1. pp.5, 9, 10.

p.41 Walter Gropius: 'Die Entwicklung moderner Industriebaukunst', *Deutscher Werkbund Jahrbuch*, Jena, 1913, pp.19-20, translated by Tim and Charlotte Benton, *Architecture and Design 1890–1939*, Milton Keynes, Open University Press, 1975. For Jeanneret's notes and movements 1914–15 and connections with Garnier see Gregh,

op.cit.; quote on Garnier, Manfredo Tafuri and Francesco dal Co, *Modern Architecture*, N.Y., Abrams, 1979, p.110: Garnier's *Une Cité Industrielle* was ready for publication years before 1917 when it finally appeared.
A tract on ultra-modern architecture; CEJ, undated letter summer 1914, see Gregh, op.cit. footnote 19, p.81.
Messaggio: I have followed Banham's translation, *Theory and Design in the First Machine Age*, pp.129-30.
p.42 City of skyscrapers: early project, see Sketchbook A2, in *Le Corbusier Sketchbooks*, Vol.1, p.89.
G. Benoît-Lévy: *La Cité jardin* (3 vols.), Paris, 1911.
p.43 Dom-ino: see Turner, 'Romanticism, Rationalism and the Domino System'; Gregh, 'The Domino Idea'; Joyce Lowman, 'Corb as Structural Rationalist', *Architectural Review*, October 1976, pp.229-33.
p.44 La Scala: for some sources see Allen Brooks, 'Le Corbusier's Formative Years at La Chaux-de-Fonds'. For role of Chapallaz, Marc E. Emery, "Chapallaz *versus* Jeanneret", *La Chaux-de-Fonds et Jeanneret (avant Le Corbusier)*, pp.23-28.
pp.44-46 Schwob: for clients see Gubler, 'Die Kunden von Jeanneret'; for design process see unpublished sketches, Bibliothèque de La Ville, La Chaux-de-Fonds, also *Le Corbusier Archive*, vol.1; also Julien Carron (alias Amédée Ozenfant), 'Une Villa de Le Corbusier, 1916'. *L'Esprit Nouveau*, Paris, 1920, pp.679-704. Classical influences on house, Colin Rowe, 'Mannerism and Modern Architecture', *Architectural Review*, 107, 1950; also William Curtis, 'Omm att transformera Palladio' ('On Transforming Palladio'), *Palladio Idag* (ed. Christer Ekelund), Liber Förlag, Stockholm, 1985. For other possible influences see M.P.M. Sekler, *Early Drawings*, p.597 for sketch of Nuremberg window; *Le Corbusier Sketchbooks*, vol.1, p.108, Sketchbook A2 for studies after Dieulafoy of Persian columns (compare to color plate detail of Schwob); Gresleri, *Viaggio in Oriente*, illustrations of Balkan house, Istanbul fountain (original photos Bibliothèque de La Ville, La Chaux-de-Fonds). For legal case, Maurice Favre, 'Le Corbusier in an Unpublished Dossier and a Little-Known Novel'. *The Open Hand*, pp.97 ff.

Chapter 4. Paris, Purism and 'L'Esprit Nouveau'

p.48 Motto: Amédée Ozenfant, *The Foundations of Modern Art*, Paris, 1916-17, see Russell Walden, 'New Light on Le Corbusier's Early Years in Paris. The La Roche Jeanneret House of 1923', *The Open Hand*, pp.117 ff.
Section d'Or: see Christopher Green and John Golding, *Léger and Purist Paris*, London, 1970.
p.49 Invariant: CEJ and A Ozenfant, *Après Le Cubisme*, Paris, 1918; I have used Banham's translation, *Theory and Design*, p.207.
p.50 Types: CEJ and A Ozenfant, *La Peinture Moderne*, Paris, 1926; Banham's translation, *Theory and Design*, p.211.
Painting into architecture: see John Summerson, 'Architecture, Painting and Le Corbusier', *Heavenly Mansions*, London, 1949; Stamo Papadaki, Le Corbusier, *Architect, Painter, Writer* (N.Y., 1948); Peter Collins, *Changing Ideals in Modern Architecture*, London, Faber and Faber, 1965.
Logic, culture: von Moos, *Le Corbusier, Elements of a Synthesis*, p.40; for Ozenfant's reminiscences on Jeanneret's gouaches of women, op.cit., p.287; see also Sketchbook A3 'Paris 1918-19', in *Le Corbusier Sketchbooks*, Vol.1, p.189.
p.51 L'Esprit Nouveau: see bibliography for journal; also R. Gabetti and C. Olmo, *Le Corbusier e L'Esprit Nouveau* (Turin, 1975).
Influential, widely read: Banham, *Theory and Design*, p.220.
Masterly, correct: Le C, *VUA*, p.16 (author's translation). I have used 'volumes' for 'volumes', whereas Etchell uses 'masses'.
p.53 Parthenon and cars: Le C, *VUA*, p.111 (Etchells' translation).
Christopher Wren: *Parentalia*, London, 1669. For suggestive connections between Classical geometries and Le Corbusier, see Emil Kaufmann, *Von Ledoux bis Le Corbusier: ursprung und entwicklung der autonem architektur*, Vienna, Leipzig, Verlag Rolf Passer, 1933.
p.54 Stone, wood: Le C, *VUA*, p.165 (Etchells' translation).
Besnus: connection to Petit Trianon discussed by von Moos, *Le Corbusier, Elements of a Synthesis*, p.78. For architect's sketches and notes see *OC 1910-1929*, p.48.

p.57 Ozenfant: see William Jordy, 'The Symbolic Essence of Modern European Architecture of the Twenties and Its Continuing Influence', *Journal of Society of Architectural Historians*, 22, October 1963, pp.177-87.

Chapter 5. Defining Types for the New Industrial City

p.60 Motto: cited by Le Corbusier, *Looking at Townplanning*, N.Y., Grossman, 1971, p.71.
p.60 For general introduction to Le Corbusier's urbanism: Evenson, *The Machine and the Grand Design*, Fishman, *Urban Utopias in the 20th Century* and von Moos, *Le Corbusier Elements of a Synthesis*; see also Manfredo Tafuri, *Progetto e Utopia*, Bari and Le Corbusier, *Urbanisme*.
Karsten Harries: 'Thoughts on a Non-Arbitrary Architecture', *Perspecta 20*, The Yale Architectural Journal, 1983, Cambridge, Mass., MIT, and London, p.16.
p.61 Taylorism: see Taylor, *Le Corbusier at Pessac*; see also Mary MacLeod, article on Le C and Taylorisation, *Art News*, Summer 1983.
Louis XIV: Le C, *Urbanisme*, p.285.
The Street: Le C, 'La Rue', *OC 1910-1929*, pp.112-15; article originally published *L'Intransigeant*, Paris, May 1929.
Fourier, Ema: see Peter Serenyi, "Le Corbusier, Fourier and the Monastery of Ema", *Art Bulletin*, 49, 1967, pp.277-86.
p.63 Classical urbanism and straight streets: see Le C, *Urbanisme*, especially pp.192-3, where he compares his geometry to that of the Tuileres and the Palais Royal. See also Anthony Vidler, 'The Idea of Unity and Le Corbusier's Urban Form', *Architect's Year Book 15*, 1968.
For Louis XV, see Pierre Patte, *Monuments érigés en France à la gloire de Louis XV*, Paris, Rozet, 1765.
St. Simon, Fourier: the most probing analysis of the ideological roots of Le Corbusier's urbanism is found in Anthony Sutcliffe, 'A Vision of Utopia: Optimistic Foundations of Le Corbusier's Doctrine d'Urbanism', *The Open hand*, pp.217 ff and Robert Fishman, "From the Radiant City to Vichy: Le Corbusier's Plans and Politics, 1928-1942", *The Open Hand*, pp.245 ff.
p.64 Pavillon de L'Esprit Nouveau: see Le C *Almanach d'architecture moderne*, Paris, 1925, for his account of the pavilion, and *L'Art décoratif d'aujourdhui*, pp.83 ff for illustrations of camp furniture, etc.
p.66 Critiques of Le Corbusier's urbanism, see especially Colin Rowe and Frederick Koetter, *Collage City*, Cambridge, Mass., 1979; Jane Jacobs, *The Death and Life of Great American Cities*, N.Y., 1957 and Norris Kelly Smith, 'Millenary Folly', *On Art and Architecture in the Modern World*, Victoria, British Columbia, 1971.
Von Moos: Le Corbusier, *Elements of a Synthesis*, p.187.
Redressment Francais: see Fishman, 'From the Radiant City to Vichy', *The Open Hand*, pp.251-53.
Pessac: see Taylor, *Le Corbusier at Pessac*, also Taylor, 'Le Corbusier at Pessac: Professional and Client Responsibilities', *The Open Hand* for problems of construction.
p.68 Steen Eiler Rasmussen, 'Le Corbusier, the Architecture of Tomorrow?', *Wasmuths Monatshefte für Baukunst 10* (1926), pp.382 ff. Translation Serenyi. For changes to houses see Philippe Boudon, *Lived in Architecture*, Cambridge, Mass., MIT, pp.161-64.
p.69 Stuttgart: for further details of Mies van der Rohe and Le Corbusier, Franz Schulze, *Mies van der Rohe, A Critical Biography*, Chicago and London, 1985, pp.131 ff.
Five points: for architects' own formulations on elements allowed by frame construction, Le C, 'Architecture d'époque machiniste', *Journal de Psychologie Normale et de Pathologie*, Paris, 1926, pp.325-50.
p.70 Comparison to Orders: von Moos, *Le Corbusier, Elements of a Synthesis*, p.74.
Racist critiques: Barbara Miller-Lane, *Architecture and Politics in Germany 1919-1945*, Cambridge, Mass., 1968, pp.69 ff.

Chapter 6. Houses, Studios and Villas

p.71 Motto: Le C, *Précisions*, p.34.
Engineers, contractors: Benton, *Les Villas de Le Corbusier*, recreates the conditions of practice in Paris of the 1920s. For clients L. Soth, 'Le Corbusier's Clients and Their Parisian Houses', *Art History 6*, June 1983.

p.72 La Roche/Jeanneret: for inaccurate version of design process Walden, 'New Light on Le Corbusier's Early Years in Paris'; more accurate is Benton's treatment in *Les Villas de Le Corbusier*, p.45 ff.

p.74 Sigfried Giedion, 'Das neue Haus-Bemerkungen zu Le Corbusier's (und P. Jeanneret's) Haus Laroche (sic) in Auteuil', *Das Kunstblatt*, x, 4, 1926, pp.153-57. Kurt Forster, 'Antiquity and Modernity in the La Roche-Jeanneret Houses of 1923', *Oppositions 15-16*, pp.131 ff.

Events from history: see *Benton, Les Villas de Le Corbusier*, p.43.

La Roche to Le C: letter 13/3/1925, Fondation Le Corbusier; later letter on prisms, January 1927, also Fondation Le Corbusier.

p.75 Pittoresque, mouvementé, *OC 1910–1929*, p.189. 'The Four Compositions' (see plate 96 of this book).

Parents' house: Le C, *Une Petite Maison*, Zurich, 1954.

Maison Cook: *OC 1910–1929*, p.130 for Le C's own statement; Benton, *Les Villas de Le Corbusier*, pp.155 ff for client and design process.

p.76 Concrete and painting: *OC 1910–1960*, p.267.

Maison Cook as urbanistic demonstration: see William J.R. Curtis, 'The Formation of Le Corbusier's Architectural Language and Its Crystallization in the Villa Savoye at Poissy', in *Le Corbusier/English Architecture 1930s* p.32; Le C's quotation, *OC 1910-1929*, section on Maison Cook.

Cook's pleasure: letter, postscript by Madame Cook to Le C, 19/3/1927, Fondation Le Corbusier.

Baizeau's rejection of designs: see Harris J. Sobin, "Le Corbusier in North Africa: The Birth of the *Brise-Soleil*", *Desert Housing*, ed. Clark, University of Arizona, 1980.

Letter: Le C to Madame Meyer, October 1925, *OC 1910–1929*, p.89.

p.79 Planeix: role of client, Benton, *Les Villas de Le Corbusier*, p.129; Quatro Colonne, p.130.

Loos: was influenced by Le Corbusier as well as influencing him, see Moller House, Vienna, 1928, which has protruding blank panel in centre of façade.

p.80 Les Terrasses: design process, see *The Le Corbusier Archive*, vol.5, and Risselada, *Ontwerpen voor die woning 1919–29*; 'cadence of repose', *OC 1910--29*, p.140 (author's translation).

p.81 James Stirling: 'Garches to Jaoul: Le Corbusier as Domestic Architect in 1927 and 1953', *Architectural Review*, 118, 1955.

p.84 Le Corbusier's own assessment of Villa Stein/de Monzie: see drawing no.31480, Fondation Le Corbusier, on which he wrote the annotation on the 25/7/59.

Abstraction of Classicism: Colin Rowe, 'The Mathematics of the Ideal Villa', *Architectural Review*, March 1947, reprinted in book of same title; Curtis, 'On Transforming Palladio'; Curtis, 'Modern Transformations of Classicism', *Architectural Review*, August 1984.

Schemata: insights into Le Corbusier's powers of transformation are given by Alan Colquhoun, 'Displacement of Concepts', *Architectural Design*, 42, 1972, p.236; and Colquhoun, 'Typology and Design Method', *Perspecta 12*, Yale Architectural Journal, 1969. See also William J.R. Curtis, *Fragments of Invention: The Sketchbooks of Le Corbusier*, Architectural History Foundation and MIT, 1981.

Chapter 7. Machine-Age Palaces and Public Institutions

p.85 Motto: Sigfried Giedion, 'The Need for a New Monumentality', *Architecture You and Me*, Cambridge, Mass., 1958, p.25.

p.86 League of Nations: Kenneth Frampton, 'The Humanist Versus the Utilitarian Ideal', *Architectural Design*, 38, 1968, pp.134-36; John Ritter, 'World Parliament; the League of Nations Competition', *Architectural Review*, 136, July 1966, pp.17-24. For a formal analysis, Colin Rowe and Slutzky, 'Transparency, Literal and Phenomenal', *Perspecta 8*, Yale Architectural Journal, 1964, pp.45-54.

p.87 Scandal: for architect's version, Le C, *Une Maison, Un palais, a la recherche d'une unité architecturale*, Paris, 1928; see also Martin Steinmann, 'Der Volkerbundspalast: eine chronique scandaleuse', *Werk/Archithèse*, 23-24, 1978, pp.28-31.

p.88 Soviet developments: Giorgio Ciucci, 'Le Corbusier e Wright in URSS', *Socialismo, città, architettura URSS 1917–1937*, ed. Tafuri, Rome, 1971, pp.171-93; also Anatole Kopp, *Town and Revolution, Soviet Architecture and City Planning 1917–35*, N.Y., 1970 and Berthold Lubetkin, 'Architectural Thought Since the Revolution', *Architectural Review*, May 1932, pp.201-14.

p.89 Alan Colquhoun, 'Formal and Functional Interactions, A Study of Two Late Works by Le Corbusier': *Architectural Design*, 36, May 1966, pp.221-22.

Mundaneum: Otlet's intentions, *OC 1910–1929*, p.190; Le Corbusier's intentions, *OC 1910–1929*, pp.192 ff.

p.90 Solomon's Temple: 'Dr. John Wesley Kelcher's Restoration of King Solomon's Temple and Citadel, Helmle and Corbett Architects', *Pencil Points VI*, November 1925, pp.69-86; Saqqara, see unpublished essay by Andreas Kultermann, 'The Conception of the Great Public Institution in the Work of Le Corbusier', in William Curtis ed., *The Architecture and Thought of Le Corbusier*, Washington University in St. Louis, Fall 1983, p.149.

p.91 Karel Teige: 'The Mundaneum', *Stavba 7*, 1928–9, pp.151-55. Le Corbusier's reply, 'Défense de l'architecture', was published in *Stavba* for 1929.

p.92 Palace of Soviets: design process sketches are in *OC 1929–1934*, p.130; comparison to Pisa, p.132; quotation on 'seductive beauty', op.cit. p.12. Quotation 'a great joy of creation', Le C, *Une Maison, Un Palais*, p.84 (author's translation). For realist critiques of modernist abstraction see William J.R. Curtis, 'Modern Architecture, Monumentality and the Meaning of Institutions: Reflections on Authenticity', *Harvard Architectural Review*, 3, Cambridge, Mass., MIT Press, 1983, pp.65 ff.

Chapter 8. Villa Savoye, Cité de Refuge, Pavillon Suisse

p.93 Motto: Henri Focillon, cited by Denys Lasdun *Architecture in an Age of Scepticism*, London, 1984, p.142.

C.I.A.M.: see Giedion, *Space, Time and Architecture*, 5th ed., pp.696-706; and Leonardo Benevolo, *A History of Modern Architecture*, Cambridge, Mass., MIT, 1971, 2 vols., vol.2, pp.497 ff.

International Style: see Hitchcock and Johnson, *The International Style*, also Curtis *Modern Architecture Since 1900*, Chapter 13, 'The International Style, the Individual Talent and the Myth of Functionalism'.

p.94, Giedion: *Space, Time and Architecture*, p.525 (1967 Edition); Rowe, "The Mathematics of the Ideal Villa".

p.96 Le C, *Précisions*, p.136; for design process and client see Benton, *Les Villas de Le Corbusier*, pp.191 ff; Risselada, *Ontwerpen voor di woning* and *The Le Corbusier Archive*, vol.7.

p.97 Four compositions, plate 96, from *OC 1910–1929*, p.189.

p.98 Classicism: see Curtis, *Modern Architecture Since 1900*, Chapter 14, 'The Image and Idea of the Villa Savoye'. For connection with procession over Acropolis, Curtis *Le Corbusier/English Architecture 1930s*; in context of 20th century abstractions of Classicism, Curtis, 'Modern Transformations of Classicism' and Curtis, 'On Transforming Palladio'.

Le C, *VUA*, caption p.167 (Etchells' translation).

p.99 Cité de Refuge: for detailed study of social context, Brian Brace Taylor, *Le Corbusier, La Cité de Refuge*, Paris, 1980.

p.102 Factory of goodness: Le C, 'L'usine du bien: La Cité de Refuge', unpublished manuscript c.1931, Fondation Le Corbusier.

Van Nelle: Le C, *Plans 12*, February 1932, p.40.

Bastions: Jerzy Soltan who worked in the Atelier in the late 1940s recalled Le Corbusier making this connection (letter to author March 1984). Ships, von Moos, 'Wohnkollektiv, Hospiz und Dampfer', *Archithèse 12*, 1971, pp.30-34.

Immense glass window: anonymous article in *Le Temps*, 8/12/33 (author's translation); for environmental deficiencies see Reyner Banham, *The Architecture of the Well-Tempered Environment*, London, 1969 and Taylor, 'Technology, Society, and Social Control in Le Corbusier's Cité de Refuge, Paris 1933', *Oppositions 15/16*, p.169.

p.104 Pavillon Suisse: for detailed treatment of design process, William J.R. Curtis, 'Ideas of Structure and the Structure of Ideas: Le Corbusier's Pavillon Suisse, 1930–31', *Journal of Society of Architectural Historians*, December 1981, XL, no.4, pp.295 ff.

p.105 Dog-bone, letter Gordon Stephenson to author, December 1978; Mr. Stephenson worked in the Atelier in the early 1930's.

p.105 Unity of conception: letter R. Fueter to Le C, 18/1/31, Fondation Le Corbusier.

Useless in present form: letter M. Ritter to L. Jungo, 3/2/31, Fondation Le Corbusier.

Curves: for major invention of curved extrusions see *The Le Corbusier Archive*, vol.8, p.212 (drawing number 15423) and p.233 (drawing 15469).

p.106 M-shaped pilotis: *The Le Corbusier Archive*, vol.8, p.222 (drawing 15441).

People without imagination: *OC 1929–1934*, p.84. For theme of urbanistic demonstrations in modern university buildings, William J.R. Curtis, 'L'Université, la Ville, et l'habitat collectif: encore de reflections sur un thème de l'architecture moderne', *Archithèse 14*, June 1975.

Era of large works: *OC 1929–1934*, p.19.

Final Report: 'Cité Universitaire de Paris, Maison Suisse, 14 September 1931', Fondation Le Corbusier.

Perfect in every way: letter Fueter to Le C, 27/12/32. Fondation Le Corbusier.

Rules of game: Le C, 'Nothing is Transmissible But Thought', *Late Works*, N.Y., 1970, p.174.

Chapter 9. Regionalism and Reassessment in the 1930s

p.108 Motto: Marcello Piacentini, 'Le Corbusier's "The engineer's Aesthetic: Mass Production Houses" ', *Architettura et Arti Decorative*, II, 1922, pp.220-223.

Conservative critics: Alexander von Senger, *Krisis der Architektur, Zurich, 1928*.

p.109 Textured façades, massive forms: Peter Serenyi, 'Le Corbusier's Changing Attitude Toward Form', *Journal of the Society of Architectural Historians*, March 1965, pp.15 ff.

p.110 My game: letter Le Corbusier to Beistegui, 5/7/29, Fondation Le Corbusier.

p.111 Chareau: Frampton, 'Maison de Verre', *Perspecta 12*, Yale Architectural Journal, 1969, pp.77-126. For probable influence of Chareau on Le Corbusier, von Moos, *Le Corbusier, Elements of a Synthesis*, p.92. For architect's remarks on Porte Molitor apartments, *OC 1929–1934*, p.144 (author's translation). For 'Ma Maison', see Frampton, 'The Rise and Fall of the Radiant City 1928–60', *Oppositions 19/20*, p.22; and *OC 1934–38*, p.131.

p.114 Mathes: *OC 1934–1938*, p.135.

p.115 Male, female: Le Corbusier, *The Modulor*, p.224.

Ironic grotto: Vincent Scully, 'Le Corbusier 1922–1965', *The Le Corbusier Archive*, vol.2, p.xiii.

p.116 Natural order: Le Corbusier, *La ville radieuse*, p.6.

Brise-soleil: Harris J. Sobin, 'Le Corbusier in North Africa: the Birth of the Brise-Soleil', *Desert Housing*, eds. K. Clark, P. Paglore, University of Arizona Press, p.155 ff; also Le Corbusier, 'Problèmes de l'Ensoleillement: le *Brise-soleil*', *OC 1938–46*, p.103. For universal 'respiration exacte', Le Corbusier, *Précisions*, p.64.

North African architectural style: Le Corbusier, 'Le Lotissement de l'Oued Ouchaia à Alger', *Architecture Vivante*, Autumn 1933, pp.48-56.

p.117 Zervos: letter to, cited *OC 1910–1960*, p.214.

Chapter 10. Politics, Urbanism and Travels 1929–1944

p.118 Motto: Frank Lloyd Wright, 'Broadacre City: a New Community Plan', *Architectural Record*, 77, no.4, April 1935, pp.243-44.

C.I.A.M.: 'Declaration of Aims, La Sarraz Switzerland 1928', see Leonardo Benevolo, *History of Modern Architecture*, vol.2, p.497.

p.119 Ville radieuse: see Le C, *La ville radieuse*: Frampton 'The City of Dialectic', *Architectural Design*, 39, October 1969; Sutcliffe, 'A Vision of Utopia'; Fishman 'From the Radiant City to Vichy'; Serenyi, 'Le Corbusier, Fourier and the Monastery of Ema'.

p.120 For ideological basis of Ville Radieuse: Fishman, *Urban Utopias in the Twentieth Century*; Mary Macleod, 'Le Corbusier's Plans for Algiers 1930–1936', *Oppositions 16/17*, 1980; Manfredo Tafuri, 'Machine et Mémoire: The City in the Work of Le Corbusier', *The Le Corbusier Archive*.

Aircraft: Le Corbusier, *Aircraft*, London, 1935. 'From Far Away', Le Corbusier, *Précisions*, 'Corollaire brésilien', p.244.

p.121 Josephine Baker: see Sketchbook B4 in *Le Corbusier Sketchbooks vol.1*, p.239 for Le Corbusier self-portrait with Baker on board ship, Rio in background; p.274 for a nude study.

Charter of Athens: Le Corbusier (with Jean Giraudoux), *Urbanisme des CIAM, La charte d'Athènes*, Paris, 1943; also José Luis Sert, *Can Our Cities Survive?*, Cambridge, Mass., Harvard, 1940.

p.122 Reyner Banham: *The New Brutalism — Ethic or Aesthetic?*, N.Y., Reinhold, 1966, p.70 ff for C.I.A.M. doctrines.

Letter: Le C to Brunel, December 1933, *La ville radieuse*, p.228.

Plan Obus: for architect's own version, see Le Corbusier, *La Ville radieuse* and *Poèsie sur Alger*, Paris, Falaize, 1950. For social context, Macleod 'Le Corbusier's Plans for Algiers 1930-36'. For influence of painting on plan, von Moos, 'Von den Femmes d'Alger zum Plan Obus', *Archithèse 1*, 1971.

p.125 Jean Cotereau: 'Un nouveau bombardement d'Alger', Macleod op.cit., p.71. New York Times 'Ideal Metropolis', 3/1/1932.

America: for architect's attitudes to U.S.A. see Curtis, *Le Corbusier at Work*, especially chapters 3 and 4, also Henry Russell Hitchcock, 'Le Corbusier and the United States', *Zodiac 16*, 1966; for reactions to American city, Curtis, 'Le Corbusier, Manhattan et le rêve de la ville radieuse', *Archithèse 17*, February 1976.

p.126 Suburbs: Le Corbusier, "What is the Problem of America?", *OC 1934–1938*, pp.65-68.

House for college president: *OC 1934–1938*, pp.132-33.

p.128 Plan Directeur: *OC 1938–1946*, pp.42 ff.

Le Corbusier on Algiers skyscraper: *OC 1938–1940*, pp.50 ff.

Le Corbusier: *Des canons, des munitions? Merci. Des logis s.v.p.*, Paris, Editions d'Architecture, 1938.

Vichy: The seminal research has been done by Fishman, 'From the Radiant City to Vichy'.

Alexandre von Senger, 'L'Architecture en péril', *La Libre Parole*, Neuchâtel, 5/5/34, reprinted in *Travaux Nord Africains*, 4/6/42.

The plan: Fishman 'From the Radiant City to Vichy', p.279.

Le Corbusier's publications: *Déstin de Paris*, Clermont Ferrand, Paris, Sarlot, 1941. *Sur les quatre routes*, Paris, Gallimard, 1941; *La Maison des hommes* (with François de Pierrefieu), Paris, Plon 1942. *Entretiens avec étudiants des écoles d'architecture*, Paris, Denoel, 1943; *La charte d'Athènes*, Paris, Plon, 1943; *Les trois établissements humains*, Paris, 1944. *Propos d'urbanisme*, Paris, Bourrelier, 1946; *Manière de penser l'urbanisme*, Paris, Editions de l'Architecture d'Aujourd'hui, Paris, 1946.

Chapter 11. The Modulor, Marseilles and the Mediterranean Myth

p.162 Le Corbusier: *When the Cathedrals Were White*, p.30.

p.163 Jerzy Soltan: 'Working with Le Corbusier', *The Le Corbusier Archive*, vol.17, p.ix.

Modulor: see Le Corbusier *Le Modulor* and *Modulor 2*, also Peter Collins, 'Modulor', *Architectural Review*, 116, July 1954, pp.5-8; Rudolf Wittkower, 'Le Corbusier's Modulor', *Four Great Makers of Modern Architcture*, N.Y., Da Capo, 1970, pp.196-204.

p.164 Einstein: *OC 1938–1946*, p.103.

Banning of Modulor: Soltan op.cit., p.xi.

Scholarly attention: Henry A. Millon, 'Rudolf Wittkower, Architectural Principles in the Age of Humanism: Its Influence on the Development and Interpretation of Modern Architecture', *Journal of the Society of Architectural Historians*, 31, no.2, May 1972, pp.83-91.

p.165 U.N.: for recent evidence of project 23-A, George Dudley, 'Le Corbusier's Notebook Gives Clues to United Nations Design', *Architecture*, September 1985, p.40. For architect's early involvement with project, Le Corbusier, *U.N. Headquarters*, N.Y., Reinhold, 1947. That Niemeyer influenced Le Corbusier is suggested by Dudley's article and a discussion between author and Gordon Bunshaft, April 1985.

Pyrenees: Le Corbusier, *Poème de l'angle droit*, Paris, 1955.

p.166 E.F. Sekler: 'The Carpenter Center in Le Corbusier's Oeuvre: An Assessment', *Le Corbusier at Work*, p.240; see also Le Corbusier, *Creation is a Patient Search*, p.247 for Totem. Quotation on re-use of elements from *OC 1946–1952*, p.225.

Abstraction, transformation: William J.R. Curtis, *Fragments of Invention: the Sketchbooks of Le Corbusier*, Architectural History Foundation and M.I.T., 1981. For Le Corbusier on tapestries, *OC 1910–1960*, p.281.

p.167 Iconostasis: for fanciful interpretation of *Poème de l'angle droit*, Richard A. Moore, 'Alchemical and Mythical Themes in the Poem of the Right Angle 1947–1965'.
Sculpture: Petit, *Le Corbusier Lui-Même*, pp.246 ff.
Soltan: 'Working With Le Corbusier', pp.xiv-xv.
p.168 Roq and Rob: for architect's intentions, *OC 1946–1952*, p.54.
p.169 Cap Martin: impressions of architect on holiday from interviews with José Luis Sert, 1971.
Unité: for architect's intentions, Le Corbusier, *L'Unité d'habitation de Marseille*, Souillac-Mulhouse, 1950. For reminiscences of design process, Soltan op.cit., Ruggio Andréini (interviews 1972), Téodoro Gonzales de Léon (discussions 1985), André Wogensky 'The Unité d'habitation at Marseille' in *The Le Corbusier Archive*, vol.16. See also Reyner Banham, '*La Maison des hommes* and *La misère des villes*: Le Corbusier and the Architecture of Mass Housing', *The Le Corbusier Archive*, vol.21. For influences on conception, see Serenyi, 'Le Corbusier, Fourier and the Monastery of Ema'; von Moos, 'Le Corbusier, Elements of a Synthesis', pp.157 ff.
p.170 Béton brut: interpretation relies on recollections of Gonzales de Léon and Andréini who both worked on the scheme. See also revealing letter by Le Corbusier to Sert, 26/5/62, *Le Corbusier at Work*, Appendix 20, in which he explains his idea of bare concrete.
p.173 Unité's influence: see Curtis, *Modern Architecture Since 1900*, ch. 21, 'The Unité d'habitation at Marseilles as a Collective Housing Prototype'; also Banham *The New Brutalism*, especially for Team X.
Tawdriness: Banham, '*La Maison des hommes* … Le Corbusier and the Architecture of Mass Housing', p.xviii.
p.174 Criticisms: see for example, Lewis Mumford, 'The Marseilles Folly', *The Highway and the City*, N.Y., 1963, pp.53-66, who rejected the idea of the interior street before seeing it with all its shops functioning.

Chapter 12. Sacral Forms, Ancient Associations

p.175 Motto: Ribard de Chamoust, *L'Ordre françois trouvé dans la Nature*, Paris 1783.
Smithson, Alison and Peter: *Ordinariness and Light*, London, 1970, p.169.
Stirling: 'Garches to Jaoul: Le Corbusier as Domestic Architect in 1927 and 1953', p.147.
p.177 Vessel of contemplation: Le Corbusier, *OC 1946–1952*, p.72.
Concave surface: Le Corbusier, *The New World of Space*, N.Y., Reynal and Hitchcock, 1948.
p.178 Stirling: 'Ronchamp: Le Corbusier's Chapel and the Crisis of Rationalism', *Architectural Review*, 119, March 1956, pp.155-161.
Couturier: for conditions of patronage see Martin Purdy, 'Le Corbusier and the Theological Program', *The Open Hand*, p.286. Also Pauly, *Ronchamp, lecture d'une architecture*.
p.179 Ineffable space: Le C, *The Modulor*, p.32.
Design process: see Danièle Pauly, 'The Chapel of Ronchamp as an Example of Le Corbusier's Design Process', *The Le Corbusier Archive*, vol.20, p.xiii; also Le C, *Le livre de Ronchamp*, Paris, 1961. pp.17 ff; for quotation, *Student Publications of the School of Design of the University of North Carolina*, 14, no.2, 1964, on Firminy church. Some of the earliest sketches of Ronchamp are in Sketchbook E18, *Le Corbusier Sketchbooks*, vol.2.
p.180 Sources of Ronchamp: for Spanish church see Sketchbook C11, *Le Corbusier Sketchbooks*, vol.1, p.55. For range of other influences, Pauly *Ronchamp, lecture d'une architecture* and Stuart Cohen and Stephen Hurtt, 'The Pilgrimage Chapel at Ronchamp: Its Architectonic Structure and Typological Antecedents', *Oppositions 19/20*, pp.143 ff. Laura S. Abbott, 'Le Corbusier's Ronchamp Chapel: Analysis and Influences on Design Development', unpublished essay, W. Curtis (ed.), *The Architecture and Thought of Le Corbusier*, Washington University in St. Louis, Fall 1983.
p.181 L'abbé Ferry, see Jean Petit, *Le Livre de Ronchamp*, p.70.
Individual, collective: Le C, *The Marseilles Block*, London, 1953, p.45.
p.182 Colin Rowe, 'Dominican Monastery of La Tourette, Eveux-sur-Arbresle, Lyons', *Architectural Review*, 129, 1961. For other portrayals, Jean Petit, *Un couvent de Le Corbusier*, Paris, 1961; A. Henze, B. Moosbrugger, *Le Corbusier, La Tourette*, Fribourg, 1966. Also Peter A. Di Sabatino, 'The Dominican Monastery of La Tour-

ette: Synthesis and Maturity for Le Corbusier', unpublished essay, W. Curtis (ed.), *The Architecture and Thought of Le Corbusier*, Washington University in St. Louis, Fall 1983.
p.184 Ondulatoires: Le C, *Modulor 2*, pp.321 ff for explanation of 'musical glazed panels'; see also Yannis Xenakis, 'The Monastery of La Tourette', *The Le Corbusier Archive*, vol.28, pp.ix ff for genesis of these elements and use of Modulor.
p.185 Spiritual mechanics: Le C, *VUA*, pp.173 ff, especially in captions which compare the mouldings to machinery.
p.186 A place of meditation: Le C, *Le Couvent Sainte Marie de La Tourette à Eveux*, Lyons, M. Lescuyer et Fils, 1971, p.84.
Total poverty: *OC 1957–1965*, p.49.
Cosmedin: Le C, *VUA*, p.129.
Truth, calm: Le C, Preface to François Cali, Lucien Hervé, *La plus grande aventure du monde: l'architecture mystique de Citeaux*, Paris, Arthaud, 1956.
Alluring fortress wall: Le C, *Voyage d'orient*, pp.127 ff.

Chapter 13. Le Corbusier in India: the Symbolism of Chandigarh

p.188 Motto: Sir Christopher Wren, *Parentalia*, London, 1750.
Chandigarh: for details of commission, Norma Evenson, *Chandigarh*, California, Berkeley, 1966; Von Moos, 'The Politics of the Open Hand: Notes on Le Corbusier and Nehru at Chandigarh', *The Open Hand*, pp.412 ff; and numerous discussions with P.L. Varma in 1983 and 1984.
p.189 Temple of New India: Nehru is quoted in Shedev Kumar Gupta, 'Chandigarh: After 20 Years', *Proceedings of EDRA III*, Los Angeles, 1972.
p.190 Maxwell Fry: reminiscences in 'Le Corbusier at Chandigarh', *The Open Hand*, p.350, also Jane Drew 'Le Corbusier as I Knew Him', *The Open Hand*, pp.364 ff.
Bed under stars: Le C Sketchbook E21E, 7-14/7/51.
Nehru, modern aspirations: Von Moos, 'The Politics of the Open Hand', pp.416 ff; see also Gupta 'Chandigarh' for Nehru's speeches.
p.191 Hindu philosophy: Le C 'Nothing is Transmissible But Thought', *Last Works*. Varma recalls that Le C stated he had been interested in Indian religious beliefs since youth. (Interview with author March 1983). See also letter Le C to Nehru 26/11/54. Fondation Le Corbusier.
192 Sketchbooks: see particularly Sketchbook F24, March 1952, in *Le Corbusier Sketchbooks*, Vol.2, pp.702 ff for early stages of Capitol buildings.
Pinjore: see Peter Serenyi, 'Timeless But of Its Time: Le Corbusier's Architecture in India', *Perspecta 20*, p.111.
p.193 Fathepur Sikri: see William J.R. Curtis, 'L'Ancien dans le Moderne: Le Corbusier en Inde', *Architectures en Inde*, ed. J.L. Véret, Paris, Moniteur, 1985; see also Alexander C. Gorlin, 'An Analysis of the Governor's Palace of Chandigarh', *Oppositions 19/20*, pp.161 ff for an attempt at linking Le C's symbolism to Hindu traditions.
p.194 Shelter of Law: the architect's intention was relayed to the author by P.L. Varma, discussions 1983, 1984. For analogy with ruined Roman Basilica of Constantine, see Serenyi, 'Timeless But of Its Time'. During the Voyage d'orient Le C took some photographs of this Basilica (and of the Pantheon and Colosseum) which are preserved in the Bibliothèque de La Ville, La Chaux-de-Fonds.
Timeless but of its time: see title of Serenyi article.
p.196 Hagia Sophia: see sketch in private collection of Jullian della Fuente, exhibited at Carpenter Center, Harvard in 1974. See also catalogue, Anthony Eardley, *Atelier Le Corbusier, 35, rue de Sèvres* for hints at the use of sketches in design process.
Son of sun: for cosmic overtones see Le C, *OC 1952–1957*, p.94.
Jura farmhouses: Allen Brooks, 'Le Corbusier's Formative Years', p.xv.
Jantar Mantar: Le C notes from Sketchbook E18, *Le Corbusier Sketchbooks*, vol.2, p.330.
p.197 Schinkel: see Rowe, *The Mathematics of an Ideal Villa*.
198 Tiger, column: the model is in the exhibition hall of the Office of the Chief Architect, Chandigarh.
Open hand: fiction of state art, Von Moos, 'The Politics of the Open Hand', p.445.

p.199 A plastic gesture: reminiscence of Ruth Nivola as reported to Mary Patricia Sekler whose article 'Ruskin, the Tree and the Open Hand', *The Open Hand*, pp.42 ff, is seminal in understanding Le C's symbols; see particularly footnote 87.

p.200 Maxwell Fry, 'Le Corbusier at Chandigarh', for criticism of commercial centre. The Open hand was, finally, erected in 1985.

For problematic aspects: Sten Nilsson, *The New Capitals of India, Pakistan and Bangladesh*, Lund, 1973, and Madhu Sarin, 'Chandigarh as a Place to Live In', *The Open Hand*, pp.374 ff.

Bold beginning: for more recent Indian modern architecture see *Architectures en Inde*, also William J.R. Curtis, 'Towards An Authentic Regionalism', *Mimar 19*, Feb.1986.

Chapter 14. The Merchants of Ahmedabad

p.202 Motto: letter Le C to Mr. Kaul (Nehru's secretary), 17/3/53. Fondation Le Corbusier.

Ahmedabad: for social context, Serenyi 'Timeless But of Its Time', also Kenneth L. Gillion, *Ahmedabad, A study in Indian Urban History*, Berkeley, Univ. California, 1968. The author has spent much time in the city talking to Le C's previous clients and collaborators.

p.203 Hutheesing request for house: letter to Le C, 19/3/51. Fondation Le Corbusier.

Climate: letter Gira Sarabhai to Le C 1/10/51. Fondation Le Corbusier.

p.205 Millowners' Building: programme and design process discussed by Balkrishna Doshi, who worked with Le C, in Spring 1983.

p.207 Little palace, see motto note to p.202.

Chimanbhai house: see *OC 1946–1952*, p.163. The early project for Millowners is on p.162.

p.208 Squabbles over fees: are a persistent theme of Le C's correspondence with his Ahmedabad clients, see for example, 'Note Pour Les Clients d'Ahmedabad', 9/1/54; also letter Le C to Bajpay, 20/6/52. For Sarabhai's cordial relations with architect see especially letters 1951–1955 between Gira ond Manorama and architect. All letters at Fondation Le Corbusier.

p.210 Shodhan: see Balkrishna Doshi, *Sarabhai House, Ahmedabad 1955, Shodhan House, Ahmedabad 1955*, photos Yukio Futagawa, *Global Architecture, ADA Edita, Tokyo, 1974*.

Traditional halls, and Shodhan: Serenyi 'Timeless But of its Time'; Le C's interest in miniatures mentioned by Doshi and supported by Indian sketchbooks.

Tropical Villa Savoye: *OC 1910–1960*, p.86.

Male, female: Le C, *The Modulor*, p.224.

Sarabhai: details of commission relayed to author by Mrs. Manorama Sarabhai, Gira and Gautam Sarabhai, and Balkrishna Doshi, 1984. I wish to thank the Sarabhais for their co-operation.

p.212 Design process: see *The Le Corbusier Archive*, Vol.26, p.114 for scheme with wooden screens.

Cherchell: Le C, *OC 1938–46*, pp.116 ff.

Paul Ricoeur, 'Universal Civilisation and National Cultures', *History and Truth*, Evanston, Illinois, Northwestern University Press, 1961, p.276.

Chapter 15. Retrospection and Invention: Final Projects

p.213 Motto: Ernst Gombrich, *Art and Illusion*, London 1977, p.78.

Cambridge: *Le Corbusier Sketchbooks*, Sketchbook N57, p.49. Jerzy Soltan, 'Working with Le Corbusier', p.xiii.

Isolation: the mood of Le Corbusier's late years was gained from a number of interviews with José Luis Sert, 1971–72.

p.214 Firminy: Anthony Eardley, *Le Corbusier's Firminy Church*, New York, 1981.

Venice and French Embassy: Colquhoun, 'Formal and Functional Interactions, A Study of Two Late Works by Le Corbusier'; see also Jullian della Fuente, 'The Venice Hospital Project of Le Corbusier', *Architecture at Rice*: no.23, Houston, 1968.

p.215 Eduard Sekler, 'The Carpenter Center in Le Corbusier's Oeuvre: an Assessment', *Le Corbusier at Work*, p.230.

Biological discipline: Le C, *Talks with Students*, N.Y., Orion Press, 1961, p.46.

p.217 Demonstration of theories: *OC 1957–1965*, p.54. For detailed analysis of design process, meaning and intentions of Carpenter Center, William J.R. Curtis, 'History of the Design' (11 chapters), *Le Corbusier at Work*, pp.39 ff. I worked in this building between 1970 and 1982.

Reaction to site: Curtis *Le Corbusier at Work*, Chapter 2.

p.218 Spiral idea, Note 'à l'Attention de Jullian', 2/2/60, Fondation Le Corbusier.

American associations: the case is made at length by Curtis, *Le Corbusier at Work*, Chapters 3 and 11.

'S' symbol: Le C, *When the Cathedrals Were White*, introduction.

Anguish of creation, Soltan, 'Working with Le Corbusier', p.xii.

p.220 Presentation of drawings, letter Le C to Sert, 29/5/61, Fondation Le Corbusier. *Le Corbusier at Work*, Appendix 16 (author's translation).

Skeleton: letter Le C to Sert, 28/2/61, *Le Corbusier at Work*, Appendix 13 (author's translation).

Béton brut: letter Le C to Sert, 26/5/62, *Le Corbusier at Work*, Appendix 20 (author's translation).

p.220 Perfect proportions: letter Le C to Sert, 29/5/61 (author's translation).

Le C, *VUA*, p.145, 'To make a plan is to determine and fix ideas. It is to have had ideas ... A plan is to some extent like an analytical contents table. In a form so condensed that it seems as clear as a crystal and like a geometrical figure, it contains an enormous quantity of ideas and the impulse of an intention' (Etchells' translation).

Conclusion: Le Corbusier: Principles and Transformations

p.223 Motto: Le C, 'Réponses à des journalistes', Petit, *Le Corbusier Lui-Même*, p.184 (author's translation).

Walter Gropius: in Petit, *Le Corbusier: Lui-Même*, p.186.

p.224 Urban ugliness: see Norma Evenson, 'Yesterday's City of Tomorrow Today', *The Le Corbusier Archive*, vol.15.

p.226 Meyer Schapiro, 'Style': *Anthropology Today*, 1951, p.291.

Sigmund Freud, 'Revision of Dream Theory', *New Introductory Lectures on Psychoanalysis*, trans. J. Strachey, Norton, 1965, p.20.

p.228 Andrea Palladio: *The Four Books of Andrea Palladio's Architecture*, ed. Isaac Ware, MDCC, London, xxviii, p.26.

Concentration camp: 'L'Univers de M. Le Corbusier c'est l'univers concentrationnaire', Pierre Francastel, *Arts et Techniques*, Paris 1956 cited by Petit, *Le Corbusier: Lui-Même*, p.186.

Touchstone of age: Kenneth Frampton, Editor's 'Introduction', *Oppositions 15/16*.

Index

Figures in italics refer to numbers of illustrations